Proceedings of the International Groundwater Symposium 2002

Published by IAHR, Paseo Bajo Virgen del Puerto 3, 28005 Madrid, Spain

First published 2002

ISBN: 90-805649-4-X

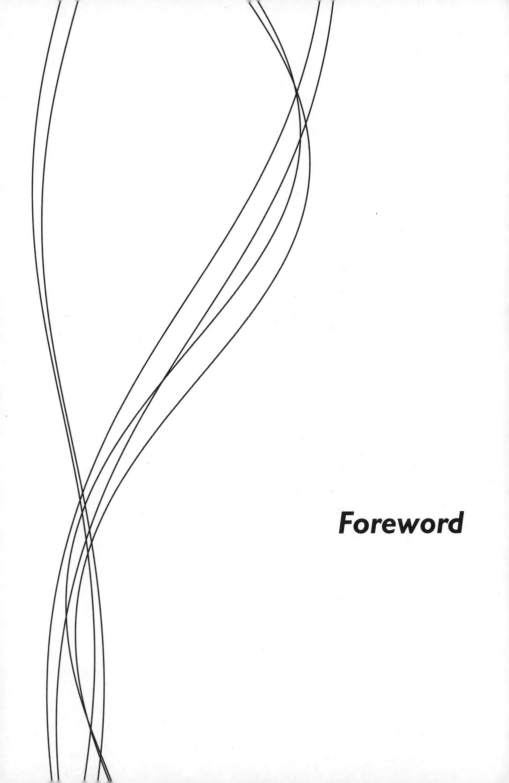

Foreword

It is widely recognized that site characterization and modeling are closely interconnected and that successful work in one requires thorough understanding of the other. The purpose of the Symposium is to bring together hydrogeologists, geologists, hydrologists, and engineers, and in particular those who focus on field measurements or lab experiments with those focused more on modeling. The aim of the Symposium is to provide a forum for the exchange of ideas, which will enhance the ability of both groups to understand better flow and transport processes in heterogeneous media. The Symposium aims also at promoting the dialog between researchers and practicing engineers and scientists.

The present printed volume contains the extended abstracts of all papers presented in the Symposium. The full manuscripts of these papers are included in an accompanying CD ROM. Because some abstracts contain Figures that were submitted by their authors in color and others had to be reduced to fit the size of the proceedings, they may have lost some of the clarity of their original form. In such cases the reader should consult the CD ROM that includes all Figures of each paper in their original colors and size.

The proceedings are organized in the following eight general themes, which correspond to the Symposium presentation sessions:

- Scaling and Uncertainty in Heterogeneous Media
- Geologic Heterogeneity: Measurements and Modeling
- Tracer tests, well testing and analysis
- Site Characterization and Case Studies
- Two phase flow in fractured rock
- Reactive transport, experiments and models
- Characterization of chemical heterogeneity and reactions, and ramifications for field-scale fate
- Unsaturated zone

Because of the nature of their subject, some papers could be classified under more than one theme. In such cases the decision to place them in one theme over another was based on practical considerations of the Symposium program.

The Symposium is organized by the International Association of Hydraulic Engineering and Research (IAHR), and co-sponsored by the International Association of Hydrological Sciences (IAHS), the Environmental and Water

Resources Institute (EWRI) of the American Society of Civil Engineers (ASCE), and the American Geophysical Union (AGU). The Organizing Committee wishes to thank all these organizations and their members for their support.

The Organizing Committee wishes to acknowledge the contribution of the keynote speakers, Drs. Gedeon Dagan, Wolfgang Kinzelbach, Ghislain de Marsily, Shlomo Neuman, Yvonne Tsang and Peter Wierenga, to the success of the Symposium. Also, the contribution of all those who provided reviews of the submitted papers, and especially the session chairs Drs. Sabine Attinger, Roger Beckie, Olaf Cirpka, Toby Ewing, Boris Faybishenko, Graham Fogg, Tim Ginn, Bob Glass, Charlie Harvey, Allen Moench, Hari Rajaram, Tim Scheibe, and Georg Teutsch, was critical for the quality of the proceedings volume.

The Organizing Committee wishes also to acknowledge the support of the Lawrence Berkeley National Laboratory, which hosted the Symposium and handled its logistics.

Finally, the Organizing Committee wishes to thank Ms. Yasmin El Harchi of the IAHR Secretariat for coordinating the publication of the proceedings, and Mr. Miguel Losada Quevedo of Pizzicato Estudio Gráfico in Spain who was responsible for typesetting the volume of extended abstracts and preparing the accompanying CD ROM.

>   The Organizing Committee
>   Angelos N. Findikakis, Bechtel National Inc.
>   Chin-Fu Tsang, Lawrence Berkeley National Laboratory
>   Rainer Helmig, Universität Stuttgart
>   Peter Kitanidis, Stanford University
>   John Nimmo, United States Geological Survey
>   Yoram Rubin, University of California, Berkeley
>   Karsten Pruess, Lawrence Berkeley National Laboratory
>   Fritz Stauffer, ETH, Zurich

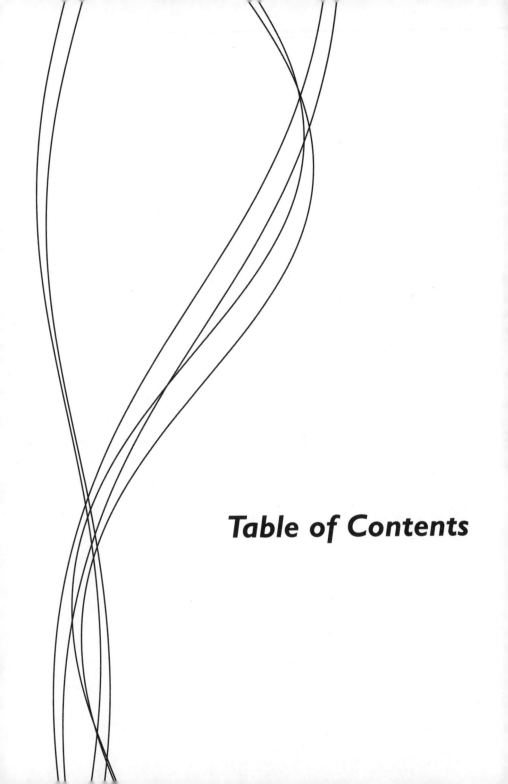

Table of Contents

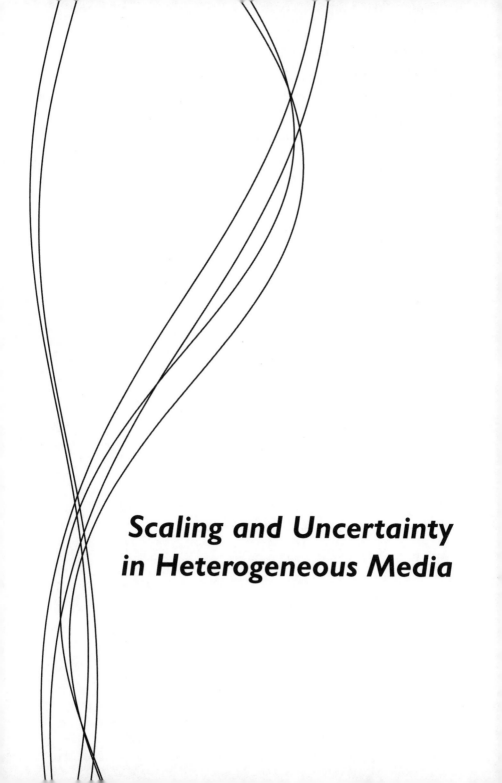

*Scaling and Uncertainty
in Heterogeneous Media*

- supports "Species model" approach...
  - but need for incorporation of soft geology...
- Regional flow & transport
  - supports use of 2D modeling — but upscaling needed.
  ✱ I should point out 2D limitation!

STOCHASTIC MODELING OF GROUNDWATER FLOW AND TRANSPORT: FROM THEORY TO APPLICATIONS

Gedeon Dagan

Faculty of Engineering, Tel Aviv University, Israel

[handwritten notes:]

- need to get stochastics into field for broader application by users & workers.
- Uncertainty: \
  - Conceptual – hard to quantify but present in all projects.
    - discrete vs. continuous models; 2D vs 3D; Conditional vs unconditional; etc.
    - Selroos et al 2002 J of H 257: 171-188 – model w/ different approaches.
  - Averaged values – scale of heterogeneity by modeling k; Scale of well screened over multiple intervals – scale of head.
- Approaches:
  1) Monte Carlo; 2) First-order approximations in σy (y = ln K) – valid for weakly heterogeneous areas & simple boundaries.
- Outstanding issues:
  - Characterize aquifers; Processes in heterogeneity; impact of wells; upscaling; complex reactions.
- OUTREACH TO WORKING HYDROLOGISTS: ① Start with simple, though limited, models; Simplify codes & create modules to attach to MODFLOW, etc; multidisciplinary approach.

INTRODUCTION

The stochastic approach regards the properties and the parameters that impact flow of water and transport of contaminants at the aquifer scale, as random. This reflects their spatial variability and the uncertainty in characterizing it. The random properties are characterized by the joint pdf (probability density function) of their values at any set of points in space. These pdf serve as input to stochastic flow and transport equations.

The beginning of the research activity in the hydrological context can be traced back to Freeze (1975), preceded by Schwydler (1962) and Matheron (1967) in the theoretical realm. It has undergone a tremendous development, manifested by instance in the large number of articles (e.g. around 180 in 2000 in various journals) and a few books (e.g. Dagan, 1989; Gelhar, 1994; Dagan and Neuman, 1997; Cushman, 1997; Kitanidis, 1997; Zhang, 2002; Rubin, in press). This development stemmed from the public and institutional interest in groundwater pollution and the willingness to invest in large scale field tests, the realization that transport of contaminants is greatly influenced by spatial varia-bility of permeability, the availability of codes that facilitate solving complex problems and last, but not least, the challenging theoretical problems posed by the approach. All these have led to the creation of a lively community and a large body of literature. The beneficial effects of these developments were the emergence of new concepts and better understanding of hydrological processes, of new approaches to analyze field experiments and to acquire data, of new modeling tools and establishing the field as one of general scientific interest.

Still, some developments are open to criticism. In parallel with a vigorous advance of the fundamentals, the stochastic approach had a limited impact on modeling and management in hydrological practice. In spite of its contributions to science, I regard the discipline as primarily of an applied nature.

Although there is room for further basic research, I believe that there is a pressing need to apply the already accumulated knowledge to solving practical problems at a greater extent. This is the main issue of the present talk.

BRIEF REVIEW OF STATE-OF-THE-ART

Hydrological variables are defined as space averages at different scales, that are enumerated and discussed. The starting point of modeling consists of the equations of flow (Darcy's Law, mass conservation) and solute transport (advection-dispersion), averaged over the pore-scale. Properties appearing in these equations, and mainly the permeability, are modeled as random space functions, characterized by their various statistical moments (average, two-point covariance,...). The dependent variables (pressure-head, specific discharge, concentrations) are also averaged at the different scales of heterogeneity, observation and application. Stochastic modeling aims at determining the statistical moments of the dependent variables, in space and time, at the appropriate scale. In the simplest approach, restricted at determining the mean behavior, the aquifer can be modeled as a homogeneous one of effective properties. The derivation of the latter is of fundamental interest.

The type of problems and solutions encountered in applications and the conceptual choices posed by them are subsequently discussed: continuous permeability distribution and discrete one (fractures), unconditional and conditional probability, direct and inverse problems, parametric uncertainty and spatial variability, two- and three-dimensional approaches.

The methods applied so far, primarily the numerical Monte Carlo simulations and first-order solutions in permeability and parameters variance, as well as the main results, are briefly reviewed. The advantages and limitations of each approach are analyzed.

It is suggested that at present the first-order approximation offers the best strategy for most applications due to its simplicity and versatility, its limitations notwithstanding.

Some aspects of a few outstanding theoretical issues, that need further research e,g, identification of aquifer structure, impact of high heterogeneity, wells hydraulics, flow and transport unsteadiness, role of increasing scales heterogeneity in space, density effects, complex reactions, are also reviewed.

FROM THEORY TO APPLICATIONS.

Past achievements of stochastic modeling e.g. the creation of a new conceptual framework, the driving force behind a few elaborate field tests, impetus to new aquifer characterization methods and application to a few major projects (mainly related to nuclear repositories), are first reviewed.

Nevertheless, stochastic modeling has not become yet a tool commonly employed in aquifer management.

It is suggested that the optimal approach to achieve this goal is to expand numerical codes of frequent use (e.g. Modflow) by incorporating stochastic components. A few strategies in three main areas are outlined in the sequel.

(i) Geohydrological characterization of properties spatial variability

A prerequisite to stochastic modeling is the estimation of statistical moments (mean, variance, integral scale) of permeability and other properties. In most applications, the hard field data are not comprehensive enough to achieve it. It is suggested to carry out a multidisciplinary effort in order to create a catalog and a methodology of estimation based on hard data, soft data and analogy. A few existing compendia may constitute the starting point.

(ii) Modeling of regional flow and transport (two dimensional)

Well established and comprehensive numerical models make possible Monte Carlo simulations. These shall incorporate both uncertainty of input parameters (recharge, boundary conditions etc) and statistics of transmissivity and storativity fields. Still, quick and simple results can be obtained by using first-order approximations in the identification stage (inverse) and in modeling of flow and transport. A few directions and outstanding problems are discussed.

(iii) Modeling of contaminant transport from point sources (three dimensional)

A few typical problems, in terms of contaminant sources and outlets, are reviewed. It is suggested that at the present stage of development of numerical codes and of data availability, simplified models based on first-order approximations shall be considered first. A few procedures are outlined and outstanding issues to be addressed are discussed.

Finally, it is submitted that in order to advance these goals a multidisciplinary collaborative effort involving stochastic and numerical modelers as well as hydrogeologists and managers is needed. This is one of the challenges of the hydrological community in the next few years.

REFERENCES

CUSHMAN, J.H., The Physics of Fluids in Hierarchical Porous Media: Angstroms to Miles, 490 p., Kluwer Academic Press, 1997.

DAGAN, G., Flow and Transport in Porous Formations, Springer-Verlag, 465 p., 1989.

DAGAN, G., and S.P. NEUMAN (editors): Subsurface Flow and Transport: A Stochastic Approach. International Hydrology Series, Cambridge University Press, 241 p., 1997

FREEZE, R.A., A stochastic-conceptual analysis of one-dimensional groundwater flow in nonuniform homogeneous media, Water Resour. Res., 11, 725-741, 1975.

GELHAR, L.W., Stochastic Subsurface Hydrology, Prentice Hall, 390 p., 1994.

KITANIDIS, P.K., Introduction to Geostatistics, Cambridge University Press, 249 p., 1997.

MATHERON, G., Elements pour une theorie des milieux poreux , Masson et Cie, Paris, 1967.

RUBIN, Y., Applied stochastic hydrology, Oxford University Press, (in press).

SHVIDLER, M.I., Flow in heterogeneous media (in Russian), Izv. Akad. Nauk USSR Mekh. Zhidk. Gaza, 3, 185, 1962.

ZHANG, D., Stochastic methods for flow in porous media: coping with uncertainties, Academic Press, 350 p., 2002

GENERATION OF ALLUVIAL AQUIFERS WITH A NEW GENETIC/STOCHASTIC SEDIMENTATION MODEL: COMPARISON WITH GEOSTATISTICAL APPROACHES BY MEANS OF GROUNDWATER FLOW SIMULATIONS

V. Teles[1,2], E. Perrier[3], F. Delay[4], Gh. de Marsily[1]

[1] *University Paris VI, UMR CNRS Sisyphe, France*
[2] *Now at MIT, Ralph M. Parsons Laboratory, Cambridge, MA*
[3] *Institut de Recherche pour le Développement, Paris*
[4] *University of Poitiers, UMR CNRS Hydrasa, France*

[Handwritten annotations:]

Approaches:
- *Inverse problem; Boolean Fracas; costats; Genetic models.* *[Focus]*
- *Categor. and cork & Foss ou Boolean!!! Didn't see TP geostats...*
- *lithology → permability - not described how!*
- *Gradual Deformation — blending different images → Eschard involved in this. Good for inverse modeling & calibration toward "truth".*

- *GENETIC MODELS:*
  - *basin models.*
  - *sedimentation models — forward process models.*

INTRODUCTION

Alluvial floodplains are extremely heterogeneous aquifers, whose three-dimensional structures are quite difficult to model. In general, when representing such structures, the medium heterogeneity is modeled with classical geostatistical or Boolean methods. Geostatistical methods use local information to infer the general statistics and the two-point covariance of spatially distributed facies (or their properties such as the hydraulic conductivity). The derived simulation techniques can create equally probable structures with the same statistical properties. These methods are efficient and handy tools that are easily conditioned to field data, but they are poorly suited to reproduce specific shapes, such as buried channels, winding shapes, point-bars, etc (e.g. Fayers and Hewett, 1992; Marsily et al., 1998). Sometimes, Boolean methods are used, particularly in simulations of oil reservoirs (e.g. Haldorsen and Daamsleth, 1990). They generate objects with a determined shape whose position and/or dimensions in space are drawn at randomly. Generally, the modeled domain has only two types of lithology (one for the generated objects, the other in the rest of the domain outside these objects). In this case, the conditioning to data is difficult. Another approach, still in its infancy, is called the genetic method because it simulates the generation of the medium by reproducing sedimentary processes (e.g. Tetzlaf and Harbaugh, 1989; Kolterman and Gorelick, 1992, 1996; Webb and Anderson, 1996).

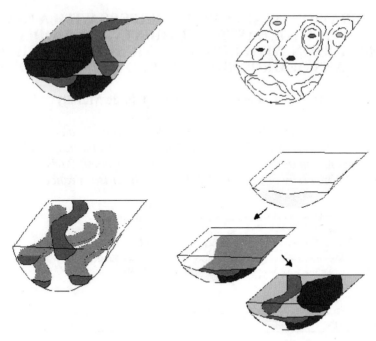

Figure 1: Schematic illustration of a real floodplain and of different methods to reproduce the 3-D heterogeneity.

MODEL STRUCTURE

We developed a new genetic model to obtain a realistic three-dimensional image of alluvial media, (Teles, 1999; Teles et al, 2001). Unlike the method proposed by Kolterman and Gorelick (1992), it does not simulate the hydrodynamics of sedimentation but uses semi-empirical and statistical rules to roughly reproduce fluvial deposition and erosion. The main processes, either at the stream scale or at the plain scale, are modeled by simple rules applied to « sediment » entities or to conceptual « erosion » entities. These rules of behavior used to simulate the construction of the plain were chosen according to empirical laws form the literature on fluvial geomorphology, or as modeling assumptions. Both meandering and braided systems are considered.

Since braided systems are highly energetic and unstable, over periods of several decades, the depositional structures appear mostly random in terms of their location in the plain, size and directional attributes. Braiding-associated dynamics are thus modeled as random processes. The basic elements are

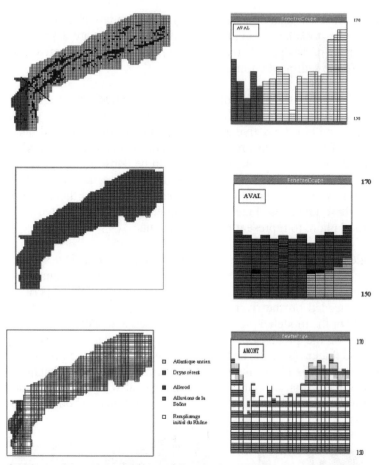

Figure 2: Planar view and cross-section of the genetic modeling of the Rhône River (France) at three different periods; A, at the end of the Bölling incision period (12,000 yrs BP); B, at the end of a deposition period called the Early Atlantic (7,000 yrs BP); C, at the end of the Mid-Atlantic period (6,000 yrs BP) during which an incision occurred in a narrower corridor.

three types of channel bars, either (i) longitudinal bars, in the stream direction; (ii) transverse bars, that grow across the stream direction, or (iii) bank-attached bars. For each time step and each bar, the location of the bar center is drawn at random in the active zone of the alluvial plain whose size is selected by the operator. The shape of the bar is chosen according to its location: in the central part of the active zone, longitudinal and transverse forms are equally probable, whereas transverse and lateral forms are equally probable on the margins of the alluvial plain. The dimensions of each bar are drawn at random, as in a Boolean process, but they are related to the width of the active area. If the floodplain is aggrading, sediment entities are deposited so that they cover the bar shape, whereas during a period of incision, erosive entities carry away the sediment entities.

Considering the spatial extent of floodplains, meandering systems are only crudely represented as a succession of sinusoidal channels from upstream to downstream within the active zone of the alluvial plain. Period, amplitude and length of the channels are drawn at random according to the plain size. If observed data are available, the model can be constrained to pass through the given observed locations. It is possible to incise the plain by flushing away sediment entities along the sinusoidal channels and then, if necessary, to fill in these channels. Fine-grain sediments can be deposited across the entire flood plain, to represent rare flood events.

The model simulates a succession of genetic periods (Fig. 2) associated with distinct climatic periods, and with the inferred associated sedimentary processes linked to the fluvial regime. As input, for each modeled period, information is needed on the river dynamics (meandering, or braided), and the magnitude of the modeled process, which is used to constrain the model. The magnitude of the processes is estimated from available quantitative data, such as the thickness of the sediments deposited during the given period, or the elevation of the top of the sediments, terraces and paleochannels. If the location of the primary channel is known, it can also be used as an additional constraint. Within a simulation, many choices are made about the processes

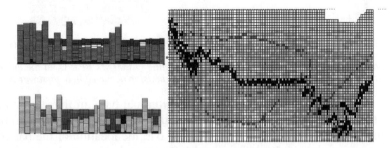

Figure 3: Results of the model applied to the Aube River (France); A, Cross-section shaded by lithology (red= gravel, white =sand, blue =clayey-loam, green = loam); B, Cross-section shaded by sediment age; C, planar view of the plain after modeling meandering channel (Boreal period, 9,000 yrs BP), shades represent deposition age.

to be modeled, the way of modeling them or the values of the model parameters. This variety of choices opens the way for generating many different realizations, but conditioning to data remains very partial and cannot be exact at any observation point in the plain.

APPLICATION TO THE AUBE RIVER FLOODPLAIN

The model was applied to a several kilometer long portion of the Aube River floodplain (France), on a scale of several kilometers. Forty-four auger-hole logs were collected (Antoine and Pastre, 1999) on a line across the floodplain. They made it possible to build a cross-section of the floodplain, and to infer its probable formation history. The model was then used to reproduce the deposition and erosion cycles that occurred during the inferred climate periods (15 000 BP to present) (Fig. 3). A three-dimensional image of the aquifer was generated, by extrapolating the two-dimensional information collected on the cross-section. Unlike geostatistical methods, this extrapolation does not use a statistical spatial analysis of the data, but a genetic analysis, which leads to a more realistic structure.

GROUNDWATER FLOW SIMULATIONS

Groundwater flow and transport simulations in the alluvium were carried out with a three-dimensional flow code (MODFLOW), using different representations of the alluvial reservoir of the Aube River floodplain : first an equivalent homogeneous medium, and then different heterogeneous media built either with the traditional geostatistical approach simulating the permeability distribution, or with the new genetic model presented here simulating sediment facies. In this case, each deposited entity of a given lithology was assigned a constant hydraulic conductivity value. Results of these models have been compared to assess the value of the genetic approach and will be presented.

CONCLUSION

The main advantage of the new approach is that it uses sedimentological information, that geologists can collect in the field, but which is generally ignored by traditional methods. This information is obtained from boreholes, auger holes, or gravel pits and includes: the age of the sediments (inferred from 14C activity of organic debris), the type of depositional environment (meandering or braided, and their succession), the grain size and nature of the deposition for a given period, and the presence of deep erosion channels filled by fine-grain sediments, such as oxbows. The position and geometry of these objects are partly random, as in a Boolean model, but the properties mat vary for each sedimentation or erosion regime according to history, and it also depends in a dynamic way on the geometry of the plain obtained at each genetic stage. The running time of the computation is very short, which makes it possible to make a large number of simulations, if desired. Our preliminary tests show that the flow and transport properties of such media are sensitive to the parameters of the genetic model, and produce transport patterns that significantly differ from those of reservoirs simulated by more conventional geostatistical techniques. Conditioning is an issue, for instance to local hydraulic conductivity values; some conditioning techniques could be considered. Calibration of a flow model using such images of the sediment structure in an alluvial plain could be made by fitting the hydraulic conductivity assigned to each facies. Calibration of the facies geometry by optimizing some of the parameters of the genetic model could also be conceived.

REFERENCES

Antoine P. and Pastre J.F. 1999. Volet paléohydrologie : rapport préliminaire concernant le transect de la vallée de l'Aube. Fonctionnement des zones humides riveraines du cours moyen des rivières, Programme National de Recherche sur les Zones Humides, Progress Reports, unpublished, Univ. Paris VI.

Fayers F.J. and Hewett T.A. 1992. A Review of Current Trends in Petroleum Reservoir Description and Assessing the Impacts on Oil Recovery, Mathematical Modelling, in Water Resources, 2, Russel T.F. et al (Eds), Computational Mechanics Publications, Elsevier, pp 3-33.

Haldorsen, H.H., Daamsleth, E. 1990. Stochastic modeling. J. of Petrol.Technol., 42, 404-412; discussion, 929-930.

Kolterman C.E. et Gorelick S.M. 1992. Paleoclimatic signature in terrestrial flood deposits : Science, v. 256, p. 1775-1782.

Kolterman C.E. et Gorelick S.M. 1996. Heterogeneity in sedimentary deposits : a review of structure-imitating, process-imitating, and descriptive approaches : Water Resour. Res., v. 32, p. 2617-2658.

Marsily G. De, Schafmeister M.T., Delay F. and Teles V. 1998. On Some Current Methods to Represent the Heterogeneity of Natural Media in Hydrogeology, Hydrogeology J., 6, pp 115-130.

Teles V. 1999. Construction de réservoirs aquifères alluviaux par modèle génétique de mise en place des alluvions, PhD Thesis University Pierre et Marie Curie Paris VI, Mémoire des Sciences de la Terre, n°99-03.

Teles V., Bravard J.P., Marsily G. de and Perrier E, 2001. Modelling of the construction of the Rhône alluvial plain since 15,000 years BP. Sedimentology , in press.

Tetzlaff, D.M., and Harbaugh, J.W., 1989 : Simulating clastic sedimentation. Van Nostrand Reinhold, New York, 202 p.
Webb E.K., Anderson M.P. 1996. Simulation of preferentiel flow in three-dimensional, heterogeneous conductivity fields with realistic internal Water Resour. Res., 32, 3, 533-545

<u>Sedimentology</u> 2001 48: 1209-1224.

- Object model: w/ rules.
    - meandering stream
        - builds point bars... But is this realistic?? DOES NOT BUILD MEANDER BENDS!!
    - braided stream deposits:
        - builds bar forms— longitudinal bars, transverse bars, lateral bars BUT, WHAT ABOUT REWORKING & OVERPRINTING?
    - successive simulations + aggradation/degradation.

- Rough, but good... nice start.

- THIS WOULD BE FUN TO PLAY WITH... CAN I USE THIS TO MODEL LLNL OR KRF?

REVISITING THE ADVECTION-DISPERSION MODEL -TESTING: AN ALTERNATIVE

Ivars Neretnieks

*Department of Chemical Engineering and Technology,
Royal Institute of Technology . SE-100 44-Stockholm, Sweden.
Tel 46-8-790 822   niquel@ket.kth.se*

Some of the basic assumptions of the Advection-Dispersion model, AD-model, are revisited. That model assumes a continuous mixing along the flowpath similar to Fickian diffusion. This implies that there is a constant dispersion length irrespective of observation distance. This is contrary to most field observations. The properties of an alternative model based on the assumption that individual water packages can retain their identity over long distances are investigated. The latter model is called the Multi-Channel model, MCh-model. Inherent in the latter model is that if the waters in the different pathways are collected and mixed, the "dispersion length" is proportional to observation distance.

Using diffusion theory it is investigated over which distances or contact times, adjacent water packages will keep their identity. It is found that for a contact time of 10 hours, two streams, each wider than 6 mm that flow side by side, will not have lost their identity. For 1000 hours contact time the minimum width is 6 cm. Such residence times are typical in many field experiments.

The MCh and AD-models were found to have very similar Residence Time Distributions, RTD, for Peclet numbers larger than 3. A generalised relation between flowrate and residence time is developed, including the so-called cubic law and constant aperture assumptions. Using the generalised relation, surprisingly, it is found that for a system that has the same average flow volume and average flowrate the form of the RTD curves are the same irrespective of the form of the relation.

Both models are also compared for a system where there is strong interaction of the solute with the rock matrix. In this case it is assumed that the solute can diffuse into and out of the fracture walls and also to sorb on the microfractures of the matrix. The so-called Flow Wetted Surface between the flowing water in the fracture and the rock is a key entity in such systems. It is found that the AD-model predicts much later arrivals and lower concentrations than does the MCh-model for strongly sorbing solutes. This can have profound influence in predicting the transport of radionuclides from a final repository for nuclear waste. In a companion paper the MCh-model is tested against field experiments.

Fractured system — not appropriate to use AD-model. But, may be modled as many independent pathways.
- Can get parallel fractures w/ minimal mixing.

SPATIAL STRUCTURE OF PERMEABILITY IN RELATION TO HIERARCHICAL SEDIMENTARY ARCHITECTURE: CENTIMETER TO KILOMETER SCALES

Ritzi[1], Robert W., Zhenxue Dai[1], David F. Dominic[1] and Yoram N. Rubin[2]

[1] *Department of Geological Sciences, Wright State University*
[2] *Department of Civil and Environmental Engineering, University of California, Berkeley*

Summarized here are the results of characterizations of permeability and associated sedimentary units across a range of scales summarized conceptually in Figure 1. The goal of this ongoing project is to statistically characterize the relevant spatial attributes (proportions, geometry and pattern) of the sedimentary units, and the spatial structure of permeability within the units. The sedimentary units exist within a hierarchical system with actually a greater number of hierarchical levels than depicted. The spatial attributes of the sedimentary units are being characterized with the transition probability at each of the hierarchical levels. Log permeability (Y) is being characterized as a continuous random variable within each of the units. The bimodal model of Rubin (1995) for the second order moments of $[Y(x), Y(x')]$ is being extended for more than two permeability modes, and across more than two hierarchical levels, to create a more general hierarchical model.

The conceptual model in Figure 1, based on thousands of actual permeability measurements, is derived from our studies of buried-valley aquifer systems in the North American mid-continent. The general ideas presented here may have application in aquifers derived from other depositional process as well. The buried-valley aquifers we have studied occur within the extent of Pleistocene glaciation. Formally pro-glacial valleys, they directed drainage away from ice margins and were in-filled during periods of aggradation. A

COOL FIGURE!!

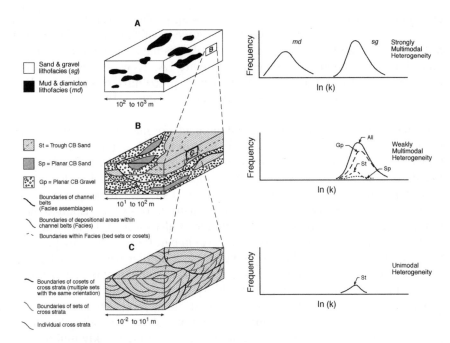

Figure 1. Hierarchical organization of lithofacies and corresponding permeability modes.

variety of depositional processes (e.g. fluvial, lacustrine, glacial) created complex mixtures of two main lithofacies: 1) a sand and gravel facies, sg, which predominates, and 2) a mud and diamicton facies, md. At the 100 m to km scale, Figure 1A, the deposits exhibit a strongly bimodal distribution of permeability corresponding to the two larger lithofacies categories. As the scale decreases to the 10 to 100 m scale , permeability becomes weakly multimodal as in Figure 1B, the modes corresponding to lithofacies which occur at the cm to 10 m scale and within which permeability appears unimodal, as in Figure 1C.

At each relevant scale we develop transition probability models which represent the volumetric proportions, geometry (mean length and variance in length in each direction) and pattern of the units, as described by Ritzi (2000).

Importantly, the real plumes occurring in buried-valley aquifers that we are familiar with are either old and large or very new and small. Older plumes are those originating from disposal decades ago. These were usually from dumps filling old gravel pits, thus local sources, which created plumes that have grown to the kilometer scale. Older plumes have sampled the strongly multimodal heterogeneity as depicted in Figure 1A. New plumes originating from recent spills or tracer tests have a high probability of only sampling heterogeneity within the sg facies, as depicted in Figure 1B.

The predominant control on the spatial moments for mass in old large plumes is the strongly multimodal aspects of heterogeneity, as represented in the transition probability models for facies sg and md. Ritzi et al. (2000) developed and compared models in a number of buried-valley locations. Transport simulations they presented are consistent with other studies in strongly multimodal media; residence time distributions for transported mass fall into fast groups of mass traveling preferentially through the high-permeability sg facies, and slow groups that travel in part through the low-permeability md facies. For the Type I plumes we are familiar with, the fast group of mass has already arrived at down-gradient receptor points and is under some remedial action. The high probability for slow groups of mass to arrive later, shown by Ritzi et al. (2000), suggests that a long term perspective is required on the arrival of contamination and on the corresponding length of time that will be required for remediation. Representing weakly multimodal heterogeneity that exists within facies sg is not important in these cases. Thus, as a practical matter, the hierarchical scaling relationship for permeability that we have developed need not be applied across all scales depicted in Figure 1.

The predominant control on the spatial moments for mass in new small plumes is expected to be the weakly multimodal aspects of heterogeneity, motivating the study of the relation between sedimentary architecture and permeability at and below the scale of Figure 1B. Here the hierarchical scaling relationship is important across a number of levels. In ongoing work we are characterizing the proportions, geometry and patterns of a hierarchy of depositional structures. This hierarchy includes laminea, groups of laminea (beds or sets), groups of beds (cosets or mesoforms), and mesoform assemblages (macroforms). The Scheibe numerical aquifer (Scheibe and Freyberg, 1995) provides an opportunity to study the hierarchical scaling relationship of second order moments on $[Y(x),Y(x')]$, in an exhaustively sampled, three dimensional representation of a lateral accretion complex, and thus an opportunity to test our model.

REFERENCES

RITZI, R.W., 2000, "Behavior of indicator variograms and transition probabilities in relation to the variance in lengths of hydrofacies," Water Resources Research, 36(11), p. 3375-3381.

RITZI, R.W., D.F. DOMINIC, A.J. SLESERS, C.B. GREER, E.C. REBOULET, J.A. TELFORD, R.W. MASTERS, C.A. KLOHE, J.L. BOGLE, AND BRENT P. MEANS, 2000, "Comparing statistical models of physical heterogeneity in buried-valley aquifers," Water Resources Research, 36(11), p. 3179-3192.

RUBIN, Y., 1995, Flow and transport in bimodal heterogeneous formations, Water Resources Research, 31(10), p. 2461-2468

SCHEIBE, T.D., AND D.L. FREYBERG, 1995, "Use of sedimentological information for geometric simulation of natural porous media structure," Water Resources Research, 31(12), p. 3259-3270.

Susan needs to look at Ritzi's work!
- not citations from petroleum literature.
- large breaks across bed types.
- multi level stochastics

INFLUENCE OF GEOSTATISTICAL INTERPOLATION OF LOG-HYDRAULIC CONDUCTIVITY ON DISPERSION AND MIXING

Olaf A. Cirpka & Wolfgang Nowak
*Universität Stuttgart, Institut für Wasserbau, Pfaffenwaldring 61,
70550 Stuttgart, Germany
Email: Olaf.Cirpka@IWS.Uni-Stuttgart.de,
Wolfgang.Nowak@IWS.Uni-Stuttgart.de*

INTRODUCTION

In stationary media with a small variance of the log-conductivity fluctuations, we can predict macrodispersion, that is, the spreading of a large solute plume, by linear stochastic theory quite accurately [Gelhar & Axness, 1983; Dagan, 1988]. While the concept of macrodisper-sion has been shown appropriate in many conservative-tracer studies, it has led to erroneous results in the transport of multiple compounds reacting with each other [Molz & Widdowson, 1988]. A basic requirement for reactions to take place is the mixing of the reacting compounds on the pore-scale. Macrodispersion, however, includes both mixing on the local scale and spreading on a larger scale, i.e., the increasing irregularity of the plume shape. The dispersion coefficient for which we expect the correct amount of mixing is the effective dispersion coefficient for a point-like injection [Dentz et al., 2000] which is strongly influenced by local dispersion. In the present study, we want to apply the closed-form expressions of mac-rodispersion and effective dispersion to log-conductivity fields arising from geostatistical in-terpolation. These fields recover the large-scale features of the true distribution quite accu-rately, whereas small-scale fluctuations are lost by smoothing. 2) We want to demonstrate that the resulting coefficients can be used in mixing-controlled reactive transport studies, leading to accu-rate mixing and correct overall reaction rates.

THEORY

Consider the log-conductivity field $Y(x) = ln(K(x))$ a stationary random function characterized by its mean $\bar{Y}$ and covariance $R_{YY}(h)$. We assume a uniform gradient $-J = \nabla \bar{\phi}$ of the mean head $\bar{\phi}$. Then, the spectrum $S_{vv}(s)$ of all seepage-velocity components v_i can be evaluated from that of log-conductivity $S_{YY}(s)$ by [*Gelhar & Axness, 1983*]:

$$\mathbf{S}_{vv}(\mathbf{s}) = \left(\mathbf{J} - \frac{\mathbf{s} \cdot \mathbf{J}}{s^2}\mathbf{s}\right)\left(\mathbf{J} - \frac{\mathbf{s} \cdot \mathbf{J}}{s^2}\mathbf{s}\right)^T \frac{K_g^2}{\theta^2} S_{YY}(\mathbf{s}) \qquad (1)$$

in which s is the vector of wave numbers, $K_g = exp\,(\bar{Y})$, θ is the porosity, and s is the absolute value of **s**. According to linear stochastic theory, the macro-dispersion tensor $\mathbf{D}^*(t)$ is in stationary velocity fields with small log-conductivity fluctuations [*Dagan, 1988*]:

$$\mathbf{D}^*(t) = \mathbf{D} + \frac{1}{(2\pi)^{d/2}} \int_{V_\infty} \left(is \cdot \bar{\mathbf{v}} - \mathbf{s}^T\mathbf{Ds}\right)\frac{1 - \exp\left(-t\left(is \cdot \bar{\mathbf{v}} + \mathbf{s}^T\mathbf{Ds}\right)\right)}{(s \cdot \bar{\mathbf{v}})^2 + (\mathbf{s}^T\mathbf{Ds})^2}\mathbf{S}_{vv}(\mathbf{s})ds \qquad (2)$$

in which **D** is the local dispersion tensor assumed uniform, d is the dimensionality, i the imaginary number, $\bar{\mathbf{v}}$ the mean seepage velocity, and t is time. For plumes of initially small size, the macrodispersion tensor $\mathbf{D}^*(t)$ applies to the moments of the ensemble-averaged con-centrations. By contrast, the effective dispersion tensor $\mathbf{D}^e(t)$ is obtained by first calculating the moments of the plumes in each realization and then ensemble-averaging the moments. Analytical expression of $\mathbf{D}^e(t)$ for a point-like injection are given by *Dentz et al.* [2000] and *Fiori & Dagan* [2000]:

$$\mathbf{D}^*(t) - \mathbf{D}^e(t) = \mathbf{D} + \frac{1}{(2\pi)^{d/2}} \int_{V_\infty} \frac{1}{(s \cdot \bar{\mathbf{v}})^2 + (\mathbf{s}^T\mathbf{Ds})^2}\Big(\left(is \cdot \bar{\mathbf{v}} + \mathbf{s}^T\mathbf{Ds}\right)\exp\left(-t\left(is \cdot \bar{\mathbf{v}} + \mathbf{s}^T\mathbf{Ds}\right)\right) \qquad (3)$$

$$-2\mathbf{s}^T\mathbf{Ds}\exp\left(-2\mathbf{s}^T\mathbf{Ds}t\right) - \left(is \cdot \bar{\mathbf{v}} - \mathbf{s}^T\mathbf{Ds}\right)\exp\left(t\left(is \cdot \bar{\mathbf{v}} - \mathbf{s}^T\mathbf{Ds}\right)\right)\Big)\mathbf{S}_{vv}(\mathbf{s})ds$$

We may use the macrodispersion and effective dispersion tensors, $\mathbf{D}^*(t)$ and $\mathbf{D}^e(t)$, derived by Eqs. (1–3), to parameterize plume spreading and mixing in transport calculations with a uniform log-conductivity value of $\bar{Y}$. If we resolve large-scale features of Y on a computational grid, we need to parameterize the spreading and mixing caused exclusively by the unresolved spatial variability.

We consider log-conductivity fields arising from geostatistical interpolation of point-measurements. Then, the interpolated field is the conditional mean, and the unresolved vari-ability is quantified by the conditional covariance $R_c(x_k, x_l)$ [*Kitanidis, 1996*]:

$$R_c\left(\mathbf{x}_k, \mathbf{x}_\ell\right) = R_{YY}\left(\mathbf{x}_k - \mathbf{x}_\ell\right) - \begin{bmatrix} \mathbf{R}_{Y(\mathbf{x})\hat{Y}} & 1 \end{bmatrix} \begin{bmatrix} \mathbf{R}_{\hat{Y}\hat{Y}} & \mathbf{u} \\ \mathbf{u}^T & 0 \end{bmatrix}^{-1} \begin{bmatrix} \mathbf{R}_{Y(\mathbf{x})\hat{Y}}^T \\ 1 \end{bmatrix} \qquad (4)$$

in which $\mathbf{u}$ is a vector consisting only of unity entries, and $\mathbf{R}_{\hat{Y}\hat{Y}}$ is the covariance matrix between all log-conductivity measurements. The conditional covariance $R_c(x_k, x_l)$ is nonstationary. For a rather dense regular grid of measurement points, we suggest to remove the non-stationarity of $R_c(x_k, x_l)$ by

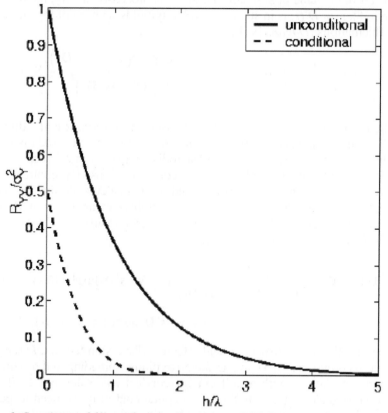

Fig. 1 Covariance of log-conductivity fluctuations. Solid line: unconditional covariance $R_{YY}(h)$; dashed line: averaged conditional for $\Delta x_{obs} = 1.25\lambda$.

taking spatial averages [*Cirpka & Nowak,* 2001]:

$$\overline{R}_c(\mathbf{h}) = \lim_{L_1,L_2,L_3 \to \infty} \frac{1}{L_1 L_2 L_3} \int_{-L_1/2}^{L_1/2} \int_{-L_2/2}^{L_2/2} \int_{-L_3/2}^{L_3/2} R_c(\mathbf{x}, \mathbf{x}+\mathbf{h}) dx_3 dx_2 dx_1 \qquad (5)$$

When we use the local dispersion tensor **D** in transport calculations on kriged hydraulic conductivity fields, we expect that half the rate of change of the second central spatial moments meet the macrodispersion and effective dispersion tensors as calculated from substituting the Fourier transform of $R_{YY}(h) - R_c(h)$ into Eqs. (1-3). We refer to the missing amount of dispersion as the correction macrodispersion tensor $D_c^*(t)$ and the correction effective dispersion tensor $D_c^e(t)$, respectively [*Cirpka & Nowak,* 2001]. Its values are calculated by substituting the Fourier transform of $R_c(h)$ into Eqs. (1-3). By applying $D+D_c^e(t)$ in transport calculations on kriged conductivity fields, we retrieve the correct amount of mixing. This will be shown in the following application.

APPLICATION TO A TWO-DIMENSIONAL DOMAIN

We generate 50 random periodic fields of 1000 x 500 cells with a size of 50 x 25 correlation lengths λ. For each realization, we collect log-conductivity values on a regular grid with a spacing of $\Delta x_{obs} = 1.25\lambda$ and perform interpolation by ordinary kriging. Fig. 1 shows the un-conditional and the averaged conditional covariance function for the given set of parameters. Fig. 2 shows the local diffusion coefficient D, the effective longitudinal dispersion coefficient $D_l^e(t)$, and the longitudinal correction effective dispersion coefficient $D+D_{cl}^e(t)$ as function of travel time, and Fig. 3 shows the difference between longitudinal macrodispersion and effective dispersion coefficients.

As an example of mixing-controlled reactive transport, we simulate a second-order irreversible bimolecular reaction of non-sorbing compounds [Cirpka, 2001]. Compounds A and B react with each other forming compound C. At the initial state, the concentration of compound A is one throughout the domain, whereas neither B nor C are present in the system. Compound B is introduced by advection with the inflow concentration of one into the domain. On the fully resolved fields, we apply D as local dispersion tensor to the simulations, whereas $D+D_{cl}^e(t)$ is used as longitudinal dispersion coefficient on the fields obtained from kriging. For comparison, we also perform simulations with D as local dispersion coefficient on the smoothed fields.

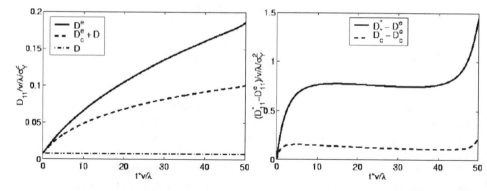

Fig. 2. Effective longitudinal dispersion coefficient Dᵉ(t), local diffusion coefficient D, and longi-tudinal correction effective dispersion coefficient Del(t) as function of travel time.

Fig. 3. Difference between longitudinal macro-disper-sion and effective dispersion as function of travel time. Comparison between unconditional and averaged conditional case.

Fig. 4 shows the total mass of the reaction product C for the different simulations, and Fig. 5 shows the second central moment of compound C. By choosing $D+D_{cl}^{e}(t)$ as local dispersion coefficient on the smoothed fields, we meet the mass balance, whereas spreading is underestimate. However, we can approximate the missing amount of spreading from the difference of macrodispersion and effective dispersion.

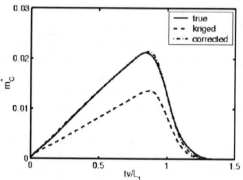

Fig. 4. Mean total mass of compound C in the domain. Comparison between the fully resolved fields ("true"), the kriged fields using D as local dispersion coefficient ("kriged"), and the kriged fields using D+Del(t) as local dispersion coefficient ("corrected").

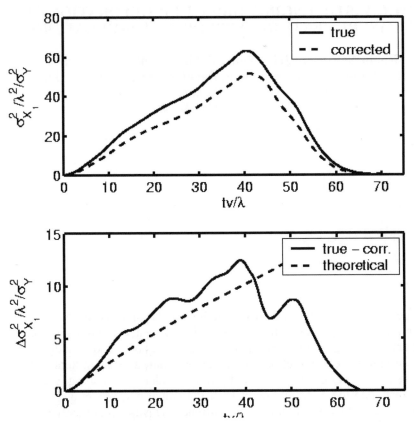

Fig. 5. Mean second central spatial moment of com-pound C. Top: Calculations on the fully re-solved fields ("true") and the kriged fields us-ing D+Del(t) as local dispersion coefficient ("corrected"). Bottom: Observed difference in the second central moment and theoretical prediction.

- REACTIVE TRANSPORT:

STOCHASTIC ENGINE: DIRECT INCORPORATION OF MEASUREMENTS INTO PREDICTIVE SIMULATIONS

Robin Newmark, John Nitao, William Hanley, Steve Carle, Abe Ramirez, Sailes Sengupta, David Harris and Roger Aines
Lawrence Livermore National Laboratory
Livermore, CA. 94550

We are creating a new method of combining disparate types of geologic observations and process simulations. Using Bayesian inferencing and an efficient search algorithm, we obtain a consolidated body of knowledge in the form of multiple configurations and parameter values of the system that are consistent with our existing data and process models. In so doing, we effectively estimate the distributions of both individual parameters and system-wide states, and their likelihood of occurrence. This is in contrast with conventional inversion methods, which produce a single deterministic solution lacking quantitative information about the distribution of uncertainty. We call this combination of probabilistic evaluation and deterministic process simulators the stochastic engine.

Our approach allows investigators to rapidly improve their understanding of system progress, making it particularly valuable for active processes like injection. The Bayesian inferencing is driven by forward process models that predict data values, such as temperature or electrical voltage, for direct comparison to measured field values. We stage the stochastic searches of possible configurations and run the simplest models, such as lithology estimators, at the lower stages. The majority of possible configurations are eliminated from further consideration by the higher stages' more complex models, such as electrical resistance models for geophysical imaging, or flow and transport models for fluid movement. The approach allows for the continuous augmentation of existing data with newly available information to enhance understanding and reduce the number of high likelihood configurations. This effectively creates a tool capable of dynamically identifying states of underground geological systems that are consistent with all available data. The stochastic engine approach will dramatically increase our understanding of large-scale complex systems and the accuracy of predicting their future behavior under natural or man-made conditions.

The stochastic engine is designed to incorporate everything from the geologists' first field observations to the millions of measurements made during a field operation such as an active remediation project, into an integrated and continuously improving understanding of the base system representation. Rather than generating the "best case" deterministic solution, it determines the most likely solutions, which conventional inversion methods cannot provide. By quantifying uncertainty, it also provides a measure of the value of additional information, and therefore can be used to design experiments as well as determine the added value of contributing data.

The stochastic engine uses data (i.e., measurements) together with forward models to determine the likely configurations within a system state space consistent with all available observations and prior knowledge. The process is shown graphically in Figure 1. We focus on improving one "base" set of data (or representation of the system) from which other parameters of interest can be calculated using process models. For geologic problems we use lithology (the general physical characteristics of a rock) as the base representation because it is typically correlated with many parameters of interest such as hydraulic conductivity. Moreover, it provides a ready means to predict the behavior of the system under forcing events such as fluid injection; when we know the lithology more accurately, we can predict the behavior of the system more accurately. The accuracy of these predictions is enhanced as our knowledge of the underlying lithologic state is increasingly refined. Thus, the question we are attempting to answer is what the lithologic configuration is in our particular problem. Using lithologic information alone (such as observations made during drilling and general geologic knowledge of the region), there is a wide range of possible states. Although some states are more likely than others, the state space is quite large and has few distinguishing peaks on the likelihood surface. An observer in Figure 1 is hard pressed to identify the highest peaks.

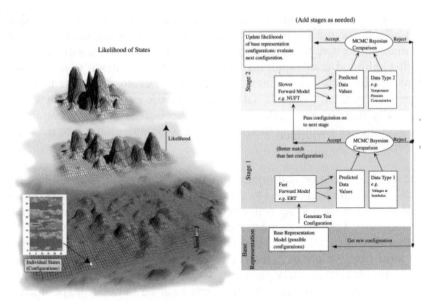

Figure 1. Conceptual depiction of the stochastic engine (right), and the effect on the total likelihood function (left) as stages with disparate data types are added to the analysis.

We next pose a hypothesis; we generate an individual configuration using the lithologic forward model (following geostatistical rules and whatever geologic observations we have available) to compare with a different configuration. The actual connection of a hypothesis to an observation is made via a forward model: for a possible subsurface configuration, the forward model predicts the values that would be observed by actual measurement. Then, these predictions are compared to the observed data, yielding a likelihood of a match relative to a specified probabilistic error model. If the match is good, the configuration is accepted. If it is not as good as the last comparison, this configuration will either be accepted or rejected according to a random rule based on the likelihood difference. If accepted, this configuration is then used in the next stage to predict a different data type using the appropriate forward model. The posterior distribution is estimated based upon the results of a sequence of these comparisons, which effectively determines the probability that any given subsurface configuration could produce the observed data. The configurations that pass all the stages form the collection of possible true configurations of the system. By staging these comparisons in a series, we can identify probable configurations using computationally efficient models early in the process. Our most computationally intensive models are only used at the top of the staging process, on configurations that are already known to be consistent with data considered at earlier stages (Figure 1 showing two stages).

In this work, we pose an example problem addressing the question of potential contaminant transport between two wells. The base representation is the lithology of the subsurface, and the observations include data from a geophysical imaging technique (electrical resistance tomography (ERT)) acquired in two boreholes and a hydraulic pump test performed between the boreholes. Thus, three quite different data types are involved; lithology, ERT measurements and a pump test. Three computational forward models are used in the analysis (a lithologic model generator, an ERT forward model and one that predicts pressure measurements resulting from a pump test). Using a synthetic "truth" case generated from the same lithologic rules and containing a permeable pathway through an aquitard unit, a two-stage analysis rapidly converges towards configurations that include the "hole" through which fluid can pass to the uppermost aquifer of interest. A posterior distribution of states is generated, from which the probability of a hole occurring can be determined. In addition to finding solutions to the question of whether there is a transport pathway for contamination to move from one well to the next, we can quantitatively evaluate the improvement of understanding achieved by incorporating each new data type (i.e., moving through the various stages). This insight has implications for efficient design of future field surveys and data collection, in addition to the simultaneous analysis of disparate data types.

This research is funded by the Laboratory Directed Research and Development (LDRD) Program at Lawrence Livermore National Laboratory (LLNL). The LDRD Program is mandated by Congress to fund director-initiated, long-term research and development (R&D) projects in support of the DOE and national laboratories. This work was performed under the auspices of the U.S. Department of Energy by University of California Lawrence Livermore National laboratory under contract No. W-7405-Eng-48.

Build many realizations - then optimize on other data - hydrologic data; chemistry; etc.

A NOVEL MULTI-SCALE ALGORITHM FOR POROUS FLOW AND TRANSPORT NUMERICAL METHODS

Bryan J. Travis

Earth & Environmental Sciences Division. EES-6/MS-T003
Los Alamos National Laboratory. Los Alamos, NM 87545

Soils and rock exhibit heterogeneity over a wide range of length scales. This multi-scale het-erogeneity presents a major challenge for numerical simulation. Traditional finite difference and finite element numerical algorithms impose a cut-off length scale through their domain discreti-zations that is usually much larger than an REV length scale. Structure (e.g., in a porous me-dium's porosity, permeability and chemical properties) smaller than this scale is lost. Unfortu-nately, it has been shown that ignoring sub-gridscale structure can lead to significant errors in estimation of flow direction and speed and consequently in transport prediction. This error is compounded for reactive transport conditions.

Recent attacks on this subgridscale structure and dynamics omission include homogenization (Jikov, Kozlov & Oleinik 1994), two-timing (two-scale per-turbation analysis, e.g., Keller 1979), renormalization (King 1989) and ran-dom walk (McCarthy 1991), explicitly solving for two scales via finite ele-ments (Hou & Wu 1997), and stochastic models (e.g., Cushman 1990; Di Federico & Neuman 1997; Guadagnini & Neuman 1999). These studies have made substantial progress in capturing the effect of small scale variability on the larger scale flow, but each has its limitations. For example, homogeniza-tion generally requires periodicity conditions, and certain material property combinations are difficult to handle. Renormalization may be time-consuming in a time-dependent situation such as unsaturated flow or for large correlation scales. The two-scale finite elements approach looks promising but requires sufficient separation of scales and hasn't been extended to 3-D or more complex flows. Stochastic methods are very powerful but are not fully developed yet for large correlation lengths and complex geometries and processes.

An alternative approach is described here which relies on the observation that important properties of soil and rock are fractal or at least approximately so over a range of scales. This al-gorithm uses fractal interpolating functions (fif) to represent multi-scale variability in soil prop-erties as well as in the dependent variables. This allows easy integration of sub-gridscale structure of a material property over a grid cell. Further, substitution of the fif form into and integration of the governing flow and transport equations result in a set of algebraic/differential equations for coefficients of the dependent variable fractal interpolating functions. Solving these provides a multi-scale solution, resolvable to any scale, which automatically couples small-scale dynamics to larger scales. The goal here is to use the fif methodology to extend traditional numerical porous flow and transport models so they can capture multi-scale heterogeneity, while keeping the classical framework, in which much time and effort has been invested. The algorithm is described and its strengths and weaknesses are discussed.

Until recently, fractals have been used mainly in a descriptive mode (e.g., Peitgen & Saupe, 1988). Predictive uses of fractals are beginning to appear; e.g., Crawford et al (1999) used fractal generators to create fractal soil structure at a highly resolved scale and then solved the governing equations directly. Scotti & Meneveau (1997, 1999) used fifs to create a sub-gridscale numerial algorithm for the nonlinear differential equations governing turbulent flow. Benson et al (2000) recently proposed a fractional dispersion model. Cushman & Ginn (2000) showed that this fractional ADE (advection-dispersion equation) is a special case of their own convolution-Fickian model. The fractional derivative of a function is known to be expressible as an ordinary derivative of a convolution of the function with a particular kernel (e.g., Oldham & Spanier, 1974), revealing that the fractional derivative is non-local.

A fractal interpolating function (fif) is similar to a classical (e.g., piecewise linear) inter-polation function, in that an fif is a continuous function that passes through a set of data points $\{(x_n, F_n), n = 0, \ldots, N; x_n > x_n-1\}$. However, it has the additional property that it is the attractor of an iterated function set (ifs) = $\{w_n, n = 1,...,N\}$. An iterated function iterates on its own output and maps a domain (e.g., the unit interval) into itself. Each member w_n maps the entire interval $[x_o, x_N]$ into a subinterval $[x_{n-1}, x_n]$. The functions w_n are affine transformations defined by:

$$w_n(x,f) = (a_n x + e_n, c_n x + d_n f + g_n) \qquad (1)$$

where the coefficients are given by:

$$a_n = \frac{x_n - x_{n-1}}{x_N - x_0} \qquad e_n = \frac{x_N x_{n-1} - x_0 x_n}{x_N - x_0}$$

$$c_n = \frac{F_n - F_{n-1} - d_n(F_N - F_0)}{x_N - x_0} \qquad (2)$$

$$g_n = \frac{x_N F_{n-1} - x_0 F_n - d_n(x_N F_0 - x_0 F_N)}{x_N - x_0}$$

In the above expressions, the scaling factors dn are free parameters but are required to lie in the range $0 \le |d_n| < 1$. They are further restricted to satisfy

$$\sum_{n=1}^{N} |d_n| \, a_n^{D-1} = 1 \qquad (3)$$

where D is the fractal dimension of the data profile. The d_ns create the 'fractalness' of the fifs. If the d_ns are all 0, then the interpolating functions reduce to piecewise linear. The w_n are applied to the points in the $[x_o, x_N]$ interval repeatedly until convergence. Barnsley (1988) has proven that the ifs defined above converges to an attractor, and that the attractor is an fif, that is, it is continuous and fits the data set. The fif can be resolved to any level of refinement desired by continued iteration of the w_ns. The fif over any subinterval, no matter how small, will resemble the profile over the entire interval, because of the self-affine nature of the fif.

Integrals of fractal interpolating functions can be defined, as well as for products of fifs. These relate the fractal integrals to integrals of the underlying piecewise linear non-fractal func-tions. These relationships are very useful in solving differential equations of flow and transport with fractal coefficients.

Multi-dimensional representations are straightforward. In two dimensions, e.g., at least two analogs of the 1-D fifs described above can be created. In the general case, rectangular elements can be defined, as a discretization of a planar region. For the special case of radial r-theta ge-ometry, periodic conditions in the theta dimension are easily achieved by setting the final interpolation point in eqns. 1-2 to be equal to the first point. Numerical solution of 2-D and 3-D fractal equations are under development.

A very simple 1-D transport example is considered, for which V is given, and V and C are fractal, and are represented by fifs as defined previously:

$$\frac{\partial C}{\partial t} + \frac{\partial}{\partial x}(VC) = 0 \quad C(x,0) = C_{init}, C(x_o,t) = CL \qquad (4)$$

C and V are treated as having dependence on x and x', where x' is small-scale behavior, and x is structure at all scales greater than the scale of x'. Eqn. (4) is first integrated over the small scale:

$$\frac{\partial \tilde{C}}{\partial t} + \frac{\partial (\widetilde{VC})}{\partial x} = -\tau, \quad \text{where} \quad \tau = \frac{\partial \psi}{\partial x} = \frac{\partial (\widetilde{VC} - \tilde{V}\tilde{C})}{\partial x} \qquad (5)$$

The "~" indicates a value that is averaged over the small x' (sub-grid) scale. y represents, roughly, the error between the coarsely resolved solution and the true multi-scale solution. The assumption of self-affinity and the fif representation allow the expression for t to be evaluated in terms of the coarser scale values of C and V. Applying a simple finite differencing, eqn 5 reduces to a set of ordinary differential equations in terms only of the values at interpolation points (or points of iteration) x_i, i=1,...N;

$$\frac{\partial \tilde{C}_n}{\partial t} + (\widetilde{VC})_n - (\widetilde{VC})_{n-1} = [A]_n (C_{pl}) \qquad (6)$$

where (C_{pl}) is the vector of C values at the interpolation points, and A is a full matrix whose components depend on δ, the x_n and V_n values, and the d_ns of eqn. 1. In the limit that all d_n's = 0, τ becomes 0 everywhere, A becomes empty and eqn 6 reduces to the classical form.

For this example the dns will change over time, and an additional equation is needed to capture the evolving dns as well as the Cn values. Following Scotti & Meneveau (1997), a transport equation for t can be derived:

$$\frac{\partial \tau}{\partial t} + \frac{\partial}{\partial x} (\tilde{V}\tau) = R(\tilde{V}, \tilde{C}, \widetilde{VC}, d_n) \tag{7}$$

This equation is discretized in a similar fashion to eqn 6. Through application of the fif repre-sentation, R can be written explicitly in terms of the coarse (~) values of C and V. Then equations 6 and 7 must be solved simultaneously for the C_n and d_n values. The full fractal profile of C can be computed at any time step by application of eqns. 1-2.

While the fif formalism allows a multi-scale representation naturally, it is not without its limitations. These include: (1) The non-local nature of integrals of fifs over sub-intervals can result in full matrices after discretization. However, the fif is a very efficient representation so that not many points are needed for good accuracy. (2) The initial scale factors {di} can be esti-mated by fitting data, such as permeability vs depth profiles. (This has proved to be very fast and robust, computationally.) This can be done assuming that data are point values or interval averages. The relationship between independent variable scale factors (such as for permeability) and dependent variable scale factors (e.g., water content or concentration) is not simple. At pre-sent, initial time profiles as well as steady state equations provide relationships. More generally, an additional transport equation can be derived for the d_n's. (3) The fractal dimension is another parameter that is required but for which there is not a unique definition. (4) Further, there is the question of whether the governing equations themselves remain valid at all scales – the fif is simply an algorithm for capturing the multi-scale interactions dictated by a set of equations whose coefficients are fractal; it implies nothing about the physical accuracy of the equations themselves over the range of scales considered.

Attractive aspects of the fif approach are: (1) Multi-scale structure is built into the algorithm. The spatial structure of the solution at any time point can be resolved as finely as desired by sim-ple iteration of the fif set. Interaction of scales is also automatically included. (2) Traditional fi-nite difference (fd) and finite element (fe) methods can incorporate the fif formalism, since the integrals of fif representations of dependent variables and products of same can be solved exactly in terms of the traditional fd or fe piece-wise linear or quadratic interpolation functions over computational grid cells. (3) The fif algorithm can be applied to flow (saturated or unsaturated) as well as to trans-port equations. (4) Exact integrals of fractal fluxes provide a new homogeni-zation method, which will be explored in two and three dimensional models.

Acknowledgement. This work is supported by a grant from the U. S. Department of Energy's Office of Basic Energy Sciences.

- Reservoir rock - Berea SS ⇒ pore geometries ...
  → lattice - Boltzmon methods.

EXPLORATION OF THE INFLUENCE OF HYDRAULIC PROPERTY CORRELATION ON PREDICTIONS OF DNAPL INFILTRATION AND ENTRAPMENT

Lawrence D. Lemke, Linda M. Abriola, and Pierre Goovaerts
The University of Michigan;
Department of Civil & Environmental Engineering
1351 Beal Avenue, Room 181 EWRE Bldg., Ann Arbor, MI 48109-2275

Used Kozeny Carman w/ d_{10} & $\phi = 36\%$.

This paper describes initial results of an investigation into the significance of aquifer property correlation on multiphase fluid migration and entrapment in a nonuniform, unconfined glacial sand aquifer located in Oscoda, Michigan. Dependent and independent porosity, permeability, and Pc-Sat parameter fields are incorporated into a cross-sectional numerical multiphase flow model used to predict PCE infiltration and redistribution at the scale of a DNAPL source zone. Earlier efforts investigating nonuniformity effects in this aquifer were conducted in support of a Surfactant Enhanced Aquifer Remediation (SEAR) pilot test (Drummond et al., 2000). Alternative spatial variability models were used to predict surfactant transport flowpaths, travel times, and concentrations across the intended SEAR sweep zone such that both the position and pumping rates of the surfactant injection and extraction wells could be effectively optimized (Drummond et al., 2000). At the same time, M-VALOR (Abriola et al., 1992), a two-dimensional immiscible fluid flow model developed at The University of Michigan by Abriola, et al. (1992) and modified by Rathfelder and Abriola (1998), was used to compare predicted PCE distributions for a vertical profile extracted from a nonuniform three-dimensional hydraulic conductivity, K, realization with a uniform homogenous profile of equivalent average K. In both cases uniform porosity was assumed. Subsequent SEAR flushing of the two profiles was simulated using MISER (Abriola et al., 1997), a two-dimensional solubilization simulator that accounts for rate limited PCE solubilization and surfactant sorption. These early simulations demonstrated that 1) small-scale nonuniformities occurring within a single depositional facies have an important influence on the infiltration and redistribution of DNAPLs within such units, and 2) variability in the organic distribution within a DNAPL source zone directly influences multiphase flow and transport model predictions of DNAPL recovery. The current study extends the prior investigation through the incorporation of a more rigorous set of procedures to model spatial variability and dependence of aquifer properties governing multiphase flow.

METHODS

Porosity and grain size distribution data collected from 167 core samples were used to estimate hydraulic conductivity and capillary pressure-saturation curves (Lemke et al., 2000). Isotropic K values were estimated from grain size distributions at 167 sample points and validated using laboratory measurements. The Haverkamp and Parlange (1986) method (HPM) was used to estimate capillary pressure as a function of effective water saturation for a given grain size distribution and values of porosity, ϕ, and irreducible wetting phase saturation, S_{wr}. Both the air entry pressure, P_b, and pore size distribution index, λ for the Brooks-Corey P_c-Sat model are estimated directly using HPM. Laboratory measurements for representative samples from each grain size distribution class made using a pressure cell apparatus developed by Salehzadeh and Demond (1999) were used to validate predicted HPM air-water retention curves. Air entry pressures for the air-water retention curve were scaled to the organic-water system using a ratio of interfacial tension, contact angle, intrinsic permeability and porosity (Leverett, 1941).

Three-dimensional, nonuniform K fields, generated at a one-foot (0.3 m) increment over an 80x60x30-foot grid conditioned to the 167 K estimates across the study area, were simulated using a three-step procedure: 1) sequential indicator simulation (SIS) (Goovaerts, 1997; Deutsch and Journel, 1998) was used to simulate the spatial distribution of six categories of grain size distributions which were identified based on KMEANS clustering of the 167 measured grain size distributions following the approach of Schad (1993), 2) d10 values were randomly assigned to each grid node based upon smoothed histograms of d10 values for each individual grain size distribution class; and 3) K values were estimated using the Carmen-Kozeny relationship (Bear, 1972). Three ensemble sets of 25 realizations were generated with different porosity, permeability, and Brooks-Corey P_c-Sat parameter distributions (Table 1).

	SIM SET 1	SIM SET 2	SIM SET 3
Porosity, ϕ	Constant	Random (SGS)	Random (SGS)
Permeability, k	SIS $k=f(d_{10})$	$k=f(d_{10},\phi)$	$k=f(d_{10},\phi)$
P_c-Sat (Brooks-Corey)	Single, constant wtd. avg. Pb and l	Single, constant wtd. avg. Pb and l	Separate Pb, l by IV class and f
Leverett Scaling	$P_b = f\left(\sqrt{k}\right)$	$P_b = f\left(\sqrt{k = f(d_{10},\phi)}\right)$	None: $P_b = f(IVclass)$

Table 1. Variable treatment of porosity, intrinsic permeability, and Brooks-Corey capillary pressure-saturation (Pc-Sat) parameters among the three alternative simulation sets.

Although SIS successfully generates stratified realizations of grain size distribution categories, random assignment of d10 values from overlapping probability distributions results in a spatial randomization of K value distributions, even when uniform porosity is assumed. Independent simulation of a spatially variable porosity field (SIM SETs 2 and 3) contributes to greater entropy in the estimated K field. In this study, SIM SETs 2 and 3 share identical porosity and permeability distributions and differ only in the assignment of capillary pressure parameters.

Spatial moments and saturation probability distributions resulting from point source DNAPL infiltration predicted by MVALOR were analyzed along two-dimensional cross sectional profiles to detect similarities and differences in model behavior for each simulation set. In each MVALOR run, 96 liters of PCE was released over 4 cells at the top of the model at a constant flux of 0.12 l/day for 400 days with an additional 330 days allowed for subsequent organic infiltration and redistribution. Horizontal and vertical grid discretization was 1 foot (0.3048m) and 0.25 foot (0.0762m), respectively; with vertical discretization fine enough to resolve capillary entry pressure effects (Rathfelder and Abriola, 1998).

RESULTS

Figure 1 illustrates simulated PCE saturations for one representative realization from SIM SETS 1, 2, and 3. PCE saturation is scaled from 0.0 to 0.04 in these figures to enhance depiction of low saturation variability, although maximum saturations each model ranged from 0.3 to 0.4 in SIM SETS 1 and

2 and up to 0.91 in SIM SET 3. Profiles from SIM SETs 1 and 2 display irregular downward migration paths or channeling of PCE due to macroscopic permeability variations in the simulation grid of the type discussed by Keuper and Frind (1991). SIM SETs 1 and 2 are quite similar when compared to SIM SET 3, which shows a greater uniformity in PCE saturations, a greater tendency for pooling above low permeability lenses, and a decreased degree of lateral spreading. Plots of σ^2_{xx} versus time confirm the observed decrease in spreading and also indicate a tendency for PCE to remain mobile for a longer period of time during the simulation. Although the PCE distributions illustrated here have not yet been compared through simulated SEAR flushing, it is clear that SIM SET 3 realizations will have a significantly different behavior in comparison those belonging to the first two simulation sets with respect to predicted breakthrough concentrations and tailing.

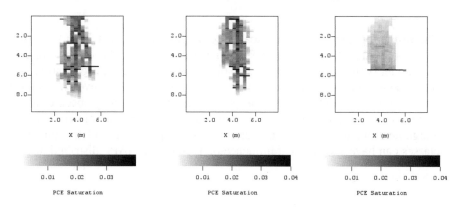

Figure 1. Simulated PCE distributions for three realizations in SIM SETs 1, 2, and 3.

Significant differences in predicted PCE infiltration and entrapment in the third simulation set result from the assignment of P_c-Sat parameters independently of the intrinsic permeability field. Leverett scaling employed in SIM SETs 1 and 2 leads to a direct correlation between P_b and k (Figure 2a) while the lack of Leverett scaling in SIMSET 3 decreases this dependency (Figure 2b). Cross-plots of P_b and λ (Figure 2c) reveal that HPM generated P_c-Sat parameter values are segregated according to grain size distribution classes in SIM SET 3 realizations. In this instance, correlation of P_b with grain size classes leads to a preservation of the spatial continuity of similar values for air entry pressures that account for the significantly different DNAPL infiltration behavior in SIM SET 3.

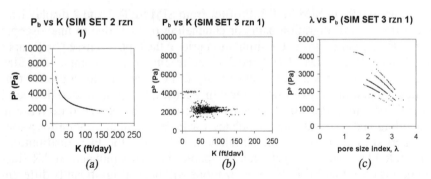

Figure 2. Cross-plots of P_b vs K for the first realizations of SIM SET 2 (a) and SIM SET 3 (b), and λ vs P_b cross-plot for the first realization of SIM SET 3 (c).

The results of this set of numerical experiments suggest that 1) independent variation in more than one aquifer parameter can increase the variance of certain model performance metrics (e.g., observed spreading), 2) correlation between pore entry pressures and permeability fields (i.e., Leverett scaling) remains important in the face of this greater variability but may obscure spatial correlation of P_c-Sat indices if the permeability field is randomized, and 3) assignment of alternative P_c-Sat indices based on spatially correlated grain size classes can have a significant influence on predicted DNAPL distributions.

UNCERTAINTY ESTIMATION OF WELL HEAD PROTECTION ZONES: A LAGRANGIAN APPROXIMATION

Fritz Stauffer, Sabine Attinger, Stephanie Zimmermann and Wolfgang Kinzelbach

Institute of Hydromechanics and Water Resources Management, ETH Hoenggerberg, CH-8093 Zurich / Switzerland Phone: +41-1-6333079; Fax: +41-1-6331061; email: stauffer@ihw.baug.ethz.ch

SUMMARY

Regulations for the protection of drinking water wells require the designation of the domain with a prescribed minimum residence time in groundwater and also of the recharge area of the well. Very often in practice only limited information is available for their delineation. There-fore such analysis should be based on stochastic concepts. The aim of the present investiga-tions is to estimate the uncertainty of well capture zones and well catchments, given the uncertainty of the spatially variable unconditional hydraulic conductivity field using a first-order approximation. For the analysis it is assumed that the flow can be modeled as a steady-state horizontal, confined or unconfined system. The well discharge rate is constant as well as the areal recharge rate. The uncertainty is estimated by considering the advective transport mechanism only, based on the reversed velocity field. The capture zone of a well for a given residence time is determined by the backward movement of many particles starting near the well. The boundary of a catchment is described by the backward movement of two single particles in the heterogeneous flow field, starting near the stagnation point of the well. Many realizations should lead to an assessment of the uncertainty by analyzing the ensemble of the particle locations and tracks. The uncertainty bandwidth of the capture zone and the catch-ment boundary is approximated by using the time dependent longi-

tudinal and transversal second moment of the transversal particle displacements, along and normal to the mean particle trajectory. Applications of the
approach are presented for a simple configuration. The results are compared
with the results from unconditional numerical Monte Carlo simulations of the
same test case. The comparison enables a first assessment of the accuracy, the
applicability, and the limits of the proposed method.

ILLUSTRATION OF THE METHOD: TEST CASE

The above mentioned semi-analytical and numerical procedures are applied
to a synthetic test case with a single well of constant discharge rate
Q_w=432m³/d and constant areal recharge rate N=0.001m/d. The domain is a
rectangular, two-dimensional unconfined heterogeneous aquifer of size L*B
(L=2000m, B=1200m) with horizontal impermeable base. The well is located at x_{w1}=995m and x_{w2}=505m. The spatial variability of the aquifer's
hydraulic conductivity K(x) is given by the variance σ_Y^2=0.1, and the correlation length IY=100m. The geometric mean Kg is 432m/d. The three bounda-
ries (x_1, x_2=B), (x_1=L, x_2), and (x_1=0, x_2) are impermeable, whereas (x_1, x_2=0)
is a fixed-head boundary with head h0=10m. Two situations are considered
here for illustration, a) the capture zone for the residence time of 50d, and b)
the catchment boundary of the well. For the semi-analytical approach the
flow field is calculated analytically. For the particle tracking a backward
Runge-Kutta scheme is used. The capture zone is calculated with 100 particles. The numerical modeling is performed using a mesh size of 10m and a
total number of m=1000 Monte Carlo runs.

The Monte-Carlo type simulation results are presented as a map of the probability to belong to the well capture zone or catchment (Figures 2 and 3, left).
The lines of probability 0.977, 0.5 and 0.023 correspond to the uncertainty
bandwidth of the semi-analytical approach (Figures 2 and 3, right). For the capture zone (Fig. 3, right) the longitudinal second moment of the particle displacements turned out to be relevant in this case for delineating the uncertainty
bandwidth. The results of the semi-analytical approach are quite similar to the
Monte-Carlo type results except the uncertainty bandwidth towards the upper
boundary (Fig. 3). The locations for the capture zone or catchment for homogeneous conditions are practically identical to the average location over all realizations. The uncertainty bandwidth deviates from the numerical results within
a zone of about two correlation lengths from the upper boundary. Note that the
semi-analytical results are obtained with a computational time being several
orders of magnitude smaller than for the numerical Monte Carlo method.

The evaluation of the time-dependent capture zone and steady-state catchment boundary of pumping wells and the related uncertainty bandwidth is of practical use. Very often only few observations are available. The presence of heterogeneities may strongly affect the uncertain-ty bandwidth of the location of protection zones.

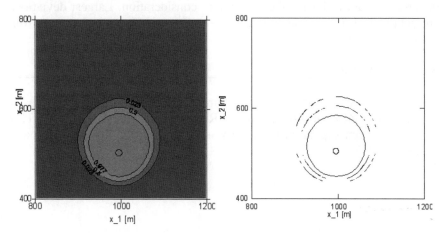

Uncertainty bandwidth (95%) of the capture zone of a pumping well for a residence time of 50 d for a test case with a flow domain of 2000m x 1200m, variance $\sigma_Y^2=0.1$, correlation length $I_Y=100m$; left: Monte-Carlo simulation with 1000 runs; right: semi-analytical Lagrangian approach.

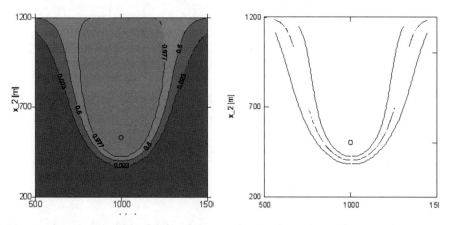

Uncertainty bandwidth (95%) of the catchment boundary of a pumping well for a test case with a flow domain 2000m x 1200m, variance $\sigma_Y^2=0.1$, correlation length I_Y=100m; left: Monte-Carlo simulation with 1000 runs; right: semi-analytical Lagrangian approach.

The comparison of the semi-analytical Lagrangian results with the Monte-Carlo type simulations shows that the method yields fair estimates of the uncertainty bandwidth for the case under consideration. Largest deviations are obtained for locations being less then two correlation lengths apart from a domain boundary.

ACKNOWLEDGEMENTS

The study was performed within the European Research Project "Stochastic Analysis of Well Head Protection and Risk Assessment" W-SAHaRA. This project has been supported by the Swiss Federal Office for Education and Science (BBT).

ON THE USE OF THE CONCEPT OF BLOCK-SCALE MACRODISPERSION FOR NUMERICAL SIMULATION OF FLOW AND TRANSPORT IN HETEROGENEOUS FORMATIONS

Alberto Bellin[1], Alison Lawrence[2] and Yoram Rubin[2]

[1]*Dipartimento di Ingegneria Civile ed Ambientale, Università di Trento, via Mesiano 77, 38050 Trento, ITALY*

[2]*Department of Civil and Environmental Engineering, University of California at Berkeley, Berkeley, California 94720, USA*

[Handwritten annotation: Hierarchy of dispersion — Macro scale ⇒ micro / block scale → micro scale. ? Sequences → Facies → internal facies scale? → my interp of Physical meaning.]

The spreading of solutes in natural formations is controlled by hydraulic property variations acting on a multiplicity of continuous and discrete scales. Stochastic modeling is often used to account for both the variations of the hydraulic conductivity, K, and un-certainty. The latter accounts for incomplete information on the actual hydraulic property variations. To capture accurately the spatial variability of , a very fine grid is required, with typical dimensions being only a fraction of the log-conductivity integral scale. The ensuing computational burden is one of the main drawbacks limiting the use of stochastic modeling in applications, and its relevance increases when stochastic modeling calls for Monte Carlo simulations. The tendency is to reduce the computational cost by using larger grid block scales, and reducing the resolution. Using large grid blocks is permitted only if measures are introduced to account for the loss of resolution caused by the ho-mogenization.

To reconcile the dichotomy between the need for high-resolution simulations and the computational cost, we follow here the idea of using an upscaled macrodispersion co-efficient, which was explored by Dagan (1994), and pursued further by Rubin et al. (1999) who derived and discussed the block dispersion tensor for ergodic plumes. In Bel-lin et al. (2001, submitted), a method is proposed which reproduces the large-scale vari-ability directly on the grid, and models the unresolved small-scale variations through suitable block-scale effective macrodispersion coefficients. In this paper, we summarize those calculations and show an example of the results.

AN EXAMPLE OF APPLICATION

To reduce the computational effort of Monte Carlo simulations, we propose simu-lating solute spreading using large grid blocks, while reproducing the effect of the sub-grid spatial variability of the hydraulic conductivity, which is not captured directly on the grid, by a Brownian motion with the time-dependent effective block-scale dispersion ten-sor obtained by Rubin et al. (1999).

The following length scales are important in numerical simulations: I_Y, the integral scale of the log-hydraulic conductivity, $Y=lnK$, which represents the hydraulic property variations of the geological formation; the characteristic size of the source, l; the charac-teristic size of the grid-blocks, Δ; and the length representing the characteristic scale of the variability reproduced

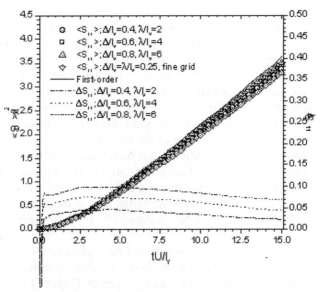

Figure 1: Comparison between the longitudinal second-order plume moments obtained while maintaining constant the ratio Δ/I_Y. The first-order solution, obtained in absence of wiped-out variability, and the fine-grid numerical solution are also shown. In all cases, the transverse source size is $l_2/I_Y=10$ and $\sigma_Y^2=0,2$. The relative difference $\Delta<S_{II}>=[<S_{II}>-<S_{II}>_{FG}]/<S_{II}>_{FG}$ is shown on the right axis. Results are obtained with 2000 Monte Carlo realizations.

directly on the grid, λ, which corresponds to the highest ob-servable fre-quency $f=1/(2\lambda)$. In applications, the latter can be roughly defined as the dimension of the zone of uniform hydraulic conductivity. Following Rubin et al. (1999) we assume that the local fluctuation of Y from its expected value, m_Y, can be split into two components $\bar{Y}'=\bar{Y}+\tilde{Y}$, where $\bar{Y}$ is the zero-mean fluctuation representing the variations captured on the grid, and $\tilde{Y}$ represents the sub-grid variability, such that the block-scale λ is proportional to I_Y, the integral scale of $\bar{Y}$.

To demonstrate the potential of the methodology proposed in Bellin et al. (2001, submitted), in Figure 1 we show the effective longitudinal second order moment $<S_{11}>$ obtained from numerical simulations conducted with several block sizes and with the wiped-out variability simulated through the block-scale dispersivity. Figure 1 also shows the relative difference $\Delta S_{11}=[<S_{11}>-<S_{11}>_{FG}]/<S_{11}>_{FG}$ between the expected values of the longitudi-nal second order moments obtained with a given grid spacing, Δ, and with $\Delta=0.25I_Y$, which is the grid size used for the fine grid simulations.

The source area is rectangular with sides $l_1=I_Y$ and $l_2=10I_Y$ along the longitu-dinal and transverse directions, respectively. The first order solution is obtai-ned for vanishing longitudinal source size and $l_2=10I_Y$.

The simulations are performed imposing the condition $\Delta/I_Y=0.25$, which leads to grid sizes of $\Delta/I_Y=0.4, 0.6$ and 0.8 for the three values of λ considered in this paper. In doing that, the ratio $R_\Delta=\Delta/\Delta_{fg}$ is 1.6 for $\lambda/I_Y=2$, and it reaches the values of 2.4 and 3.2 for $\lambda/I_Y=4$ and $\lambda/I_Y=6$, respectively. The relative differences between large- and fine-grid simulations vary between 2.2% and 4.6% for $\lambda=2I_Y$, and bet-ween 6.9% and 9.7% for $\lambda=6I_Y$. In both cases, the smaller relative difference is observed at the larger times. The case $\lambda=4I_Y$ lies in between the other two cases.

Furthermore, Figure 1 shows that the numerical $<S_{11}>$ is larger than the corre-sponding fine-grid solution and that as λ increases it approaches the first-order solution. This result shows that the effects on the solute spreading of the wiped-out variability can be reproduced through the effective block-dispersi-vity concept with the above limitation for the grid's size, although the relative importance of the neglected higher-order terms increases with λ, as more variability is reproduced through the block-scale dispersion coefficients.

The main conclusion that can be drawn from this work is that the block-scale mac-rodispersion coefficients can be used to model the wiped-out variability occurring when blocks larger than a fraction of log-conductivity integral scale are used in numerical simulations. This leads to the reduction of the computational cost of the numerical simu-lations. However, the need to obtain an accurate reproduction of the large-scale variabil-ity, which is repro-duced directly on the computational grid, imposes an upper limit on the grid size that can be used in numerical simulations of solute transport.

REFERENCES

BELLIN, A., A. LAWRENCE, and Y. RUBIN, On the concept of effective-block-macrodispersi-vity and its use in modeling flow and transport in heterogeneous for-mations, Water Resour. Res., 2001, submitted.

DAGAN, G., Upscaling of Dispersion Coefficients in Transport Through Heterogeneous Formations, In: Computational Methods in Water Resources X, Peters et al., eds., Kluwer Academic Press, The Netherlands, pp 431-439, 1994.

RUBIN, Y., A. SUN, R. MAXWELL, and A. BELLIN, The concept of block-effective macrodis-persivity and a unified approach for grid-scale- and plume-scale-dependent trans-port, J. of Fluid Mech., 395, 161-180, 1999.

APPLICABILITY OF UNIMODAL STOCHASTIC APPROACHES IN SIMULATING FLOW IN BIMODAL HETEROGENEOUS FORMATIONS

Zhiming Lu, Dongxiao Zhang, Elizabeth Keating
Hydrology, Geochemistry, and Geology Group (EES-6)
MS T003, Los Alamos National Laboratory
Los Alamos, NM 87545

Most existing stochastic models assume that the porous medium being studied can be characterized by one single correlation scale. However, hydraulic properties exhibit spatial variations at various scales, thus stochastic models developed for unimodal media may not be applicable to flow and transport in a bimodal heterogeneous medium. The aim of this study is to investigate under what circumstances the second-order moment-based stochastic models are applicable to the bimodal porous medium.

We assume that two materials (categories) in the porous medium may have a different mean, variance, and correlation scale. The distribution of materials in the domain is characterized by indicator random functions, whose correlation structures are assumed to be independent of the statistics of the two materials in the previous studies [Rubin and Journel, 1991; Rubin, 1995; Russo et al., 2001]. We derived expressions for the covariance of indicator random variables in terms of statistics of two materials

$$C_{I,ij}(h) = p_i(\delta_{ij} - p_j)\, e^{-h/\lambda_I} \qquad (1)$$

where p_i is the proportion of the ith material in the porous medium, h is the separation distance, and λ_I is the correlation length of the indicator random variables

$$\lambda_I = L_1 L_2 / (L_1 + L_2) \qquad (2)$$

which is the harmonic mean of the mean lengths of two materials. It should be emphasized that if the mean lengths depend on directions, the correlation length λ_I is also direction-dependent. In this case, the indicator random variables are anisotropic. For a stationary field, the anisotropy ratio between any two directions is equal to the ratio of the mean lengths of a category in these two directions. Once the covariances of the indicator random functions are known, the variance and the correlation length of the composite field can be found. The mean, variance, and correlation length of the composite field are used to define the "equivalent" unimodal field.

To investigate the applicability of the second-order moment-based stochastic model to a bimodal porous medium, we simulated four cases with different degree of the symmetry of the $Y = \ln K_s$ distribution and the contrast of between-en $\{Y_1(x)\}$ and $\{Y_2(x)\}$ of two materials. For each case, we conduct two sets of Monte Carlo simulations and compare results against those from the second-order moment-based stochastic models [Zhang and Winter, 1999; Zhang and Lu, 2001]. The first set of Monte Carlo simulations, termed as "bimodal Monte Carlo," is performed for flow in a porous medium with two materials. The second set of Monte Carlo simulations, called "unimodal Monte Carlo," is done for the "equivalent" unimodal fields with an exponential covariance. The bimodal Monte Carlo simulation results are considered the "true" solution that is the basis for comparisons between different approaches.

The second-order moment-based stochastic model [Zhang and Winter, 1999; Zhang and Lu, 2001] is applied to the "equivalent" unimodal field with a single correlation length. For the purpose of comparison, we also applied the second-order moment-based stochastic model to the field with a bimodal covariance C_Y, which is a summation of several exponential terms. We call the former the unimodal moment-based approach, and the latter the bimodal moment-based approach. The main purpose of this study is to discuss the applicability of the unimodal moment-based and unimodal Monte Carlo approaches to flow in a bimodal porous medium. It is also of interest to see if the second-order bimodal moment-based stochastic model will make any improvement, comparing to the second-order unimodal moment-based stochastic model.

It is found that, for all cases considered, the head variance obtained from the bimodal moment-based stochastic model is essentially the same as that computed from the unimodal moment-based stochastic model. This is understandable as the covariance of the composite log hydraulic conductivity field for the cases considered can be well approximated by an exponential covariance of a single correlation length.

Our numerical results show that, when the total variance of the $\ln K_s$ is small, for example $\sigma_Y^2 < 1.0$, no matter what the $\ln K_s$ distribution is, the mean head and its variance from both the unimodal and bimodal moment-based stochastic models as well as those from the unimodal Monte Carlo simulation are close to the bimodal Monte Carlo simulation results. This indicates that the unimodal moment-based stochastic models are applicable to a bimodal system in this case.

When the total variance the $\ln K_s$ is large, the symmetry of the $\ln K_s$ distribution has a great effect on the applicability of the stochastic moment approaches. When the $\ln K_s$ distribution is symmetric, results from both unimodal and bimodal moment-based models are very close to those from bimodal Monte Carlo simulations for the composite variance as large as 4.0. As the composite variance increases, the agreement between the second-order moment-based models and the bimodal Monte Carlo simulations deteriorates. When the $\ln K_s$ distribution is asymmetric, results from two sets of Monte Carlo simulations may be in close agreements, due to the fact that one material dominates the distribution and thus the bimodal porous medium may be well represented by its equivalent unimodal porous medium. For this case and when the composite variance is about 3.5, the results from both unimodal and bimodal moment-based models are significantly different than those from the corresponding Monte Carlo simulations, indicating that the second-order moment-based stochastic models do not work for a relatively large composite variance under these conditions. The applicability of the second-order moment-based stochastic models to a bimodal porous medium is further limited by the fact that in realty the mean log hydraulic conductivities between different materials may differ by several orders of magnitude, thus the composite variance of the $\ln K$ may be very large.

REFERENCES

Rubin, Y., and A. G. Journel, Simulation of non-Gaussian space random functions for modeling transport in groundwater, Water Resour. Res., 27(7), 1711-1721, 1991.

Rubin, Y., Flow and transport in bimodal heterogeneous formations, Water Resour. Res., 31(10), 2461-2468, 1995.

Russo, D, J. Zaidel, and A. Laufer, Numerical analysis of flow and transport in variably saturated bimodal heterogeneous porous media, Water Resour. Res., 37(8), 2127-2141, 2001.

Zhang, D., and Z. Lu, Stochastic analysis of flow in a heterogeneous unsaturated-saturated system, Water Resour. Res., Submitted, 2001.

Zhang, D., and C. L. Winter, Nonstationary stochastic analysis of steady-state flow through variably saturated, heterogeneous media, Water Resour. Res., 34, 1998.

GENERALIZED COARSE-GRAINING-PROCEDURES FOR FLOW IN POROUS MEDIA

S.Attinger
*Institute of Hydromechanics and Water Resources Management,
ETH Zurich, Switzerland*

Measurement results of soil properties that are spatially variable crucially depend on the resolution at which they are resolved. This paper focuses on heterogeneous soil permeabilities and the impact their resolution has on the solution of the piezometric head equation.

We present a systematic approach to derive a resolution dependent head equation where small scale heterogeneities up to an arbitrary length scale are averaged out and large scale heterogeneities are still resolved. For this purpose, we choose a method called coarse-graining. Basically, it is a partial volume averaging procedure developed in the context of large eddy simulations in the theory of turbulence. Iteration of coarse-graining over stepwise coarser averaging volume allows one to formulate the coarse-graining procedure in terms of a differential equation which becomes a renormalisation group equation. Renormalisation group analysis is equivalent to a summation of higher order perturbation theory contributions. Therefore, the results are valid for highly heterogeneous media as well.

We find an explicit form for the head equation on intermediate scales: small scale fluctuations in the heterogeneous permeabilities are averaged out up to an intermediate scale, yet they show an impact on the head equation in the form of a scale dependent equivalent permeability. We present explicit results in two and three dimensional domains: For no coarse-graining, the equivalent permeability is given by the arithmetic mean whereas it is equivalent to the effective permeability in the case of large Coarse Graining scales. For intermediate scales, we find scale dependent values.

In our talk, we also present results of numerical simulations. The aim of this part of study was to test whether the coarse-grained pressure equation still models essential physical features of the heterogeneous flow behavior. As a reference case, we performed a flow simulation through a heterogeneous medium on a very fine grid solving the local equation and measured the total water balance. Gradually, we coarsened the numerical grid as shown in figure 1 and solved the pressure equation defined on the coarser resolution scale. Additionally, we solved the equivalent homogeneous pressure equation for the case of global upscaling. The total water balance has to be conserved in all simulations due to mass conservation. We tested it and found it conserved within a standard deviation of 8 percent. Moreover, we compared our approach (moving frame average or block average in figure 2) with other averaging procedures as arithmetic averaging, harmonic averaging and geometric averaging permeabilities over the coarsening blocks. The results are plotted in figure 2 for a two-dimensional domain with isotropically distributed permeability values.

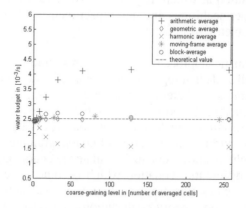

Figure 2: Total water balance for different coarsening levels and different averaging procedures.

The results can be used in order to reduce the computational effort in numerical modeling: A reduction of the grid-block resolution can be performed without a big loss of information.

Figure1:

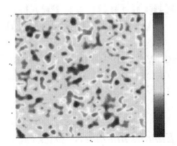

Fine resolved heterogeneous permeability field (256x256)

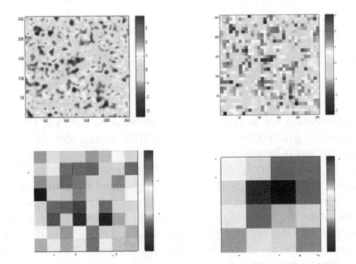

Four coarsening levels: Averaging over 2x2, 8x8, 16x16, 32x32 cells

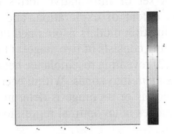

Equivalent homogeneous permeability field

OBTAINING INFORMATION FOR SUBSTANTIATION OFHYDROGEOLOGICAL PREDICTIONS WITH A SPECIFIED ERROR

Prof. Nikolay Ognyanyk & Dr. Nina Paramonova
The Institute of Geological Sciences of the NAS of Ukraine
55b, O.Gonchara-st, Kiev, Ukraine, 01054
Tel: + 38 044 2169550
Fax: + 38 044 2169334
E-mail: timophei@bricks.Kiev.ua.

Initial information for model development must be optimal, i.e. providing predictions at a given time and with a specified error under minimum costs. Hydrogeological information is optimized in the following consequence: an accuracy of design works _ an accuracy of predictions _ a model accuracy _ an accuracy of hydrogeological information obtained at the field-scale and by inverse task solution. A method for research of survey point density is described including the following stages: (1) establishment of a parameter variability model and the optimal mode for arial parameter approximation, (2) zoning an area in terms of variability, (3) development of a regression model, in which approximation errors are functions of exploring network density and parameter variability, for all distinguished sites, (4) organization of feedback and model adaptation. A set of informative terms describing geological parameter variability, an extent of exploration, and quality of variability representation by approximation models is obtained during calculations and a variogram analysis. Zoning consists of two stages: (1) classification of sites using informative terms; (2) revealing resemblance between different couples of classes and combining them into zones. Within each zone an average distance between mapping points or its range is determined by substitution of specified errors or their ranges in an optimal regression model.

ENTROPY-BASED APPROACH TO REMOVE REDUNDANT MONITORING WELLS FROM REGIONAL-SCALE GROUNDWATER NETWORK

Zhihua Chen[1], Gang Chen[1], M.Leshoele[2], Xuejun Chen[3]
[1] Dept. of Env. & Hydrogeology, China University of Geosciences
[2] Graduate College, China University of Geosciences
[3] Guilin Institute of Technology

INTRODUCTION

Redundant monitoring wells (RMW) within a groundwater-monitoring network are those observations wells that have contributed little or no information to our understanding of the groundwater system being monitored RMW are abundant in the monitoring networks that were founded prior to or in 1960's. The reasons for the occurrence of RMW in the networks possibly resulted from two cases: First, as the design of monitoring networks was mainly based on the hydrogeological approach, the number and location of monitoring wells were based on local hydrogeological conditions. The existence of RMW in the network designed at that time was an almost unavoidable due to the limitations of knowledge and information about groundwater system. Secondly, for economic reasons, boreholes that were drilled for geological and hydrogeological investigations, pump testing and other purposes were adopted for many monitoring networks. Hence, dense distribution of wells in an area with high permeability and good accessibility, and sparse distribution of wells in an area with low permeability and/or difficulty to access should not surprise.

The aim of this research is to extend the entropy–based methods to hydrogeology, and identify RMW in monitoring networks in terms of the information relationships among different monitoring wells. The dataset used in this case study are taken from the water level observations of a regional-scale monitoring network in Hebei Plain, China. It included 140 monitoring wells and their 10-year observations (1981-1990).

ENTROPY-BASED APPROACH

Since a monitoring network has an ability to transmit hydrological information, groundwater-monitoring networks can be considered as a signal communication system. All monitoring wells in a network are the receivers of water level signals. Three inherent characteristics of the communication system in signal transmission exist in the monitoring network: (1) signal transferring; (2) signal decaying; (3) signal identifying. The variations of groundwater levels are the signals presenting various states of groundwater system; there should be some differences in the signal characteristics because the monitoring wells are located in different hierarchical groundwater systems and/or different geological formation. These differences in signal characteristics can be described by their probability distributions and used to identify their relationships. We can adopt the concepts of entropy to quantitatively measure the info-relationships among monitoring well pairs and then to recognize RMW from groundwater monitoring networks.

For a monitoring well, its information content relies on the statistical structure of its observations. The more complicated the fluctuations of water level are, the higher entropy the monitoring well has. Therefore, the entropy can be applied to measure the capability of a monitoring well to provide information of groundwater.

Entropy is formulated in terms of probabilities for a discrete set of observations

$$H(X) = -\sum_{i=1}^{N} p(x_i)\ln p(x_i)$$

Here $H(X)$ = entropy, described as the information contained in monitoring well X.

Another important concept gained from communication theory is the mutual information $T(X_i, X_j)$, which represents the information transfer between monitoring well pair X_i and X_j. Mutual information has the following basic properties: (i) when two random observations of monitoring wells X_i and X_j are independent of each other, $T(X_i,X_j)=0$. (ii) If there is a statistical relationship between monitoring well pair X_i and X_j, $T(X_i,X_j)>0$, which shows that there is an information transfer between X_i and X_j.

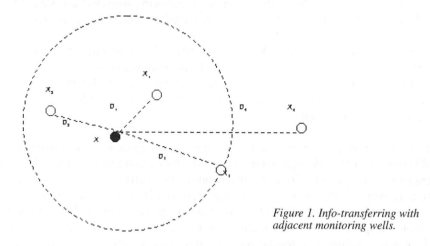

Figure 1. Info-transferring with adjacent monitoring wells.

Before removing RMW from a monitoring network we need a criterion to identify where the potential RMW are located and which monitoring wells are the RMW. In this investigation, the information transmission $T(X_i,X_j)$ between a pair of monitoring wells has been adopted as a measurement, which is information standard instead of standard errors or assembly average. With this method, we can find out accurately those RMW in a network. For example, there are 5 monitoring wells in a certain area (shown in Fig.1), the questions are: Is it necessary to include all the monitoring wells? Which are superfluous among these monitoring wells? And which could replace another while their information transferring is high enough? The procedure of using mutual information $T(X_i,X_j)$ to identify the RMW from a network is described as follows.

Generally, monitoring well **X** has information transfers $T(X_i,X_j)$ (i=1,2,3,4) with its surrounding monitoring wells X_1, X_2, X_3, X_4. Since the information transfer among monitoring wells is essentially a function of distances between their locations, i.e., the amount of info-transmission will decrease while the distance Di increases. So, if the aquifer media is homogeneous and $D_1<D_2<D_3<D_4$, it is true for the relation: $T(X,X_1)>T(X,X_2)>T(X,X_3)>T(X,X_4)$.

Suppose $T(X_i,X_j) \geq \eta$, when the information transfer $T(X_i,X_j)$ between well pair is high enough that either of the well can be replaced. Therefore, one of the wells can be recognized as the redundant monitoring well. η is the information transfer threshold. For instance in Fig.1, if $T(X,X_3) \geq \eta$, the monitoring wells X_1 and X_2 are considered as the redundant monitoring wells as they have same information as the monitoring well X and therefore should be eliminated.

For the monitoring well pair **X**, X_4, since their information transfer $T(X,X_4) < T(X,X_3) < \eta$, that means the formation from monitoring well X is different from that of monitoring well X_4, and new information can be obtained from X_4's observations. So, it is necessary to keep X_4 as another information source about the groundwater.

From the procedures mentioned above we can conclude that the existence of RMW in the network depends mostly on the monitoring well's capabilities to transfer information within nearby monitoring wells. A high information-transferring capability of a monitoring well implies it can keep strong info-relationships with its adjacent wells. That is the information from the well about the groundwater has significant representation in a wide coverage. Therefore, evaluating information-transferring capacities of monitoring wells is the foundation for identifying RMW in the network.

APPLICATION

The approach is demonstrated by using the data from the monitoring network of Hebei Plain, China, it covers an area over 6.0×10^5 km^2. Geologically, various unconsolidated deposits included diluvial, alluvial and marine compose the main aquifers. The complicated deposition history of the unconsolidated sediments resulted in the aquifers with high heterogeneities.

Summarizing the statistical relations between D_{ij} and $T(X_i,X_j)$, it is a nonlinear relationship and can be matched best with logarithmic equations; the relationships become more definite after the data pairs are grouped according to the flow directions and geological properties; The monitoring wells located at diluvium have higher ability than those in alluvium to transfer information since diluvial sediments have higher transmissibility.

Identification of RMW is the searching procedure of RMW judged by the specific thresholdη. It includes two steps: (i) Calculating the $T(X_i,X_j)$ between each pair of monitoring wells within the radius; (ii) If the information transfer $T(X_i, X_j) \geq \eta$, then compare their entropies $H(X_i)$ and $H(X_j)$. Generally, high threshold of information transfer means the network will have a high density and more accurate. In this study, we have designed several information transfer thresholds (η= 1.6, 1.4, 1.2, 1.0, 0.8) to identify the redundant monitoring wells in the network. The identified RMW corresponding to various thresholds and their relative errors when the RMW were removed is listed in Table 1.

Table 1   the list of info-transfer thresholds & relative errors (R.E.)

Threshold (Napier)	RMW	Percent of RMW (%)	R. E. (%) Δ=5m	R.E.(%) Δ=10m	R.E.(%) Δ=20m
1.6	6	5.00	1.28	**0.57**	0.32
1.4	18	12.6	3.66	**1.77**	0.53
1.2	29	20.7	7.34	**3.63**	1.77
1.0	39	27.9	9.45	**6.64**	3.32
0.8	56	32.8	13.55	**9.75**	3.51

This study shows that the entropy-based approach is a recommendable method to optimize and redesign the existing networks. The obvious benefit of the Entropy-based approach is that it can exactly identify those redundant monitoring wells if they exist in the network. Moreover, it also allows user or expert's judgments in the selection process of monitoring wells. Finally, the information transfer criterion can be adjusted easily to match those different motoring networks with various purposes and/or scales. However, the determination of the information-transferring criterion is still an issue that needs further research in hydrology and hydrogeology.

THE VALUE OF CONDITIONING DATA FOR PREDICTION OF CONSERVATIVE SOLUTE TRANSPORT AT THE OYSTER SITE, VIRGINIA

Timothy D. Scheibe
Pacific Northwest National Laboratory, tim.scheibe@pnl.gov
Richland, WA, USA

The large and diverse body of subsurface characterization data generated at a field research site near Oyster, VA provides a unique opportunity to test various approaches for characterizing field-scale heterogeneity in aquifer properties and modeling subsurface flow and transport. We are using observed bromide breakthrough curves (BTCs) from injection experiments conducted in 1999 and 2000 at two experimental plots within the South Oyster Site (flow cells) as a baseline for evaluating data worth and model effectiveness. BTCs are available at 24 multi-level samplers, eight ports each (192 total sampling points) in one flow cell, and at a lesser number of locations in a second, more heterogeneous flow cell. Each BTC is a time series of measured concentrations, spaced two to twelve hours apart over the seven-day field experiment. A detailed model, implemented using the RAFT code, is used to simulate breakthrough curves at the sampler locations. This model requires the specification of spatial distributions of hydrologic parameters such as hydraulic conductivity. This in turn involves the integration of data of various types and amounts into a conceptual model framework. Characterization information available at the field site includes direct measurements of hydraulic conductivity using borehole flowmeter and well test methods, geological observations and grain size measurements from borehole cores, high-resolution geophysical data (both surface and cross-borehole radar), and detailed observations of conservative tracer and bacterial transport. The number of possible conceptualizations and methods for data integration is nearly limitless, and each gives rise to a different prediction of bromide breakthrough at sampling points. To evaluate the relative appropriateness of each approach, and the value of the data utilized therein, we simulate BTCs at each sampler location and quantitatively compare them to the observed BTCs. The conclusions derived from comprehensive studies based on complete data from the first flow cell will be applied and tested using a more limited data set from the second flow cell.

FLUCTUATION APPROACH TO ASSESSMENT OF THE RELIABILITY OF RADIOACTIVE WASTE DISPOSAL

L. A. Bolshov, A.M. Dykhne, and P. S. Kondratenko
Nuclear Safety Institute, Russian Academy of Sciences,
52 Bolshaya Tul'skaya St., Moscow 113191, Russia
Phone: (095) 955 2291, Fax: (095) 958 0040, E-mail: kondrat@ibrae.ac.ru

One way to solve the problem of high-level radioactive waste (RW) is their disposal in unsaturated rock massifs. In this framework, the radionuclide migration within low-permeable geological media must be approximated in the assessment of RW disposal reliability. In real rock massifs, however, fractures are, at least temporarily, partially water-saturated and provide contaminant transport due to advection. The fracture system is characterized by geometrical and other properties of individual cracks as well as by their relative positions. It is very important that these systems are to a high extent irregular, so the fractures as to their role in radionuclide transport are to be described by the fracture parameter's distribution.

In this paper, some consequences, which result from the irregularity of the geological medium, are deduced regarding RW disposal reliability. These consequences deal with the choice of optimum geometrical repository characteristics and limits on possible accuracy of reliability assessment of RW disposal in geological media. In the course of the analysis, the concepts developed in the theory of irregular solid systems (see Lifshitz et al. (1982), Raikh and Ruzin (1991)) are taken advantage of.

The storage reliability criterion is formulated in terms of appropriately defined dimensionless quantity R named as a risk factor that should be less than unity. The risk factor R is proportional to product of the initial repository radionuclide concentration N/V (N and V are the total number of repository radionuclides at the initial moment and the repository volume, respectively), the repository-medium contact area S and the effective rock transmittance $\tilde{\sigma}$ providing radionuclide transport to the water table.

The quantity $\tilde{\sigma}$ is determined by the sparse and randomly distributed fracture configurations referred as punctures. The ensemble-average of the surface density of punctures in the dependency on a specially defined dimensionless transmittance u is determined by the expression:

$$\rho(u) = \frac{1}{S_0} \exp\left[-\Omega(u)\right] \tag{1}$$

where S_0 has dimension of an area and $\Omega(u)$ is a function possessing the following features:

$$\Omega(u) \gg 1 \qquad \frac{\partial \Omega}{\partial u} < 0 \qquad \frac{\partial^2 \Omega}{\partial u^2} > 0 \tag{2}$$

The analysis based on these features resulted in that the statistical averaged value of the risk factor $<R>$ is characterized as a non-monotonic function of the repository-medium contact area S. There are two regions differing in behavior of the quantity $<R>$ in dependence on S. If S exceeds the value of some characteristic area   of the geological medium, the quantity $<R>$ is determined by optimum punctures independent on the area S and corresponding to dimensionless transmittance $u=u_{opt}$ which is determined from the equation:

$$\left(\frac{\partial \Omega(u)}{\partial u}\right)_{u=u_{opt}} + 1 = 0 \tag{3}$$

The averaged risk factor $<R>$ slightly decreases as the contact area S increases at $S>S_c$.

In the region $S<S_c$, the quantity $<R>$ is determined by punctures with dimensionless transmittance $u=u_f$ given by the equation:

$$\frac{S}{S_0} \exp\left[-\Omega(u_f)\right] = 1$$

In this range of the contact area S, the averaged risk factor depends on S in a non-monotonic way, having a maximum at $S=S_{max}$ close to S_c. At contact areas in the range $S<S_{max}$, a rather rapid decrease of the quantity $<R>$ occurs as the area S decreases.

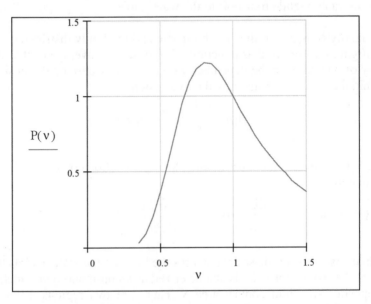

Figure 1. Behavior of the averaged risk factor in the dependence on the dimensionless contact surface area v (schematically). $P(v) \equiv < R(v) > / < R(1) >$

The dependencies of the normalized value of the average risk factor on the area S, expressed in terms of dimensionless parameter

$$v = \frac{\ln(S/S_0)}{\Omega_{opt}} \qquad (4)$$

are given by the relations:

$$P(v) \equiv \frac{< R(v) >}{< R(1) >} = \exp\left[-\frac{1}{2}(v-1)\Omega_{opt}\right] \qquad v>1 \qquad (5)$$

$$P(v) = \exp\left[-\left(u_f - u_{opt}\right) + \frac{3}{2}(1-v)\Omega_{opt}\right] \qquad v<1 \qquad (6)$$

Note that the value $v=1$ corresponds to $S=S_c$ which equals

$$S_c \equiv S_0 \exp\left(\Omega_{opt}\right) \tag{7}$$

Fig.1 schematically illustrates the behavior of $P(v)$ as function of parameter v.

Another consequence resulting from the irregularity of the geological medium consists in statistical uncertainty of the factor R. The coefficient of the statistical uncertainty can be defined as

$$\Delta = \frac{\left(< (\delta R)^2 >\right)^{1/2}}{< R >} \tag{8}$$

The uncertainty is small at $S \gg Sc$ $(\Delta \ll 1$ when $v > 1)$. On the contrary, the statistical uncertainty becomes to be large in the region $S < Sc$. There is $\Delta \sim 1$ when $v < 1$ and $\Delta \gg 1$ when $v \ll 1$.

A possible recommendation following from the results obtained, with respect to RW repository geometrical characteristics, can be as follows. The most favorable situation to minimize the risk factor corresponds to the case when a linear repository dimension L is noticeably smaller than the characteristic correlation length determined by the equality

$$L_c = \sqrt{S_c}$$

From the standpoint of the repository reliability, the expediency is not ruled out that a large repository having dimension $L > L_c$ could be divided into a number of small ones having characteristic dimension $L < L_c$ and located at a distance much larger than L_c from each other.

REFERENCES

LIFSHITZ, I.M., GREDESKUL, S.A., and PASTUR, L.A., Introduction to the Theory of Irregular Systems, Nauka, Moscow, 1982, in Russian.

RAIKH, M.E, and RUZIN, I.M.,. Transmittancy Fluctuation in Randomly Non-Unioform Barriers and Incoherent Mesoscopics in Mesoscopic Phenomena in Solids Ed. by B.L. Altshuler, P.A. Lee and R.A. Webb, Elsevier, pp. 315-368, 1991.

UPSCALING HYDRAULIC CONDUCTIVITY FROM THE PORE SCALE TO THE CORE SCALE

Peter A. Lock, Xudong Jing, and Robert W. Zimmerman
*Department of Earth Science and Engineering, Imperial College,
London, UK*

INTRODUCTION

The overall goal of our work has been to develop a method for predicting directionally-dependent single-phase permeabilities of sedimentary rocks, using only a small number of SEM images, with a minimum of computational effort. The scheme used here is a refinement of that developed by Schlueter (Ph.D., UC Berkeley, 1995) for isotropic rocks, and applies image analysis to SEM photographs of sandstone pores. The hydraulic radius approximation is used to compute the individual conductivities of the pores. Stereological correction factors are applied to determine the true cross-sectional shapes from the images, and to determine the true number density of pores per unit area. A constriction factor accounts for the effect of the variation of the cross-sectional area along the tube length. Some method of upscaling is then needed to derive an equivalent conductance from the observed distribution of conductances. In the present paper we focus on this aspect of the problem. We have used the effective-medium approximation of Kirkpatrick (Rev. Mod. Phys., 1973), its anisotropic extension by Bernasconi (Phys. Rev. B, 1974), the generalized perturbation ansatz of Gelhar and Axness (Water Resour. Res., 1983), and exact network simulations using the code NETSIM (Jing, Ph.D., Imperial College, 1990) to carry out this upscaling step. The individual pore conductances are derived from images of several consolidated North Sea sandstones, with permeabilities ranging from 10-500 mD.

PORE CONDUCTIVITY DATA

The data set consisted of a collection of backscattered electron micrographs prepared from the core extractions of a commercial well that lies inside the UK Continental Shelf (UKCS), supplied by Enterprise Oil. The sandstones were mostly fine-grained, ranging from a very fine to medium granularity with moderate to poor sorting. Porosities ranged from 8-14%. Grain size distributions were not calculated, but mean pore sizes, defined by $r_{eq} = \sqrt{A / \pi}$, ranged from 12-125 μm.

Back-scattered electron images are taken of each thin section. The images are then digitized, after which gray-level thresholding is applied to identify individual "pores". The perimeter P and area A of each remaining pore are estimated with the Scion Image for Windows image analysis program. Stereological correction factors are applied to convert the observed perimeters and areas into "actual" values. The hydraulic conductivity of each pore is estimated from the hydraulic radius approximation, $C = A^3 / 2P^2$ A multiplicative constriction factor, found by integrating the Poiseuille equation, is applied to account for converging/diverging nature of the pores. The details and accuracy of the steps outlined above are discussed by Lock (Ph.D., Imperial College, 2001). We merely argue here that the pore conductances thus obtained should be more realistic than the idealized lognormal or normal distributions used in most previous tests of the various effective-medium upscaling methods. A histogram of the conductances of the individual pores from one thin section can be found in the extended paper, and in Lock (2001).

NETWORK MODELING OF PERMEABILITY

As a benchmark to establish the exact permeabilities, we have used NETSIM (Jing, 1990), a network simulation code that models transport phenomena through a cubic lattice of pore tubes. Individual conductances are chosen from the measured distribution, and assigned randomly to locations on the lattice. The computed results are sensitive to the number of elements used in the simulations, and also vary slightly from one realization to another, even if the same underlying conductance distribution is used. For any lattice size, the geometric mean of the permeabilities was taken over several realizations. The means tended to level out to a constant value after about twenty realizations, for all lattice sizes. The lattice size was then increased until grid convergence was achieved, which tended to occur when a 30x30x30 lattice was reached.

The purpose of an effective-medium approximation is to allow the replacement of each conductor C_i in a network by a conductor having some "effective value" C_e. According to the isotropic effective-medium approximation of Kirkpatrick (1973), the effective conductance is found by solving the following implicit equation:

$$\sum_{i=1}^{N} \frac{C_e - C_i}{[(z/2) - 1]C_e + C_i} = 0 \qquad (1)$$

where the co-ordination number z represents the number of conductors that meet at each node, and N is the total number of conductors. For a cubic lattice, $z = 6$. Equation (1) can be solved using either the bisection algorithm, or a one-dimensional Newton-Raphson procedure.

Bernasconi (1974) extended Kirkpatrick's model to a cubic lattice in which the conductivity distributions in the three orthogonal directions may differ. The three effective conductances $\{C_e^x, C_e^y, C_e^z\}$ are computed by solving three simultaneous algebraic equations of the form

$$\sum_{i=1}^{N_x} \frac{C_e^x - C_i^x}{C_e^x \left\{ \dfrac{\tan^{-1}[((C_e^x C_e^y + C_e^x C_e^z + C_e^y C_e^z)^{1/2} / C_e^x]}{\tan^{-1}[C_e^x / (C_e^x C_e^y + C_e^x C_e^z + C_e^y C_e^z)^{1/2}]} \right\} + C_i^x} = 0 \qquad (2)$$

with the other two equations found by cyclically permuting the superscripts $\{x,y,z\}$.

Gelhar and Axness (1983) suggested the following expression, sometimes called the Generalized Perturbation Ansatz (GPA), for the effective permeability for an isotropic heterogeneous three-dimensional aquifer with a lognormal permeability distribution:

$$K_{eff} = K_G \exp\left[\frac{\sigma_{\ln K}^2}{6} \right] \qquad (3)$$

where K_G is the geometric mean of the permeability distribution, and $\sigma_{\ln K}^2$ is the log variance.

UPSCALING OF ACTUAL PORE CONDUCTANCES

Permeabilities were estimated for each set of orientated thin sections belonging to each of the separate cores in accordance with the procedure outlined above. The prediction for the permeability in, say, the x-direction of core 2 was made by using only the pore conductivities that were observed in this image, which are assumed to represent those pores that are aligned (roughly) in the x-direction. Hence, although the Kirkpatrick model is inherently isotropic, by using three different input data sets for the three directions, our method can yield different permeabilities in the three directions. Similarly, when using NETSIM, we took only those conductivities from the x-direction, but used these values to populate the entire lattice in an isotropic manner.

The table below lists the predicted permeabilities, compared with the measured values. The integers are core identifiers, and the "X,Y,Z" labels refer to the three orthogonal faces of the cores. Permeabilities are given in milliDarcies. The predictions made using Kirkpatrick's effective-medium approximation are within a factor of two of the measured values in almost every case. If absolute values are considered, the average error is 48%. For comparison, it should be noted that previous isotropic network models that utilized two-dimensional imaging, such as that of Koplik et al. (J. Appl. Phys., 1984), overpredicted the permeability by about a factor of ten.

CORE	ϕ	k (measured)	k (Kirkpatrick)	k (NETSIM)
1X	0.08	18	29	29
1Y	0.08	18	52	53
2X	0.12	137	222	227
2Y	0.12	119	209	213
2Z	0.12	109	265	270
3X	0.11	202	198	201
3Y	0.11	196	175	180
3Z	0.11	222	179	182
4X	0.08	83	87	89
4Y	0.08	72	56	57
4Z	0.08	28	35	36
5X	0.14	470	239	245
5Z	0.14	500	275	279
6X	0.11	275	188	191
6Z	0.11	228	189	192
7X	0.09	109	96	98
7Y	0.09	109	95	97
7Z	0.09	69	115	117

This method, although based on an inherently isotropic model, gives qualitative indications of anisotropy, provided that the measured anisotropy is large enough to exceed the measurement error bars. The only unambiguously anisotropic core is 4, which has a measured anisotropy of about {6:5:2}, and a predicted anisotropy of {5:3:2}. In this case, the three principal permeabilities were predicted to within 25%, and the ordering of the permeabilities was predicted correctly.

It was thought that the use of an inherently anisotropic effective-medium model such as that of Bernasconi (1974) might lead to improved permeability predictions. The three-dimensional version of the anisotropic effective-medium theory was applied to sample 4 (see full paper). The permeability estimations made using the Bernasconi model agreed very well with the output of NETSIM used in its anisotropic mode, by using the pore conductivities estimated from image 1X to populate only those bonds that are aligned in the x-direction, etc. The predictions of the anisotropic model were only slightly different from those obtained using the isotropic model.

This work was supported by Enterprise Oil, plc.

RISK ANALYSIS OF CONTAMINATION USING THE TWO-PHASE FLOW MODEL AND STOCHASTIC APPROACH

Guan-Zhi Chen, Kuo-Chin Hsu and Cheng-Haw Lee
Department of Resources Engineering, National Cheng-Kung University
Tainan, Taiwan 70101, R.O.C, (06)2757575 ext 62840 ext 32
gzchen.tw@yahoo.com.tw

Recent studies on hydrogeology have shown that the hydraulic properties of natural porous media often display high spatial variability. Theoretical analyses and field experiments indicate that this spatial variability dominantly controls the behaviors of flow and solute transport in the aquifer. The classical deterministic approach has difficulty in treating the spatial variability due to the inherent randomness of the medium and scarcity of available data. On the contrasty, the stochastic approach treats the soil properties as random variables and is able to take the spatial variability into account in the analysis. In particular, the stochastic approach is useful for the risk analysis of groundwater problems.

In this study, a stochastic approach was proposed to investigate the effect of the heterogeneity on groundwater flow and solute transport in both saturated and unsaturated zones. We first investigate the effect of the two-phase flow model on the unsaturated flow. The two-phase flow model is more realistic than the single-phase flow model for modeling unsaturated flow and solute transport. The two-phase flow model may induce smaller water content than that from the single-phase flow model and leads to a larger polluted area in the unsaturated zone. By combining the Turning Bands method and a multi-phase transport code TOUGH2, an automatic process is used for Monte Carlo simulation of the solute transport. The approach is applied to a potentially polluted site in Taiwan and results are compared to the deterministic approach.

A total of 1000 realizations are simulated in the Monte Carlo simulations. The result of the probability exceeding the MCL on the 104th day is shown in Figure 1. Figure 1 indicates that the plume in the unsaturated zone is symmetric about the source area and the regional groundwater may be polluted on the 104th day with a probability of less than 0.05. For comparison, we also perform the deterministic simulation using the average soil properties. Figure 2 shows the result for the deterministic case. In the deterministic approach the contaminant front of the MCL will not reach the regional groundwater while the stochastic result shows a possibility of pollution in groundwater at the same time.

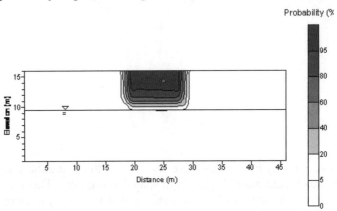

Figure 1. Probability distribution contour of chlorite in 104th day

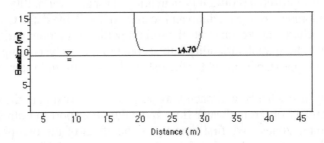

Figure 2. The contaminant front of the MCL in 104th day

Figures 3 and 4 are the same for the stochastic and the deterministic approaches on the 365th day, respectively. Both approaches show that both saturated and unsaturated zones are polluted at this time. The stochastic approach provides information on risk distribution of the contaminant. The highest risk area (probability greater than 0.95) is about 4 meters below the water table and extends to 10 meters from the center of the source. Outside the domain there is a low probability of pollution at this time. The deterministic result in Figure 4 shows the contaminant has passed over the boundary at this time. Although the deterministic approach requires less labor, it doesn't provide the information of prediction uncertainty. On the other hand, the stochastic approach does provide a probability distribution of the contaminant for the risk analysis.

Our results lead to the following conclusions:

1. The water content from the two-phase flow model will be smaller than that derived from the single-phase flow model. This may lead to a faster flow field and a larger contaminant plume in the two-phase modeling.

2. A stochastic approach using the two-phase flow model is applied to a potentially polluted site in Taiwan. The results for concentration exceeding the MCL on both the 104th day and the 365th day are presented. The stochastic approach provides useful risk information, which is not available from the deterministic approach.

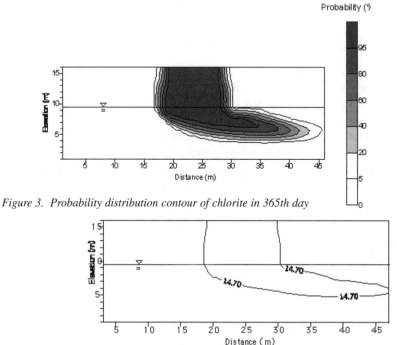

Figure 3. Probability distribution contour of chlorite in 365th day

Figure 4. The contaminant front of the MCL in 365th day

SPATIAL CORRELATION STRUCTURE IN THE THREE-DIMENSIONAL PERMEABILITY FIELD ACCOMPANIED BY SHALLOW FAULTS

Shinji Nakaya[1], Taiyoh Yohme[1], Akihisa Koike[2], Tetsuhiro Hirayama[3], Toshiaki Yoden[3] and Makoto Nishigaki[4]

[1] *Department of Civil Engineering, Faculty of Engineering, Shinshu University, Nagano, Japan*
[2] *Kansai Electric Power Co., Osaka, Japan*
[3] *NEWJEC Inc., Osaka, Japan*
[4] *Department of Environmental and Civil Engineering, Faculty of Environmental Science and Technology, Okayama University, Okayama, Japan*

INTRODUCTION

Faults always have been considered to induce macroscopic heterogeneity for permeability fields in geologic bodies because of (1) fracture networks of the damage zone along fault that may form conduits and channels with respect to flow; (2) the central gouge or core zone in fault that may act as a permeability barrier. Therefore, in basement rocks accompanied by faults, the hydrogeological structure increases heterogeneity of the permeability fileds. To evaluate permeability of rock formations, researchers always need consider whether the faults will work as a barrier, conduit, or barrier-conduit system.

For heterogeneous permeability field induced by faults, three-dimensional spatial correlation structure (SCS), which is expressed by semivariogram, must be determined. Though line-directional semivariograms, drawn from data pairs sampled on lines in a same direction, have been conventionally calculated in multi-directions, it can not be easily detected from in situ data because of sparse sampling.

In this paper, instead of line-directional semivariogram, introducing the idea of plane-directional semivariogram to the in situ permeability data of basement rocks accompanied by shallow faults in a dam site, the three-dimensionally heterogeneous permeability field is geostatistically estimated. The three-dimensional SCS of permeability is compared with major trend of faults. The preferential flow path in the estimated permeability zone is discussed from observation of groundwater level.

METHOD

Geostatistical method, the block kriging needs the semivariogram $\gamma(h_{ij})$ of distance, hij in the direction from i to j. The semivariogram $\gamma(h_{ij})$ is usually calculated from the coordinates of i and j using the variogram model curve in which represents the relationship between hij and $\gamma(h_{ij})$ in multi-line directions obtained from observations. Here, the plane-directional semivariogram gp that is obtained from values of permeability on P-plane in the Q-direction (Figure 1) is introduced instead of $\gamma(h_{ij})$ in a line direction to modeling the spatial correlation structure of permeability. Figure 2 shows the relationships between L_{p1} or L_{p2}, which are the radii of semi-major and minor axes for variogram range of P-plane, L_p-ellipse, and Q direction, and between strike direction of fault and the width. The L_{p1} shows the directional anisotropy close to ellipse, while the L_{p2} is nearly isotropic. The direction of the largest directional anisotropy of L_p (N-S~N30°W direction) is concordant with that of the major trend of shallow faults.

RESULTS AND DISCUSSION
HYDROGEOLOGICAL CHARACTERISTICS OF THE STUDY SITE

Study area is located in Gifu prefecture, central Japan along the Kiso River. The basement rocks of the study area, which are unconformably overlain by soft modern sediments, consist of the Mesozoic sedimentary formations, overlying cretaceous Nohhi rhyolitic rocks and intruded by Cretaceous granite. Figure 3 shows the contour lines of groundwater level, inferred fault lines and borehole locations. Hydrologically, this area is characterized by the groundwater flow around the dam from the upper of dam to the lower through basement rocks of mountain side, because large hydraulic gradient occurs around the dam. The zone of water level lower than 185-m contour above sea level (ZWLL) is in contrast to that of water level higher than 185-m contour and lower than 210-m one (ZWLH). The trend of both zones, which extend in north-south direction, is concordant with the major trend of the faults.

Using the exponential semivariogram model with L_p-ellipse for Q axis of N15°W direction on horizontal plane, which shows the largest directional anisotropy of L_p, sill = 0.62(variance of all measured permeability) and nugget = 0.0, the three-dimensional spatial distribution of permeability of the study area is estimated by block kriging. Figure 4 shows the typical estimation results of permeability at a horizontal slice with fault lines. It is estimated that continuous zone of permeability higher than 10 Lugeon (CZPH) and that of permeability lower than 1 Lugeon (CZPL) are formed in heterogeneous permeability field. From previous studies on fault zone architecture and in situ fault observation, the CZPL is correlative with central gouge or core zone, while the CZPH is correlative with bounding damage zone, though the area of the CZPH decreases with depth. The existence of CZPL is supported by the field observation that faults in this area are accompanied by fault clay. Comparing the estimated permeability distribution with the measured groundwater level in study area (Figure 3), it is pointed out that CZPH is concordant with ZWLH, while CZPL is concordant with ZWLL. The CZPL and the CZPH are inferred to work as a permeability barrier and as a preferential flow path, respectively.

CONCLUSIONS

Introducing the idea of plane-directional semivariogram to the in situ permeability data of basement rocks accompanied by shallow faults in a dam site, the three-dimensionally model for spatial correlation structure was determined and then using it, the three-dimensional heterogeneous permeability field was estimated by block kriging. The following major conclusions can be drawn:

1. The directional anisotropy of semivariograms appears in three-dimensional spatial correlation structure for the permeability field in the study area. Direction of the largest anisotropy of the spatial correlation to the permeability is concordant with that of the major trend of shallow faults.

2. It is estimated that continuous zones of higher permeability and that of lower permeability are formed in heterogeneous permeability field. From previous studies on fault architecture and in situ fault observation, the continuous zone of lower permeability is correlative with central gouge or core zone, while the continuous zone of higher permeability is correlative with bounding damage zone.

3. Since the continuous zones of higher permeability and of lower permeability are concordant with the zone of higher water level and with that of lower water level, respectively, they are inferred to work as a permeability barrier and as a preferential flow path, respectively.

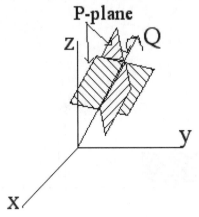

Figure 1. Definitions of Q axis, Q-direction, and P-plane.

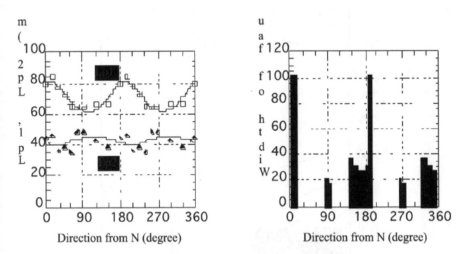

Figure 2. Relationships between Lp1 or Lp2 and between strike direction of faults and the widths.

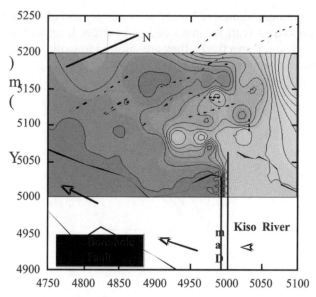

Figure 3. Contour lines of groundwater level   in March, 1995, inferred fault lines and bore-hole locations in study area.

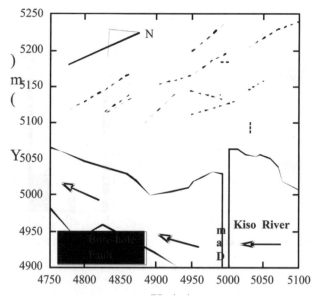

Figure 4. Estimated result of the permeability at a horizontal slice (180 m above sea level) in study area.

A PARAMETER SCALING CONCEPT FOR ESTIMATING FIELD-SCALE HYDRAULIC FUNCTIONS OF LAYERED SOILS

Z. Fred Zhang, Andy L. Ward, and Glendon W. Gee
Pacific Northwest National Laboratories , Richland WA

Predicting flow and transport in unsaturated porous media is often hampered by insufficient and uncertain constitutive property information. Some studies have used inverse flow modeling for parameter estimation to overcome these limitations. However, determination of the soil hydraulic parameters of layered soils remains a challenge since inverting for too many parameters can lead to the non-uniqueness of parameter values.

Yeh and Harvey (1990) determined the effective hydraulic conductivity by treating the layered sand as being uniform. Abbaspour et al., (1997) proposed a sequential uncertainty domain parameter fitting (SUFI) procedure to inversely estimate soil hydraulic parameters. A limitation of SUFI is that the number of simulations for each iteration may become too large to be acceptable.

Vogel et al. (1991) introduced the linear variability concept that expresses the soil hydraulic properties in terms of a linear transformation and used three mutually independent scaling factors for K, ψ, and θ. The linear scaling method is based on the traditional scaling theory in that the hydraulic properties $\psi(\theta)$ and $K(\theta)$ rather than hydraulic parameters are scaled. However, it is well known that parameters such as the pore-size distribution parameters, which are texture dependent, cannot be accommodated in hydraulic property scaling. Scaling of the parameters rather than the properties might offer a more robust approach for characterization of heterogeneous soils.

In this research, we introduce the concept of parameter scaling as a method to consider the vertical heterogeneity of soils. With parameter scaling, the hydraulic parameters of all the soil textures are scaled to a reference texture. The vertical variability of soil properties is then described by the spatial distribution of the mutually independent scaling factors. Reference parameters of the heterogeneous soils are then inversely estimated from field observations of water flow and knowledge of the spatial distribution of the scaling factors.

PARAMETER SCALING AND DEFINITION OF SCALING FACTORS

Soil hydraulic properties are commonly described by many empirical functions to allow incorporation into numerical models (Brooks and Corey, 1964; van Genuchten, 1980). Assume a layered soil comprised of M different textures with each texture characterized by a set of hydraulic parameters β.

The concept of parameter scaling is different from traditional scaling in that we scale the soil hydraulic parameters of the hydraulic functions rather than the hydraulic properties. In the method, we select a single texture as the reference texture described by a set of reference parameters, β. The jth parameter of the ith texture, b_{ij}, are related to the reference parameters through a set of mutually independent linear scaling factors, γ_{ij}, for i = 1 to M textures, i.e.

$$\beta_{ij} = \gamma_{ij}\, \tilde{\beta}_j \qquad (1)$$

Similarly, a logarithmic scaling factor is defined as

$$\ln(\beta_{ij}) = \gamma_{ij}\, \ln(\tilde{\beta}_j) \qquad (2)$$

Parameter scaling has the following characteristics: (1) it does not require the constitutional materials to be similar. As long the hydraulic properties of the soil materials can be described by a hydraulic function (e.g., Brooks and Corey, 1964; van Genuchten, 1980), parameter scaling is applicable. (2) Instead of scaling the hydraulic properties [i.e., the $\theta(\psi)$ and $K(\psi)$] relations, the hydraulic parameters are scaled. As a result, the flow equation can always be expressed in real time and space regardless of the soil heterogeneity. This has the potential to overcome the difficulty in estimating hydraulic parameters for heterogeneous system using inverse procedures. (3) After the scaling, the values of the hydraulic parameters of all the soil textures perfectly reduce to the reference values. No scaling error is introduced and hence the application of an inverse scaling will return the original parameter values. (4) The spatial variability of each hydraulic parameter can be expressed by the scaling factors. Different parameters may have different variability structures within the same soil domain. (5) When the parameters are to be estimated by an inverse procedure, the number of unknown variables is reduced by a factor of M.

CALCULATION OF SCALING FACTORS

Although the parameter values at the local scale are often different from those at field scale, it is reasonable to assume that local-scale values of gij are equal to those at the field-scale, i.e.

$$(\gamma_{ij})_{LS} = (\gamma_{ij})_{FS} \tag{3}$$

where subscript LS denotes local-scale and FS field-scale. In this context, local scale means the range represented by an individual observation and field scale is the three-dimensional range of an experimental site. Equation [3] essentially means that the relationship between the parameters of different textures is scale invariant. For example, if at the local-scale the saturated hydraulic conductivity, $(K_s)_{LS}$, of the ith texture is $10 \cdot (K_s)_{LS}$, we expect that the field-scale value, $(K_s)_{FS}$ of the ith texture to be $10 \cdot (K_s)_{FS}$. Thus, the scaling factors can be determined with Eq. [1] or [2] using the parameter values measured at the local scale or in the laboratory.

ESTIMATING THE FIELD-SCALE REFERENCE PARAMETER VALUES

After determining the values of the scaling factors as discussed above, the field-scale reference parameter values are estimated by fixing the values of the scaling factors and solving an inverse problem. Solution of the inverse problem requires minimization of the objective function, $S(\tilde{\beta})$, with respect to the soil hydraulic parameters. The objective function is a measure of the fit between simulated values and observations and is defined as

$$S(\tilde{\beta}) = \sum_{k=1}^{N} w_k [y_k - \hat{y}_k(\tilde{\beta})]^2 \tag{4}$$

where y_k are observations of any data type, e.g., θ or ψ; $\hat{y}_k(\tilde{\beta})$ are the corresponding simulated values; w_k are the weights associated with each observation and is defined as the reverse of the variance of the measurement error; and N is the total number of observations.

After applying parameter scaling in a layered soil with M textures, the number of hydraulic parameters to be estimated using the inverse procedure is reduced by a factor of M. The only unknown variables are the reference parameters. The reduction of the number of parameters to be estimated greatly reduces the uncertainty of the estimates and accelerates the convergence during inverse modeling.

RESULTS

The parameter scaling method was tested using two infiltration-drainage experiments in layered soils. The numerical simulator, STOMP (White and Oostrom, 2000), was combined with the inverse modeling program, UCODE (Poeter and Hill, 1998), to estimate the hydraulic parameters. Using the values of the scaling factors determined using local-scale parameters, the field-scale reference hydraulic parameters were inversely estimated and their corresponding 95% LCI are given. Since parameters $\tilde{K}_s$ $\tilde{\alpha}$, and $\tilde{n}$ were log-transformed when they were estimated, their 95% LCIs are expressed as the mean values multiplied or divided by a factor, which has the minimum value of unity. The 95% LCIs for parameter $\tilde{K}_s$ for both soils have the largest uncertainty, which vary with factors of 1.57 and 1.25, respectively. The 95% LCIs for parameters $\tilde{\alpha}$ and $\tilde{n}$ vary with a factor less than 1.18. Both $\tilde{\theta}_s$ and $\tilde{S}_r$ have relatively small ranges that is equal or less than ±0.011.

When the field-scale parameter estimates were used to simulate the flow, the simulation errors were significantly reduced. When compared to the use of local-scale parameters, parameter scaling reduced the sum of the squared weighted residue by 96% for the Hanford experiment and by 93% for the Andelfingen experiment.

REFERENCES

Abbaspour, K.C., M.T. van Genuchten, R. Schulin, and E. Schlappi. 1997. A sequential uncertainty domain inverse procedure for estimating subsurface flow and transport parameters. Water Resour. Res., 33,1879-1892.

Brooks, R.H., and A.T. Corey. 1966. Hydraulic properties of porous media affecting fluid flow. Proc. ASCE J. Irrig. Drain. Div. 92:61-88.

Poeter, E.P., and M.C. Hill. 1998. Documentation of UCODE, a computer code for universal inverse modeling. U.S. Geological survey, water-resources investigations report 98-4080.

Rockhold, M.L., M.J. Fayer, and G.W. Gee. 1988. Characterization of unsaturated hydraulic conductivity at the Hanford site. PNL-6488, Pacific Northwest Laboratory, Richland, Washington.

Vogel, T., M. Cislerova, and J.W. Hopmans.1991. Porous media with linearly variable hydraulic properties. Water Resour. Res. 27: 2735-2741.

White, M.D., and M. Oostrom. 2000. User's guide of STOMP - Subsurface transport over multiple phases. PNNL-12034 UC-2010, Pacific Northwest National Laboratory, Richland, Washington.

van Genuchten, M.Th. 1980. A closed form equation for predicting the hydraulic conductivity of unsaturated soils. Soil Sci. Soc. Am. J. 44: 892-898.

Yeh, T.-C. J., and D.J. Harvey. 1990. Effective unsaturated hydraulic conductivity of layered sands. Water Resour. Res. 26:1271-1279.

DEVELOPING THERMALLY ENHANCED IN-SITU REMEDIATION TECHNOLOGY BY EXPERI-MENT AND NUMERICAL SIMULATION

T. Theurer, A. Winkler, U. Hiester, H.-P. Koschitzky
VEGAS, Institute of Hydraulic Engineering, University of Stuttgart

SUMMARY

The state-of-the-art technology to remove non-aqueous phase liquids from the unsaturated zone is the 'cold' Soil Vapour Extraction (SVE). In heterogeneous media limitations arise due to insufficient ventilation of low permeable layers and low vapour pressure of the contami-nant. At VEGAS, the research facility for subsurface remediation at the University of Stutt-gart, a thermally enhan-ced SVE is being developed. The vapour pressures of the contaminants are increased by heating the low permeable zones in the subsurface by thermal wells to a tem-perature above 100°C. To show the feasibility of this techno-logy, a series of experiments con-cerning heat and mass transport in porous media were conducted on different scales. In paral-lel to the experiments, numerical modeling was used for sensitivity analysis and upscaling.

INTRODUCTION

Soil vapour extraction (SVE) is used to remediate contaminations of volatile phase liquids. The contaminants evaporate and diffuse into the soil air, which is extracted and treated. The process of evaporation into the gas phase, though, is strongly limited by the vapour pressure of the contaminant. For low vapour pressures, only a small equilibrium concentration of the contaminant in the

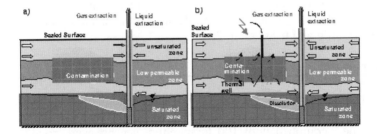

Figure 1: Principle of "cold" soil vapour extraction. a) and application of thermal wells to heat contaminated, low permeable layers b)

soil air can be achieved. In that case, the SVE has an unacceptably low efficiency. The same applies, if the contaminant is present in a low permeable zone of the subsurface, where almost no ventilation occurs (see Fig. 1a).

By increasing the temperature in these low permeable target zones (see Fig. 1b), the contami-nant will evaporate at higher rates, resulting in migration into the more permeable layers. There, it can be extracted with the soil air, where the output efficiency is greatly increased.

1D-EXPERIMENTS FOR HEAT AND MASS TRANSPORT

To investigate the physical and thermodynamic principles of heat and mass transport experi-ments were conducted in a glass column (Winkler et al, 2000), which was equipped with a heating element on top and temperature sensors. Mass output was monitored in all phases. In a first set of experiments, only the heat transport mechanisms were under regard, and the following aspects could be ratified:

• Heat transport occurs mainly by heat conduction.
• Heat transport occurs by evaporated liquids in the gas phase.
• Energy is transported by fluids, which are warmed up and mobilised due to a loss in surface tension and viscosity (Mobilisation).

Numerical modeling with the non-isothermal model MUFTE_UG (HELMIG, 1997) was used to validate the experiments. To obtain input data, capillary pressure-saturation-relationships and viscosity were measured as a function of temperature. During calibration, it could be shown that almost all parameters involved in the processes (e. g. interfacial tension σ, viscosity v, residual saturation S_{wr}, density ρ) are affected by the increase in temperature (Class & Helmig and Class et al, 2001).

2D-Experiments

To investigate the effect of gravity on and heterogeneity of the subsurface on the heat- and mass transport, two-dimensional experiments in a flat stainless steel "flume", equipped with 100 temperature sensors were conducted. A flow field similar to "natural" conditions could be imposed. Heat transport and contaminant removal from low permeable layers was tested in the experiments. Downward mobilisation of NAPL did only occur at a very small rate due to the small temperature gradients. After 72 hours, 90% of the contaminant was removed in the gas phase, as the mass balance of the soil vapour sampling indicated.

A two-dimensional numerical model was used to obtain qualitative information about the pa-rameters that could not be measured. The high energy losses, which occurred during the ex-periments, could not be taken into account, which left the computed results unfit for quantita-tive analysis of the problem situation. It could be visualized, that heat transport happens inde-pendently of permeability, which is an advantage against steam injection, where low perme-able layers take a long time to be heated. Heat is additionally transported by the soil air, which has a very low heat capacity. Initial contamination is escaping the temperature gradient and during the experiment partitioning into the gas phase.

The flume experiments lead to the important conclusion, that the remediation scheme to be developed was qualitatively feasible, if residual saturation of contaminant was not too high, and a greatly increased transport rate of NAPL could be achieved in the gaseous phase (Theurer et al, 2001). However, criteria needed to be developed for necessary heating tem-peratures, distance of thermal wells and their arrangement and soil vapour extraction rate.

Future Work

To answer the remaining questions, a series of three-dimensional experiments in a large tank is planned at the VEGAS-facility. A large stainless steel container with the dimensions of ap-proximately 6.0 m*6.0 m*4.5 m will be used to investigate the three-dimensional performance of the remediation technology at nearly field scale under defined laboratory conditions.

Figure 2 shows the setup: A layer of fine sand, where contaminant can be injected, is confined between two layers of coarse media, where transport of vapours occurs. Thermal wells are placed with a distance of approximately one meter and can be heated above, below and in the fine layer. Soil vapour wells are screened in different depths to obtain a flow field with the best benefit for contaminant transport.

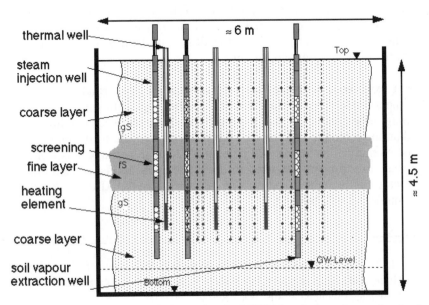

Figure 2: Cross section through the steel tank al VEGAS and planned setup for the three-dimensional experiments on large scale.

Three-dimensional experiments reflect natural conditions as far as soil layering is concerned. Also, losses can be eliminated, and handled equipment is near field scale.

Numerical modeling was used for the detailed planning of the experimental setup. The simu-lations for the dimensioning of the experiments include:

- Which distance for the thermal wells is to be chosen?
- How is the "natural" state of water saturation to be implemented?
- How can the contaminant be infiltrated?

CONCLUSIONS AND OUTLOOK

A thermally enhanced remediation strategy for contaminants with low vapour pressures, con-fined in low permeable soils, is to be developed. The strategy of using thermal wells for in-crease of the vapour pressure of the contaminants was analysed in small-scale experimental setups. It was shown, that the remediation technique is feasible and results in a high cleanup efficiency. Considering the non-isothermal properties of the relevant cleanup processes, a numerical model was developed and calibrated by results from small-scale experiments. It has been used for the design of large-scale experiments, which are costly and time-consuming.

To gain experience with the field site application of thermal wells, some experiments on large scale with "natural" soil heterogeneities and dimensions are going to be conducted. It is to be proven, that under such conditions the remediation technique has the desired efficiency, and has no limiting side effects. Numerical modeling will be better validated by the results from the large-scale experiments and used for field site applications, concerning the temperature, arrangement and number of thermal wells. Also, three-dimensional modeling will be used.

REFERENCES

CLASS, H., HELMIG, R., BASTIAN, P., 2001: Numerical Simulation of Nonisothermal Multiphase Multicom-ponent Processes in Porous Media – 1. An Efficient Solution Technique, submitted to Adv. Water Resour.

CLASS, H., HELMIG, R., 2001: Numerical Simulation of Nonisothermal Multiphase Multicomponent Proc-esses in Porous Media – 2. Appliations for the Injection of Steam and Air, submitted to Adv. Water Resour.

HELMIG, R., 1997: Multiphase Flow and Transport Processes in the Subsurface – A Contribution to the Modeling of Hydrosystems, Springer Verlag.

THEURER, T., WINKLER, A., KOSCHITZKY, H.-P., 2001: Heat Transfer in the Vadose Zone: Experiments and Numerical Evaluation, Proceedings of the XXVI General Assembly, EGS 2001, 25–30 March 2001, Nice

WINKLER, A., THEURER, T., SCHMIDT, R., KOSCHITZKY, H.-P., 2000: Thermal In-Situ Remediation of Low Permeable Soils: Theory and Experimental Results, Proceedings of the 7th International Conference on Contami-nated Soil, 18-22 September 2000, Leipzig, Vol. 2, pp. 1127 - 1128.

ADAPTATION OF PROBABILITY MODEL TO PROCESS INFORMATION ABOUT PESTICIDES' DISTRIBUTION IN SOIL UNDER UNCERTAIN CONDITIONS

O.Molozhanova, Y.Chaika

Lev I. Medved Ecohygiene and Toxicology Institute, Kiev, Ukraine

The deterministic modeling of pollutant migration in the subsurface hydrosphere is usually characterized by the inclusion of interaction mechanisms within the subsurface water (solution)-rock system, assessing as well as physical-chemical conditions of water-exchange system. Hence, predictive models in hydrochemistry are developed on the basis of chemical thermodynamic approach and kinetics.

The limited application of the thermodynamic approach, which is based on estimated equilibrium states, is due to relatively high subsurface water velocities in the upper hydrodynamic zone, and the non-equilibrium state of the system as a whole. The lack of thermodynamic constants necessary for calculation makes it even more difficult to use this approach for real prediction of pesticide migration.

We consider that the development of models based on physical-chemical hydrodynamics and kinetics makes it possible to perform a comprehensive analysis of the system, which would take into account the convective transport of the constituents, the pollution sources, and the kinetics within the water-soil system. Generally, this method can be used for prediction if the following data is available: (1) filtration rates (including filtration parameters and hydraulic gradients); (2) convective diffusivities and values of effective porosity; (3) suitable data on parameters specifying the diffusion, sorbtion, and desorbtion under different conditions; (4) information about surface chemical changes within the phases in interaction; and (5) kinetic parameters and processes in the heterogeneous system of moving solutions.

A simpler, more rigid prediction of migration is based on consideration of inert pollutant transport coupled with a flux of filtration water, without taking into account the physical-chemical interactions. But, even this simplest and idealized model requires a special schematization of filtration, which differs from the schematization used for routine geofiltration problems. The reason is that in this case, the averaging of filtration parameters by migration area is acceptable within a considerably narrower range than in the case of pure filtration predictions. Hence, the stricter requirements must be made to include the characteristic dimensions of filtration heterogeneity. As a result, the typical filtration model is unsuitable to assess the filtration component in pollution migration. Moreover, it is necessary to obtain a more detailed information about the subject of inquiry.

The geofiltration models are even less suitable to account for the profile pattern of the pollutant mass transport. The average prediction according to such models may be considered only as a very rough approximation. Methods available in hydrogeological studies in principle do not allow the inclusion of vertical filtration heterogeneities within poorly permeable beds or aquifers within the reasonable limits of the field filtration tests. These heterogeneities cause the migration interaction between multilayered water-bearing formations within the water-exchange system, as well as the anisotropic effects of the boundary conditions from above on the system as a whole (the so-called "infiltration recharge").

It is yet more difficult to take into account a complex of physical-chemical factors in modeling hydrogeological units. This requires an evaluation of a number of parameters and constants in suitable mass-transport equations, which is, in fact, a complicated subject requiring a separate study. In addition, there is a practical problem of migration schematization of the system. Namely, this includes special schematizations of the physical-chemical interactions of subsurface water and specific rocks, physical-chemical conversions directly in the subsurface water, the migration flow pattern and its variation in time, and migration boundary conditions.

It must be noted that reactions which proceed directly in aqueous solutions are kinetic in character and, in simplest case, may be considered by means of a generalized constituent destruction (decay) factor, varying as a function of the physical-chemical features of the particular pollutant in the solid/liquid phase. The most complex are the processes involving interaction between pesticides and their derivatives and heterogeneous organic matter in the subsurface water and solids. These processes occur at different stages of metamorphosis and have so far been studied from a physical-chemical point of view.

This overview of the prediction of pesticide behavior in nature shows that, in terms of deterministic models, there is a great number of difficult problems. Hence, it remains a strategic project to implement a wide application of deterministic models that allow prediction under conditions of specific large-scale hydro-geological systems and determine pesticide transportation in soil rock-water system in conditions of uncertainty.

Clearly, real improvement of deterministic models of limited hydrogeological units characterized by quasi-natural or highly disturbed flow conditions depends on collection of suitable initial data and improvement of special techniques of field filtration and migration tests. Such units enable prediction by means of physical simulation, based on the similarity theory application.

Depending on the degree of detail in the design of such analog units, the similarity criteria, as well as corresponding criterion equations, may be set by means of analytical treatment of the following parameters:

• Corresponding differential equations and boundary conditions;

• Values of the quantities, defining the process of pesticide migration within hydrogeological system.

The first approach is promising under conditions of rather detailed filtration and migration studies of the analog units. The second one is applicable in short-term predictions and can already be used for empirical prediction. For all this, there is a probability of the occurrence of factors which are not considered significant but which can increase the error of prediction. Therefore, as new information appears we must analyze the feedback and take the next steps to improve the model.

Such models allow us to look for empirical dependencies which are significant for prediction on the basis of connection between the pesticide and related factors, and permit us to do this without a rigorous and complete description of the migration process. Among such predictive methods, it is note-worthy to highlight the MGRA (Method of Group Registration of Arguments) probability model. It allows not only to find predictive dependencies, but also to optimize them, taking into account the degree of precision attainable in the study of connections between pollution and other relevant factors.

In order to implement the advanced predictive models we need to look into the real space-time distribution of pesticides among the elements of subsurface hydrosphere, taking into account the multiplicity of effects from interacting factors.

Thus, we identify the individual block elements with characteristic properties and factors within the water-exchange geosystem, such as the aeration zone, the soil water-bearing horizon, the poorly permeable strata, and artesian aquifers. Depending on the specific nature of the problem, a topsoil layer may be included in the system as a component of boundary conditions. These boundary conditions are also set by the vegetation cover, atmospheric, hydrological, and landscape features, as well as the affected anthropogenic environment.

The scientific evidence accumulated over many years of work in this field allows us to define specific factors which predetermine pesticide behavior within the subsurface hydrosphere. They may be classed as follows:

- Geological and hydrogeological factors, which determine the natural protection of subsurface water (lithologic and petrographic composition and thickness of aeration zone, poorly permeable deposits and aquifers; geological position and consistency of poorly permeable rocks; relationships between levels of multilayered water-bearing formations);

- Landscape and climatic factors, which govern both recharge and pollutant ingression (the estimation of annual precipitation and evaporation and their seasonal distribution; rainfall intensity; the bearing of prevailing apparent winds and their forces; special features of the vegetation cover and topography, including surface and vertical discontinuities of the terrain, its orientation, etc.);

- Physical-chemical factors within water-exchange geosystems (chemical properties of water, chemical composition and physical-chemical properties of subsurface water, water-bearing and poorly permeable rocks, soils, bottom silts, etc.);

- Physical-chemical characteristics of pesticides (solubility in water and fats; stability over a wide range of pH values; volatility, etc.);
  Variables in pesticide sources (range of products; time, method, and quantity of utilization; persistence time; source type, etc.); and

- Factors of accompanying anthropogenic pollution sources.

An enormous amount of materials for constructing the model are received as a result of monitoring investigations of pesticides in subsurface water. Investigations were conducted in different areas, in soil and climatic conditions of Ukraine (forest, forest-step and step zones).

Work is currently still under way in accordance with the overall scheme, with a general methodical approach to the selection of suitable observation areas, water and soil sampling, and chemical analyses. Concurrently, we accumulate information about the model's inputs, including, but not limited to, the amount of pesticide use, pollution indices per hectare of terrain, geological and hydrogeologic conditions, and climatic features. We research approximately fifty characteristics of the main factor group pertaining to uncertain conditions.

As a result of our research, it was established the presence of pesticides in subsurface water and underlying interstitial water-bearing horizons. The range of compounds identified includes more than twenty pesticides, which are derivatives of different compound classes, such as: organochlorine - DDT (DDE, o,p,-DDN, DDD); hexachlorocyclohexane isomers; dilor, heptachlor, kelthane; organophosphoric - metaphos, carbophos, rogor; derivatives of carbamic acid - sevin, cynebe; derivatives of 2,4-D group; symmetrical triazines (simazine, atrazine, agelone), etc. The levels of contamination are distributed over a wide range, and vary within the subsystem by two to three orders of magnitude and between the units by four to five orders of magnitude.

There may be several types of pesticide migration within or between units: (1) convective (water transport); (2) biological (transfer by plant root systems and soil biota); (3) diffusive; and (4) transfer as a result of human activities (agrochemical measures associated with soil loosening, plowing with soil turnover, drainage and irrigation projects, geological engineering surveys, etc.).

We have used experimental mathematical design to demonstrate the role of individual and cumulative influences of the factors, such as pesticide properties, environment, temperature, precipitation and humidity, and their double and triple combinations. The design factors for pesticide migration in soil-rock-water systems for different rocks (sand, sandstone, marl, claystone, limestone, loam and clay), involving 23 substances, were obtained by means of simulated modeling. The results (see part of them in Table 1) permit us to evaluate absorption properties of soils and rocks and identify real and potential pesticide accumulators. Examples of such soils are, for instance, ordinary black earths, turf soil, meadow and meadow-peat soils, which are rich in humus (4-8 %) and have considerable absorption capacity (100-150 mg-equiv./100 g of soil) and predominance of physical clay (more than 30 %).

Based on generalized information from the monitoring of subsurface water pollution we developed classifications of indices characterizing the persistence and migration of agents within the subsurface hydrosphere, for physical and mathematical modeling of specific processes within subsystems.

Based on generalized information from the monitoring of subsurface water pollution we developed classifications of indices characterizing the persistence and migration of agents within the subsurface hydrosphere, for physical and mathematical modeling of specific processes within subsystems

In view of the three-dimensional character of water-exchange geosystems, the optimum procedure is to design interim models for separate units and boundary conditions, for the purpose of subsequent synthesis into an integrated complex model.

The predictive model of pesticide dynamics in soil which defines boundary conditions within the subsurface hydrosphere, may be considered as an example of the system element model. The physical sense of the model is the consideration of a complex four-component system: pesticide-soil and plant-utilization conditions. Of 35 factors studied (such as fat solubility, stability over a range of pH, biochemical composition of plants, particle size of soils, availability of K_2O, P_2O_5, etc.) only 15 parameters are involved in the generalized model. The probability model that we developed helps to receive precise information in uncertain conditions is highly beneficial in the field of environmental protection. From the standpoint of predicting the static and dynamic pesticide distributions within the object of inquiry, it is also helpful in creating a number of predictive estimation maps, such as an absorption soil zoning map, a map of the ability of vegetation to absorb pollutants from soil, a ground water protection map, etc., which permit to evaluate the main factors in pesticides' impact on pollution of soils and groundwater.

SIMULTANEOUS INVERSION OF HYDRAULIC HEAD AND PERMEABILITY FOR HYDROGEOLOGICAL SITE CHARACTERIZATION: THEORY AND APPLICATION TO THE LLNL SUPERFUND SITE

S. Ezzedine[1], J. Ziagos[2], K. Mansoor[2]
[1]Weiss Associates,
[2]Environmental Restoration Division
Lawrence Livermore National Laboratory, L530
7000 East Avenue, Livermore, CA-94550

Natural heterogeneities and spatial variability of petrophysical properties of the subsurface control groundwater flow. Therefore, a 3D image of the heterogeneous subsurface, mainly permeability, is needed to enhance groundwater cleanup performances, and to optimize management strategies and other decisions. Aquifers are, generally, highly heterogeneous, and petrophysical properties can vary over very short distances. Consequently, there may not be enough point measurements for a comprehensive subsurface characterization. Measurements such as head (H), flow rate (Q), and permeability (K), are usually sparse and available at only a few locations, at disparate scales. Hence, a reliable interpolation is needed for a complete map of the subsurface.

A novel approach forward-inverse adaptive technique (FIAT) has been developed to meet hydrogeologists' needs for a unique, most favorable, solution. FIAT simultaneously solves the inverse and forward partial differential equations (PDEs) through an implicit scheme to assure consistency between the governed physical processes. Adaptive-grid, Galerkin finite element methods are applied to solve the system of PDEs. The problematic nature of the hyperbolic inverse PDE is alleviated using a regularization method. Associated boundary value assignments are modified to unspecified boundary conditions. To ease the numerical problems associated with the point-well singularity, the observed Hs, Ks and Qs are projected onto concentric, equivalent, well radii using an analytical solution.

Data collected at the LLNL Superfund Site. At LLNL (Figure 1) were used Volatile organic compounds (VOC) were used as solvents when the site was an active Naval Air Station in the 1940's. Fuel petroleum hydrocarbons associated with gasoline spills have also contaminated the underlying aquifer. The VOCs are mainly Trichloroethylene (TCE), Tetrachloroethylene (PCE) and Chloroform. The site is located in an unconsolidated alluvial basin. The hydrogeology of the area is very complex, but a considerable amount of geological, geophysical, hydraulic and geochemical data is available. These data provide a unique opportunity to study the relationship between hydraulic conductivity and sediment texture. The contaminants are distributed within a thick, complex sequence of unconsolidated alluvial sediments. A hydrostratigraphic analysis has been conducted to divide sequence of layers into hydrostratigraphic units (HSUs). Our analysis is focused on HSU5 shown in Figure 2.

Three stress periods were analyzed: pre-stressed period (1995), pre-developed period (1997), and the current state (2001). Because of the limited subsurface characterization of HSU5, only five wells were installed to remediate the VOC plumes within the LLNL superfund site boundaries. Table 1 shows the pumping scenarios. Head boundary conditions are also time dependent. On the west (east) side the head BC are maintained at 159.5m (171m), 160.5m (172.5m) and 158.5m (170m), for 1995, 1997, and 2001, respectively. The north and south side head BCs are considered impervious. Figure 3a depicts the 2D geometry of HSU5 and the initial finite elements mesh. Dense mesh regions represent head, permeability measurement and extraction well locations. The number of head measurements and pumping wells differs from one stress period to another.

The initial transmissivity and head map based on cokriging of the head and the transmissivity measurements are given on Figure 3b and 3c, respectively. Only head map initial guess based 2001-stress period is shown on Figure 3c. FIAT optimal transmissivity map inversion is depicted in Figure 4. FIAT honors K and H measurements, pumping history, and more importantly the mass balance and the boundary conditions. FIAT acts as a higher order nonlinear optimal filter for the given data and the flow equation. To illustrate further the successful K-inversion, the head maps are reported for all three stress periods on Figures 5a-c. Not surprisingly, the measured and calculated head is in good agreement. Results show that FIAT acts as a non-linear filter that honors not only data measurements but also the governing mass balance equations.

ACKNOWLEDGMENTS

This work was performed under the auspices of the U.S. Department of Energy by the Univer-sity of California, Lawrence Livermore National Laboratory (LLNL) under contract No. W-7405-Eng-48. Additional financial support from DeepLook Fluid Imaging Collaboration (a consortium of oil and service companies) to LLNL under contract No. 0878-66 is appreciated. S. Ez-zedine would like to thank Dr. Said Doss and Fredric Hoffman for fruitful discussions.

Well/Year	1995	1997	2001
W-1310	Off		140 (m³/d)
W-0359	Off		55 (m³/d)
W-0566	Off	85 (m³/d)	50 (m³/d)
W-0907	Off		55 (m³/d)
W-1114	Off	55 (m³/d)	

Table 1: Pumping scenarios at LLNL site within the Hydrostratigraphic Unit (HSU) 5

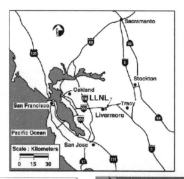

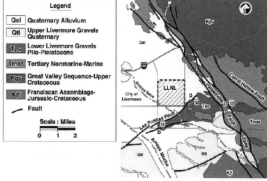

Figure 1: Aerial view of the location of LLNL and the complex geological setting in its vicinity.

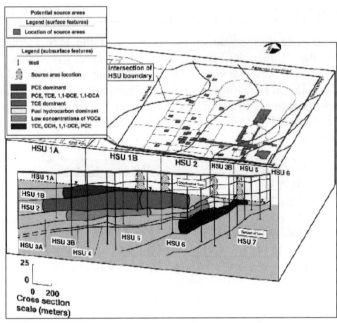

Figure 2: Site map of LLNL showing HSUs and contoured VOCs.

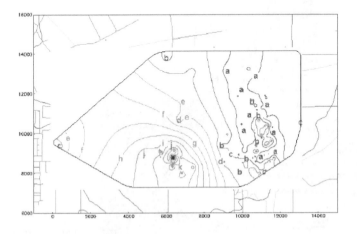

Figure 4: Inverted K field which honors not only K and H data measurements but also head and flux boundary condi-tions.

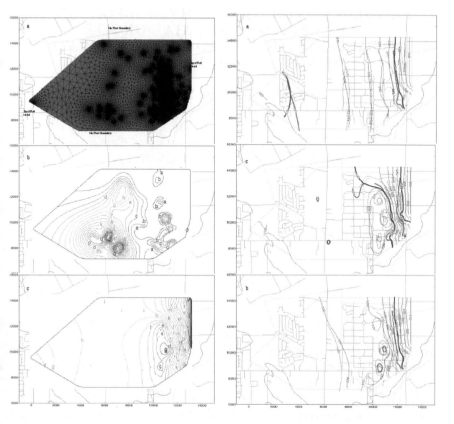

Figure 3: a) Initial finite elements mesh. b) Initial K distri-bution obtained by cokriging the K and H measurements. c) Initial head (H) distribution obtained by cokriging H and K measurements for the

Figure 5: Measured (red) and inverted (blue) results using FIAT a) stress period 1992, b) stress period 1996, and c) stress period 2001.

BAYESIAN INTEGRATION OF HYDROGEOLOGICAL AND GEOPHYSICAL DATA FOR SITE CHARACTERIZATION: THEORY AND APPLICATION TO THE LLNL SUPERFUND SITE

Souheil Ezzedine[1] and Yoram Rubin[2]

[1] *Weiss Associates, ERD. Lawrence Livermore National Laboratory, L530. 7000 East Avenue, Livermore, CA-94550.*
[2] *Civil and Environmental Engineering. University of California, Berkeley. 440 Davis Hall, Berkeley, CA-94720.*

A stochastic Bayesian approach for combining well logs and geophysical surveys for enhancing subsurface characterization is presented. The main challenge we face is in creating the bridge to link between ambiguously related geophysical surveys and well data. The second challenge is imposed by the scale disparity between the geophysical survey and the well logs. Our approach intends to integrate and transform the well log data to a form that can be updated by the geophysical survey and this tends to be a convoluted process.

Ideally, the geophysically measured attributes correlate well with the hydrogeological ones and the conversion from one to the other is straightforward. In reality, however, the conversion is convoluted and non-unique. Hence, a conceptual, data-driven approach for lithology mapping based on the well log data is developed. The proposed approach is general in its basic principles, but not universal since the employed petrophysical models are site specific. The general approach is stochastic given the large uncertainty associated with crosswell interpolation, the petrophysical models and the interpretation of the geophysical surveys. The Bayesian approach allows us to condition estimates on what is clearly a set of complex and nonlinear petrophysical models linking different geological attributes. The proposed approach comprises several steps, each of which intended to explore, model and utilize the aspects of the data that are needed for relating between the survey data and the well logs.

Our methodology consists of sequentially generating a series of collocated attributes. At the basis of the hierarchy, images of the lithology are generated, conditional to well logs. Each lithology image serves then as the basis for generating a series of shaliness images conditional to well data. The shaliness images are then used to correlate the survey resistivity with the hydrogeological attributes obtained experimentally. The series of generated images all have in common the well data and the same underlying spatial structure and hence they are all physically plausible. The variations between the images constitute a measure of the spatial variability and estimation uncertainty. We focus here on estimating resistivity, which can be converted to conductivity using well-known or site-specific models. After the exploratory data and the geostatistical analysis is performed, we proceed in four steps as described below:

a- Generation of the lithology images using sequential indicator simulation (SIS). The lithology is defined through an indicator variable I according to: i=1 if x is located in a silt body, 0 otherwise. Boldface letters denote vectors, i.e., x is the location coordinates vector. Lower-case i is a realization of the spatial random function (SRF) I. I is characterized through its expected value con-ditional to the borehole data, $p^c = E^c\{I\} = E\{I \mid \text{measurements}\}$, with a superscript "c" denoting conditional. Since I is binary, p^c is statistically exhaustive. Its spatial variability is defined through the semivariogram and is shown in Figures 1a-b.

b- Generation of shaliness images using se-quential Gaussian simulation (SGS). This step is similar in principle to the previous one. The differences are due to the fact that (i) the shaliness S is not a binary variable and (ii) the pattern of spatial variability of the shaliness may be different between the sand and silt lithologies, i.e. γ_{Sli}, the semivariogram of the shaliness S, depends on the lithology i=0 or 1. SGS algorithm is adopted here to generate shaliness images. Shaliness S is defined by its mean m_{Sli}, its semivariogram γ_{Sli} (Figures 2a-b) for a given facies i.

c- Computing the resistivity prior pdf. Once x is identified as being either sand or silt and is as-signed a shaliness value, a prior pdf for the resistivity $f_R(x)(r|I=i, S=s)$ can be defined through Figure 3a. R and S denote the SRF of the resistivity and the shaliness, respectively, and r and s denote their realizations. Figure 3b illustrates the joint pdf of R and S given I=0 (i.e., sand) and the mar-ginals $f_R(r|I=0)$ and $f_S(s|I=0)$. Conditioning further on $S=s_0$ leads to $f_R|_S(r|S=s_0, I=0)$, which is our

Bayesian prior. Scarcity of data led us to condition on ranges of S values rather than on single values. These pdfs are the Bayesian prior pdfs of the resistivity, and hence our stochastic estimation for the resistivity R at x in case no additional data become available through surveying. Synthetic "true" images of the geological setting and the resistivity image are given in Figure 4. To illustrate the updating process, a single realization of the lithology and resistivity images are given in Figure 5. These images will be updated using the following step.

d- Updating $f_{R(x)}$(r|I=i, S=s) based on crosswell electromagnetic resistivity survey $\rho(x)$. Defining $f_{R(x)}$(r|I=i, S=s) = $f'_{R(x)}$(r) for brevity, and given a collocated survey resistivity $\rho(x)$ (Figure 6), the posterior pdf f"R(x)(r|ρ) can be defined through Bayes' rule:
$f''_{R(x)}$(r|ρ) = C_R L(ρ|r) $f'_{R(x)}$(r); where L(ρ|r) is the likelihood function, and C_R is a nor-malized factor. In general, ρ is defined over a support volume larger than the support volume of ρ. In the case of a high resolution geophysical survey ρ(x)-- ρ(x) and Bayesian updating is unnecessary. This, however, is not generally the case and the alternative is to update $f'_{R(x)}$(r) given r. Typically we are interested in R representative of a block of scale ~1m while r is defined by blocks of scale ~3m or greater. The inference of the like-lihood function, L(ρ|r), is critical for the successes of the updating process. Once f"$_R$(r|ρ) is defined, a realization of R at x can be drawn. The whole process is repeated for all x until a complete image of the resistivity field is completed (Figure 7). Similarly, the lithology images can be improved through the resistivity survey despite the non-linear and non-unique relationship displayed in the cross-plot. Our approach calls for Bayesian updating of pc as well, through the relationship: $p^{c'}$ = C_I L(ρ|I) p^c, where L(ρ|I) is the likelihood function, of a similar nature to L(ρ|r), only relating r to I rather than R. C_I is a normalized factor similar to C_R (Figure 8). At this stage the Bayesian approach becomes the key for data assimilation, its robustness stems from its ability to express vague relationship as probabilistic rules and to bridge over scale disparity issues. This brings us to refer to the approach presented here as a set of tools rather than as a clear road map.

We have found that the benefits in estimating high-resolution subsurface resistivity (Figure 7) given a low-resolution resistivity survey (Figure 6) are more significant than those gained in estimating lithology (Figure 8). The LLNL data showed good correlation between resistivity and lithology at the small scale (Figure 3a), but at lower resolution the correlations deteriorate. This observation is supported by the fact that the resistivity surveys were non-informative for updating the lithology images. Resistivity-shaliness-lithology relations may show perfect correlation at a fine scale but can appear to have large scatter when using a larger observation scale. We explored the limits of the approach through synthetic surveys of different resolutions and error levels, employing the relationships between the geophysical and hydrological attributes which are weak or non-linear or both. The synthetic surveys closely mimic the conditions at the LLNL Superfund site. We show that the proposed stochastic Bayesian approach improves hydrogeological site characterization even when using low-resolution resistivity surveys (Figure 9).

ACKNOWLEDGMENTS

Funding for this study was provided by the NSF pro-ject EAR-9628306 and the DOE, EMSP Grant DE-FG07-96ER14726. This work was performed under the auspices of the U.S. Department of Energy by University of California, Lawrence Livermore National Laboratory under contract No. W-7405-Eng-48. The authors wish to thank: G. Mavko and T. Mukerji, Stanford Univ. R. Bainer, R. Blake and F. Hoffman, Lawrence Livermore National Laboratory. D. G. Hill, Weiss Associates. J. Rector, F. Morrison and R. Hatch, Univ. of California, Berkeley.

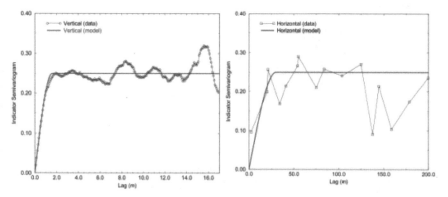

Figure 1: Indicator experimental and theoretical semivariograms: a) vertical direction, b) horizontal direction. Theoretical semivariograms are exponential.

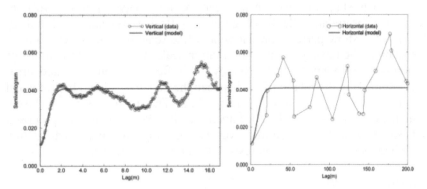

Figure 2: Shaliness experimental and theoretical semivariograms: a) vertical direction, b) horizontal direction. Theoretical semivariograms are Gaussian.

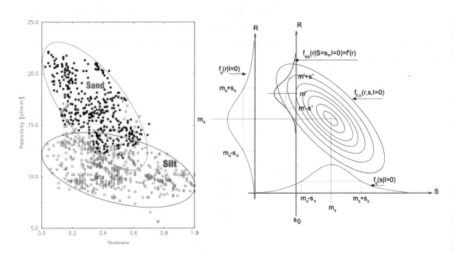

Figure 3: a) True petrophysical relationship between shaliness and resistivity plotted from available data. b) Generic scheme for constructing conditional (prior) resistivity pdfs to lithology and shaliness

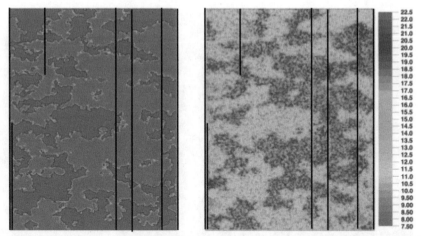

Figure 4: "True" geological setting. a) SIS of the lithology conditional to borehole data. Red and purple colors represent sand and silt, respectively. b) True resistivity image built by projecting the "true" shaliness image using the petrophysical relationship depicted on Figure 3a. Straight lines depict vertical wells.

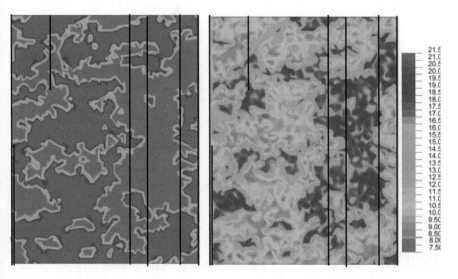

Figure 5: a) A realization of the lithology image. b) A realization of the resistivity image built similarly to Figure 4b.

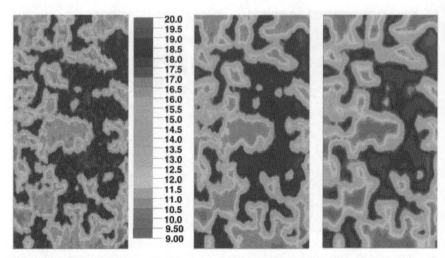

Figure 6a-c: Examples of the resistivity surveys obtained by geometric averaging of the "true" resistivity image (Figure 4b) over a) 3x3, b) 6x6, and c) 9x9 small-scale blocks.

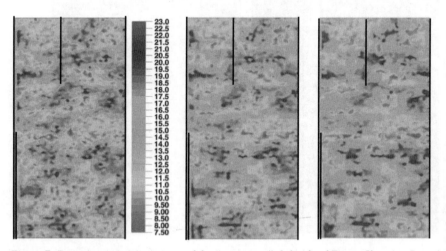

Figure 7: Posterior resistivity images of the "testing set", left side of Figure 5b, using Bayes' rule, and the resistivity surveys: a) 3x3, b) 6x6, and c) 9x9 resistivity survey (Figure 6a-c) and the posterior lithology (Figure 8a-c).

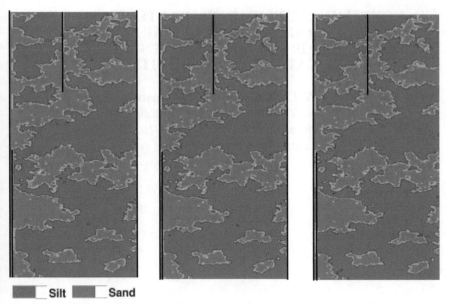

Silt   Sand

Figure 8a-c: Posterior lithology image of the "testing set", left-hand side of Figure 5a, using Bayes' rule, and a) 3x3, b) 6x6, and c) 9x9 resistivity survey (Figure 6a-c).

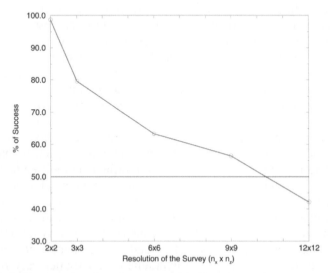

Figure 9: Percentage of number of successes of the Bayesian up-dating approach for different survey resolutions and different errors in the surveys.

CONTAMINANT PLUME CHARACTERIZATION IN A HETEROGENEOUS ALLUVIAL AQUIFER: A CASE HISTORY OF A HAZARDOUS WASTE TANK LEAK AT THE HANFORD SITE, USA

V. G. Johnson and F. A. Spane
Pacific Northwest National Laboratory, P.O. Box 999, Richland, Washington 99352; Phone number: (509) 376-0916; FAX (509) 372-1704; email: Vernon.Johnson@pnl.gov

Investigations of leaks at hazardous waste-storage sites commonly involve evaluation of the rate and extent of contaminant migration in shallow aquifers. At sites with deep aquifers, however, hydrogeological characterization is often very costly and difficult to obtain. To reduce the costs of site characterization, the combination of limited field data, together with predictive modeling can be used in estimating the likely impact of hazardous waste leaks. Here we report an evaluation of contaminant dispersal in a relatively deep, heterogeneous alluvial aquifer, near a subsurface nuclear waste-storage tank at the Hanford Site in south-central Washington State, USA.

At the Hanford Site, several underground single-shell tanks containing radioactive and hazardous waste from the plutonium production era have leaked into the vadose zone. Groundwater monitoring data indicate that mobile contaminants (technetium-99, nitrate, chromate, uranium, and iodine-129) have slowly migrated through 60 to 80 m of glaciofluvial sediments and into the underlying aquifer. Intercalated layers of sand, gravel and silt-clay, with irregular cementing, produce a heterogeneous aquifer of varying permeability. At the tank farm with the highest groundwater contaminant concentrations (the main focus of this paper) hydraulic conductivities vary from <1 to16 m/day and Darcy flow velocities range between 20 and 100 m/yr within an estimated plume area of approximately 75 x 200 m. Discrete depth sampling indicates that tank waste constituents are restricted to the upper 10 m of the aquifer at this location.

Investigations are underway at those waste management areas where significant groundwater contamination occurs (e.g., where contaminant concentrations are greater than 10 times the drinking water standards). The objective of the facility investigation phase is to determine the nature, extent and rate of contaminant migration in both the vadose zone and the underlying aquifer. The first of these studies was initiated at a site in the 200 West Area of the Hanford Site known as Waste Management Area S-SX (WMA S-SX). This paper is based on information from the groundwater investigation being conducted for the Department of Energy in response to a regulatory directive from the State of Washington.

APPROACH

A 3-dimensional, analytical dispersion model (PLUME –3D) was used to simulate the contaminant arrival time of Tc-99 at a downgradient well, to approximate the plume shape and to help estimate the lateral extent of contamination from the source area. The simulation of contaminant arrival times and breakthrough patterns at known well distances from a contaminant source has been shown to be particularly valuable for determining groundwater-flow velocity and longitudinal dispersion.

The numerical analysis procedure included an initial simulation of the Tc-99 contaminant arrival time profile to obtain preliminary estimates for hydrologic and transport parameters (e.g., groundwater-flow velocity, longitudinal and transverse dispersivities) within the contaminant plume area. The well used for the initial simulation is located near the plume center and approximately 125 m from the contaminant source. For initial input parameters for the simulation, the following values were utilized:

- A contaminant source input rate ranging between 6.6E-6 and 6.6E-7 kg/day (based on vadose zone core sample data from the tank leak site, a source area of 400 m² and an infiltration rate of 10 cm/yr)
- Ambient groundwater-flow velocities ranging between 0.03 and 0.10 m/day and an aquifer effective porosity of 0.25 (based on single-well tracer test results)
- Transverse and longitudinal dispersivities of 1.2 m and 8.5 m, respectively (empirically derived from existing contaminant plumes in the vicinity

- Initial contaminant arrival at the water table in ca 1990
- A constant eastward flow direction (based on a trend-surface analysis of water-level data for the nearest wells)
  Homogenous aquifer properties were assumed and concentrations were computed for the top of the aquifer (where the highest observed concentrations occur)

RESULTS

Simulation efforts using the initial input values for dispersivity were not successful in matching the observed arrival-time profile at the test well. Consequently, dispersivities were lowered significantly (D_x, D_y and D_z = 0.5) to match the observed arrival pattern consisting of an abrupt or very sharp increase in concentration. This response pattern suggested very little dispersion had occurred over the ~125 m distance between the tank source and the well. The effects of channelization (i.e., boundaries) that commonly occur in alluvial-type aquifers and uniformity of groundwater flow conditions has been noted by others as a possible cause for low observed dispersion values, particularly transverse dispersivity. In addition, the relatively small area investigated may also contribute to the low calculated dispersivities and may not be representative of large-scale transport behavior. The calculated groundwater flow velocity (0.05 m/d) obtained from the arrival time analysis also compares favorably with a single-well tracer test (0.04 m/d) conducted in the central plume area.

A comparison of predicted and observed areal contaminant distribution was also undertaken using the dispersivity values obtained from the arrival-time analysis. Reasonable agreement was found between the predicted and observed areal distribution data. The analytical model, therefore, was found to approximate the general shape suggested by the observed distribution. Additional analytical and numerical modeling is needed to further explore depth variation of contaminants within the aquifer as well as lateral dispersion. None of the commercially available analytical models, however, can account for localized variations in aquifer lithology that lead to deviations from a symmetrical plume pattern.

CONCLUSIONS

Predictive results from a 3-D analytical model (PLUME-3D) were compared with data obtained from monitoring well observation points within a heterogeneous alluvial aquifer to assess the representativeness of hydrologic characterization data, and to evaluate the extent of groundwater contamination from a past-practice hazardous waste storage tank leak. To accomplish this, dispersivities that are commonly used in transport modeling of homogeneous aquifers had to be significantly lowered to simulate contaminant distribution within the heterogeneous, channel-type alluvial deposits exhibited at the study site. This is justified since contaminant dispersion within this type of setting would be significantly constrained by the geometry and permeability structure of the channel deposits. This would be particularly relevant for areas in close proximity to the contaminant source location.

The experience described in this case history illustrates the interplay between practical modeling and the reality of field conditions where near-term cleanup or mitigation decisions must be made on the basis of limited aquifer characterization data under less than ideal conditions. Results presented in this paper suggest the modeling approach can also be used to design more efficient monitoring networks for detecting and evaluating the extent of contamination and exposure potential at other tank-leak sites at this large nuclear waste management complex. Also, the experience in applying simple analytical transport models at this site demonstrated their potential usefulness as a planning tool for more efficient allocation of resources for field characterization data.

CONDUCTIVITY OF A BIMODAL
HETEROGENEOUS MEDIUM

Sergey Pozdniakov[1] and Chin-Fu Tsang[2]

[1] Faculty of Geology, Moscow State University, 119899 Vorobiovy Gory, Moscow, Russia, Email sppozd@geol.msu.ru
[2] Earth Science Division, Lawrence Berkeley National Laboratory, One Cyclotron Road, Berkeley, CA 94720, USA, Email cftsang@lbl.gov

A self-consistent approach for estimating effective hydraulic conductivity of a 3-D medium with a binary distribution of local hydraulic conductivities is considered. The medium heterogeneity is represented by a combination of matrix medium conductivity with spatially distributed sets of in clusions. Estimation of effective conductivity is based on a self-consistent approach introduced by Shvidler (1985). The tensor of effective hydraulic conductivity is calculated numerically by using a simple system of equations for the main diagonal elements. Verification of the method is done by comparison with theoretical results for special cases and numerical results of Desbarats (1987). The effective parameters obtained by this approach generally agree with numerical 3-D modeling results. Further, our 2-D result on percolation threshold agrees with the percolation theory, while the result for a 3-D medium exceeds the percolation threshold by almost a factor of two. Further studies of the limitations and applications of the current approach are underway.

APPLICATION OF GEOSTATISTICAL INVERSE MODELING TO CONTAMINANT SOURCE IDENTIFICATION AT DOVER AFB, DELAWARE

Anna M. Michalak and Peter K. Kitanidis
Department of Civil and Environmental Engineering, Stanford University, Stanford, California

Interest in techniques aimed at identifying sources of environmental contaminants has been growing over the past several years. The ability to conclusively identify the source of observed contamination can not only help in the remediation process, but can be critical to the identification of responsible parties. One category of methods based on analyzing the contamination distribution is inverse methods. A subset of these uses a function estimate to characterize the source location or release history, in which case the source characteristics are not limited to a small set of parameters. This category includes methods that use a deterministic approach and others that offer a stochastic framework. In stochastic approaches, such as geostatistical methods, parameters are viewed as jointly distributed random fields, and estimation uncertainty is recognized and its importance can sometimes be determined.

Analysis of subsurface soil cores from the site of a field-scale groundwater remediation experiment at Dover Air Force Base, Delaware, has revealed that tetrachloroethene (PCE) and trichloroethene (TCE) contamination extends into an aquitard underlying a groundwater aquifer. In this paper, aquitard cores are analyzed using geostatistical inverse methods to infer the contamination history in the overlying aquifer. These data sets have previously been examined by Ball et al. (1997) and Liu and Ball (1999). Ball et al. (1997) assumed that the history was made up of one-step and two-step constant concentrations at the aquifer/aquitard interface, whereas Liu and Ball (1999) applied Tikhonov regularization to obtain a function estimate of the concentration history. Whereas both these methods are deterministic and identify a single estimate of the source function, a geostatistical approach allows for more in-depth analysis. This approach results in a best estimate that is the median of all possible contamination histories, as well as confidence intervals about that best estimate. Furthermore, conditional realizations can be generated which allow for better visualization of the unknown process. Finally, structural parameters that describe the continuity of the contamination-history function are optimized using the data itself.

This work represents the first application of the geostatistical approach to contaminant source identification to the interpretation of field data. This paper also reports on the first demonstration of the applicability of this approach to a physically non-uniform domain. Finally, we develop a Markov Chain Monte Carlo method for enforcing concentration non-negativity while maintaining the statistical rigor of the geostatistical methodology. Specifically, a Metropolis-Hastings algorithm is applied to conditional realizations generated using a cubic semivariogram and modified to be nonnegative using Lagrange multipliers. The candidate constrained conditional realizations generated in this fashion are accepted or rejected based on their posterior probability relative to that of the last accepted realization. The chain is run until the probability space has been appropriately sampled.

In general, results presented by Liu and Ball (1999) fall within the statistical confidence intervals obtained using this stochastic approach. The current approach, however, allows for the uncertainty associated with the estimated boundary conditions to be quantified. Furthermore, the ability to generate confidence intervals and conditional realizations greatly improves the ability to interpret obtained results. For example, conditional realizations show the variety of concentration histories that may have lead to the observed aquitard contamination. Overall, current results indicate that the diffusive process that lead to the contamination of the aquitard, combined with the significant concentration measurement error, result in relatively wide confidence intervals about the estimated contamination history in the overlying aquifer. However, the introduction of additional information into the system in the form of a non-negativity constraint greatly reduces the width of the confidence intervals.

REFERENCES

BALL, W. P., C. LIU, et al. (1997). "A diffusion-based interpretation of tetrachloroethene and trichloroethene concentration profiles in a groundwater aquitard." Water Resour. Res. 33(12): 2741-2757.

LIU, C. and W. P. BALL (1999). "Application of Inverse Methods to Contaminant Source Identification from Aquitard Diffusion Profiles at Dover AFB, Delaware." Water Resources Research 35(7): 1975-1985.

MANAGING UNCERTAINTY IN RISK-BASED REMEDIATION DESIGN: AN OPTIMIZATION FRAMEWORK USING A NOISY GENETIC ALGORITHM

Barbara S. Minsker[1], Gayathri Gopalakrishnan[2] and David E. Goldberg[3]

[1] Civil and Environmental Engineering, 3230 Newmark Laboratory, 205 N. Mathews Avenue, University of Illinois, Urbana, Ilinois, 217-333-9017, minsker@uiuc.edu
[2] Civil and Environmental Engineering, University of Illinois, Urbana, Ilinois (Now at Geomatrix Consultants Inc., Minneapolis, MN)
[3] General Engineering, University of Illinois, Urbana, Illinois

INTRODUCTION

Cost and technology limitations are now causing a shift in the hazardous waste field towards risk-based remediation of contaminated sites. Under risk-based remediation, contaminants are removed only to the extent necessary to protect human health and the environment. A major difficulty in risk-based remediation is negotiating an appropriate risk-based limit and a reasonable corrective action approach, particularly given all of the sources of uncertainty in predicting risk. The risk-based criteria are usually developed by negotiating an acceptable risk level with regulators (e.g., a risk of 1 in a million, or 10-6, of developing cancer in an individual lifetime) and then calculating a contaminant concentration target corresponding with that risk level under conservative assumptions. However, this approach can lose valuable information on the relationships among risk, uncertainty, cost, cleanup duration, and remediation design.

To aid in the design and negotiation process, an optimization framework is being developed that combines a noisy genetic algorithm with risk assessment models in order to simultaneously predict risk and propose cost-effective and reliable strategies for reducing the risk. The model can be used to improve understanding of the critical factors involved in a risk-based remediation. This paper provides an overview of the algorithms used in the framework and develops guidelines for effective use of the noisy genetic algorithm. A case study is presented that demonstrates how the algorithm efficiently identifies highly reliable designs.

RISK MANAGEMENT MODEL OVERVIEW

The management model combines a genetic algorithm with a fate and transport simulation model and risk assessment module to identify promising remediation designs. The current simulation models implemented in the management model are Modflow and RT3D, but other models can easily be substituted. These models are used to predict contaminant concentrations that would be measured in the contaminant source area for each possible design solution, which consists of well locations and pumping rates for extraction wells. The risk assessment module uses an analytical model to predict contaminant concentrations at off-site exposure wells given concentrations in the source area and estimates human health risk associated with the predicted concentrations. Using a specified management objective, the genetic algorithm automatically searches for remediation designs that best meet this objective while satisfying user-specified constraints. Currently the model can either be run to evaluate tradeoffs between cost and risk without considering uncertainty (using a nondominated sorted genetic algorithm, or NSGA) or to minimize cost given a specified maximum risk level under conditions of uncertainty (using a noisy genetic algorithm). Research is ongoing to combine these two approaches and implement uncertainty within the NSGA (creating a noisy NSGA). This paper focuses solely on the noisy genetic algorithm, with an objective of minimizing remediation costs. The constraints, which specify a maximum allowed risk level, are incorporated into the objective function using a penalty function. The resulting "fitness function" is the sum of the cost and a penalty for violating the constraints.

NOISY GENETIC ALGORITHMS

Simple genetic algorithms (GAs) have been used in numerous engineering design applications within water resources to identify optimal solutions. Genetic algorithms (GAs) search for the optimal solution to a problem using techniques that are analogous to Darwinian "natural selection". The decision variables defined for the optimization model are usually coded as a string of binary digits. These strings, each representing a decision variable, are linked to form a "chromosome". Each chromosome represents a single trial design.

Several chromosomes or trial designs are grouped together to form a "population", which in turn forms a "generation". Using three classic Darwinian operators, the population is evolved to more and more "fit" designs, where fitness is defined by the objectives and constraints of the problem.

A GA that operates in a noisy environment is referred to as a "noisy GA". The noisy GA uses sampling from the noisy fitness function to evaluate fitness of candidate solutions. Sampling is performed by taking the mean of multiple noisy fitness evaluations for a given trial design, similar to Monte Carlo simulation. However, unlike Monte Carlo simulation modeling, which requires extensive sampling, the noisy GA with the sampling fitness function performs best with few samples. As the population evolves, any strings that fail to perform well under a variety of sampled conditions will be outperformed by more robust designs and eliminated from the population using the evolutionary operators.

OPTIMAL SAMPLING IN THE NOISY GENETIC ALGORITHM

Although the noisy genetic algorithm requires relatively few samples to evaluate each trial design, the fitness evaluation process can still be quite time consuming when computationally-intensive groundwater fate and transport models must be run for each sample. Hence, it is important that the sampling be as efficient as possible. A three-step methodology for determining the appropriate sample size has been developed as follows:

> Step 1: Determine the population size and other GA parameters. To determine the population size that will result in the best performance, the three-step method developed previously for the simple GA can be used. However, the population-sizing equation is replaced by an equation that considers noise. Other standard GA parameters (crossover probability and mutation probability) can be readily estimated using previous methods.

> Step 2: Estimate the noise variance and fitness variance. Once the standard GA parameters are set in Step 1, the optimal sample size for the noisy GA must be estimated. The first step of the process is to estimate the noise and fitness variances, which are needed for estimating bounds on the optimal sample size in Step 3. The noise variance is the variance of the fitness of a single design across multiple samples. The fitness variance is the variance of the fitness across all designs in the population, ignoring noise.

Step 3: Identify the optimal sample size. Once the variances are calculated in Step 2, lower and upper bounds for the optimal sample size can be estimated. A number of sample sizes between the lower and upper bounds can also be eliminated using a "pareto pruning" technique. For problems with computationally-intensive fitness functions (such as the risk-based remediation design problem), the lower bound sample size will usually be less than one, so a sample size of one can be used initially. The sample size can then be increased in successive runs until the same optimal solutions are obtained (indicating that the sample size is large enough) or the model no longer converges within the allowed computing time.

CASE STUDY

To evaluate the performance of the management model, a case study was developed using data from the Borden site, as detailed by Smalley et al. (2000). Applying the three-step optimal sampling methodology for the noisy GA (described above) to the case study resulted in the following parameters: population size of 75, crossover probability of 0.5, mutation probability of 0.01, a lower bound on the sample size of one, and an upper bound on the sample size of 31. The pruning methodology identified possible optimal sample sizes as 1-13, 15, 17, 19, 21, 25, and 31. As noted earlier, the best sample size would usually be identified by starting with a sample size of one and increasing the sample size until the optimal solution stabilizes or the model no longer converges within the allowed computational time. In this case, we tested a larger number of sample sizes to more thoroughly assess the performance of the model for different sample sizes. The optimal designs identified for each sample size were then evaluated using 5,000 Monte Carlo simulations to determine their reliability. The results showed that designs with 98% reliability were identified with a sample size as small as 5. For a sample size of 7, designs with a range of reliabilities between 68% and 98% were identified within a fairly narrow range of costs. These results indicate that, for this simple case study, higher reliability can be achieved without much increase in costs. In all four cases, the optimal well location is identical and the pumping rates vary only between 173 and 200 m3/day.

CONCLUSIONS

A risk-based remediation design model was presented that combines a noisy genetic algorithm with risk assessment models to simultaneously assess risk and identify cost-effective and reliable designs. The noisy genetic algorithm evaluates candidate designs using sampling of the fitness function, which is the sum of the objective function and constraints. A three-step methodology for determining the optimal sample size was also summarized. Application of the model to a case study demonstrated that highly reliable designs can be identified with minimal sampling, revealing the efficiency of the noisy GA approach. Several designs were identified with a range of reliabilities, providing useful information in assessing the tradeoffs between cost and reliability. Research is ongoing to complete development of the risk management model, which will ultimately allow tradeoffs among cost, risk, cleanup time, and uncertainty to be considered in a multi-objective format during the remediation design process. With such information available, remediation negotiations will be able to focus on the design issues that have the most effect on the cost and reliability of the remediation.

REFERENCE

SMALLEY, J. B., B. S. MINSKER, and D. E. GOLDBERG, Risk-based in situ bioremediation design using a noisy genetic algorithm, Water Resources Research, 36(10), 3043-3052, 2000.

THE SIGNIFICANCE OF GROUNDWATER GRADIENT MAGNITUDE ON FLOW PATHS IN SIMULATIONS OF HETEROGENEOUS AQUIFERS

Dean Oliver[1] and Derrik Williams[2]
*[1] ENVIRON Corporation, 6001 Shellmound St. #700, Emeryville,
CA 94608; doliver@environcorp.com, 510-420-2542
[2] 4032 Brighton Ave., Oakland, CA, 94602
derrikw@mindspring.com, 510-336-7030*

In heterogeneous systems, it is widely assumed that contaminant migration follows preferential pathways. The impact of heterogeneity on particle tracks under various aquifer stresses has not been examined. This is particularly important at contaminated sites where releases have occurred under natural gradients, but remediation by pump and treat induces a more significant gradient. This issue has arisen in litigation cases where current patterns of contamination can be combined with historical pumping stresses to allocate costs to different parties. It is also an important issue when designing a groundwater model to evaluate the effectiveness of remediation.

To study the impact of modeled heterogeneity on travel distance, we look at the average distance traveled by contaminant particles released some distance from an extraction well. Steady-state flow simulations are carried out using MODFLOW (McDonald and Harbaugh, 1988). Forward particle tracking is carried out through MODPATH (Pollock, 1994).

The groundwater model consists of seven layers. The top two layers (layer 1 and 2) represent an upper aquifer, layers 3 and 4 represent an aquitard, and layers 5 through 7 represent a lower aquifer. The hydraulic conductivities in each model layer are homogeneous, and incorporate a vertical anisotropy of 1:10. A series of random conductivity fields is developed for each subsequent simulation with different correlation lengths and variances. Table 1 summarizes the variance and correlation lengths incorporated into each random conductivity field. Two additional models are created: the first incorporates a homogeneous and isotropic conductivity field based on the weighted average conductivity of the simple layered model; the second uses the same homogeneous horizontal conductivity field as the first model, but incorporates a vertical anisotropy of 1:10.

With each of the models, extraction rates between 3000 ft^3/d (15.6 gpm) and 10,000 ft^3/d (51.9 gpm) are induced at a hypothetical extraction well located in layers 6 and 7. Particles are released from a hypothetical source location in layer 1. The particle path lengths are measured under each stress. Figure 1 shows the relationship between average transport distance and pumping rate for each of the random K-filed simulations. In general, the average travel distance is related to variance, not correlation length; conductivity fields with high variance show longer transport distances than those with low variance. Figure 1 furthermore shows that average travel distances may not approach the same asymptote value for all simulations.

Table 1: Conductivity Field Parameters

	Variance of log K			**Correlation Length (ft)**	
Label	**Layers 1-2**	**Layers 3-4**	**Layers 5-7**	**Horizontal**	**Vertical** [1]
K5	0.13	0.7	0.35	500	20, 30
K5s	0.18	1.08	0.48	200	20, 30
K5i [2]	0.13	0.7	0.35	500	20, 30
K6	0.56	1.48	1.37	500	20, 30
K6f	0.46	1.55	1.49	500	20, 30
K6s	0.82	2.25	1.75	200	20, 30
K6I	0.56	1.48	1.37	500	20, 30

Notes *1 First number is correlation in layers 1-4, second number is correlation in layers 5-7*
2 K5 is identical to K5i except that the vertical anisotropy is increased.

The results of simulations with random conductivity fields are then compared with results from the layered model and the two homogenous models. These models simulate the common modeling techniques employed in many non-academic situations. While these approaches are more commonly employed and simpler, they are often a less accurate representation of field conditions.

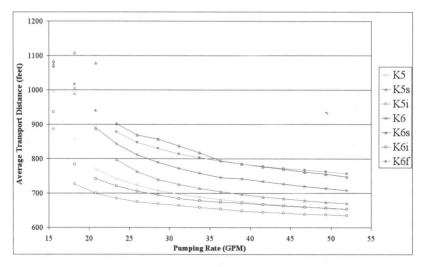

Figure 1: Average distance traveled by particles in each random conductivity field as a function of extraction rate at the well. Note that the lines on each curve begin when all particles are captured.

Figure 2 is similar to Figure 1, with results from the three additional simulations plotted. The three additional simulations are labeled iso (the homogeneous, isotropic simulation), ani (the homogeneous, anisotropic simulation) and lyr (the layered simulations). Figure 2 shows that the iso and ani cases tend to blend into the heterogeneous cases fairly well, though they tend to have shorter transport distances than the high-variance K6 series. The lyr case – the most common way of modeling – has a very different shape to it, however, having generally larger average transport distances.

Figure 3 shows the percentage of particles that are not captured as a function of extraction rate. This illustrates that the iso case pretty well matches the capture percentage of the K5 and K6 cases, the ani case does better with the shorter correlation range K5 and K6 cases, and the lyr case inadequately matches any heterogeneous case.

These results generally suggest that the uniform layering commonly used in models may be the worst representation of reality if particle trajectories are what are important. These results demonstrate that capture of particles is badly underestimated with a layered representation.

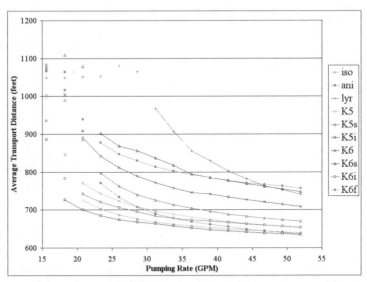

Figure 2: Average distance traveled by particles in all conductivity fields as a function of extraction rate at the well. Note that the lines on each curve begin when all particles are captured.

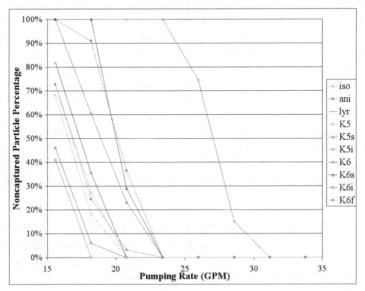

Figure 3: Percentage of the 220 released particles that are not captured at the extraction well as a function of the extraction rate.

POTENTIAL GROUNDWATER RECHARGE AND THE EFFECTS OF SOIL HETEROGENEITY ON FLOW AT TWO RADIOACTIVE WASTE MANAGEMENT SITES AT THE NEVADA TEST SITE

Daniel G. Levitt and Vefa Yucel
Bechtel Nevada, POB 98521, Las Vegas, NV, 89193

SUMMARY

Two low-level Radioactive Waste Management Sites (RWMSs), consisting of shallow land burial disposal units at the Nevada Test Site (NTS), are managed by Bechtel Nevada for the U.S. Department of Energy, National Nuclear Security Administration. The NTS has an arid climate with annual average precipitation of about 17 cm at the Area 3 RWMS and about 13 cm at the Area 5 RWMS. The vadose zone is about 490 m thick at the Area 3 RWMS, and about 235 m thick at the Area 5 RWMS. Numerous studies indicate that under current climatic conditions, there is generally no groundwater recharge at these sites. Groundwater recharge may occur at isolated locations surrounding the RWMSs, such as in large drainage washes. However, groundwater recharge scenarios (and radionuclide transport) at the RWMSs are modeled in support of Performance Assessment (PA) documents required for operation of each RWMS. Recharge scenarios include conditions of massive subsidence and flooding, and recharge resulting from deep infiltration through bare-soil waste covers. This paper summarizes the groundwater recharge scenarios and travel time estimates that have been conducted in support of the PAs, and examines the effects of soil hydraulic property heterogeneity on flow.

VADOSE ZONE HYDROLOGIC CONCEPTUAL MODEL

The vadose zone hydrologic conceptual model identifies four zones from the ground surface to the water table: an upper zone, a few meters of alluvium from the ground surface where climate and vegetation strongly control the movement of water, an intermediate zone where relatively steady upward movement of water occurs, a static zone below the intermediate zone where essentially no liquid flow is currently occurring, and a lower zone where flow is steady and downward due to gravity. In the upper zone the magnitude and direction of both liquid and vapor fluxes vary seasonally and often daily, and, except for periods following precipitation events, water contents are quite low. In the intermediate zone, the stable isotope compositions of soil pore water confirm that evaporation is the dominant process. This region extends to depths ranging from approximately 3 to 49 m (10 to 160 ft) in Area 3, and from approximately 3 to 40 m (10 to 131 ft) in Area 5. The static zone begins between approximately 49 to 119 m (160 to 390 ft) in Area 3, and between approximately 40 to 90 m (131 to 295 ft) in Area 5 (Shott et al., 1997, 1998). Stable isotope compositions of pore water from the lower zone indicate that infiltration into this region must have occurred under cooler, past climate conditions. If water were to migrate below the currently static region, movement to the groundwater would be extremely slow due to the low water content of the alluvium.

RECHARGE FROM SUBSIDENCE AND FLOODING SCENARIOS

Simulations of water flow at the Area 5 RWMS were conducted assuming that the waste cells in the RWMS subsided to a uniform depth of 2 m (caused primarily by collapse of void spaces in the waste), and then completely filled with flood waters from three consecutive 200-year floods in three consecutive years. The probability of occurrence of such flooding in 10,000 years is approximately 1 in 800. This modeling was conducted as a bounding assessment of recharge for the Area 5 PA (Shott et al., 1998). The modeling was conducted using ODIRE (Lindstrom et al., 1995), as well as VS2DT (Healy, 1990). Simulations indicate that ODIRE and VS2DT yield comparable results. Travel times of the wetting front to the groundwater table ranged from 140 to 190 years.

RECHARGE FROM DEEP INFILTRATION THROUGH WASTE COVERS

Conservative one-dimensional modeling studies have been conducted to predict flow through monolayer-ET waste covers at the RWMSs. These studies indicate that some drainage (10 percent of rainfall at Area 3, and 1 percent of rainfall at Area 5) may occur under non-vegetated conditions. Redistribution of that infiltrated water was modeled using VS2DT (Healy, 1990) to estimate travel times to groundwater. These simulations resulted in travel times of water through the vadose zone to groundwater of 500,000 years at the Area 3 site.

Simulations were also conducted to calculate travel times of water through the vadose zone to groundwater at the Area 5 site under ambient conditions. These simulations were conducted using stochastic distributions of soil hydraulic properties, and Darcy's law, and assuming no influence from evapotranspiration. 7,500 Monte Carlo realizations were conducted, resulting in a wide distribution of travel times. The mean travel time to groundwater was approximately 52,000 years.

EFFECTS OF HYDRAULIC PROPERTY HETEROGENEITY ON FLOW

Simulations of flow were also conducted using data from boreholes drilled into the floor of a nuclear subsidence crater (U-3bh) at the Area 3 RWMS. (Nuclear subsidence craters are used for waste disposal at the Area 3 site.) Redistribution of soil water beneath the U-3bh crater was modeled using two scenarios: a homogeneous soil profile, and a layered-soil profile in which soil layers consisted of subtle yet distinct differences in hydraulic properties. For both modeling scenarios, initial water content conditions were taken from the actual water content profile data from soil core collected from beneath the U-3bh crater. The model runs simulated 100 years of redistribution. For the homogeneous profile scenario, one set of van Genuchten hydraulic parameters were calculated from the mean of the van Genuchten parameters (logmean for Ksat and alpha). For the layered-soil scenario, 10 sets of van Genuchten hydraulic parameters were calculated by grouping all the U-3bh data into 10 categories, where each category included soil layers having similar water retention curve shapes.

Results of the model runs indicate significantly different rates of redistribution between the two scenarios. For the homogeneous profile scenario, a wetting front moved to a depth of 80 m below U-3bh in about 100 years. For the layered-soil scenario, although some redistribution occurred between soil layers, there was no significant downward movement of a wetting front out of the layered section of the profile.

These simulations and the neutron logging data that were collected in the two cased boreholes indicate that subtle layering of hydraulic properties cause water flow to be significantly less than if a single set of hydraulic properties are used. These results suggest that some of the modeling studies described in this paper, which used single sets of hydraulic properties, are overly conservative, and likely have underestimated travel times to groundwater. Limitations of these studies include the use of one-dimensional modeling geometries.

REFERENCES

BECHTEL NEVADA, 1998. Hydrogeologic Characterization of the Unsaturated Zone at the Area 3 Radioactive Waste Management Site. Vol. 1: Data Interpretations, Vol. 2: Data. Bechtel Nevada. DOE/NV/11718--210. February 1998.

BECHTEL NEVADA, 2001. 2000 Waste Management Monitoring Report, Area 3 and Area 5 Radioactive Waste Management Sites, Nevada Test Site. DOE/NV/11718--582.

CROWE, B., W. HANSEN, R. WATERS, M. SULLY and D. LEVITT, 1998. The Consequences of Disposal of Low-level Radioactive Waste from the Fernald Environmental Management Project: Report of the DOE/Nevada Independent Panel, Los Alamos National Lab Report No. LA-13453-MS.

FAYER, M.J. and T.L. JONES, 1990. UNSAT-H Version 2.0: Unsaturated soil water and heat flow model. Pacific Northwest Laboratory, Richland, WA. PNL-6779 UC-702.

HEALY, R.W., 1990. Simulation of solute transport in variably saturated porous media with supplemental information on modifications to the USGS's computer program VS2D. USGS Water-Resources Investigations Report 90-4025.

LINDSTROM, F.T., D.E. CAWLFIELD, and H. WEAVER, 1995. A dynamic one-dimensional vertical and isothermal vadose zone water and water vapor flow model. Reynolds Electrical and Engineering Co. Inc., Las Vegas, Nevada. DOE/NV/11432—179.1A.

SHOTT, G.J., V. YUCEL, M.J. SULLY, L.E. BARKER, S.E. RAWLINSON and B.A. MOORE, 1997. Performance Assessment/Composite Analysis for the Area 3 Radioactive Waste Management Site at the Nevada Test Site, Nye County, Nevada, Revision 2.0. Bechtel Nevada. DOE/NV--491. September 1997.

SHOTT, G.J., L.E. BARKER, S.E. RAWLINSON, M.J. SULLY, and B.A. MOORE, 1998. Performance Assessment for the Area 5 Radioactive Waste Management Site at the Nevada Test Site, Nye County, Nevada (Rev. 2.1). Bechtel Nevada. DOE/NV/1171--176. January 1998.

SIMUNEK, J.M. and M.Th. VAN GENUCHTEN, 1996. HYDRUS2D. Simulating water flow and solute transport in two-dimensional variably saturated media. International Ground Water Modeling Center, IGWMC-TPS 53.

STOCHASTIC GROUNDWATER FLOW MODELING IN 2-D HETEROGENEOUS ANISOTROPIC MEDIA

Deliana Gabeva
Department of Civil Engineering,
University of Queensland, St. Lucia, Qld 4072, Brisbane, Australia

Any aquifer as a natural system is characterized with a spatial variability of its properties. The system is affected by a variety of factors that determine its stochastic behavior. The stochastic behavior of the aquifer places a special requirement on the methodology of the flow and contaminant transport modeling for accounting the availability of limited information about the spatial variation of the parameters of the system (hydraulic conductivity, porosity, dispersivity, retardation factor). The limited information is, indeed, the source of uncertainty, which propagates through the solution of the flow and transport equations to the output variables. A good alternative for solving the problem of uncertainty are the methods of Geostatistics, which are extremely powerful tools for modeling the spatial variability of the hydrogeological parameters.

The current investigation deals with the modeling of the spatial variability of hydraulic conductivity and how this parameter affects the hydraulic head prediction. This parameter has a large variability, which is often considered as a primary source of uncertainty for field-scale flow and transport.

The present paper offers a technique for stochastic groundwater flow modeling in heterogeneous anisotropic aquifers with a presentation of hydraulic conductivity as a random field. The technique includes the implementation of the sequential Gaussian simulation method for modeling random hydraulic conductivity fields and stochastic modeling of hydraulic head with a hybrid method combining the boundary integral equation method (BIEM) and finite element method (FEM).

Numerical solution of the 2-D steady-state groundwater flow in a homogeneous saturated aquifer is achieved with a BIEM-FEM hybrid method. The governing equation of the groundwater flow is the partial differential equation of Poisson. The equation is solved under the Dirichlet, and Neumann boundary conditions.

The stochastic modeling of groundwater flow is based on the governing equation where hydraulic conductivity is treated as a random function $K(x)$. This means that any point of area A is characterized with certain hydraulic conductivity realizations obtained from the SGS implementation. The stochastic modeling of the hydraulic head is achieved with the numerical solution of the groundwater flow problem over each hydraulic conductivity realization related to a point of the domain and with appropriate boundary conditions. In this way the modeling meets the requirement for homogeneity at a given point of the domain. The number of the SGS realizations for hydraulic conductivity determines the number of solutions for hydraulic head. The joint stochastic solution for the area investigated represents a sample of the solutions for hydraulic head where each hydraulic head solution is valid to a point of the domain with a certain hydraulic conductivity realization. In this way the heterogeneity and anisotropy of the aquifer that is taken into account in random hydraulic conductivity fields propagates through the stochastic modeling of the groundwater flow.

OBJECT OF INVESTIGATION

The aquifer investigated is represented by alluvial deposits concluded between two rivers. The aquifer area is characterized by a high variability of hydraulic conductivity (K) within the range of 0.01 to 200.0 [m day^{-1}].

Two variants of stochastic interpretation of hydraulic conductivity are considered: source sample of 42 and 548 measurements of hydraulic conductivity. The two variants are chosen in order to investigate the influence of different levels of hydraulic conductivity uncertainty on the hydraulic head forecasts.

RESULTS OF HISTOGRAM MODELING

The location of the discharging and observation wells giving information about hydraulic conductivity for the first variant is shown in Fig.1(a), and the relevant histogram is presented in Fig.1(b). The distribution of the values of hydraulic conductivity indicates large filtration heterogeneity of the aquifer. It is not obvious that the data obey a lognormal distribution. For this reason, the hydraulic conductivity data are transformed using a nonlinear normal-score transformation to mean of zero and unit variance, and the relevant histogram is illustrated in Fig.1(c).

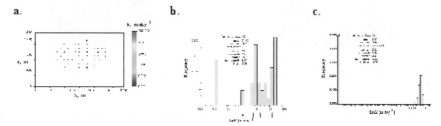

Figure 1. Sampling location map (a) and histogram of hydraulic conductivity – variant 1

RESULTS OF VARIOGRAM MODELING

The variogram modeling of the spatial variability of hydraulic conductivity is done and the lag distances used between the points of measurements is 25 meters. The selection of the most suitable function to adequately describe the spatial behavior of the hydraulic conductivity is based on testing different semivariogram models. The Gaussian model (Fig. 2a,b) has the best goodness of fit observed in comparison with other theoretical models used as spherical, exponential, power and hole-effect models. The analysis of the experimental semivariograms shows that the anisotropy is clearly defined and it is an inherent property for the hydrogeological medium investigated in the present case study.

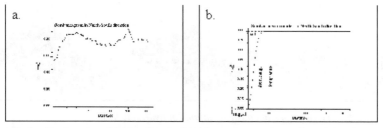

Figure 2. Semivariogram of hydraulic conductivity: (a) experimental model in North-South direction; (b) theoretical model fitted in North-South direction.

RESULTS OF SEQUENTIAL GAUSSIAN SIMULATION

The implementation of the sequential Gaussian simulation deals with the two variants of investigation described initially. The results obtained are graphically illustrated in Fig.3 (a,b) as a map of the spatial distribution of hydraulic conductivity. The map defines a heterogeneous anisotropic media.

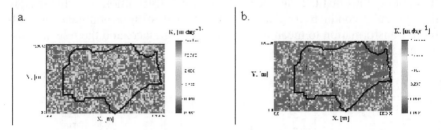

Figure 3. SGS models of hydraulic conductivity for variant 1 (a) and variant 2 (b)

The analysis of the results for both variants indicates that the SGS method has the potential to improve the representation of the spatial distribution of hydraulic conductivity depending on the number of initial sample measurements used. Obviously the increase of the number of the measurements leads to a significant improvement of the spatial distribution of hydraulic conductivity.

RESULTS OF HYDRAULIC HEAD MODELING

The hydraulic head modeling in the present case study is based on the implementation of numerical and stochastic modeling of the flow problem.

The calculation procedures on the numerical modeling of the groundwater flow are done with the author's computer code BIEMH written in FORTRAN

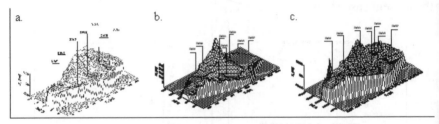

Figure 4. 2-D numerical and stochastic solutions of hydraulic head

[Gabeva, 1993]. The results of the numerical solution are illustrated in Fig.4(a) which shows a map of hydroisohypses. The solution is obtained with the average assessments of hydraulic conductivity that are related to the division of the area into 3 filtration zones. The analysis of the map of hydroisohypses indicates the location of the cones of water level depression.

The stochastic modeling of hydraulic head is based on the SGS generations of hydraulic conductivity for both variants of investigation. The results obtained are graphically illustrated in Fig.4 (b,c). Fig.4 (b) shows the 2-D stochastic solution of hydraulic head based on the sample of 42 measurements and 45763 generations of hydraulic conductivity. Fig.4(c) deals with the 2-D stochastic solution of hydraulic head based on the sample of 548 measurements and 45763 generations of hydraulic conductivity. The analysis of both figures indicates that the number of hydraulic conductivity measurements of the source sample affects the adequacy of modeling. Stochastic solution demonstrates a sensitivity in the zones of discharging wells. The stochastic solution of the flow problem provides a higher degree of the modeling adequacy as it accounts the heterogeneity and anisotropy of the aquifer. The calculation procedures on the stochastic hydraulic head modeling are done with the author's computer code BIEM-STOCH written in FORTRAN.

The technique presented in the paper provides a solution of the complex problem for stochastic modeling of groundwater flow. The solution is developed for a 2D steady-state groundwater flow in heterogeneous saturated aquifer, which governing equation treats a stochastic hydraulic conductivity. The hydraulic conductivity random fields are modeled with the sequential Gaussian simulation method that takes into account the heterogeneity and anisotropy of the aquifer. The stochastic modeling of hydraulic head is achieved with the numerical solution of the groundwater flow problem over each hydraulic conductivity realization related to a point of the domain. The results obtained from a case study show that the technique provides a high level of adequacy of the stochastic modeling of groundwater flow.

STOCHASTIC MODELING OF INDUSTRIAL POLLUTUON IN HETEROGENEOUS MEDIA

Deliana Gabeva[1] and Kevin Burrage[2]
[1] Department of Civil Engineering,
[2] Department of Mathematics
University of Queensland, St. Lucia, Queensland, 4072, Brisbane, Australia

Stochastic modeling of contaminant transport in porous media has become a subject of wide interest and intensive research in the last two decades. This can be explained with the possibilities of this type of modeling to account for the heterogeneity of aquifers as an inherent property of the real hydrogeological media.

The heterogeneous nature of flow influences to a large extent the solute transport in porous formations, which results from the spatial variability of the hydraulic conductivity. That is why the stochastic approach is an alternative for more accurate prognoses as it makes the relations between the spreading of a solute plume and the spatial variability of the hydraulic conductivity, the other aquifer parameters, the boundary and recharging or discharging conditions.

The contaminant transport problem is formulated as a prediction of the pollutant concentration in time and space. The problem solution is considered as an implementation of numerical-analytical and stochastic transport models which description is provided below.

The migration process of the different chemical contaminants in pore homogeneous aquifers is described with the governing equation:

$$R \frac{\partial C}{\partial t} = D_L \frac{\partial^2 C}{\partial x^2} - v_x \frac{\partial C}{\partial x} + \frac{q_s}{\theta} C_s - \lambda C \qquad (1)$$

The initial concentration in the domain of interest is zero everywhere. The boundary conditions describe that the initial concentration of the pollutant on the boundary is zero, and the concentration of the tracer solution is C_0. for times from 0 to t_0 and than is 0 for all time more than t_0.

The solution of the contaminant transport model is obtained with the implementation of numerical BIEM/FEM approach for predicting the hydraulic head and stream function solution as well as the use of an analytical solution of the contaminant transport. The numerical-analytical approach covers two stages. The first stage deals with the solution of the hydrodynamic (filtration) part of the problem, i.e. building the hydrodynamic net (stream and equipotential lines, and equivalent streamtubes), which is a 2-D solution. The 2-D hydrodynamic model determines the geometry of the streamtubes, their flow rate, hydraulic gradient and streamtube area. The second stage deals with the solution of the migration part of the problem, i.e. determination of the pollutant concentration at different points of each   2-D streamtube and moment of time using the method of equivalent streamtubes and the solutions for 1-D migration model with the implementation of Laplace-Carson transform.

The hydrodynamic flow net represents a net of equipotential lines and streamlines. The equipotential lines are determined from the solution of hydraulic head. The streamlines are determined suing the concept of stream function.

The prediction of migration of pollutants is based on the governing equation (1). The migration of the pollutant concentration is modeled in each streamtube from the boundary of the area towards the discharging well (along x coordinate). Each streamtube is considered separately. The 2-D space is presented by the hydrodynamic net, which determines the geometry of the stream tubes. The solution of the governing equation for the case of variation of the entrance pollution concentration on the boundary is as follows:

$$C = C_0\, f(Pe, h, \overline{\gamma}, \overline{\varphi}, b)\,, \qquad (2)$$

where: C is the pollution concentration in a point at a distance x from the boundary in time t; C_0 is the entrance pollution concentration:

$$C_0 = at^b e^{-\varphi t} \tag{3}$$

a, b, φ - constants; $f(Pe, \eta \cdot \overline{\gamma}, \overline{\varphi}, b)$ – function that can be assessed by the expression:

$$f = \sqrt{\frac{Pe.e^{Pe}}{4\pi\eta}} \int_0^1 (1-y)^b \exp\left[\left(\overline{\varphi} - \frac{\eta Pe}{4} - \overline{\gamma}\right)y - \frac{Pe}{4\eta y}\right] \frac{dy}{y\sqrt{y}} \tag{4}$$

The stochastic contaminant transport model takes into account the spatial variability of pollutant concentration, which is affected mainly by the spatial variability of hydraulic conductivity, flow velocity, and hydraulic head. The procedure for stochastic log-hydraulic conductivity modeling implements the Sequential Gaussian simulation method. This procedure includes histogram modeling of the aquifer parameters, variogram modeling of the spatial variability, and Sequential Gaussian simulation of random fields.

The generations of random hydraulic conductivity fields by the Sequential Gaussian simulation method are used for the stochastic prediction of hydraulic head through the implementation of the BIEM/FEM solution. The stochastic hydraulic head predictions are used as an input in the analytical solution of the contaminant transport problem where the pollutant concentration is also a random field.

A hypothetical hydrogeological object is considered in the present study. A variant of stochastic interpretation of hydraulic conductivity is treated using a source sample of 42 measurements. Hydraulic conductivity varies from 0.01 to 200.0 m/day, and transmissivity parameter varies within the range of 0.1 to 2000 m²/day. The aquifer area is divided into three zones having average assessments of hydraulic conductivity of 40.92, 40.26 and 150 m/d and transmissivity of 409.2, 402.6, and 1500 m²/day respectively. The area includes 7 discharging wells (DW1-DW7). Each well works with a discharge of 30 m³/day. The water pollution with sulfates is due to industrial objects located near the aquifer area. The presence of sulfate pollutant is considered. A case of water infiltration from rainfalls is also taken into account as a recharge source.

The migration parameters for sulfate pollutant are as follows: dissolved concentration (C) – 48 mg/l; sorbed ability of the medium (n_s) – 0.5; dispersion coefficient (D) – 0.3 m²/day; irreversible elimination γ=0. The distribution of the initial concentration of the sulfate pollutant in time along the aquifer boundary is described with equation (14), which represents a power-exponential model. The assessments of the model coefficients are: a = 48, b = 0.8 and j = 0.032.

The results for the numerical-analytical contaminant transport model are graphically interpreted in Fig.1-2. For example, Fig.1a shows the model of the sulfate plume evolution in the 15th day from the pollution commencement. The models related to the 30th, 100th and 350th days are presented in Fig. 1b, 2a and 2b respectively. The analysis of the models indicates that there is an increase of the pollutant concentration around the discharging wells in time. The concentration is spread fast from the first day of the pollution commencement. The behavior of the sulfate pollutant shows that certain threshold concentration of 250 mg/l is exceeded and keeps that level till the end of the first month. After that period the concentration slowly decreases up to the primary concentration.

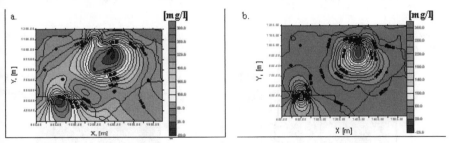

Fig. 1. 2-D model of sulfate pollution in the 15th day (a) and in the 30th day (b)

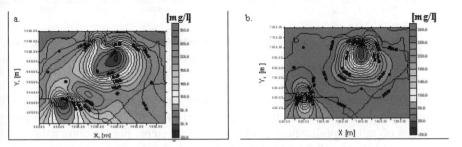

Fig. 2. 2-D model of sulfate pollution in the 100th day (a) and in the 350th day (b)

The Stochastic Gaussian simulation method is implemented with the use of a source sample of 42 measurements of hydraulic conductivity. The simulation results in a generation of random hydraulic conductivity field of 45763 realizations using the lag tolerance of 25 meters. The results of this generation are described in [Gabeva, 2002] and they are used in the stochastic modeling of hydraulic head and stream function.

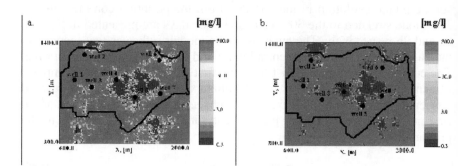

Fig. 3. Stochastic models of sulfate pollution in the 15th day (a) and in the 30th day (b) from the pollution commencement

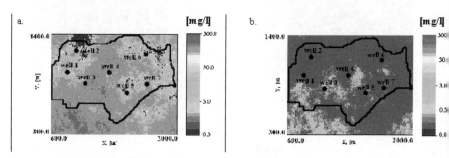

Fig. 4. Stochastic models of sulfate pollution in the 100th day (a) and in the 350th day (b) from the pollution commencement

The results obtained for the stochastic contaminant transport model are interpreted graphically for each time step discretisation of the solution. The prediction of sulfate pollutant is made with 4 time steps. Fig. 3a shows the stochastic model of sulfate pollutant in the 15th day from the pollution commencement. The stochastic models for the 30th, 100th and 350th day are illustrated in Fig.3b, 4a, and 4b. The analysis of the models obtained indicates that the stochastic modeling has the ability to reveal the detailed picture of the predicting variability of the sulfate pollutant in heterogeneous medium. After the 30th day the pollutant concentration begins decreasing and in the end of the first year it almost disappears.

The stochastic approach of contaminant transport modeling presented in the paper represents an attempt to finding a solution of the problem for increasing the adequacy modeling. The approach combines successfully an analytical solution of the contaminant transport with a numerical solution of hydraulic head prediction in heterogeneous medium. It uses the Sequential Gaussian simulation method to model the spatial variability of hydraulic head. The main advantage of the stochastic approach developed is that it has the potential to predict the stochastic behavior of the sulfate pollution process investigated. The results obtained from the case study confirm its efficiency at the solution of 2-D contaminant transport problem.

EXPERIMENTAL AND NUMERICAL INVESTIGATION OF MACRODISPERSION OF DENSITY-DEPENDENT FLOW AND TRANSPORT IN STOCHASTICALLY HETEROGENEOUS MEDIA

M. Koch and B. Starke

Department of Geohydraulics and Engineering Hydrology,
Kurt-Wolters Str. 3, University of Kassel, D-34109, Kassel, Germany
Email: kochm@uni-kassel.de ; bstarke@uni-kassel.de

While the physics of density-independent flow and transport in both homogeneous and heterogeneous media has sufficiently been observed and documented, this is less the case when variable density flow and transport is considered. Although the last decade has seen a wealth of experimental and numerical studies of density-dependent phenomena which occur in many facets in groundwater hydrology such as, for example, (1) seawater intrusion in coastal aquifers; (2) saltwater upconing in formation aquifers; (3) vertical seepage of brackish water from open ocean canals; (4) movement of brine solutions in salt domes that have been targeted as possible nuclear waste repositories; and (5) infiltration of dense aqueous (miscible) or non-aqueous (immiscible) phase liquids, to name a few, many of the governing processes driving density-dependent flow and transport are not well understood, namely in a stochastically heterogeneous porous media.

To this avail experiments of macrodispersion for the hydrodynamically stable case of density-dependent flow within a stochastic heterogeneous medium have been carried out in the new plexiglas tank (10 m x 1.2 m x 0.1 m) of the University of Kassel. Several experiments with saltwater concentrations ranging from 250 ppm (fresh water) to - at the time of this writing - 35000 ppm (seawater) and two inflow velocities u = 1 and 4 m/day each are carried out for an anisotropically packed sand structure with a relatively small variance of the (ln) permeability of $\sigma_y^2 = 0.25$ and correlation lengths $\lambda_x = 20$ cm and $\lambda_z = 5$ cm and a small average grain size d = 0.6 mm. A stable density-stratified two layer situation is created by injecting freshwater into the upper halve of the tank above a layer of saline water that is injected into the lower halve of the tank. The two inflow velocity cases are created by appropriate adjustment of the horizontal hydraulic flow gradients across the tank by varying the heights of the two small inflow/overflow containers with respect to the outflow/overflow container and measuring the freshwater and saltwater inflows by means of two flowmeters. Once the plume concentration has reached a steady-state (after one to two weeks, depending on the flow velocities) sampling of the fluid concentration is performed by extracting a tiny amount of fluid by means of asyringe at about 126 sampling ports places along 6 vertical columns over a time span of about 5 days and measuring its electric conductivity. With the help of previously established calibration curves the NaCl- concentration is then determined.

The understanding of much of the physics of the macrodispersion processes in the density-dependent flow and transport experiments relies on the interpretation of the curves of relative concentration, the width of the mixing zone – as measured approximately from the difference of the z-locations for the $C/C_0 = 0.16$ and $C/C_0 = 0.84$ and position of the layer centroid.

For calibration and validation purposes the experiments are accompanied by numerical simulations using the 2D density-dependent flow and transport SUTRA. In this finite element modell each sand block was represented numerically by 8 x 4 elements in the numerical grid, resulting in a total of n_x x n_y = 392 x 98 = 38416 elements. Hydrostatic Dirichlet boundary conditions (BC) for the pressure are specified at the in- and outflow vertical boundaries of the tank, whereby the upper half of the inflow side corresponds to that prevailing in the freshwater layer and the lower part to that of a saltwater layer of given concentration C_0.

Whereas the numerical models reveal density effects by exhibiting a lowering of the centroid of the mixing zone for already small salt concentrations (~1000 ppm), this appears not to be the case for the experiments. One reason for this departure is that the piezometric heads in the fresh- and saltwater inflow chambers had to be slightly varied through the experiments to ensure identical inflow, as measured by the flowmeters, resulting in significant variations of the vertical position of the mixing zone. This resulted in more or less significant variations of the vertical position of the mixing zone.

Simulations with the SUTRA-model shows that the position of the mixing zone is extremely sensitive to the pressure gradients.

Both experiments and numerical models indicate for the same concentration-contrast C_0 a larger sinking of the mixing layer with decreasing inflow velocity and, at the same time, an apparent increase of the lateral dispersion coefficient D_T. On the other hand, in contrast to results of other experimental studies and also to theoretical predictions, no decrease of D_T with increasing C_0 is observed here. It is postulated that this is, on one hand, due to the low pore-scale Peclet-numbers of $Pe = O(7)$ of the experiments which is in the regime where hydrodynamic dispersion is theoretically still dominated by molecular dispersion and, on the other hand, due to the low degree of heterogeneity of the tank packing that is characterized by only a small variance and small average grain sizes. Finally, there is some evidence at the time of this writing that the experiments discussed so far with boundary conditions that keep the inflow velocities constant for different concentrations are to be interpreted differently from experiments with constant head boundary conditions that are presently being carried out.

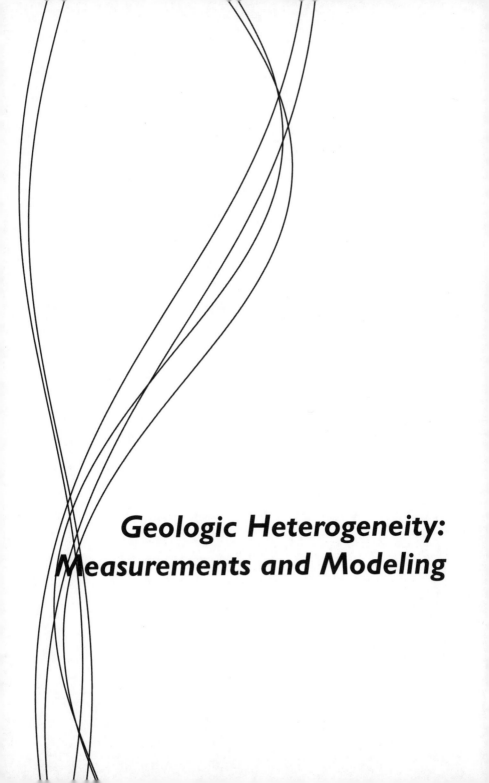

Geologic Heterogeneity:
Measurements and Modeling

HIGH-RESOLUTION ESTIMATION OF NEAR-SUBSURFACE WATER CONTENT USING GPR GROUND WAVE INFORMATION

Susan Hubbard[1], Katherine Grote[2], Michael B. Kowalsky[2] and Yoram Rubin[2]

[1] *Lawrence Berkeley National Laboratory, Berkeley, CA 94720*
sshubbard@lbl.gov

[2] *Dept. of Civil and Env. Engineering, UC Berkeley, Berkeley, CA 94720*

Information about near surface soil water content is a vital component for vadose zone, agricultural and ecological studies, as well as for climate models that require input about flux across air-ground surface interface. Our research focuses on investigating the applicability of a surface geophysical method, ground penetrating radar (GPR), for use as a water content estimation tool. To test the potential of GPR methods under natural field conditions, we have developed a field site within a Cabernet Sauvignon vineyard. The volume and frequency of water application within the vineyards is important for optimizing crop yields, achieving maximum vine performance and fruit quality, and for achieving high irrigation efficiencies. California uses the largest volume of water of any state in the nation, and as vineyards consume more rural acreage, competition for water resources is increasing. As a result, water content information is also necessary to ensure that surface water supplies do not degrade in water-scarce agricultural areas. Conventional measurements of water content (such as from time domain reflectometry [TDR], neutron probe, or gravimetric techniques) are intrusive and provide information at a 'point' scale, which is usually insufficient for managing a crop. Remote sensing data can provide information over much larger spatial areas in a rapid manner. However, it still is a challenge to obtain information about soil water content from remote sensing data in the presence of a crop cover such as agricultural areas. At the scales of space and time necessary to describe dynamic vineyard environments, reliance on only sparse, high-resolution point samples or on coarser remote sensing proxy information could generate large uncertainties when used as input to precision farming decisions. Incorporation of water content information potentially available from GPR methods could lead to improved crop management decisions. Similarly, dense and accurate information about water content could lead to improved vadose zone and climatic models.

Our overall project goal is to develop GPR interpretational techniques for providing volumetric water content information, and to assess the potential and limitations of this method as a field tool. In unsaturated geologic materials, the velocity of the GPR signal is very sensitive to water content. Our research involves careful development and application of GPR data acquisition and analysis techniques to quantify the variations in GPR attributes as a function of water content. A secondary goal of the project is to compare the results obtained from GPR data with information available from plant-based and remote sensing measurements to investigate which method or combination of methods is most helpful for precision vineyard management. This research focuses on a single aspect of the investigation involving use of ground wave GPR travel time (velocity) information to estimate near surface volumetric water content over our field site.

To test the concept of using GPR methods to estimate moisture content under natural heterogeneous conditions, we have developed a field site at the Robert Mondavi Winery in Napa County, California. At this field site, several different types of data have been collected, including water content measurements from conventional point sample tools, soil texture data, surface and crosshole GPR, and remote sensing imagery. We initially performed several detailed studies to understand the responses of GPR to moisture variations at the site. These investigations included trenching, infiltration studies, tomographic data analysis, and comparison of the GPR responses with other co-located measurements collected using time domain reflectometry (TDR), gravimetric techniques, neutron probe, soil texture, and remote sensing data. These studies suggested that GPR ground wave data had the potential to provide dense information about near surface water content in a rapid and non-invasive manner.

To investigate spatial and temporal variations in near-surface water content over the entire Mondavi Site, full grids of GPR data were collected at four different times throughout the year. The arrival times of the 900 MHz air and ground waves from the GPR data were picked and compensated for zero-time starting delays. The ground wave travel times were converted into velocities and then the velocity values were converted into dielectric constants. Using a petrophysical relationship between dielectric constant and water content, the spatially dense dielectric constant values were converted into estimates of near surface volumetric water content. As illustrated by Figure 1, the two-dimensional grids of estimated water content over the Mondavi Field Site reveal areas that are wetter and dryer. Comparison of all the GPR grids collected at different times during the year suggests that there is a spatial persistence of the water content distribution at the field site. Our analysis suggests that near-surface soil texture, precipitation and irrigation influence these patterns. We are currently quantifying the influence of soil texture on water content estimates and the link between the water content and the soil texture with the remote sensing imagery.

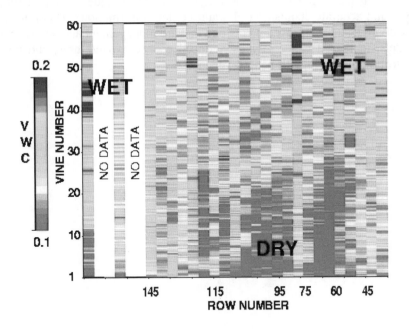

Figure 1 Estimates of volumetric water content (VWC) obtained from 900 MHz GPR data collected over the entire study site during a single data acquisition campaign. GPR measurement sampling interval along the rows is 10 cm, and GPR lines were collected every 5th Row. Both row and vine spacing are 4 feet, so the study area shown above encompasses 134,400 sq. feet, or about 3 acres. Analysis of all GPR grids suggests that there is a persistence of the spatial patterns of water content over time, and that these patterns are likely controlled by shallow soil texture.

Our analysis shows that estimation of water content using 900 MHz ground wave travel time data yielded high-resolution information about volumetric content of the very near surface. Comparison of the GPR-obtained estimates with conventional measurements (TDR and gravimetric measurements) of water content suggests that the GPR approach provided useful information about water content in a spatially dense and non-invasive manner. This study has focused on use of GPR ground wave travel time information using a single central frequency. We are extending the analysis by considering inclusion of information available from lower frequency ground wave travel times and amplitudes as well as reflected energy into the analysis to obtain a high-resolution, 3-D volume of GPR-obtained water content estimates as a function of time. We are also in the processes of investigating the spatial correlation functions associated with the different types of data as a function of season. Successful development of GPR interpretation techniques could facilitate rapid and accurate acquisition of water content information. This information could lead to improved precision vineyard management and vadose zone models, increased water savings, reduced energy expenditures, and better control on the ecology of natural vegetation.

APPLICATIONS OF ELECTRICAL RESISTIVITY TOMOGRAPHY IN MAPPING ROCK DISPERSIVITY AND MONITORING WATER FLOW IN HETEROGENEOUS MEDIA

Qi You Zhou[1], Hiroya Matsui[1], Jun Shimada[2] and Akira Sato[3]
[1] Tono Geoscience Center, Japan Nuclear Cycle Development Institute, Gifu, Japan; zhou@tono.jnc.go.jp; matsui@tono.jnc.go.jp
[2] Department of Earth Science, Kumamoto University, Kumamoto, Japan; jshimada@sci.kumamoto-u.ac.jp
[3] Engineering Development Section, Kowa Company, Niigata, Japan; a-satou@kowa-net.co.jp

INTRODUCTION

Compared with seismic tomography or elastic wave tomography, and ground-penetrating radar, electrical resistivity tomography (ERT) has several advantages. One of them is that ERT not only can give us the spatial distribution of material resistivity at a given time, but also can be used to continuously monitor the variations of this spatial distribution. Thus it is possible to use the method to investigate the water flow and solute transport processes in the media. The another advantage of ERT is that it can be conducted at different scales and directions in the field. This is especially useful in characterizing fractured rocks where the fluid flow is often highly heterogeneous and the hydraulic parameters usually vary substantially over short distance. Based on ERT measurements made on two rock blocks, the purpose of this study is to map the dispersivity of the rock and investigate the flow process in fractured rocks.

MATERIALS AND METHODS

Experiments were conducted on two 40 cm x 40 cm x 20 cm initially dried rock blocks (pumiceous tuff). The blocks came from a quarry near Oya, Tochigi, Japan, and had a 0.39 porosity and a 9.52 x 10-10 cm/s saturated hydraulic conductivity in the direction perpendicular to the 40 cm x 40 cm surface. Except that one rock block has an artificial Y-shape fracture (called Y-fractured block), the experiments for the two blocks are the same. In the front surface of each block, a total of 64 cylindrical stainless steel electrodes (diameter 12mm and height 60mm) were installed at a depth of 2.5 cm so as to form an 8 x 8 grid, with the electrode interval in horizontal and vertical directions equal to 5 cm. A 30 cm x 10 cm x 25 cm tank made of acrylic plates was settled in the central 30 cm x 10 cm area of the top surface for each block.

During the experiments, the tank was filled to 22-24 cm water depth with a NaCl solution that had an electrical conductivity of 330-380 ms/cm. During the infiltration, the water level in the tank went down. Once the water level decreased below 22 cm, NaCl solution with the same electrical conductivity was added to keep the water level in the tank between 22 and 24 cm.

Before and after the water infiltration experiment began, ERT measurements in the front surface of the blocks were made by Wenner array method. A 10 mA and 2 Hz alternative direct current, which was initially set at 300 V, was applied through two electrodes and the electrical resistance between another two electrodes was measured by a multichannel dense electrode electrical prospecting system (Next-400, made by Kowa Company, Japan). The measurements were conducted for different electrode combinations (each combination uses four electrodes and gives one electrical resistance) along horizontal (56 measurements), vertical (56 measurements) and two oblique directions (58 measurements) with a total of 170 measurements for each measurement scan. One measurement scan took about seven minutes and the scan was repeated initially every two or three, then every twelve or twenty-four hours.

As the water infiltration in the block can be considered an approximate one-dimensional vertical flow, the electrical resistances measured along the horizontal direction were considered to be the best for estimating the dispersivities. For a particular electrode combination, each measured electrical resistance can be converted to a dimensionless resistance $\overline{R}_T$ which is defined by

$$\overline{R}_T \equiv \frac{R_0^{1/b}}{\left(R_i^{1/b}e^{k(t_i-t_0)/b} - R_0^{1/b}\right)} \frac{\left(R_i^{1/b}e^{k(t_i-t)/b} - R^{1/b}\right)}{R^{1/b}}, \qquad (1)$$

where R_i and R_0 are the medium resistances corresponding to the initial and saturated conditions, t, t_i and t_0 are the temperatures corresponding to the medium resistances R, R_i and R_0, k is the medium resistance decay coefficient accounting for the temperature effect, and b is a constant relating solution resistivity with solute concentration (0.9525 for NaCl solution here). Because $\overline{R}_T$ corresponds to the dimensionless solute concentration in the medium, it would be able to fit the theoretical solution about solute transport in the media. For one-dimensional water flow and solute transport, this means that

$$\overline{R}_T = A + B\left\{erfc\left[\frac{z - vt}{2(\alpha vt)^{1/2}}\right]\right\}, \qquad (2)$$

where z is the transport distance (positive downward), α is the longitudinal dispersivity, v is the flow velocity, A and B are two additional fitting parameters. The ideal values of A and B are 0 and 0.5, respectively. Therefore, by fitting the dimensionless resistance calculated by (1) to (2), the rock dispersivity α and flow velocity v in the rock can be estimated. In this study, we let k=0.026 and use the measured maximum resistance as Ri, and the measured minimum resistance as R_0 in the calculation of $\overline{R}_T$. The fitting was conducted using the 'NonLinearRegress' command in the software Mathematica (Version 4.0, made by Wolfram Research Company). The estimated parameters were plotted at the central position of the four electrodes. For other electrode combinations, the same processes were repeated. Therefore, a total of 56 dispersivities and 56 flow velocities at different positions were obtained. To image the infiltration process in the rock blocks, first the measured resistance was converted to apparent resistivity ρ_a. Then $\log_e\rho_a - \log_e\rho_a^i$, where rai is the apparent resistivity before the water infiltration, was calculated and the result was plotted at the central position of the four electrodes used. For other electrode combinations, the same calculations were conducted. Based on these data, two-dimensional (2-D) distribution of the $\log_e\rho_a - \log_e\rho_a^i$ was obtained by a 2-D distance-weighted interpolation method. Thus, the 2-D infiltration process in the rock blocks was imaged.

DISPERSIVITIES ESTIMATED FOR THE UNFRACTURED BLOCK

The estimated dispersivity ranges from 0.14 cm to 3.56 cm. The D is distributed between 0.06 X 10^{-10} m^2/s and 11.83 X 10^{-10} m^2/s, consisting with the order of diffusion coefficients (5.3-9.3 X 10^{-11} m^2/s for 40mmϕ X 30mm samples) reported by Kita et al. [1989] for the tuff rock. This means that the estimated dispersivities are quite reliable. A comparison with the dispersivity values reported by Gelhar et al. [1992] also indicates that the estimated dispersivities are reasonable for the block scale.

SPATIAL VARIATIONS OF THE ROCK DISPERSIVITY IN UNFRACTURED BLOCK

The results show that the dispersivity increases with the transport distance in all of the sections. Gradients of the dispersivity near the top surface ($Z<10$ cm) are relatively small, while from $Z=10$ cm to $Z=25$ cm, the gradients are much larger. When $Z> 25$ cm, the gradients seem to become small again, and some of the dispersivity values even decrease with increasing transport distance. One possible reason for this decrease is the data fitting in the unsaturated breakthrough curves. Another possible reason is the effect of block boundary. The resistance measured near the boundary represents a measurement region more near the inner side of the block than that measured far from the boundary does. Probably, the small gradients of the dispersivity near the top surface also are the results of the boundary effect. A comparison between 5 cm electrode interval and 10 cm electrode interval indicates that the dispersivities based on the 10 cm electrode interval measurements are generally larger than those based on the 5 cm electrode interval measurements. Since the 10 cm electrode interval measurement samples more rock volume than the 5 cm electrode interval measurement does, this supports the statement that the dispersivity increases with the sample scale.

From the two-dimensional distribution of the dispersivities obtained from the 5 cm electrode interval measurements, it is clear that although the rock is considered homogeneous, the variation of the dispersivity in the X direction is still clear. For $Z<25$ cm, the dispersivities at the left side of the image seem generally smaller than those at the right side. While for $Z>25$ cm, there is a region with relatively high dispersivity at the left side of the block. Because the use of the unsaturated breakthrough curves in the parameter estimation and the effect of block boundary would result in an underestimated dispersivity, the relatively high dispersivity at the lower left side of the image probably indicates the variations of rock property in this area.

INFILTRATION PROCESS IMAGED BY THE CHANGES OF APPARENT RESISTIVITY IN Y-FRACTURED BLOCK

The temporal variations in the distribution of logera-logerai clearly indicated the interactions between matrix and fracture in the conduction of water. The water infiltration began at 10:00 on July 10, 2000. Five hours later (at 07/10.15:00), we see that the apparent resistivity along the vertical fracture changed greatly. The water rapidly infiltrated downwards and passed through the block. No clear apparent resistivity change was observed in the matrix except at the upper left corner. During the initial period of the infiltration, matrix suction showed little influence on the water flow in the fracture. However, we see that with continuing infiltration, the water conduction in the matrix gradually became important. At 07/17.09:00, the advancement of water in the matrix was clearly seen. The water flow in the vertical fracture was reduced. At 07/26.06:00, we see that the area invaded by the water further expanded and the water flow in the vertical fracture was further reduced. When it was 08/07.06:00, the area invaded by the water almost covered the entire area, indicating that the water suction and infiltration in the matrix was playing an important role in the conduction of water. So, we see that in the rock block with fracture, there is a transition process from fracture to matrix in the significance of conducting water. The transition process was not observed in the rock block without fracture. This demonstrated that the infiltration in the fractured rocks differs from that in the homogeneous rocks greatly.

CONCLUSIONS

Based on continuous ERT measurements made on a rock block without fracture and data fitting between dimensionless resistance breakthrough curve and the solution of one-dimensional solute transport equation, the rock dispersivity was estimated and mapped. Although there are several factors that affected the parameter estimation, the estimated dispersivity was proved to be reasonable. Application of ERT to a rock block with an Y-shape fracture indicated the effectiveness of ERT in monitoring flow process in the fractured rocks, and revealed that the infiltration in the fractured rocks is different from that in the homogeneous rocks.

REFERENCES

GELHAR, L. W., C. WELTY, and K. R. REHFELDT, A critical review of data on field-scale dispersion in aquifers, Water Resour. Res., 28(7), 1955-1974, 1992.

KITA, H., T. IWAI, and S. NAKASHIMA, Diffusion coefficient measurement of an ion in pore water of granite and tuff, Journal of the Japan Society of Engineering Geology, 30(2), 84-90, 1989

CHARACTERIZATION OF THE UNSATURATED ZONE AROUND A CAVITY IN FRACTURED ROCKS USING ELECTRICAL RESISTIVITY TOMOGRAPHY

Qi You Zhou[1], Hiroya Matsui[1] and Jun Shimada[2]

[1] Tono Geoscience Center, Japan Nuclear Cycle Development Institute, Gifu, Japan; zhou@tono.jnc.go.jp; matsui@tono.jnc.go.jp
[2] Department of Earth Science, Kumamoto University, Kumamoto, Japan; jshimada@sci.kumamoto-u.ac.jp

INTRODUCTION

In many engineering projects, understanding the three-dimensional distribution of the unsaturated zone around cavity in the fractured rocks is an important work, but remains a great challenge. One reason is that the fractured rocks are usually highly heterogeneous and the fluid flow is often limited to a few fractures. Thus the formation and development of the unsaturated zone around a cavity in the fractured rocks usually is much more complex than that in the homogeneous media. Another reason is that there is still no suitable technique that can effectively, non-invasively and three-dimensionally monitor the desaturation process around the cavity. Based on experiments conducted on the end-wall surface of a tunnel, the purpose of this paper is to verify the effectiveness of electrical resistivity tomography (ERT) in monitoring groundwater movement in fractured rocks, and try to use ERT to characterize the unsaturated zone around a cavity.

EXPERIMENTAL SITE AND METHODS

The experiments were conducted in a tunnel located at 140 m depth in Tono Mine, Gifu, Japan. The experimental site is a 3.4 m x 2.2 m end-wall surface of the tunnel. Although the site mainly is weathered granite, the rock properties at the site are extremely heterogeneous. Because water seepage can be observed at the surface, the rock at the site is considered saturated.

Within the 3.4 m x 2.2 m end-wall surface of the tunnel, a total of 134 stainless steel electrodes (2 cm x 6 cm cylinder) were installed to a depth of 2.5 cm, with horizontal and vertical spacing between the electrodes approximately equal to 20 cm. Then, the electrodes were connected to a multichannel dense electrode electrical prospecting system (Next-400, made by Kowa Company, Niigata, Japan). A 30 mA and 2 Hz alternative direct current, which was initially set at 300 V, was input through two current electrodes and the voltage between another two potential electrodes was measured. Thus, every combination of four electrodes gives out a voltage datum. Both pole-pole arrays, and Wenner arrays with unequal electrode interval were used in the electrode combination. The measurements were conducted along X, Y, XY and -XY four directions and at every given time interval. With these data, the rock apparent resistivity tomography was conducted.

During the experiments, a 3 m depth borehole, perpendicular to the end-wall surface and having a 116mm diameter, was drilled at the central part of the site. The drilling took three days and recycling water was used. The measurement scanning continued throughout the drilling. Electrode positions where water leakage was observed were recorded before and after the drilling.

TEMPORAL VARIATIONS IN THE SPATIAL DISTRIBUTION OF WATER SEEPAGE SITE

A comparison in the spatial distribution of water seepage site before and after the drilling shows that before the drilling, the water seepage occurred mainly in the central vertical zone and at the right side. The water seepage was not observed at the lower left side, nor on the upper side where X values were in the range of 0.2 m to 0.9 m. The spatial distribution of the seepage position shows great heterogeneity. After the drilling, the spatial distribution of the seepage position retreated greatly. The water seepage at the central upper side of the wall surface was rarely observed. The seepage site at the right side also reduced to a small area. The highly heterogeneous spatial distribution of the desaturated zone around the borehole is clearly indicated.

From the temporal variations in the spatial distribution of water seepage site, it is clear that the reduction of water seepage also occurred in the region lower than the borehole position. The reason probably is that the desaturating process above the borehole position resulted in a reduction in the water supply to the region below the borehole position. In addition, the breakage of hydraulic connectivity between the upper and lower parts of the borehole may also reduce water supply to the lower region. Although compared with the site scale, the borehole scale seems too small to result in the water supply reduction to the region below the borehole and break the hydraulic connectivity between the upper and the lower parts of the borehole. However, if the borehole cut through some water conductive fractures in the rocks, the situation would become different. Because fractures with larger apertures can be observed on the wall surface of the borehole, this most probably is the case. Thus, formation of the unsaturated zone around the cavity may result from two reasons, the water drainage above the borehole position and the water supply reduction below the borehole position.

TEMPORAL VARIATIONS OF THE ROCK RESISTANCES

The temporal variations of the rock resistances show that the borehole drilling resulted in extensive changes in the rock resistances. Even at the position highest above the borehole position, there is a resistance change, indicating that the range of the unsaturated zone may have expanded to this area. With drilling of the borehole, we see that the resistance generally decreased. Because less water content in the rocks would result in larger resistance values, this decrease of the resistance probably is the result of the use of recycling water during the drilling. The increased temperature, which resulted from lighting, may also have contributed to the decrease of the resistance to some extent. After the drilling, the resistances increased, some fast, some slowly. Difference in the resistance responses to the drilling is very clear. This difference in the resistance response reflected the complexity of the flow system around the borehole.

TEMPORAL VARIATIONS IN THE SPATIAL DISTRIBUTION OF ROCK APPARENT RESISTIVITY

The temporal variations of contour lines with the same range of apparent resistivity increment indicate the expanding process of high apparent resistivity area around the borehole. If the increase of the rock apparent resistivity exclusively resulted from the desaturating process in the fractured rocks, this suggests the gradual expansion of the unsaturated zone around the borehole. Consistent with that observed in the temporal variations of the water seepage site, here we also see that the desaturating process not only occurred at the area above the borehole, but also happened at the area below it.

The results also indicate the difference in the expanding speed. For example, the expanding toward the upper left direction is faster than that toward the upper right direction. The contour lines seem to have a shape elongated in the direction of upper left to lower right. This suggests that the water conductivity in this direction may be larger than that in other directions. Temporal variations of the water seepage site also support this statement. Thus, a prediction that the water flow in the experimental site is from the upper left to the lower right is rational.

The difference in the expanding speed not only occurred at different directions, but also happened in the same direction. The desaturating process advances fast one moment and slowly next. We interpret this interesting fluctuation phenomenon as the result of media heterogeneity and predict that the discharge rate in the borehole would exhibit a nonlinear dynamic behavior.

FRACTURE NETWORK CONNECTIVITY OBSERVED IN THE TEMPORAL VARIATIONS OF ROCK APPARENT RESISTIVITY DISTRIBUTION

From the two-dimensional distribution of the apparent resistivity increment in the depth of 25 cm at 2001/06/04.06:00, it is clear that the area with a relatively high increment value did not symmetrically distribute around the borehole, but extended from the borehole toward the lower right and upper right directions. At the upper right side, it again divided into two branches, one toward the right, the other toward the upper left. If we assume that the increase of the apparent resistivity exclusively resulted from the desaturation in the fractured rocks, the distribution pattern of the high apparent resistivity increment may suggest the characteristics of fracture network connectivity or the water flow paths around the borehole. This further demonstrated that the desaturating process in the fractured rocks is highly preferential.

With the above results, the desaturating process which occurred around the borehole may be described like this. First, the water discharge from the borehole results in the water drainage above the borehole position. Then, the water supply to the areas below the borehole position decreases because of the water discharge from the borehole. Consequently, the desaturating process also occurs at the area below the borehole position. The desaturating process first advances along the preferential paths in the fractured rocks, then from these highly conductive paths gradually expands to the less conductive sites. This process may advance to the area far from the borehole or cavity.

CONCLUSIONS

Based on experiments conducted on end-wall surface of a tunnel, we investigated the effectiveness of ERT in characterizing unsaturated zone around a borehole in the fractured rocks. The results demonstrated the effectiveness of the ERT and revealed that the desaturating process around the borehole not only occurred at the area above the borehole position, but also happened at the area below the borehole position. However, because the experimental site here is a highly heterogeneous one, and our analyses were based on the rock apparent resistivity only, the results obtained here are still to be verified both for other cases and with the inversely calculated 3-D rock real resistivity data.

ACKNOWLEDGMENTS

This work is part of a research project of using electrical resistivity tomography to characterize the fractured rocks in the field, which is supported by Japan Nuclear Cycle Development Institute, Japan (JNC). However, any opinions, findings, conclusions, or recommendations expressed herein are those of the authors and do not necessarily reflect the views of JNC. The authors are grateful to Yukio Miura, Hiromi Hayashi and Shigeo Nakama for their support in the experiments.

MODELING ALLUVIAL FAN AQUIFER HETEROGENEITY AT MULTIPLE SCALES THROUGH STRATIGRAPHIC ASSESSMENT

Gary S. Weissmann[1], Zhang Yong[2], Graham E. Fogg[2,3], Richard G. Blake[4], Charles D. Noyes[4], and Michael Maley[4]

[1] Dept. of Geological Sciences, Michigan State University, 206 Natural Sciences Building, East Lansing, MI 48824, weissman@msu.edu;
[2] Hydrologic Sciences, University of California, Davis, California;
[3] Dept. of Geology, University of California, Davis, California;
[4] Lawrence Livermore National Laboratory, Livermore, California.

Heterogeneity exists at multiple scales in complex, stream-dominated alluvial fan aquifer systems (Figure 1), significantly influencing contaminant fate and transport. Variability at the large-scale represents potentially significant changes in the depositional system character through time and is delineated by sequences that are bounded by regional unconformities. In stream-dominated alluvial fans, these unconformities are typically marked by laterally extensive, relatively mature paleosols. Hydrofacies distributions (e.g., gra-

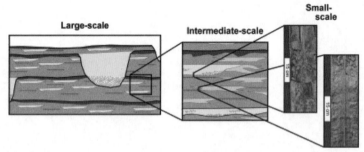

Figure 1: Multiple scales of heterogeneity in a stream-dominated alluvial fan. Large-scale units or sequences are bounded by laterally extensive paleosols, intermediate-scale units encompass hydrofacies or facies assemblages within the deposit (e.g., channel assemblage, overbank assemblage), and small-scale heterogeneities are formed from cross-bedding or lamination within the various hydrofacies or facies assemblages.

vel, sand, muddy sand, mud, or paleosol) within each sequence control the intermediate-scale aquifer variability, and small-scale heterogeneity is associated with variability within each hydrofacies unit.

Each scale of heterogeneity should be modeled by different means. Deterministic models based on stratigraphic analysis can determine sequence boundary and systems tract geometries, thus delineating the large-scale heterogeneity. Transition probability geostatistics is useful in modeling the intermediate-scale hydrofacies distributions within each sequence. Contaminant dispersion due to small-scale heterogeneity can be modeled using appropriate dispersivity tensor values. Alternatively, sequential Gaussian simulation, or other similar approaches, can be used to model smaller-scale variability within each facies unit if sufficient conditioning data exist. By modeling each scale of variability separately, we avoid violating assumptions of stationarity and more accurately represent the aquifer heterogeneity.

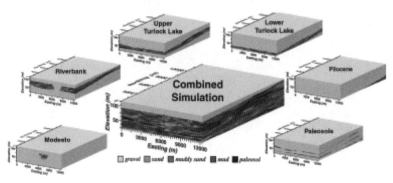

Figure 2: Individual sequence and combined final realizations for the Kings River Alluvial Fan site. Large-scale sequence boundaries, marked by paleosols, were modeled deterministically. Intermediate-scale hydrofacies distributions and paleosol thickness were modeled using conditional simulation in transition probability geostatistics.

Examples from the Kings River Alluvial Fan, located southeast of Fresno, California (Figure 2), and the alluvial fan deposits at Lawrence Livermore National Laboratory, located in Livermore, California (Figure 3), show application of this approach. Though rivers of very different sizes produced each alluvial fan system, and, therefore, a different magnitude of sedimentologic variability exists in each system, this approach captures the relevant scales of heterogeneity within each system.

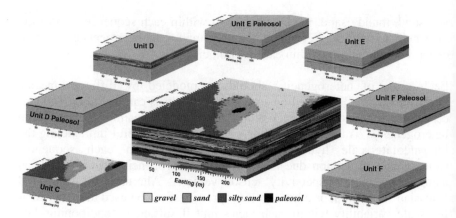

Figure 3: Individual stratigraphic unit realizations and the final combined realization for the Lawrence Livermore National Laboratory site. Large-scale stratigraphic unit boundaries were modeled deterministically, and intermediate-scale hydrofacies distributions were modeled using conditional simulation in transition probability geostatistics.

USING ^{222}Rn TO ASSESS THE FRACTURE APERTURES IN FRACTURED CRYSTALLINE ROCK

Ivars Neretnieks

Department of Chemical Engineering and Technology, Royal Institute of Technology . SE-100 44-Stockholm, Sweden. Tel 46-8-790 8229
niquel@ket.kth.se

The concept of Flow Wetted Surface, FWS, is used to describe the interaction of a solute carried by the flowing water in fractured rocks with the rock surfaces in contact with the flowing water in fractures. The larger the surface a given flowrate of water contacts, the larger can be the exchange of solutes between the flowing water and the stagnant water in the pores in the rock matrix. This exchange permits the uptake of a contaminant that is carried by the water in the fractures into the larger water volume in the rock matrix. The solute will also access the large inner surfaces in the rock matrix and sorbing solutes may sorb there. The propagation downstream of a contaminant can be retarded very much in relation to the water velocity.

Several ways have been proposed of estimating the magnitude of the specific FWS by using hydraulic measurements and by tracer tests.

It has also been suggested that a naturally generated tracer such as ^{222}Rn could be used as a supplementary method to measure the FWS. The underlying idea is to measure the concentration of ^{222}Rn in the water and use the known (measured) concentration of ^{222}Rn in the rock and/or the infill material in the fractures to determine how much ^{222}Rn is generated. With a known generation rate and the measured concentration in the water the fracture surface that generates this amount of ^{222}Rn can be assessed. This could then be used to determine the FWS. It is found that a commonly used model does not account accurately for the effects of matrix diffusion. This can lead to very large errors in determining the fracture apertures. A model including the matrix diffusion effects in steady state conditions is proposed. It is also found that although the FWS per volume of flowing water, which is equivalent to fracture aperture, can be estimated in this way the information cannot be used to determine the FWS per volume of rock without additional independent measurements of e.g. flowing fracture frequency.

SIMULATIONS OF SOME IN-SITU TRACER EXPERIMENTS IN FRACTURED CRYSTALLINE ROCK AT ÄSPÖ

Ivars Neretnieks and Luis Moreno
Department of Chemical Engineering and Technology, Royal Institute of Technology. SE-100 44-Stockholm, Sweden. Tel 46-8-790 8229
niquel@ket.kth.se

Some recent, converging flow, tracer tests at the ÄSPÖ Hard rock laboratory in Sweden using non-sorbing as well as sorbing tracers in fractured crystalline rocks were analysed and simulated. Laboratory data on diffusion and sorption properties were used to predict the Residence Time Distribution, RTD, of the sorbing tracers. The field explorations were mainly aimed at assessing the hydraulic properties of one specific fracture that was deemed to be the main flow conduit, the so-called Feature A. It was found that the residence time distributions could not be explained if it was assumed that all flow takes place in only Feature A. An approximately 30 times larger Flow Wetted Surface or 1000 times larger matrix diffusivity or sorption coefficients than laboratory data indicated would be needed.

A hypothesis that the flow took place in many fractures in a three dimensional pattern and not only in the two dimensional Feature A is tested in this paper. Transmissivity measurement in five boreholes in the rock volume containing Feature A show that there is a high frequency of water conducting fractures. The conductive fracture frequency was found to be about 2/m which gives a Flow Wetted Surface about 30 times larger than in Feature A. Using our Channel Network model, breakthrough curves for three strongly sorbing tracers were predicted using only laboratory data, the transmissivity measurements and the pumping flowrate. No information on the water residence time as obtained by the non-sorbing tracer tests was used. The predictions were surprisingly accurate considering that no adjustments of any parameter values have been.

A Multi Channel model that is presented in a companion paper was also tested with encouraging results.

DELINEATION OF FAST FLOW PATHS IN POROUS MEDIA USING NOBLE GAS TRACERS

G.B. Hudson and J. E. Moran
Analytical and Nuclear Chemistry Division, Lawrence Livermore National Laboratory, Livermore, CA, 94551 USA

In some areas of the arid western USA, water purveyors use artificial recharge to augment natural recharge to groundwater basins where water demand is high. In coastal regions of California, USA, artificial recharge replenishes basins that were subject to overdraft, mitigates seawater intrusion, and provides benefits to water quality. Artificial recharge facilities usually consist of abandoned quarries or injection wells, with high capacity, public water supply wells located down-gradient. Source water for artificial recharge may be water captured from the watershed, imported water, or recycled wastewater. For the latter case, the proposed regulations for the potability of water of wastewater origin stipulate a minimum subsurface residence time of one year and dilution of ≥50% with a non-wastewater source.

In order to demonstrate compliance to the proposed regulations, and to improve the understanding of groundwater flow in the affected basins, a tracer may be added to the artificial recharge source water. Movement of the tracer is observed at down-gradient points in the groundwater basin. In practice, the period of observation is on the time scale of several months to a couple of years; shorter than for natural (or bomb pulse) isotopic tracers such as tritium, 14Carbon, or stable isotopes of oxygen, but longer than the time scale for pump tests. The data acquired from such a tracer experiment can be used to calibrate groundwater flow models and to identify fast flow paths.

Delineation of fast flow paths is important, because the portion of water that travels most quickly from surface sources to production wells may have the greatest impact on water quality.

The fact that multiple surface water sources supply public drinking water wells dictates the choice of tracers. Dissolved noble gases are chemically inert, colorless and odorless, and are non-radioactive, thereby posing no real or perceived health risks. By using tracers of the same element enriched in different isotopes, recharge from multiple sources can be examined using a single noble gas isotopic analysis from a well water sample. Furthermore, the low natural abundance of certain isotopes of naturally-occurring dissolved noble gases means that by using even a small volume of tracer with a highly altered isotopic content, a large dynamic range can be achieved during dilution with native groundwater. Dissolved noble gases do not sorb to aquifer materials and are not retarded relative to water flow. The only difference in saturated zone transport properties between water molecules and dissolved noble gases is in their rates of diffusion, but this is a negligibly small effect under the rates of advective transport that apply.

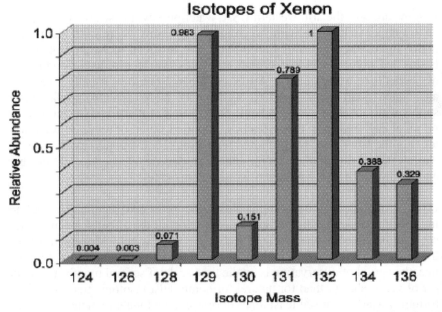

Figure 1. Natural abundance pattern of Xe isotopes. An artificial tracer has a highly altered isotopic content, e.g., 99% 124Xe.

Xenon has nine stable isotopes, five of which are good candidates for isotopically enriched tracers. Figure 1 shows the natural abundance pattern for Xe; the isotopically enriched tracers used in these studies have highly altered abundance patterns. The Xe gas is pre-dissolved into a small volume of water for introduction into the recharge water body. Sampling for dissolved noble gases in water is accomplished by pumping the water through a 3/8" copper tube under pressure (so that the gases stay in solution), and pinching the tube at both ends with metal clamps, to make an air-tight seal. Analysis of the dissolved tracer gases is by noble gas mass spectrometry (VG5400) with sample introduction by multiport gas handling manifold. The precision for 124Xe/132Xe is 0.5% and the precision for ^{136}Xe/^{132}Xe and ^{129}Xe/^{132}Xe are 0.1%. At a cost of $1USD per 103 m^3 per isotope, a tracer concentration (C/C0) of 1% can be readily detected.

RESULTS

In an experiment at the Alameda County Water District, artificial noble gas tracers were added to two recharge ponds, as shown in Figure 2, and move-

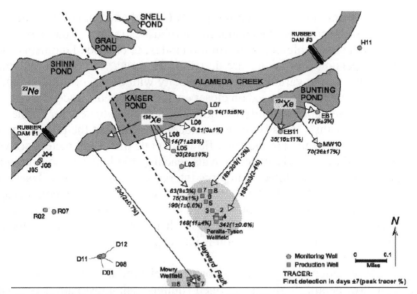

Figure 2. Recharge facilities at the Alameda County Water District. Tracer loading and arrivals at monitoring and production wells are shown. Tracer elution curves were determined for each well. Both Xe tracers were detected in a few samples from the Peralta-Tyson wellfield.

ment of the tracer was monitored in the groundwater wells shown, over a period of one and a half years. Dissolved ^{124}Xe tracer was loaded into Bunting Pond and ^{136}Xe tracer was loaded into Kaiser Pond (Figure 2). Tracer was released by gravity flow through a plastic tube, in one location near the center of the pond. The process of tracer introduction was repeated once per week for four weeks. The rationale for introducing tracer over a period of four weeks was to provide a tracer pulse in wells such that sampling could be spaced at reasonable time intervals.

The most striking features of the tracer data are the very short travel time for a small fraction of the water pumped at some of the production wells, and the low tracer concentrations observed at nearly all the wells. The short travel time (60 days) to the production wells indicates a maximum velocity of 2100 m/yr. This value does not represent the velocity of the center of mass (and hence is not necessarily the advective speed), but rather is the rate of travel for that portion of the surface water that reaches the wells fastest. Given the low hydraulic gradient (.002), and low pumping volume ($2x10^6$ l) over the first sixty days of the tracer study, the fast arrival was somewhat unexpected.

Because of limitations in sampling points (spatial and temporal availability, and long well screens), one cannot make robust estimates of the mass distribution in the tracer plume, of the dilution index, or of second moments (from which dispersion coefficients are derived). However, some semi-quantitative estimates of the variation of flow velocity with depth, of dilution, and of dispersion can be made based on closer examination of the tracer curves. For instance, these data exemplify the utility of noble gas tracers for delineation of fast flow paths. Mass balance considerations rule out the possibility that a major portion of the groundwater flows at a rate of several meters per year. Wells that showed early tracer arrivals reaching the highest concentrations, are those with the shallowest sampling intervals (top-of-screens). Tracer was not detected at wells with the deepest top-of-screens. Furthermore, a drop in tracer levels occurs during times of high production and a rise occurs during times of low production, indicating that when water rises in the wellbore, a zone of higher tracer concentration is intercepted.

These observations suggest that a zone of preferential flow is likely present at a shallow depth. In this unconfined aquifer, such a fast path may exist at or near the phreatic surface. In contrast to the very fast movement of the small volume of water containing tracer, groundwater ages measured by the Tritium-^{3}Helium method give mean ages (residence times for water since recharge) in the AHF sub-basin of 3 to 9 years. Therefore, while the bulk of the water resides in the sub-basin for several years, a high conductivity layer near the water table likely provides a path for much faster transport for a small fraction of the artificially recharged water.

These fast travel times indicate that contaminants that are not retarded relative to water flow will reach water supply wells quickly, before remediation methods are in place. Furthermore, de-activation of viruses may require longer times in the subsurface than the travel times observed in these coarse grained alluvial aquifers. The work described here demonstrates that noble gas isotope tracers allow collection of hydrogeologic information on a large scale, and with unprecedented detail.

This work was performed under the auspices of the U.S. Department of Energy by the University of California, Lawrence Livermore National Laboratory under contract No. W-7405-ENG-48.

USE OF DUAL LATEROLOG AT THE DETERMINATION OF FRACTURE PARAMETERS IN HARD ROCK AQUIFERS

Vilmos Vasvári

Geoteam GmbH. Consultants for Hydrogeology, Geothermics and Environment, Austria. A-8200 Gleisdorf, Weizerstr. 19 Tel.: +43-3112-6515; Fax: +43-3112-6830 e-mail: geoteam@aon.at

INTRODUCTION

Within the scope of a research project the geophysical borehole measurement methods were investigated and selected which are suitable for the characterization of fracture parameters and determination of hydraulic properties in fractured aquifers. New imaging technologies, such as the Formation MicroScanner (FMS) and Formation MicroImager (FMI), can yield data to determine fracture porosity, aperture and dip of fractures (Luthi & Souhaité, 1990; Hornby & Luthi, 1992), but these measurements and their evaluation are expensive in comparison to others. Furthermore, the data evaluation requires special knowledge and specific hardware and software. Therefore, the Dual Laterolog tool (DLL) was chosen which is used in deep thermal water exploration routinely and allows the estimation of fracture parameters in hard rocks quantitatively as well. By using the Dual Laterolog, based on resistivity anomalies and separation between shallow (LLs) and deep laterolog (LLd) and on mud conductivity, fracture zones can be detected; in addition the fracture porosity and the fracture aperture of horizontal and vertical fractures can be estimated easily. The applicability of the calculation methods was tested in carbonate and crystalline aquifers.

ESTIMATION OF FRACTURE PARAMETERS

Due to the inverse relationship between resistivity and porosity, the Dual Laterolog can be used to compute the porosity of the rock according to Archie's equation, which can be applied if the sediments/rocks do not contain any clay or if the contribution of surface conduction to the signal is negligible. The fracture porosity can be estimated from the separation between the deep and shallow measurements based on the observation that the former is sensitive to the presence of horizontal conductive features only, while the latter responds to both horizontal and vertical conductive structures.

FRACTURE POROSITY

The first equation for estimation of total porosity based on measurement on core data was developed by Archie (1942). Archie has found a power function, which yields the total porosity of formation depending on the relationship between the resistivity of formation and formation water:

$$\Phi_{tot}^{m} = \frac{a \cdot R_W}{R_0} \qquad (1)$$

where Φ_{tot} = total porosity; R_W = formation water resistivity (Ωm); R_0 = resistivity of a nonshaly formation rock (Ωm); a = constant (mostly about 1); m = Archie's cementation exponent.

Using charts the total porosity in fractured media can be reduced to the fracture porosity, $\Phi_{frac} = f(\Phi_{tot}, m)$. If a value of m is available, the chart can be used to estimate the portion of fracture porosity of the measured total porosity. The graphs in the chart can be good approximated by power functions, which were determined and used at numerical calculations. Fractured formations generally have a cementation exponent less than 2.

In order to estimate the fracture porosity in hard carbonate formations Boyeldieu & Winchester (1982) developed Archie's formula further and worked out the following equation:

$$\Phi_{frac}^{m_{frac}} = \frac{C_{LLs} - C_{LLd}}{C_m} \qquad (2)$$

where Φ_{frac} = fracture porosity (-); m_{frac} = Archie's cementation exponent (usually around 1.4); C_{LLs} = conductivity measured by the shallow laterolog, $1/R_{LLs}$ (S/m); C_{LLd} = conductivity measured by the deep laterolog, $1/R_{LLd}$ (S/m); C_m = mud conductivity measured by mud log, $1/R_m$ (S/m).

FRACTURE APERTURE

In fractured rocks large separations are observed between shallow and deep laterolog curves. In high-contrast formations the Dual Laterolog response is controlled by four parameters: the resistivity of the formation blocks, the resistivity of the invading fluid, the extent of invasion and the fracture opening. With a few simplifying assumptions Sibbit & Faivre (1985) developed a numerical finite-element model for the Dual Laterolog measurement in a borehole in order to solve the inverse problem and to determine the fracture aperture. For modeling a resistivity contrast of $R_b/R_m > 10^4$ was assumed. Two cases were distinguished: horizontal and vertical fractures. The model calculations resulted in the equation for long vertical fractures:

$$\varepsilon_v = \frac{C_{LLs} - C_{LLd}}{4 \times 10^{-4} \cdot C_m} \tag{3}$$

where ε_v = fracture aperture of vertical fractures (mm); further variables see above.

For horizontal fractures:

$$\varepsilon_h = \frac{C_{LLd} - C_b}{1.2 \times 10^{-4} \cdot C_m} \tag{4}$$

where ε_h = fracture aperture of horizontal fractures (mm); C_b = conductivity of the non-fractured host rock (S/m); further variables see above.

In addition, the authors have discovered that isolated horizontal fractures can be identified by a sharp decrease in resistivity with a total width at the inflection points of around 0.8 m and that DLL may show negative separation.

In the equations (2), (3) and (4) the variables $C_{LLs} (1/R_{LLs})$ and $C_{LLs} (1/R_{LLd})$ are measured directly by Dual Laterolog. $C_m (1/R_m)$ is taken from the mud log measured in the borehole. In thermal water wells the borehole is mostly filled by water or a weak mix of water and mud. R_w is measured as a log with the temperature or calculated by means of a measured value and the temperature log. The formation water resistivity may be calculated from its laboratory temperature to any formation temperature and therefore for the overall borehole by ARP´s empirical formula (John, 1999). C_b, the conductivity of the non-fractured host rock is calculated from Rb, which may be different from

R_t, the overall resistivity of the formation. In zones of non-fractured rock masses the values of R_b can be replaced in sections by the maximum values of R_{LLd}.

FRACTURE DENSITY

In order to estimate a next fracture parameter, the fracture density, which can not be measured by DLL directly, was derived from the fracture porosity and aperture of horizontal fractures. Since the DLL has a vertical resolution of 0.61 m, the fracture aperture calculated by equation (4) represents an average value of the measured section. Therefore, the fracture density can be regarded as an apparent fracture density:

$$app.\ fracture\ density = \frac{1000 \times fracture\ porosity}{mean\ fracture\ aperture\ (mm)} \qquad (5)$$

A rough control of the fracture aperture of horizontal fractures allows the parallel plate model using cubic law. If transmissivity or hydraulic conductivity are known by pumping test, for example, and the joint spacing can be estimated, the mean aperture can be calculated assuming laminar flow (Bear et al. 1993).

$$k = \frac{\rho \cdot g}{\mu} \cdot \frac{b^2}{12} \cdot \frac{b}{l} = c(T) \cdot \frac{b^3}{l} \qquad (6)$$

where k = hydraulic conductivity (m/s); ρ = density of water (kg/m^3); g = acceleration due to gravity (m/s^2); μ = dynamic viscosity of water (Pa·s); b = mean fracture aperture (m); l = mean joint spacing (1/m).

CONCLUSION

For the first estimation of fracture porosity calculated for water bearing horizons the cementation exponent of 1.4 yields values in a plausible field. But the investigations show, that the exponent can range from 1.1 to 1.7 at similar rocks and fracture systems. The exponent can be adjusted by core samples and it is valid only for the rock in the drilling.

The fracture apertures were estimated both, by empirical calibration of the formula (4) and by formula (6). The differences in the fracture apertures which amount to two orders can be explained by following reasons: The conditions assumed at the derivation of the equations for hydrocarbon differ from those, for water bearing horizons. A resistivity contrast $R_b/R_m > 10^4$ between mud and unfractured host rock must also be given. That's why the fracture apertures especially of horizontal fractures in low resistivity rocks are calculated too high. However, after standardization of the calculated values can be also estimated, how much larger the apertures in the water bearing horizons are as usual in the drilling.

The calculation by the parallel plate model results in an effective hydraulic aperture whereby a constant distance between the fractures and parallel and smooth fracture surfaces are assumed. The flow conditions in the fractures are laminar. The field of validity of the parallel plate model is limited for fractures in which fracture roughness in comparison to the mean aperture is small. The hydraulics of fractures weathered by chemical and hydrothermal processes or filled by minerals can not be reproduced by conventional parallel plate models. This can be especially assumed at the investigated carbonate aquifers.

The estimate of R_b, which can't directly measured by DLL and it is derived from the maximum resistivity values between fractures zones, influences the results fairly. But the determining factor at the calculation is the resistivity contrast. By means of laboratory measurement on cores empirical adjusting of the formulas seems to be possible by modification of the constants. However, this requires further investigations by numerical models.

Furthermore, isolated horizontal fractures could also be detected by DLL, but their identification is difficult because of the interpretation of sharp decrease in resistivity.

As a consequence of the work, the application of the equations (1) to (4) is recommended to estimate only the fracture porosity of fractured aquifers. On the other hand the fracture evaluation is only successful in high resistivity rocks with fracture apertures below 1 mm.

REFERENCES

ARCHIE, G. 1942. The electrical resistivity log as an aid in determining some reservoir characteristics. Trans. AIME, 146. pp. 54-62.
BEAR J, TSANG, C-F., & MARSILY, G. (eds.) 1993. Flow and Contaminant Transport in Fractured Rock. Academic Press, Inc. San Diego London.
BOYELDIEU, C. & WINCHESTER, A. 1982. Use of the Dual Laterolog for the Evaluation of

the Fracture Porosity in Hard Carbonate Formations. Offshore South East Asia Conference, Singapore.

HORNBY, B. E. & LUTHI, S. M. 1992. An integrated interpretation of fracture apertures computed from electrical borehole scans and reflected Stoneley waves. In: HURST, A., GRIFFITHS, C. M. & WORTHINGTON, P. F. (eds.), 1992. Geological Applications of Wireline Logs II. Geological Society Special Publication No. 65, pp. 185-198.

LUTHI, S. M. & SOUHAITÉ, P. 1990. Fracture apertures from electrical borehole scans. Geophysics, Vol. 55, No. 7, pp. 821-833.

JOHN, H. 1999. Basics of Oil and Gas Log Analysis. Kansas Geological Survey, Doveton.

SIBBIT, A. M. & FAIVRE, O. 1985. The Dual Laterolog Response in Fractured Rocks. Trans., paper T, SPWLA 26th Annual Logging Symposium, 1-34, Dallas.

INVESTIGATION OF FRACTURED POROUS MEDIA -SYSTEMATIC EVALUATION OF TRACER TESTS ON LABORATORY SCALE

Brauchler, R.[1], Leven, C.[1], Sauter, M.[2], Lield, R.[1], Teutsch, G.[1] and Dietrich, P.[1]

[1] *University of Tuebingen, Applied Geology, Institute of Geology*
[2] *University of Jena, Institute of Geoscience, Dept. of Hydrogeology*

For a reliable investigation and identification of transport processes and the quantification of transport parameters in fractured porous media the availability of a large amount of various transport data is an essential prerequisite. This paper introduces two independent approaches for the classification of tracer experiments. The approaches are illustrated by transport data obtained from 51 high resolution gas tracer tomography experiments conducted to a fractured cubic sandstone block on laboratory scale. For the interpretation of these transport experiments it is necessary to choose techniques, which allow the processing of a large number of transport data in a maintainable timeframe without neglecting the differential physical properties and the geometry of the investigated media. Therefore a deterministic and a statistical approach were developed to attribute the breakthrough curves into characteristic groups. The basic principle of the deterministic classification is the geological mapping of the sandstone block. The objective statistical classification is based on flow rates and the statistical moments of the breakthrough curves. The comparison of the results between the deterministic and statistical approach shows a nearly perfect conformity.

INTRODUCTION

In this paper the first results of two independent approaches are considered for the systematic evaluation of tracer tests. Firstly, a deterministic classification was performed with respect to the fracture network and sedimentary structures. Secondly, based on the acquired data sets of transport experiments, a variety of parameters was measured or determined, e.g. flow rates, statistical moments of breakthrough curves, in order to characterize different transport phenomena. In addition, multivariate statistical techniques like factor analysis and cluster analysis were applied to the set of transport parameters. The physical properties and the preparation of the sandstone block as well as the experimental setup are described in detail in the CD-ROM version.

DATA BASE

The data base of the interpretations comprises 51 helium breakthrough curves (Figure 1a).

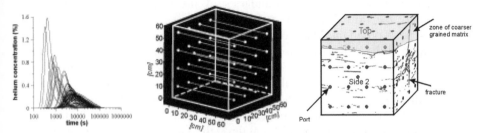

Figure 1: a) Breakthrough curves of all 51 tracer experiments. b) Illustration of the 17 used port-port connections for one of three spatial directions. c) The diagram of the fractured block illustrates the fracture network and the zone of coarser grained matrix. On each side are seventeen ports for injection and extraction of the tracer.

The transport experiments which are discussed in this paper were conducted by using one port for injection and the port on the opposite side for extraction of the tracer. The distance between the opposed ports in each experiment is 60 cm. Figure 1b) summarizes the used port-port connections for one spatial direction. For the other two directions the same relative positions of the ports were chosen.

DETERMINISTIC APPROACH

The deterministic approach is based upon a simple classification of the transport experiments in order to obtain differentiated classes of breakthrough curves (in the following called "Btcs") which allow the identification of trends and the coherence of different transport characteristics. Firstly, the data are classified with respect to the texture of the matrix at the location of the ports, because the upper part of the sandstone block consists of a coarser grained matrix (Figure 1c). Secondly, the influence of the fracture network is assessed. For this purpose, the Btcs are arranged into the following two groups a) matrix connections b) combined fracture-matrix and fracture-fracture connections.

The comparison of the classes with respect to texture and fracture network results that the transport experiments are dominated by the properties of matrix texture, while the system is influenced by the fracture network to a lesser degree.

STATISTICAL APPROACH

It can be expected that the spatial position of the injection and extraction ports with respect to the boundaries of the sandstone block influences strongly the flow field. Subsequently, for the statistical approach Btcs are chosen, recorded under uniform boundary condition in order to avoid a falsification of the statistically ascertained results. Btcs recorded with the geometrical boundary conditions illustrated in Figure 2 a) and b) were chosen because of the availability of a large amount of Btcs. The following statistical investigations were conducted with the commercial software package Systat®9. The conducted statistical investigations are based on the following variables: time of the initial breakthrough (T-initial), peak arrival time (T-peak), time when 50% of the mass is recorded (T-median) and logarithm of the flow rate (ln flow rate).

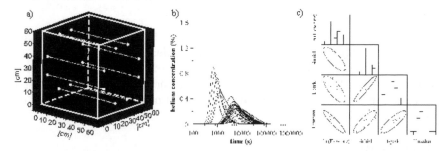

Figure 2: a) Illustration of 8 used port-port connections for one of three spatial directions. b) Btcs (24) selected for the statistical approach. c) Illustration of the pearson correlation matrix and the frequency distribution (n=24).

The first step was to generate a correlation matrix to identify relationships between the different parameters describing the Btcs (Figure 2c). Furthermore, the correlation matrix serves as starting point for the principal components analysis. The aim of the following principal components analysis is the clear illustration of the relationships among the variables. The analysis of the principal components indicates the best conformity between ln (flow rate) and factor 2 and between T-peak and factor 1 (Figure 3a). Hence, the system can be described to a large degree by the variance of the two variables T-peak and ln (flow rate).

The next step of the statistical procedure is cluster analysis. The aim of this analysis is the detection of natural groupings in data.

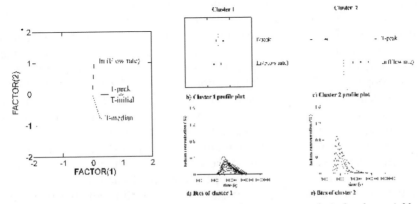

Figure 3: a) Factor loadings plot of the principal component analysis for the variables T-initial, T-peak, T-median and the logarithm of the flow rate. The illustrations b) and c) show the results of the cluster analysis. The vertical dashed line in b) and c) indicates the grand mean across all data. The variable mean within each cluster is marked by a dot. The horizontal lines indicate one standard deviation above and below the mean. Figure d) and e) show the Btcs of the two clusters.

Before the cluster analysis was conducted the variables T-peak and ln (flow rate) were standardized to put the measurements on a common scale. The k-means clustering procedure splits the Btcs into two clusters by maximizing variations between clusters and minimizing variations within a cluster. The Btcs of the two clusters (Figure 3d, e) indicate a completely different transport behavior. The Btcs of cluster 1 are characterized by mainly broad and flat breakthrough curves due to lower transport velocities and tailing effects caused by the less permeable rock matrix. The lower transport velocities become apparent if the mean values of the flow rate of the two clusters are being compared. In cluster 1 the mean value of the ln (flow rate) is smaller than the grand mean across all data in contrast to cluster 2 (Figure 3b, c). Furthermore, the Btcs of cluster 2 exhibit small values of T-peak and T-initial corresponding to a fast transport of the tracer through the system. The comparison between the Btcs of cluster 2 and the Btcs which are recorded from direct connections to the coarser grained matrix shows a nearly perfect conformity. This means that the statistical investigations are an objective tool to attribute the Btcs into characteristic groups.

SUMMARY AND CONCLUSIONS

This paper presents a classification procedure for Btcs obtained from high resolution gas tracer experiments by employing a deterministic and a statistical approach. The deterministic approach is based on the simple classification of the transport data with respect to the texture of the matrix and the fracture network. This approach enables the recognition of significant factors dominating the transport behavior. Furthermore, it is possible to attribute the breakthrough curves to characteristic groups with similar transport properties. As opposed to the deterministic approach, the realization of the statistical approach can be transferred to a real fractured aquifer. The first step of the statistical approach was to identify the coincidences between the used variables. The correlation matrix indicates linear coincidences between all variables. For a reliable reduction of the multivariate problem, factor analysis was conducted which enables it to describe the system with only two variables. These two variables are used for the following cluster analysis. The two characteristic groups resulting from the cluster analysis allow an objective identification of the variability of different transport processes.

EXAMPLES OF QUANTIFICATION OF PORE SCALE FLUID FLOW AND TRANSPORT PROCESSES USING X-RAY COMPUTATIONAL MICROTOMOGRAPHY (CMT)

J.W. Hopmans[1]*, D. Wildenschild[2], V. Clausnitzer[3] and M.L. Rivers[4]

[1] *Hydrology, Department of Land, Air and Water Resources, University of California, Davis, CA 95616, USA, jwhopmans@ucdavis.edu*
[2] *Environmental Resources, Technical University of Denmark, 2800 Lyngby, Denmark, dw@er.dtu.dk*
[3] *WASY GmbH Waltersdorfer Strasse 105, D-12526 Berlin-Bohnsdorf, Germany, vc@gfz-potsdam.de*
[4] *Consortium for Advanced Radiation Sources, University of Chicago, USA, rivers@cars.uchicago.edu*

INTRODUCTION

A common problem regarding an improved understanding of flow and transport in porous media is the general lack of microscopic geometry and pore-scale flow and transport measurements. However, recent numerical advances have allowed simulation at the pore scales, using network or pore-scale modeling (e.g. Celia et al., 1995), and Lattice-Boltzmann modeling (e.g. Ferréol and Rothman, 1995). Although macropore and preferential flow are suggested as important mechanisms for accelerated breakthrough of contaminant, to fully understand the significance of immobile water regions, dispersion and diffusion processes, and the control of pore fluid connectivity and tortuosity, it is becoming increasingly clear that pore-scale measurements are needed. Plausibly, an argument can be made that a fundamental understanding of flow and transport mechanisms in porous media can only be achieved by studying processes at the pore- or micro-scale.

Mechanisms operating at the pore-scale cannot be measured with traditional macroscopic experimental techniques, whereas electromagnetic (EM) methods can. Although various sources of electromagnetic (EM) radiation are available for noninvasive porous medium measurements, such as the light transmission technique [Tidwell and Glass, 1994] and gamma rays [Brown et al., 1993], we report on recent developments of x-ray computerized microtomography (x-ray CMT), for determining the internal structure of an object. The physical basis of the x-ray technique lies in the absorption and scattering of the penetrating x-rays or photons, of which the magnitude is proportional to the atomic density profile of the scanned object.

Following the introduction of x-ray CT in the medical sciences, the technique was adopted by earth-science research in the early 1980's. Linear relationships were established between attenuation and soil bulk density [Petrovic et al., 1982; Anderson et al., 1990], and volumetric water content [e.g. Hopmans et al., 1992]. X-ray tomography has also been used to monitor the transport and breakthrough of solutes in porous media [e.g. Vinegar and Wellington, 1987; Clausnitzer and Hopmans, 2000]. In the last 5 years, the applications of CT have progressed to characterization of specimen pore space with respect to variables such as spatial correlation, connectivity, and tortuosity [Coles et al., 1998], porosity, pore-volume-to-surface-ratio, permeability, electrical resistivity, and wetting phase residual saturation [Auzerais et al., 1996; Klobes et al., 1997; Clausnitzer and Hopmans, 1999]. Among the most recent applications is the use of CT to describe the physically complex pore space as used in network and pore-scale simulation models [Hazlett, 1995; Ferréol and Rothman, 1995; Coles et al., 1998]. In a very recent publication, Held and Celia [2001] call for direct measurement techniques capable of resolving and quantifying phase interfaces in porous media, the existence of which would resolve difficulties associated with evaluation of new model development using current indirect measurement techniques. Interfacial areas have thus far been measured indirectly, but with the advances in high-resolution imaging using CMT it may be possible to track interfacial area and curvature as a function of phase saturation or capillary pressure at a spatial resolution of about 1 micrometer. Example experiments will demonstrate the application of CMT to (1) measure spatial variability of solute breakthrough, and (2) measure spatial water distribution in variably-saturated soils. We present results from industrial tomograms, and the synchrotron-based microtomography facility (GSECARS, sector 13) at the Advanced Photon Source at Argonne National Laboratory.

ACKNOWLEDGEMENTS

Work supported in part by IGPP Grant 00-GS-012, by the Danish Technical Research Council, and by the EMSP of the DOE Office of Science under contract No. W-7405-ENG-48. Use of the Advanced Photon Source was supported by the DOE Basic Energy Sciences, Office of Science, under Contract No. W-31-109-ENG-38. We are also grateful to John Steude and Brett Simon of Scientific Measurement Systems, Austin, Tex., and to Patrick Roberson and Dan Schneberk of the Nondestructive Evaluation Division at Lawrence Livermore National Laboratory for their valuable support and assistance. Research was supported in part by USDA NRI Proposal No. 95-37107-1602.

REFERENCES

AUZERAIS, F.M., J. DUNSMUIR, B.B. FERREOL, N. MARTYS, J. OLSON, T.S. RAMAKRISHNAN, D.H. ROTHMAN, and L.M. SCHWARTZ, Transport in sandstone: A study based on three dimensional microtomography, Geophysical Research Letters, 23(7), 705-708, 1996.

ANDERSON, S. H., R. L. PEYTON, and C. J. GANTZER, Evaluation of constructed and natural soil macropores using X-ray computed tomography, Geoderma, 46:13-29, 1990.

BROWN, G..O. M.L. STONE, and J.E. GAZIN, 1993, Accuracy of gamma ray computerized-tomography in porous media, Water Resour. Res.29:479-486.

CELIA, M.A., P.C. REEVES, and L.A. FERRAND, Recent advaces in pore scale models for multi-phase flow in porous media, Rev. of Geophys., 33, 1049-1057, 1995.

CLAUSNITZER, V, and J.W. HOPMANS, 1999. Determination of phase-volume fractions from tomographic measurements in two-phase systems. Advances in Water Resour.22:577-584.

CLAUSNITZER, V., and J.W. HOPMANS, 2000. Pore-scale measurements of solute breakth-rough using microfocus x-ray tomography, Water Resour. Res., 36(8), 2067-2079.

COLES, M.E., R.D. HAZLETT, E.L. MUEGGE, K.W. JONES, B. ANDREWS, B. DOWD, P. SIDDONS, A. PESKIN, P. SPANNE, W.E. SOLL, Developments in synchrotron x-ray microtomography with applications to flow in porous media, SPE Reservoir Eval. and Eng., Aug. 1998, 288-296. 1998.

FERREOL, B. and D.H. ROTHMAN, Lattice-Boltzmann simulations of flow through Fontainebleu sandstone, Transport in Porous Media, 20, 3-20, 1995.

HAZLETT, R.D., 1995. Simulation of capillary-dominated displacements in microtomogra-phic images of reservoir rocks. Trans. Porous Media, 20, 21-35.

HELD, R.J. and M.A. CELIA, 2001. Modeling support of functional relationships between capillary pressure, saturation, interfacial area and common lines, Adv. Water Resour., 24, 325-343.

HOPMANS, J. W., T. VOGEL, and P. D. KOBLIK, X-ray tomography of soil water distribution in one-step outflow experiments, Soil Sc. Soc. Am. J., 56(2):355-362, 1992.

KLOBES, P., RIESEMEIER, H., MEYER, K., GOEBBELS, J. and K. H. HELLMUTH, Rock porosity determination by combination of x-ray computerized tomography with mercury porosimetry. Fresenius Journal of Analytical Chemistry, 357: 543-547, 1997.

PETROVICH A. M., J. E. SIEBERT, and P. E. RIEKE, Soil bulk density analysis in three dimensions by computed tomographic scanning, Soil Sc. Soc. Am. J., 46:445-450, 1982.

TIDWELL, V.C., and R.J. GLASS, 1994, X ray and visible light transmission for laboratory measurement of two-dimensional saturation fields in thin-slab systems, Water Resour. Res. 30:2873-2882.

VINEGAR, H. J., and S. L. WELLINGTON, 1987. Tomographic imaging of three-phase flow experiments, Rev. Sci. Instrum., 58(1):96-107.

A THREE-DIMENSIONAL HYDROSTRATIGRAPHIC FRAMEWORK MODEL OF THE PAHUTE MESA - OASIS VALLEY AREA, NYE COUNTY, NEVADA

Sigmund L. Drellack, Jr., Lance B. Prothro, and Jose L. Gonzales
Bechtel Nevada, Las Vegas, Nevada

A three-dimensional hydrostratigraphic framework model for the Pahute Mesa - Oasis Valley area has been built to support investigations of the effects of underground nuclear testing on groundwater at the Nevada Test Site and adjacent areas. The model area of over 2,700 square kilometers encompasses the northwestern portion of the Nevada Test Site and adjacent lands to the west managed by the U.S. Air Force and the U.S. Bureau of Land Management.

This large study area with generally sparse subsurface data is geologically complex and includes Mesozoic-age thrust faults, at least six Tertiary-age calderas, several intrusive bodies, and many relatively recent basin-and-range normal faults. Published and unpublished data from geophysical investigations, surface geologic maps, and nearly 200 drill holes (mainly on the Nevada Test Site) were used to develop a hydrostratigraphic framework that will form the foundation for subsequent groundwater flow and contaminant transport models.

Using lithologic information from drill holes and outcrops, nine hydrogeologic units were identified: alluvial aquifer, welded-tuff aquifer, vitric-tuff aquifer, lava-flow aquifer, tuff confining unit, intracaldera intrusive confining unit, granite confining unit, clastic confining unit, and carbonate aquifer.

These hydrogeologic units were used to organize the complex stratigraphic setting of the area into 46 hydrostratigraphic units ranging in composition from a single hydrogeologic unit of limited extent, to very thick and extensive "composite" hydrostratigraphic units consisting of complex networks of lava-flow aquifers and tuff confining units. Six caldera structural and topographic margins, 27 normal faults, 9 structural zones, 2 thrust faults and 1 detachment fault were used to define the structural framework for the model. Additionally, geophysical and surface geologic data were integrated with drill hole data to construct cross sections through areas of little data, and structure maps of the tops of selected hydrostratigraphic units at a scale of 1:62,500. The above interpretive products along with available hard data (drill hole information, surface geology, digital elevation models) were imported into Dynamic Graphic's EarthVision®, a proprietary modeling software system.

This modeling effort integrates and builds on over 30 years of previous hydrogeologic studies in the area. This work was conducted by a multi-disciplinary team of scientists from Bechtel Nevada and a consortium of International Technologies Corporation, Science Applications International Corporation, and GeoTrans, Inc. Scientists at the Los Alamos National Laboratory, Lawrence Livermore National Laboratory, and the U.S. Geological Survey also provided data and guidance under the auspices of the U.S. Department of Energy, National Nuclear Security Administration Nevada Operations Office. The work supports the Underground Test Area Project of the Department of Energy's Environmental Restoration Program for the Nevada Test Site.

This work was supported by the U.S. Department of Energy, National Nuclear Security Administration Nevada Operations Office, under Contract No. DE-AC08-96NV11718. DOE/NV/11718- -646-ABS

AN EMPIRICAL METHOD FOR THE EVALUATION OF EQUIVALENT CONDUCTIVITY OF LOW-PERMEABLE MATRICES WITH HIGH-PERMEABLE INCLUSIONS

Christen Knudby[1], Jesús Carrera[1] and Graham E. Fogg[2]
[1]. Departament Enginyeria del Terreny i Cartogràfica, Universitat Politècnica de Catalunya, Barcelona, Spain
[2]. Department of Land, Air and Water Resources, University of California, Davis, California, USA

INTRODUCTION

A large portion of the upscaling literature within hydrogeology has restricted its analysis to multi-Gaussian log-K distributions with small variance and restriction upon the spatial correlation model. As a result, the obtained results are of limited use when the problem at hand is an estimation of equivalent conductivity, Keq, of non-Gaussian geologic media with high variance. In formations composed of a low-permeable matrix with correlated high-permeable inclusions (e.g. alluvial settings), high variances and non-Gaussian distributions should be expected. For such media, which are frequently investigated in hydrogeology, very few upscaling methods exist. A computationally inexpensive method which, based upon obtainable geologic data, could predict Keq with reasonable precision would therefore definitely be of great use.

UPSCALING FORMULA FOR SINGLE HIGH-PERMEABLE INCLUSION

We present and evaluate an empirical formula for prediction of Keq of a two-component mixture. The formula is based on the results of Bumgardner (1990) who simulated permeameter-type flow through a low-permeable matrix (clay) with an embedded high-permeable inclusion (sand). We reproduced his numerical results and found, as he did, an approximately linear relationship between 1/Keq and the normalized inclusion length/width ratio. By use of this relationship, an estimate of Keq, K*eq, is found as

$$\frac{1}{K_{eq}^{*}} = \left(\frac{1}{K_A} - \frac{1}{K_H} \right) \frac{R - p_s}{1/p_s - p_s} + \frac{1}{K_H} \quad , \quad R = \frac{B_x / D_x}{B_y / D_y} \in \left[p_s, \frac{1}{p_s} \right] \quad (1)$$

where K_A and K_H are the arithmetic and the harmonic means of point K values, respectively. $p_s \in [0,1]$ is the proportion of sand whereas R is the sand body ratio normalized by the domain dimension ratio D_x/D_y. For one series of fields for which domain size, material proportions and sand and clay conductivities were kept constant, fig. 1 compares the linear relationship given by (1) to estimates of Keq obtained as $K*_{eq} = q*D_x/(D_y*\Delta h)$, q being the flow rate and Δh the head difference across the domain.

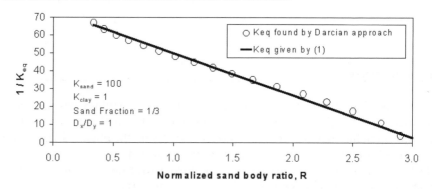

Figure 1 - $1/K_{eq}$ vs. normalized sand body ratio, R, for a single sand body embedded in clay.

MODIFICATION OF FORMULA FOR THE APPLICATION TO STOCHAS-TICALLY GENERATED FIELDS

The upscaling formula was modified in order to become applicable to stochastically generated fields. When more than one sand body is present in the domain, it becomes necessary to determine an average normalized value for the sand body ratio. We modify (1) to

$$\frac{1}{K_{eq}^{*}} = \left(\frac{1}{K_A} - \frac{1}{K_H} \right) \frac{R' - p_s}{1/p_s - p_s} + \frac{1}{K_H} \quad , \quad R' = \frac{B_x' / D_y'}{B_y' / D_x'} \quad (2)$$

where B' is an averages of individual body lengths and D' is an average of "local domain" dimensions which represent the area around each sand body. The average distance between bodies in the direction of flow, L_x, was determined as the arithmetic mean of individual distances between bodies whereas. The average sand body length B'_x was determined as a weighted average of individual sand body sizes. Having found L_x and B'_x, the normalization lengths, which assure $K^*_{eq} \in [K_A, K_H]$, are found from

$$D'_x = L_x + B'_x \quad , \quad D'_y = \frac{D_x D_y}{\beta D'_x} \qquad (3) - (4)$$

where b is the total number of sand bodies. The modified upscaling formula presented above was tested on a number of binary stochastic fields generated using TPROGS (Carle, 1999) which implements transition probability theory. MODLFOW-2000 was used to simulate the flow whereas GEO_OBJ (Deutsch, 1998) was used to identify and count the individual sand bodies in the realizations. Predictions of K_{eq} obtained using (2) were compared to predictions using the self-consistent approach and to averages of the Cardwell and Parson (CP) bounds. For a binary medium with dimension D, the self-consistent approach leads to (Dagan, 1979)

$$K^*_{eq} = \frac{1}{D} \left(\frac{p_s}{(D-1)K^*_{eq} + K_s} + \frac{1 - p_s}{(D-1)K^*_{eq} + K_c} \right)^{-1} \qquad (5)$$

The CP bounds for a rectangular domain are determined as

$$K^{CP}_{lower} = K^x_H \left(K^y_A \right) \quad , \quad K^{CP}_{upper} = K^y_A \left(K^x_H \right) \qquad (6)$$

where, for example, $K^x_A(K^y_H)$ is the arithmetic mean of the harmonic means of point conductivities on each cell line parallel to the y-axis.

RESULTS

Fig. 2 compares the predictions obtained by use of (2) to the self-consistent approximation and geometric averaging of CP bounds for a series of 50 stochastic fields of dimension 256 x 64, a sand proportion around 20% and a mean sand body length, Bx, and mean sand body width, B_y, of approximately 24 and 4, respectively. For this run, the conductivities were set to 100 and 1. As indicated in the figure, the upscaling formula presented in this paper has

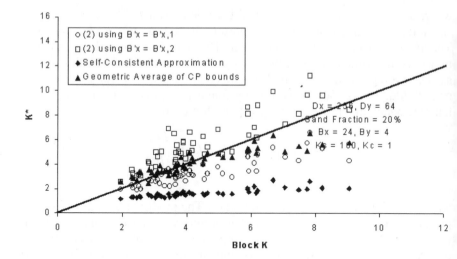

Figure 2 - Keq estimated from (2), (5) and averaged bounds. Full line corresponds to Darcian approach

been applied using two different methods for the determination of the average sand body length B'_x. The results marked ($B'_x = B'_{x,1}$) were produced taking B'x as a weighted average of the average individual body lengths. The results marked ($B'_x = B'_{x,2}$) were produced taking B'x as a weighted average of the individual body lengths. The used weights summed to unity and were proportional to the body size. We find that the use of $B'_x = B'_{x,1}$ in general works well when the fields present no channeling of the flow whereas the use of $B'_x = B'_{x,2}$, which results in a higher normalized body ratio, works well when the fields makes flow channeling possible. Due to the underlying assumption of non-interaction, the self-consistent approach works well for small K contrasts and when non-interaction is a reasonable assumption. However, when significant interaction is present, the approach fails considerably for the correlated fields to which it was applied. The geometric average of the CP bounds works well for the fields analyzed in fig. 2, but tends to underestimate K_{eq} for large block K and grossly overestimates K_{eq} when the K contrast becomes greater than 1000.

DISCUSSION AND CONCLUSIONS

The upscaling formula presented in this paper is simple, and shows promising results for upscaling of geologic media where a low-conductivity material surrounds high-conductivity inclusions. The necessary information on facies lengths can be obtained from outcrop studies of analogous formations, from closely spaced well data (e.g. Weissman and Fogg, 1999), and from studies of modern depositional systems that are the same or similar to subsurface deposits. We conclude that the method must be considered as an alternative when trying to upscale binary media with high contrasts in hydraulic conductivity.

REFERENCES

BUMGARDNER, J., 1990: Characterization of Effective Hydraulic Conductivity in Sand-Clay Mixtures. Master Thesis, Univ. of California, Davis

CARLE, S.F., 1999: T-PROGS: Transition Probability Geostatistical Software, v. 2.1. UC Davis

DAGAN, G., 1979: Models of Groundwater Flow in Statistically Homogeneous Porous Formations. Water Resour. Res. 15(1), 47-63

DEUTSCH, C.V., 1998: FORTRAN programs for calculating connectivity of three-dimensional numerical models and for ranking multiple realizations. Computers and Geosciences 24(1), 69-76

WEISSMANN, G.S. and FOGG, G.E., 1999: Multi-scale alluvial fan heterogeneity modeled with transition probability geostatistics in a sequence stratigraphic framework. Journal of Hydrology 226, 48-65

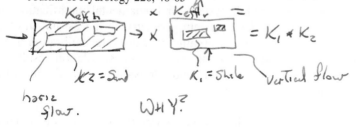

THE EFFECT OF KARST NETWORK GEOMETRY ON STEADY-STATE PARAMETER CALIBRATION

By Attila Kovacs, Laszlo Kiraly & Pierre-Yves Jeannin
CHYN, University of Neuchâtel, Emile Argand 11, CH 2007 Neuchâtel,
Attila.Kovacs@unine.ch

This study aims to investigate the possibility of modeling steady-state groundwater flow in a shallow karst aquifer. In addition the study attempts to answer the question whether it is feasible to abide by the measured hydraulic parameters and observed conduit system, or fundamental modifications of flow parameters or observed karst system geometry are necessary. In other words we examine the possibility of obtaining steady-state calibration of the model and the effect of karst network geometry on simulation results. In order to have realistic input parameters and comparative data, the model is based on a real karst aquifer.

The research site (Bure-plateau in NW Switzerland) on 83 km² area is located at the southern margin of the Plateau Jura, to the west of the southern ending of the Rhine Graben.

This plateau consists of horizontal layers of limestones and marls of Triassic – upper Jurassic age (Lambhart & Decrouez 1997).

The Malm sediments form the main aquifer, having a total thickness of 300-400 m. The aquifer is bounded from below by the Oxfordian marls (100m thick). The underlying sediments of Dogger age are considered hydraulically independent (Gretillat 1996). The sequence is 300-400 m thick, delimited from below by a thick sequence of marls, containing one considerable (40m thick) marl intercalation. The Malm plateau is dissected by NS, NW-SE and NE-SW oriented faults, which form a succession of long horst and graben structures (Kiraly et al. 1971). The vertical displacement along faults is generally in the range of 20-40 m.

The explored conduit system (called Milandrine) contains an 4.6 km long underground river with mainly free surface flow; only the downstream part (500 m) is phreatic. River discharge ranges between 20 – 1500 l/s.

We applied the combined discrete channel and continuum approach (Kiraly & Morel 1976, Kiraly 1985,1988) for simulating groundwater flow. This approach allows a combination of 1-D, 2-D and 3-D linear or quadratic finite elements to be used. Using the code FEN1 saturated, steady-state groundwater flow in two or three dimensions can be calculated.

In our model two horizontal sheets of two-dimensional linear finite elements simulate the aquifer geometry and represent aquifer volumes separated by the Sequanian "Astartes marls". The horizontal layers are connected only through vertical two-dimensional finite elements, which represent faults (Fig. 1). In other words the marls act as hydraulic barriers. Chains of one-dimensional finite elements, embedded in the two-dimensional element network represent karst conduit network.

Figure 1. Finite element network

Boundary conditions were defined along main rivers (fix-head boundaries), and along mountain ridges and stratigraphical borders (no-flow boundaries).

We simplified our conceptual model to confined flow. Hydraulic conductivities of the rock volume were measured from borehole tests or derived from experimental values. We applied an average of measured values as uniform hydraulic parameters to the entire model domain. Transmissivity values were set proportional to the varying thickness of the aquifer layers. Hydraulic conductivity values of the conduit system and of the fractures are estimated values. We aimed approximate model calibration. As calibration parameters we used maximum and average water levels, and average spring discharges for certain springs (we were mainly interested in the discharge of the Milandrine subsurface river).

We tested several conceptual models (Fig. 2): First we attempted to abide by observed hydraulic parameters and karst conduit network (model RKREF). Subsequently we tried to roughly calibrate the model by changing hydraulic parameters of different components one at time (models RKCALR & RKCALF). Finally, we extended the observed karst network, in order to test the possibility of calibration on conditions that we abide by initial hydraulic parameters (model TK). The extended network follows a hierarchical trial-and-error structure converging on known karst springs.

MODEL	K rock volume (m/s)	K fractures (m²/s)	K karst network (m³/s)	KARST NETWORK GEOMETRY	H max (m)	Q Milandre (m³/s)	MO... RES...
REFERENCE VALUES	1.00E-06	1.00E-04	1.00E+01	OBSERVED	580	0.155	
MODEL RKREF	1.00E-06	1.00E-04	1.00E+01	SAME AS OBSERVED	4693	0.354	N... CALIE
MODEL RKCALR	1.30E-05	1.00E-04	1.00E+01	SAME AS OBSERVED	560	0.278	ROU... CALIE
MODEL RKCALF	1.00E-06	>>REF	1.00E+01	SAME AS OBSERVED	-	-	CALIE IMPO
MODEL RKCALK	1.00E-06	1.00E-04	>>REF	SAME AS OBSERVED	-	-	CALIE IMPO
MODEL TK	1.00E-06	1.00E-04	1.00E+01	EXTENDED	525	0.218	ROU... CALIE

Figure 2. Input parameters and simulation results for applied model versions.
(>>REF means that calibration failed even at considerably higher values than reference)

Our steady-state flow simulations show, that in order to obtain observed hydraulic potentials, without extending the observed karst network, considerably higher conductivities than measured values have to be applied for the rock volume (model RKCALR, Fig. 7). The model also demonstrates, that by only increasing the hydraulic conductivities of observed discrete features (faults or caves), no calibration is possible (models RKCALF & RKCALK). In the case that we intend to abide by realistic hydraulic parameters, the extension of observed karst conduit system to the whole model domain becomes essential (model TK).

REFERENCES

GRETILLAT, P-A. 1996. Aquiferes karstiques et poreux de l'Ajoie (Jura, Suisse). Thèse, CHYN, Université de Neuchatel, 209 p.

KIRALY, L. 1985. FEM-301 – A three dimensional model for groundwater flow simulation. NAGRA Technical Report 84-49, 96 p.

KIRALY, L. 1988. Large-scale 3D groundwater flow modeling in highly heterogeneous geologic medium. In: Custoido et al. Eds., Groundwater flow and quality modeling, pp. 761-775, D. Riedel Publishing Company.

KIRALY, L. 1998. Modelling karst aquifers by the combined discrete channel and continuum approach. Bulletin du Centre d'Hydrogeologie, Neuchatel, Vol. 16, pp. 77-98.

KIRALY, L., MATTHEY, B. & TRIPET, J.P. 1971. Fissuration et orientation des cavités souterraines. Région de la Grotte Milandre. Bull. Soc. Neuchateloise des Sciences naturelles. Tome 94, pp. 99-114.

KIRALY, L. & MOREL, G. 1976. Etude de regularisation de l'Areuse par modele mathematique. Bulletin du Centre d'Hydrogeologie, Neuchatel, Vol. 1, pp. 19-36.

LABHART, T & DECROUEZ, D. 1997. Géologie de la Suisse. Delachaux et Niestlé SA, Lausanne – Paris.

JEANNIN, P-Y & GRASSO, A.D. 1995. Estimation des infiltrations efficaces journalières sur le bassin karstique de la Milandrine (Ajoie, JU, Suisse). Bulletin du Centre d'Hydrogeologie, Neuchatel, Vol. 14, pp. 83-89.

JEANNIN, P-Y & GRASSO, A.D. 1995. Recharge respective des volumes de roche peu perméable et des conduits karstiques, role de l'épikarst. Bulletin du Centre d'Hydrogeologie, Neuchatel, Vol. 14, pp. 95-111.

RELATIONSHIPS BETWEEN RELATIVE VOLUMES, SPECIFIC SURFACES AND TYPICAL LINEAR DIMENSIONS OF PHASES IN HETEROGENEOUS ENVIRONMENTS

Y.M.Denisov, A.I.Sergeev
Central Asian Hydrometeorological Research Institute
Tashkent, Uzbekistan

When studying multiphase and multicomponent environments (soils, snow cover, timber and other) such their characteristics as relative volumes of phases (α_i), specific contact surfaces of i-phase with j-phase, total specific phases surfaces bi and typical linear dimensions of phases (their thickness or hydraulic radiuse) $\delta_i = k_\delta \, \alpha_i / \beta_i$ where k_δ - non-dimensional coefficient of proportionality which changes from 2 to 3 for flat or bulbous figures.

An important circumstance for above environments is the fact that indicated features are not independent ones but are strongly connected.

Our investigations have shown that all obtained relations between phase characteristics include total specific surface of skeleton of indicated environments. Revealing the dynamics of this surface change have shown that there is non-linear dependence between relative volume of skeleton and surface's initial value. It has been turned out that there is a such relative volume of skeleton under which its total specific surface reaches maximum value.

END MEMBER SIMULATION OF HYDRAULIC FAULT PROPERTIES: FIELD MEASUREMENTS VERSUS MODEL RESULTS

Gernot Paulus[1] and W. Lansing Taylor[2]
[1] *School of Geoinformation, Carinthia Tech Institute, Europastrasse 4, A-9524 Villach, Austria ; e-mail: paulus@cti.ac.at*
[2] *Department of Geological and Environmental Sciences, Stanford University, Stanford CA, 94305-2115, USA*

Subsurface fluid migration is a multi-parameter process that depends on the tectonic and climatic history of a region, facies and lithology variation, hydrochemistry, and hydraulic properties of fluids, rocks and fault material. Understanding fluid migration is a key component of petroleum and geothermal exploration and production in sedimentary basins. Hydraulic heads, isotopes and hydrochemical data are routinely used to investigate regional flow systems in sedimentary basins. However, such regional interpretations frequently neglect the structural evolution of the system and rarely address the influence of faulting on fluid flow. In order to quantify uncertainty in the prediction of hydraulic head distributions from spatially limited data, we have simulated fluid flow at the basin scale in a faulted system, and considered how the pressure distribution and flow paths change as a function of the hydraulic properties of faults.

Faults are hydraulically complex structures that may have a strong influence on both basin scale head distributions and fluid flow pathways. We use a hydrologic model based on the work of Smith et al., 1990, where the fault consists of an inner zone and an outer zone. For simplicity, we assume that the zones are symmetrically distributed and invariant along the length of the fault, though neither of these conditions is believed to be characteristic of all naturally occurring faults. We propose a re-definition of the terms barrier, conduit, and barrier-conduit as they relate to faults so that they are defined by the effective permeability of the entire fault zone rather than by the internal structures. We extend the model of Smith et al., 1990, to include four end-member permeability distributions that can be observed in naturally occurring fault zones.

If the relative permeability of both the inner and outer zones is less than one, the fault will be called a barrier (figure 1). If both the inner and outer zones have a relative permeability that is greater than one, the fault will be called a conduit. If the inner zone has a relative permeability less than one and the outer zone has a relative permeability greater than one, the fault will be called a barrier-conduit. And, if the inner zone has a relative permeability greater than one and the outer zone has a relative permeability less than one, the fault will be called a conduit-barrier. Faults where the inner and outer zones have the same relative permeability are referred to as mono-permeability faults, while those with two distinct relative permeabilities are referred to as duo-permeability faults. This classification only applies to a limited set of all the possible permeability distributions in fault zones. More complex permeability distributions can, as a group, be referred to as n-permeability faults.

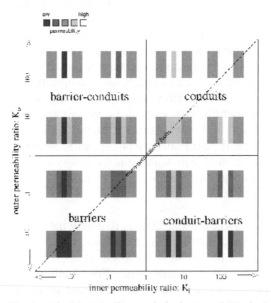

Figure 1: Classification of symmetrically zoned, dual-permeability faults. Barriers, conduits, barrier-conduits, and conduit-barriers are defined by the relative permeability of the inner and outer zones of the fault (from Taylor et al., in review).

In order to quantify uncertainty in the prediction of hydraulic head in complex fault systems, we have modelled basin scale fluid flow in the Molasse Basin, Upper Austria, and tested the sensitivity of head distribution to the hydraulic and geometric properties of faults. Using end member simulations with faults represented as either conduits or barriers, we found that faults cause characteristic perturbations in the flow field. Conduits are characterised by low pressure gradients within the fault zone and local pressure pertur-

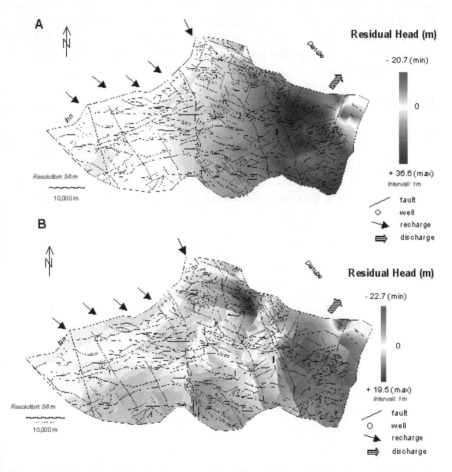

Figure 2 Residual head distribution caused by different hydraulic behaviour of faults in the Molasse basin. General flow direction is from west to east. Blue colours indicate areas where the residual heads are above the regional hydraulic gradient, Red colours where the heads are below it. (A) Faults are represented as conduits, (B) Faults are represented as barriers.

bations near the fault terminations. In contrast, barriers show pressure support and high gradients across the fault, with the head distribution strongly compartmentalised by faults that are part of a connected network across the region. We have found that flow velocities are more sensitive to fault properties than head distributions. By comparing the regional hydraulic gradient with the local flow velocities, it is possible to distinguish whether faults are behaving as conduits or barriers from only a limited spatial sampling of the pressure distribution (figure 2). However, when predicting head distributions from a limited data set, our simulations suggest that it is important to consider the position of the sample points in relation to any faults since fluid pressure depends strongly on the geometry and hydraulic properties of faults in the surrounding area.

REFERENCES

SMITH, L., FORSTER, C.B., and EVANS, J.P., 1990 Interaction of fault zones, fluid flow, and heat transfer at the basin scale. in: Hydrogeology of low permeability environments, International Association of Hydrogeologists, v. 2, p.41-67.

TAYLOR, W. L., G. PAULUS, and S. K. MATTHAI, (in review) Sensitivity of Regional Head Distributions to Effective Fault Permeability, submitted to Journal of Geophysical Research

SIMULATING UNSATURATED FLOW FIELDS BASED ON GROUND PENETRATING RADAR AND SATURATION MEASUREMENTS

Nils-Otto Kitterød[1] and Stefan Finsterle[2]

[1] *University of Oslo, Department of Geophysics, ++ 47 228 55825,*
nilsotto@geofysikk.uio.no
[2] *Lawrence Berkeley National Laboratory, University of California,*
Earth Sciences Division

Large amounts of de-icing chemicals are applied at the airport of Oslo, Norway. These chemicals pose a potential hazard to the groundwater because the airport is located on a delta deposit over an unconfined aquifer. Under normal flow conditions, most of the chemicals degrade in the vadose zone, but during periods of intensive infiltration, the residence time of contaminants in the unsaturated zone may be too short for sufficient degradation. To assess the potential for groundwater contamina-tion and to design remedial actions, it is essential to quantify flow velocities in the vadose zone. The main purpose of this study is to evaluate theoretical possibilities and practical limitations of using results from ground penetrating radar (GPR) and measurements of liquid saturation in combination with inverse modeling for the estimation of unsaturated flow velocities. The main stratigraphic units and their geometry were identified from GPR measurements and borehole logs. The liquid saturation measurements reveal the smaller-scale heterogeneities within each stratigraphic unit. The relatively low sensitivity of flow velocities to the observable saturation limits the direct inference of hydraulic parameters. However, even an approximate estimate of flow velocities is valuable as long as the estimate is qualified by an uncertainty measure. A method referred to as simulation by Empirical Orthogonal Functions (EOF) was adapted for uncertainty propagation analyses. The EOF method is conditional in the sense that statistical moments are reproduced independent of second-order stationarity. This implies that unlikely parameter combinations are discarded from the uncertainty propagation analysis. Simple forward simulations performed with the most likely parameter set are qualitatively consistent with the apparent fast flow of contaminants from an accidental spill. A field tracer test performed close to the airport will be used as an independent dataset to confirm the inverse modeling results.

Flow in the vadose zone is decisive for recharge processes and transport of contaminants to the groundwater. Due to spatial heterogeneity in the natural environment and temporal variation in precipitation and evaporation, there are significant practical and theoretical challenges to find a unique set of effective flow parameters that reproduce the main character of the system. A number of field-scale tracer experiments have been conducted in the last decade that elucidate important flow processes in the unsaturated zone. A main conclusion is that tracers seem to be transported much more rapidly than expected, and that flow patterns are very irregular. Even in apparently homogeneous soils, flow is observed to be concentrated in very small zones, and a significant portion of released tracers or contaminants are being transported to depth along preferential fast-flow paths. These observations imply that tracer tests in the unsaturated zone are very difficult to monitor and analyze. Nevertheless, tracer tests are considered very valuable, and are used here to confirm the predictive capabilities of a calibrated flow model.

The purpose of this paper is (1) to discuss the possibility of using liquid saturation as the primary data for estimating unsaturated hydraulic parameters, (2) to compare the transport simulations with field tracer test data, and (3) to propose proper orthogonal decomposition for simulation of conditional uncertainties in the estimated flow parameters.

Evaluating liquid saturation as primary data is of interest because this variable can be mapped with high spatial resolution by indirect methods, such as ground penetrating radar tomography, Time Domain Reflectometry or—as done in this project—a combination of neutron scattering measurements and interpolation by kriging. Large-scale flow modeling relies on structural mapping of the geological formation. Because there is a relation between liquid saturation and hydraulic properties, spatially continuous images of liquid saturation also reflect the geological structure. Parameter estimation is conducted in the framework of the Bayesian Maximum Likelihood method.
The preliminary evaluation of the EOF simulation reveals the importance of including the cross-correlations between the flow parameters in the error pro-

pagation analysis. This is done by decomposing the cross-correlations (or the covariance matrix) into eigenfunctions and eigenvalues. By including the eigenfunctions and the eigenvalues directly in the simulation procedure, the EOF method discards automatically unlikely parameter combinations, thus reducing prediction uncertainties. Note that the EOF method as presented here applies to Gaussian stochastic processes. Unlike many other methods, the assumption of second order stationarity of statistical moments is not necessary.

The present study indicates that observations of liquid saturation alone are not sufficient for robust estimation of unsaturated flow parameters. Independent information about the geological framework is necessary, along with independent estimates of the flow parameters. A small perturbation in the a priori information results in different estimation results, indicating that the inversions of saturation data are strongly conditioned on prior information. Further-more, inaccuracies in specifying unit interfaces may have introduced systematic errors, highlighting the importance of the sedimentological framework model. The simulated tracer test indicates, however, that the derived flow parameters are reasonable. Recall that the observations from the tracer test are not included in the inverse modeling procedure, i.e., they serve as an independent test of the appropriateness of the calibrated flow model.

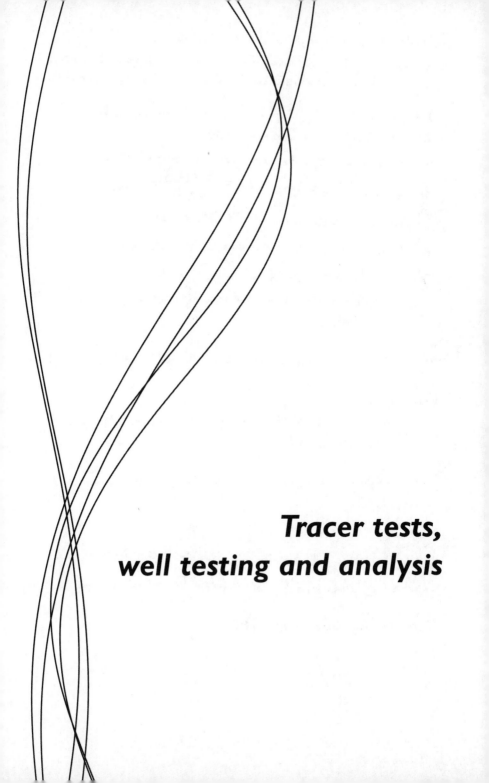

Tracer tests,
well testing and analysis

- Shlomo's aquifer concept is still not realistic...
  - because of this, the analytical solutions don't seem to cut it.
    - if facies variability exists, these solutions don't work out...

1) plot head vs log(distance) - include pumping wells
2) fit straight line through points
3) At some point, there is a deviation from curve.
4) Determine T_G = geom mean = $\dfrac{2.303\, Q}{2\pi T_G}$ = slope.
5) Plot dimensionless head $\hat{h} = 2\pi T_G\, h_c / 2.303\, Q$
6) match w/ semi-log type curve to evaluate σ^2
7) evaluate $\lambda = r/2\sigma r$ from horiz. match.
    - Can match & get variance of heterogeneity ... not a perfect match...

✱ Can we get an analytical solution for well test that is meaningful?

⎛ Fractured rock -
⎜   - allowed for borehole storage by modeling hole as very porous &
⎜   permeable material...
⎝
↘ If conceptual framework is not realistic, how can you understand
   results???

Did a test -
  - looked @ obs wells & got leaky aquifer tests — 40 ft/d
  - looked @ pumping well, got different T. — Theis soln got 40 ft/day.

→ deMarsily knows this stuff —

STATISTICAL ESTIMATION OF HETEROGENEITIES: A NEW FRONTIER IN WELL TESTING

S.P. Neuman[1], A. Guadagnini[2], M. Riva[2], V.V. Vesselinov[3] and W.A. Illman[4]

[1] *Departament of Hydrology and Water Resources, University of Arizona, Tucson, Arizona 85750.*
[2] *Dipartamento di Ingegneria Idraulica Ambientale e del Rilevamento, Politecnico di Milano, Piazza L. da. Vinci, 32, 20133 Milano, Italy.*
[3] *Hydrology, Geochemistry and Gology Group, Los Alamos National Laboratory, MS C306, Los Alamos, NM 87545.*
[4] *Departament of Feoscience, University of Iowa, 121 Trowbridge Hall, Iowa City, IA 52242.*

[handwritten annotations:] Assume homogeneous/stationary/heterogeneity in a zone – use geostats... No facies changes.
– cell size is 25 × 35 m → fractured tuff.
Future – geostatistical inverse of multiple pressure interference tests – Dec 2001 WRR.
– hydraulic tomography.

INTRODUCCTION

Well-testing methods have traditionally relied on analytical solutions of groundwater flow equations in relatively simple domains, consisting of one or at most a few units having uniform hydraulic properties. Among the latter

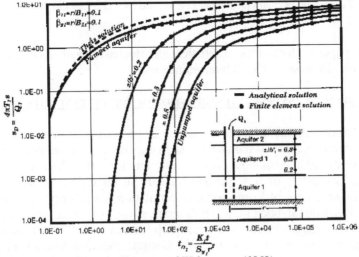

Figure 1. Multiaquifer solution by Neuman and Witherspoon (1969).

is a multiaquifer solution (Figure 1) developed by Neuman and Witherspoon (1969), part of which has recently been incorporated into the popular well-testing software package AQTESOLV (Duffield 2000).

In recent years, attention has been shifting toward well-testing methods and solutions that would allow one to characterize subsurface heterogeneities in greater detail. Among deterministic solutions developed for this purpose we mention those of Chu and Grader (1991, 1999) for transient interference tests in composite aquifers. An aquifer may contain up to three uniform, isotropic regions of finite or infinite extent. Regions may have various configurations, some of which are illustrated in Figure 2. Active and inactive wells may be placed at diverse locations within the composite system. Constant flow rate, pressure or slug test conditions may be prescribed at active wells having zero or finite radius, the latter including storage and skin. Boundary skins between regions can be used to simulate faults or boundaries between fluid banks.

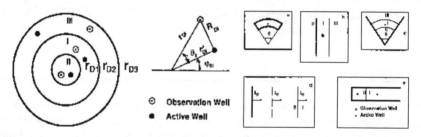

Figure 2. Examples of composite aquifer flow systems considered by Chu and Grader (1991).

In this paper we focus on geostatistical and stochastic methods to assess heterogeneity by means of well interference tests.

GEOSTATICAL INVERSE INTERPRETATION OF INTERFERENCE TESTS

A recent development has been the use of geostatistical inversion to assess the spatial variability of parameters, such as permeability and porosity, on the basis of multiple cross-hole pressure interference tests. The approach yields detailed estimates of how parameters vary in three-dimensional space, as well as measures of corresponding estimation uncertainty. It amounts to three-dimensional pneumatic "tomography" or stochastic imaging of the rock, a concept proposed some time ago by Neuman (1987) and discussed by several authors in recent years. We illustrate the idea through pneumatic injection tests conducted in unsaturated fractured tuff at the Apache Leap Research Site (ALRS) near Superior, Arizona, by Illman et al. (1998).

Geostatistical inverse interpretation of cross-hole pneumatic interference tests at the ALRS is described by Vesellinov et al. (2001a-b). Figure 3 shows the setup of three cross-hole tests (PP4 – 6) and a corresponding estimate of how log (base 10) air permeability varies in three-dimensional space across the site. The estimate was obtained by simultaneous numerical inversion of pneumatic pressure records from multiple observation intervals in all three tests. Similar estimates were obtained for air-filled porosity.

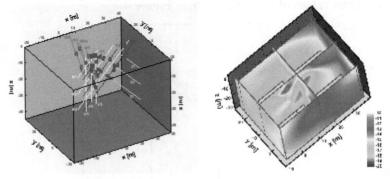

Figure 3. Setup of cross-hole tests PP4 - 6 at the Apache Leap Research Site and a corresponding estimate of log (base 10) air permeability (after Vesselinov et al., 2001b).

ENSEMBLE MEAN INTERPRETATION OF WELL TESTS

Analytical solutions are being developed to describe the mean and variance of flow to a well in a randomly heterogeneous medium. Based on these and corresponding Monte Carlo simulations, we have started developing standard method of well test interpretation that yield statistical parameters of medium heterogeneity. We illustrate the idea in the context of steady state radial flow to a well that pumps water at a constant rate Q from a bounded, randomly heterogeneous confined aquifer. A corresponding analytical solution was developed by Riva et al. (2001).

The aquifer has a statistically homogeneous and isotropic log transmissivity field $Y = \ln T$ with mean $\{Y\}$, variance σ^2 and integral scale λ. A fully penetrating well of radius $r_w \ll \lambda$ pumps at a constant rate Q. Constant head H_L is maintained at a radial distance $L \gg \lambda$ from the axis of the pumping well.

Fully penetrating observation wells record head $h(r_i,\theta_i)$ at discrete radial and angular locations (r_i,θ_i).

It can be shown that when $L>>\lambda$, the ensemble mean head $\{h\}$ is given quite accurately by

$$\langle h(\alpha)\rangle = \langle h(1)\rangle + \frac{Q}{2\pi T_G} W(\alpha,\sigma^2)$$

where $\alpha=r/(2\lambda)$, $T_G=\exp\langle Y\rangle$ is the geometric mean transmissivity, and W is a "well function". The latter is plotted versus dimensionless radial distance α and various values of the variance σ^2 in Figure 4.

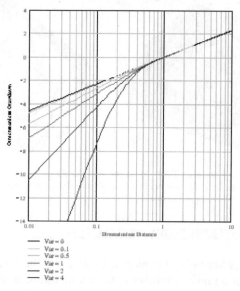

Figure 4. Dimensionless mean drawdown W versus dimensionless radial distance for various values of σ^2.

To analyze data from a pumping test, one (1) plots h_i versus r_i on semi-logarithmic paper; (2) fits a straight line to h_i data corresponding to the highest range of r_i values; (3) determines T_G from the slope, $2.303Q/(2\pi T_G)$, of the straight line; (4) plots dimensionless head, $\tilde{h}_i=2\pi T_G h_i/(2.303Q)$, versus r_i on semilogarithmic paper; (5) matches the plot of $\tilde{h}_i$ versus r_i with one of the semilogarithmic type curves; (6) reads or interpolates the corresponding variance value σ^2; (7) selects an arbitrary match point; (8) from the corresponding values of r and α, calculates $\lambda = r/(2\alpha)$. The approach is demonstrated on synthetic random data.

Similar methods are being developed for statistically anisotropic media and transient flow regimes.

Solutions for composite materials. Composite of different materials. Still don't look geologically realistic.

REFERENCES

CHU, L. and A.S. GRADER, Transient pressure analysis of three wells in a three-composite reservoir, SPE Paper # 22716, Proc. SPE Annual Conference and Exhibition, Dallas, TX, 5-9 October, 1991.

CHU, L. and A.S. GRADER, Transient pressure and rate analysis for active and interference wells in composite systems. In Situ, 23(4), 297-332, 1999.

DUFFIELD, G.M., AQTESOLV, HydroSOLVE Inc., 2000.

ILLMAN, W.A., D.L.THOMPSON, V.V. VESSELINOV, and S.P. NEUMAN, Single-Hole and Cross-Hole Pneumatic Tests in Unsaturated Fractured Tuffs at the Apache Leap Research Site: Phenomenology, Spatial Variability, Connectivity and Scale, Rep. NUREG/CR-5559, prepared for U.S. Nuclear Regulatory Commission, Washington, D.C., September, 1998.

NEUMAN, S.P., Stochastic Continuum Representation of Fractured Rock Permeability as an Alternative to the REV and Fracture Network Concepts, pp. 533-561, Rock Mechanics: Proceedings of the 28th U.S. Symposium, Tucson, Arizona, edited by I.W. Farmer, J.J.K. Daemen, C.S. Desai, C.E. Glass, and S.P. Neuman, A.A. Balkema, Rotterdam, 1240 p., 1987.

NEUMAN, S.P., and P.A. WITHERSPOON, Theory of Flow in a Confined Two Aquifer System, Water Resour. Res., 5(4), 803-816, 1969.

RIVA, M., A. GUADAGNINI, S.P. NEUMAN, and S. FRANZETTI, Radial flow in a bounded randomly heterogeneous aquifer, Transport in Porous Media, 45(1), 139-193, 2001.

VESSELINOV, V.V., S.P. NEUMAN, and W.A. ILLMAN, Three-dimensional numerical inversion of pneumatic cross-hole tests in unsaturated fractured tuff: 1. Methodology and borehole effects, Water Resour. Res., in press, 2001a.

VESSELINOV, V.V., S.P. NEUMAN, and W.A. ILLMAN, Three-dimensional numerical inversion of pneumatic cross-hole tests in unsaturated fractured tuff: 1. Equivalent parameters, high-resolution stochastic imaging and scale effects, Water Resour. Res., in press, 2001b.

QUANTIFYING PARAMETER UNCERTAINTY IN WELL-TEST ANALYSIS

Randall M. Roberts[1], Richard L. Beauheim[1] and John D. Avis[2]
[1] Sandia National Laboratories
[2] Duke Engineering and Services

Well-test analysis is the method by which hydraulic parameters of interest are inferred from transient pressure and flow-rate data – it is an inverse problem. As such, it is open to the following questions: 1) how uncertain are the estimated values of the fitting parameters; 2) how long must a test run to reduce the uncertainty to an acceptable level – it is possible to collect both too little data (large uncertainty) and too much data (effectively redundant and, therefore, a waste of time and money); 3) which test sequences provide the most information in the least amount of time; and 4) which types of data transforms increase sensitivity to the hydraulic parameters of interest? The overall premise is simple – one would like to get the most information in the least amount of time and have well-constrained estimates of the parameters of interest that are statistically meaningful and defensible.

A new well-test analysis code nSIGHTS (n-dimensional Statistical Inverse Graphical Hydraulic Test Simulator) has been developed that allows the analyst to address these questions in real time, i.e., the inherent uncertainties can be quantified statistically as a test is being run. The statistics are investigated graphically to provide an intuitive approach to the problem. Taking this statistical approach a step further, nSIGHTS can be used to generate synthetic test responses based on available information and also to add expected amounts of noise to the data. The statistical tools can then be used to optimize a test design by investigating all of the above questions before mobilizing and starting a field test. Jacobian analysis is used to determine which part of a test provides information about a particular parameter. Joint-confidence regions, perturbation analysis, and solution-space maps reveal optimal constraints

-a pumping test is an inverse problem w/ uncertainties !!

n SIGHTS code - beta release. - trying to implement code.
   - handles non-ideal tests.
   - graphics in code.
   - includes "messy" systems.
   - have (four secondary fitting parameter.!/

THE ATTEMPT TO CHARACTERISE THE HYDROGEOLOGICAL PROPERTIES OF A FRACTURED SHEAR ZONE BY MODELLING OF SEVERAL TRACER DIPOLE TESTS

Wilfried Pfingsten

Paul Scherrer Institut, Waste Management Laboratory, CH-5232 Villigen PSI, Switzerland
phone: +41 56 310 2418, e-mail: wilfried.pfingsten@psi.ch

For more than 10 years, tracer migration experiments have been performed at the Grimsel Test Site to improve the understanding of radionuclide transport in fractured rocks and to develop and test models that describe these experiments. Models are needed for performance assess-ment modelling of nuclear waste repositories. Most experiments have been performed in the Migration (MI) shear zone AU96 (Frick, et al., 1992). A new type of reactive transport experi-ment is foreseen in a parallel, neighbour shear zone, AU126, to investigate the interaction of a high pH solution with the fractured rock and its influence on radionuclide migration within a long-term experiment. In advance of the planned long-term reactive transport experiment, it is necessary to characterise its hydrogeological and transport properties as well as to identify the relevant transport processes. The Grimsel granodiorite is characterised by the presence of ductile shear zones that include mylonite bands. In the shear zones, brittle fractures developed, mainly in the mylonite bands, and including a highly porous fault gauge material (crushed mylonite). A detailed description can be found in (Bossart and Mazurek, 1991). Ten boreholes (7 m to 17 m long) have been drilled from the access tunnel through the shear zone in order to get information on its hydro-geological properties. Their distance from each other in the shear zone is from 0.77 m to 16.26 m. Six boreholes intersect the shear zone within a 2 m by 2 m area (Fig. 1). At a time, two of them have been used to install the dipole flow field. A step-pulse injection of different tracers was performed (Table 1) by an injection loop parallel to a pumping loop that preconditioned the stationary flow conditions during the dipole ex-peri-ments. The tracer is monitored by a fluorescence signal at the injection and extraction side of the dipole. Four independent tracer dipole experiments between different boreholes have been conducted under different dipole geometries, pumping rates and orientation to the back-ground water flow to deduce transport properties of the shear zone and test the model applicability.

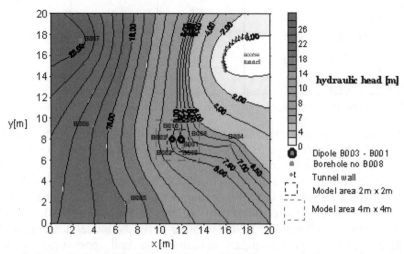

Figure 1: Hydraulic head distri-bution within the HPF shear zone by kriging interpo-lation from values measured in the packer intervals of the boreholes. The indi-cated model areas are used for two-dimen-sional transport calcu-lations.

Two different modelling approaches are used to model the dipole tracer experiments. One is the double porosity transport model RANCHMD (Jakob, 1990), which was exten-sively used to model MI experiments performed in a neighbour, more permeable shear zone. The second is the reactive transport code MCOTAC (Pfingsten, 1996 &, 2001). The double porosity ap-proach was applied in analogy to the modelling of the MI experiments (Hadermann and Heer, 1996; Heer and Hadermann, 1994; Heer and Smith, 1997). Tracer transport is approximated to take place in open fractures in one dimension. In addition, matrix diffusion in the diffusion-accessible porosity is considered perpendicular to the fracture.

The two-dimensional reactive transport code, MCOTAC, was applied to fit the tracer experiments and to allow for predictions for dipole set-ups of the long-

Dipole experiment	1	2	3	4
Boreholes (distance [m])	B003 to B001 (0.77)	B003 to B001 (0.77)	B002 to B001 (1.02)	B003 to B001 (0.77)
Orient. to backgr. flow	parallel	parallel	45°	parallel
Tracer	Uranine (0.5 ppm)	Pyranine (0.5 ppm) T3 (5 ppm)	Perylene (2 ppm) UV-1 (10 ppm)	Uranine (0.368 ppm)
Pumping rate (injection / extraction [ml/min]	~7.5 ~2.1	~1.1 ~0.9	~1 ~0.9	~0.92 ~0.76
Tracer injection Δt	45 min	24 h	12 h	3 h
Time for experiment [h]	100	160	300	670
Peak arrival time [h]	6.1	36	23	18

Table 1:   Summary of four dipole tracer experiments performed in the HPF shear zone.

term reactive transport experiment. Its application seems necessary, as modelling of the long-term dipole experiment 4 by a single flow path double porosity approach was not successful. MCOTAC takes into account advection, dispersion and diffusion in a two-dimensional heterogeneous porous medium of variable thickness in the third dimension in space and includes a finite differences flow model. Tracer transport is calculated by random walk of multispecies particles (Pfingsten, 1996). In order to fix the model domain and the hydraulic and transport boundary conditions, several approximations were made related to the background hydraulic head distribution and the model area (Fig. 1). Due to experimental constraints, injection and extraction rates have to be moderate and are in the same order of magnitude. This translates into a wide dipole flow field. In the model domain, background hydraulic head (water flow) and the shear zone thickness have been interpolated from measurements in ten boreholes to a finite grid. Transport parameters, as diffusion and dispersion coefficients, are also related to a finite difference grid. Integral measurements of the hydraulic conductivity in the model area do not show large variations, however, structural geologic analysis of bore cores and borehole images indicate for large local heterogeneity in the dipole area. To take into account this heterogeneity consistently, the local hydraulic conductivity was assumed to be related to the porosity, i.e. by a non-linear function. Then, the porosity distribution, which influences both hydraulic and transport modelling, and the dispersion coefficients are used to fit the measured breakthrough curves. The short-term dipole experiments could be modelled by the double porosity approach with a few free parameters (Fig. 2). The reason could be that experiments did not last long enough to show differing tailing properties as measured for experiment 4. A single mean flow path probably dominates the initial breakthrough. Parameter values used for fracture width, pore diffusion constant, matrix porosity and thickness are: $9.3 \cdot 10^{-5}$ m, $2.5 \cdot 10^{-11}$ m^2/s, 0.062 and $5 \cdot 10^{-2}$ m, respectively, to fit the HPF breakthroughs, which are in the same range as reported in (Heer and Smith, 1997) for the MI experiments: $5\text{-}6 \cdot 10^{-5}$ m, $1\text{-}2.5 \cdot 10^{-11}$ m^2/s, 0.06-0.1 and $1 \cdot 10^{-2}$ m, respectively, except that the water flow velocity in the open fracture was assumed to be much smaller: 90-1500 m/y for HPF compared to 17181 m/y for the MI Uranine experiment. However, the long-term tracer experiment 4 was not possible to be modelled by a double porosity approach with a single flow path, because the slope was no longer reproducible. Only a two-dimensional heterogeneous approach was successful in reproducing the measured tracer breakthrough. Variation of the porosity distribution in the near-field of the applied dipole leads then to a fit shown in Fig. 2, which is not a unique solution due to the number of free parameters for the two-dimensional modelling. In summary, it still was not possible to discriminate between several transport processes:

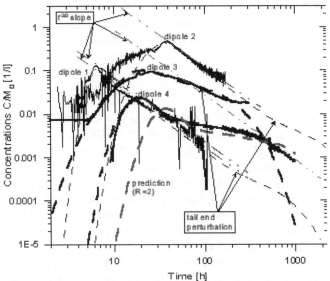

Figure 2: Measured and calculated break-through curves for four tracer dipole experi-ments per-formed in the HPF shear zone. Dipoles 1, 2 and 4 are directed from borehole B003 (injec-tion) to B001 (extraction), dipole 3 from B002 to B001: Solid lines - experiments, dashed lines - calculations. Dipoles 1, 2 and 3 have been modelled by RANCHMD, dipole 4 by MCOTAC. A predic-tion for a reactive tracer (R=2) is calculated by MCOTAC for a dipole experiment 4 set-up.

For a double porosity approach, matrix diffusion is characterised by a $t^{-3/2}$ slope in the break-through curve (Heer and Hadermann, 1994), as well as by a tail end perturbation in case of limited matrix diffusion, indicated in Fig. 2. The $t^{-3/2}$ slope is obvious in dipole experiments 1, 2 and 4, but this characteristic feature of transport in a dual porous medium is reproducible also by a two-dimensional heterogeneous porous medium approach. Also the tail end pertur-bation, calculated by the double porous medium approach, could not be observed in the experiments. Experiments and modelling leave it an open question if transport in shear zone AU126 will take place in open fractures or in a heterogeneous porous medium. Additional dipole experiments with other dipole geometry may reduce this uncertainty, especially, if a sorbing tracer can be used together with a non-sorbing tracer in the same dipole experiment. The double porosity and the two-dimensional heterogeneous porous medium approach will have different characteristics in the breakthrough for sorbing and non-sorbing tracers (Heer and Smith, 1997). This will allow the discrimination between dominant and negligible processes, e.g. heterogeneous flow field versus matrix diffusion. A predicted breakthrough curve for a sorbing tracer is included in Fig. 2. Finally, additional uncertainties remain for the approximations used for both model approaches. Some will be reduced only after the long-term experiment by analysis of the resin-impregnated and excavated shear zone material.

REFERENCES

BOSSART, P. and MAZUREK, M. (1991): Structural Geology and Water Flow-Paths in the Migration Shear Zone, Technical Report 91-12, NAGRA, Wettingen, Switzerland.

FRICK, U., ALEXANDER, W.R., BAEYENS, B., BOSSART, P., BRADBURY, M.H., BUEHLER, C., EIKENBERG, J., FIERZ, T., HEER, W., HOEHN, E., MCKINLEY, I.G. and SMITH, P.A. (1992): The radionuclide migration experiment - overview of investigations 1985-1990, Technical Report 91-04, NAGRA, Wettingen, Switzerland.

HADERMANN, J. and HEER, W. (1996): The Grimsel (Switzerland) migration experiment: integrating field experiments, laboratory investigations and modelling, J. Cont. Hydrology, vol. 21, pp. 87-100.

HEER, W. and HADERMANN, J. (1994): Grimsel Test Site: Modelling Radionuclide Migration Field Experiments, PSI Bericht 94-13, Paul Scherrer Institut, Villigen, Switzerland.

HEER, W. and SMITH, P.A. (1997): Modeling the Radionuclide Migration Experiments at Grimsel. What Have We learned? in Proc. 21st Int. Symp. on the Scientific Basis for Nuclear Waste Management (I. G. McKinley and C. McCombie, Eds.), Davos, Switzerland, Mat. Res. Soc., vol. 506, pp. 663-670.

JAKOB, A. (1990): RANCHMD - RAdio Nuclide CHain transport with Matrix Diffusion,

Manual, Paul Scherrer Institut, Villigen, Switzerland.

PFINGSTEN, W. (1996): Efficient Modeling of Reactive Transport Phenomena by a Multispecies Random Walk Coupled to Chemical Equilibrium, Nuclear Technology, vol. 116, pp. 208-221.

PFINGSTEN, W. (2001): Indications for self-sealing of a cementitious L&ILW repository, PSI Bericht 01-09, Paul Scherrer Institut, Villigen, Switzerland.

ACKNOWLEDGEMENTS

Partial financial support by the Swiss National Cooperative for the Disposal of Radioactive Waste (Nagra) is gratefully acknowledged.

DIFFERENT APPROACHES TO ANALYSING SINGLE-WELL AND MULTIPLE-WELL TRACER TESTS IN FRACTURED-ROCK AQUIFERS

Kornelius Riemann and Gerrit van Tonder
University of the Free State, Bloemfontein, South Africa

Correct analysis of tracer tests in fractured-rock aquifers requires specific information about the geometry of the fracture network, which is often not available. To estimate the flow velocity from tracer tests the through-flow area must be known. The most common model for calculating the through-flow area is using the equivalent aperture of the fracture (parallel plate model). The equivalent fracture aperture is calculated either from the mean residence time of a tracer (mass balance aperture) or the transmissivity of the fracture (cubic law aperture). In the radial flow model the area is calculated from the thickness of the aquifer or length of the tested section. Riemann & van Tonder (2001a, 2001b) introduced the non-integer flow dimension to calculate the through-flow area, used in the estimation of the flow velocity from tracer tests. The non-integer flow dimension can be estimated using the method of Barker (1988) for analysing hydraulic test data.

These three approaches were used independently to analyse point dilution tracer tests, conducted in the vicinity of an abstraction borehole, which was then used for radial convergent tests to compare and eventually to verify the results. The tests were conducted on the Campus Test Site of the University of the Free State in Bloemfontein, South Africa.

The co-called Karoo aquifer is the main aquifer type in South Africa. Karoo aquifers consist mainly of sandstones, mudstones, shales and siltstones.

Isostatic upliftment, together with the intrusion of lavas and dolerites, caused intensive fracturing. There is normally at least one horizontal bedding-plane fracture, which is usually found in the sandstone layer. On the Campus Test Site, located at the campus of the University of the Free State, 30 observation boreholes exist, 11 of which intersect the single, bedding-plane fracture at a depth of 21 to 24 m. The thickness of the fracture zone can be assumed to be about 20cm, according to borehole videos and acoustic logs.

Hydraulic and tracer tests were conducted on several boreholes, including the boreholes UO5 and UO26, intersecting the main fracture zone. Applying the method of Barker (1988) to the hydraulic test data the flow dimension n was estimated to 1.75 and 1.85 respectively (i.e. between bi-linear and radial flow), while the flow extent b was estimated to 0.15 and 0.16 respectively. The transmissivity of the fracture obtained from analytical and numerical models is estimated as 700 and 750 m2/day respectively (Chiang and Riemann, 2001).

To estimate groundwater velocity, effective thickness of the fracture zone and the kinematic porosity, radial convergent tests were conducted between boreholes UO5 and UO20, which are 15 m apart (called the UO5-tracer test), and between boreholes UO26 and UO28, which are 14 m apart (called the UO26-tarcer test), whereby the injection of the tracer was used as a point-dilution test. These point-dilution tests in the boreholes UO20 and UO28 were analysed with the different approaches as mentioned above. The results are shown in Table 1 and 2.

PARAMETER	RADIAL FLOW MODEL	FRACTIONAL FLOW DIMENSION	MASS BALANCE APERTURE	CUBIC LAW APERTURE
Transmissivity (m²/d)				700
Mean residence time (min)			424	
Flow dimension	2.0	1.75	2.0	2.0
Fracture zone or aperture (m)	1.0 (tested section)	0.15 (from RCT)	0.036	0.0024
Darcy velocity (m/d)	3.48	24.9	96.8	1455

Table 1. Parameter values obtained from the UO20 point dilution test (injection for the UO5 radial convergent test) with different approaches.

The data of the radial convergent tests were analysed by fitting the parameters flow velocity, dispersivity and thickness of through-flow to the breakthrough curve of the tracer in the abstraction borehole. Both tests yielded a flow

PARAMETER	RADIAL FLOW MODEL	FRACTIONAL FLOW DIMENSION	MASS BALANCE APERTURE	CUBIC LAW APERTURE
Transmissivity (m²/d)				750
Mean residence time (min)			395	
Flow dimension	2.0	1.85	2.0	2.0
Fracture zone or aperture (m)	2.0 (tested section)	0.15 (from RCT)	0.027	0.0024
Darcy velocity (m/d)	0.73	9.44	54.2	596.5

Table 2. Parameter values obtained from the UO28 point dilution test (injection for the UO26 radial convergent test) with different approaches.

velocity of 51 m/day, which is then compared to the estimation of the Darcy velocity (see Table 1 and 2) and to the estimation of the flow velocity from hydraulic test data. The results are shown in Table 3.

PARAMETER	HYDRAULIC TEST	RADIAL FLOW MODEL	FRACTIONAL FLOW DIMENSION	MASS BALANCE APERTURE	CUBIC LAW APERTURE
UO5 Test					
Darcy velocity (m/d)		3.48	24.9	96.8	1455
Kinematic Porosity		0.07 [1]	0.49 [1]	1.0 [2]	1.0 [2]
Flow velocity (m/d)	**57.35**	**51.0**	**51.0**	**96.8**	**1455**
UO26 Test					
Darcy velocity (m/d)		0.73	9.44	54.2	596.5
Kinematic Porosity		0.01 [1]	0.19 [1]	1.0 [2]	1.0 [2]
Flow velocity (m/d)	**60.8**	**51.0**	51.0	**54.2**	**596.5**

1) Porosity is calculated from the relation between Darcy velocity and flow velocity
2) Porosity is set equal to 1 due to the chosen model

Table 3. Estimated flow velocities obtained from both the UO5 and UO26 tracer test, using different approaches.

The comparison of the results from the two tests (see Table 3) indicates that the parallel plate model, using the equivalent aperture of the fracture, will yield values that are too high for the groundwater velocity. There is also evidence that the estimated cubic law aperture is far too small and therefore will yield velocity values, which are 10 to 20 times higher than those obtained from the radial convergent test. The estimation of the flow velocity using the hydraulic test data and Darcy's law compares good to the results from the radial convergent tests.

CONCLUSION

- The use of the parallel plate model with the cubic law aperture for estimation of groundwater velocity from a single-well tracer test in fractured rock aquifers is not an appropriate approach. The results do not seem to be reliable. By using the mass balance aperture the results are much closer to the flow velocity estimated from the radial convergent test, but can still yield an overestimation.
- On the other hand using the radial flow model with the length of the tested section in a point-dilution test can result in an underestimation of groundwater velocity in the fracture, if the thickness of the fracture zone is not known or assumed correctly.
- Therefore it is recommended to use the fractional flow dimension model (Riemann and van Tonder, 2001a and 2001b), because the through-flow area during a tracer test depends on the flow geometry, which is best described by the parameters n (flow dimension) and b (flow extent). These parameters can be obtained from hydraulic test data applying the Barker-method.

ACKNOWLEDGEMENT

The financial support of the Water Research Commission of South Africa is gratefully acknowledged. We would like to thank Mr Kevin Pietersen of the Commission for his support.

REFERENCES

BARKER, J.A. 1988. "A generalized radial flow model for hydraulic tests in fractured rock". Water Resources Research. 24(10): 1796-1804

CHIANG, W.H. and K. RIEMANN. 2001. "Guidelines for aquifer parameter estimation with computer models". WRC Report No 1114/1/01, Water Research Commission, Pretoria

DROST, W. and F. NEUMAIER. 1974. "Application of single borehole methods in groundwater research." In Proceedings, Symposium on Isotope Techniques in Groundwater Hydrology, 1974, Vienna, pp. 241-254

NOVAKOWSKI, K.S., P.A. LAPCEVIC, J. VORALEK and G. BICKERTON. 1995. "Preliminary interpretation of tracer experiments conducted in a discrete rock fracture under conditions of natural flow." Geophysical Research Letters. 22(11): 1417-1420

NOVAKOWSKI, K.S. 1996. "Course in fractured rock aquifers", presented at the Institute for Groundwater Studies, Bloemfontein.

RIEMANN, K. and G. VAN TONDER. 2001a. "Interpretation of tracer tests in fractured aquifers using fractional flow dimensions". In Proceedings, Fractured Rock 2001, 2001, Toronto

RIEMANN, K. and G. VAN TONDER. 2001b. "The fractional flow dimension of fractured aquifers, obtained from and used with single-well and multiple-well tracer tests". In Proceeding, New approaches to characterizing groundwater flow, XXXI. IAH Congress, 2001, Munich

SAUTY, J-P. 1980. "An analysis of hydrodispersive transfer in aquifers." Water Resources Research. 16(1): 145-158

TSANG, Y.W. 1992. "Usage of "Equivalent Apertures" for Rock Fractures as Derived From Hydraulic and Tracer Tests". Water Resources Research. 28(5): 1451-1455

THE STEADY-STATE DIPOLE-FLOW TEST: A SUMMARY OF THE FIRST TEN YEARS

Zlotnik, Vitaly A.[1], Zurbuchen, Brian R.[2], Halinah, Todd[3] and Ptak, Thomas[4]

[1] *Department of Geosciences, University of Nebraska-Lincoln, 214 Bessey Hall, Lincoln, NE 68588*
[2] *Nebraska Department of Environmental Quality, 1200 N St., Lincoln, NE 68509*
[3] *School of Geology, Oklahoma State University, 105 NRC, Stillwater, OK 74078*
[4] *Institute of Geology, University of Tübingen, Sigwartstrasse 10, D-72076 Tübingen, Germany*

INTRODUCTION

The emergence of the dipole-flow test (DFT) method was stimulated by studies of recirculation wells that became widely used for groundwater remediation. Such wells have screened sections or use packers to separate two active sections (chambers) in wells with a continuous screen. Investigations of the recirculatory flow for remediation purposes led to recognition of other potential applications by Herrling et al. (1991). Kabala and Xiang (1992) and Kabala (1993) proposed the use of the recirculation principle specifically for single-borehole aquifer testing. They introduced the term "dipole-flow test" and developed algorithms for parameter identification from transient chamber drawdown in different aquifer types.

Zlotnik and Ledder (1994, 1996) provided quantitative analysis of the kinematic flow structure in the aquifer near the DFT, showed that the scale of influence of the DFT is limited, and concentrated efforts on the steady-state DFT for obtaining hydraulic conductivity (K) or horizontal hydraulic conductivity (K_r) profiles. After Zlotnik and Zurbuchen (1998) demonstrated the feasibility of the technique in the field, the DFT and the dipole probe (DP) were applied at several sites for characterization of variability of K in unconsolidated and consolidated formations (e.g. Zlotnik et al., 2001; Halihan and Zlotnik, 2002).

The objectives of this paper are to summarize the theory, methodology, field applications, and verification of the DFT using comparisons with other single-borehole tests conducted on similar scales.

The theory of the DFT is based on a linear boundary value problem for head changes in groundwater flow near the DP. The chamber lengths can be equal (DFT or symmetric DFT) or unequal (asymmetric DFT). The major variables of interest are the measurable uniform heads on the surface of the upper and the lower chambers under a constant recirculation rate. Various special cases were investigated for a range of conditions.

Homogeneous Anisotropic Media. The steady-state DFT was investigated by Kabala and Xiang (1992), Kabala (1993), Zlotnik and Ledder (1994, 1996). Theory of transient DFT was given by Kabala (1993) and Zlotnik and Ledder (1994, 1996). Zlotnik and Ledder (1994, 1996) provided a quantitative analysis of the kinematic flow structure of the DFT. It was shown that the flow is localized near the chambers at a scale on the order of the distance between chamber centers of the DP, and the drawdown rapidly reduces with distance from the DP in the aquifer. Therefore, the DFT is generally insensitive to the aquifer boundaries.

Structured Heterogeneity. Studies of the DFT flow considered cylindrical skin, layered aquifers, or their combination (Kabala and Xiang, 1992; Xiang and Kabala, 1997; Peursem et al., 1999). It was found that the effect of high K skin decreases with the increase of chamber separation distance, decrease of the well skin thickness, and decrease of the contrast between aquifer and skin.

Stochastic Model of Heterogeneity. Indelman and Zlotnik (1996) determined the mean hydraulic head distribution as a function of mean K, variance of ln K, and correlation scale using a theory of non-uniform flow in statistically homogeneous formations with a log-normal K distribution with a finite vertical correlation scale.

The methodology of the DFT includes several components. Well design requires optimal parameters of well screen length and minimization of the aquifer disturbance by selecting the appropriate drilling method (type, tool diameter, and circulation fluid) and well completion technique (gravel pack versus natural collapse, well development). Geotextile rings filled with clay pellets have the potential to reduce vertical short-circuiting of flow along the borehole annulus (Ptak and Teutsch, 1994). Long screened sections that provide space for at least several DFTs are preferred (Zlotnik and Zurbuchen, 1998). In consolidated formations a well screen is not needed (Halihan and Zlotnik, 2002). Other technical aspects of methodology include selection of packer "length-to-radius" ratio above 10 to prevent short-circuiting of the flow between chambers and other well sections (Cole and Zlotnik, 1994); estimates of flow rate by the pump performance curves (Zlotnik and Zurbuchen, 1998); different water recirculation methods (Halihan and Zlotnik, 2002); use of control transducers above and below the DP to test the packer seal; field verification of the linearity of the chamber response to flow rate changes (Zlotnik and Zurbuchen, 1998).

Different interpretations of the DFT in heterogeneous aquifers can yield various resolutions of K. The head difference between chambers yields a K estimate that is characteristic of the zone adjacent to the DP. Use of drawdown of each individual chamber ("by-chamber interpretation") yields a K estimate that is characteristic of the smaller zone adjacent to the each chamber. At this time, the steady-state DFT model of an isotropic uniform aquifer of infinite extent seems to be the most practical approach for DFT interpretation (Zlotnk and Zurbuchen, 1998; Hvilshøj et al., 2000; Zlotnik et al., 2001; Halihan and Zlotnik, 2002).

Applications of the DFT have involved both consolidated and unconsolidated formations. In some cases, data from other tests – pumping tests (PT), multilevel slug tests (MLST), borehole flowmeter tests (BFT) – are also available at these sites for comparison.

Management Systems Evaluation Area (MSEA), Nebraska, USA, is located on an alluvial terrace within the Platte River valley (Zlotnik and Zurbuchen, 1998). The approximately 14 m thick unconfined sand and gravel aquifer is separated from the lower aquifer (Ogallala Group) by a silt-clay layer (aquiclude). The water level in the aquifer fluctuates between 3 and 5 m below land surface. A 16-m long, 10-cm diameter testing well was drilled using a hollow-stem auger 0.26 m in diameter. Data from 153 DFTs at 24 depths in this well were processed using the head-difference interpretation. The comparison of K_r profile with results of the grain-size analysis using Hazen's formula demonstrated good resolution of the DFT method.

Hokheimer Insel Site, Germany, is located near Heilbronn, in the Neckar Valley (Ptak and Teutsch, 1994; Zlotnik et al., 2001). The unconfined thin aquifer exists in a 2.5- to 4.0-m thick sequence of poorly sorted Holocene alluvial sand and gravel deposits, of which approximately 3 m are saturated. The aquifer has a wide range and variance of K. It is overlain by 5- to 6-m of mostly clayey flood deposits and underlain by a hydraulically tight clay and limestone formation of Middle Triassic age. Fourteen 15-cm diameter monitoring wells with screens extending through the entire saturated thickness were tested. Some wells had geotextile rings. Comparison of the DFT data from 14 tested wells with data from other tests shows that the DFT is capable of estimating K_r in the range from 49 to 6000 m/day with variance of ln K_r on the order of 1 to 2.

Vejen Site, Jutland Peninsula, Denmark is underlain by 10-m thick glacio-fluvial sediments of the Quaternary period (Hvilshøj at al., 2000). The aquifer is composed of rather homogeneous sand with embedded at some locations discontinuous clay, silt, or coarser grained sand and gravel lenses. The water table is about 5 m below the ground surface. Three 12.5-cm diameter wells were installed using cable drilling to minimize formation disturbance. The well screen extended over all saturated thickness. The analysis of this study indicates that estimates of anisotropy are less reliable from the transient DFT, than K estimates from the steady-state DFT.

Bissen Quarry, Wisconsin, USA, is located approximately 7 km southwest of Sturgeon Bay (e.g., Muldoon and Bradbury, 1998; Halihan and Zlotnik, 2002) and produces the Silurian Byron Dolomite. Nineteen 7.6-cm diameter wells were installed at an approximate 3-m spacing grid, most to 11 m in depth on 40-m x 25-m area of exposed dolomite with visible vertical fractures. Previous studies identified four major horizontal fractures, two dissolution zones, a diagenetic zone, and an orthogonal set of sub-vertical fractures. The continuum theory was applied to this fractured media. Spatial analysis of data confirmed theory of Zlotnik and Ledder (1996) on inverse-quadratic decrease of drawdown with distance from the DP center. Comparing the specific drawdown (drawdown per unit pumping rate) between chambers verified the applicability of the continuum concept and previous findings on fracture connectivity.

Verification of the DFT by direct comparison with other hydraulic tests in the same borehole has been limited. Towards this goal, a field program was designed in the alluvial aquifer at the MSEA site (see above).

The DFT, MLST, and BFT are based on different principles, kinematic flow structure, and shape and size of the corresponding support volume. We compared these techniques for estimation of K_r profiles using two additional wells that were identical in design. The experimental design of the DFT, the MLST, and the BFT employed an identical test scale – the length of tested screen interval ≈ 60 cm. Profiles obtained from all three techniques were similar in each well. The by-chamber interpretation (upper chamber) was used for the DFT data. K_r profiles in the tested wells ranged over 260 m/day, and exhibit a strong correlation in spite of the differences between tests. Correlation between the DFT and the MLST, which have identical tested screen lengths, was especially strong, with narrow 95%-confidence bands. Correlation between the BFT data and the other tests was less significant. The variance from both the DFT and the MLST slightly exceeded that from the BFT, but in general, the data were in a good agreement. Summary statistics for the three tests confirm the theoretical concept that variance in K_r (or ln K_r) is strongly dependent on the test scale.

SUMMARY

Approximately 2000 DFTs have been conducted in various configurations at different sites and locations. Examples include nine wells in Nebraska, fourteen wells in Germany, three wells in Denmark, one well in Wisconsin, etc. Previous DFT research includes theory, field methodology, and data interpretation techniques to estimate K_r. Comparison with other testing techniques indicates that the DFT scale is determined by the individual chamber length. Several new applications of the DFT in various environments are in progress. They include use of the DFT for estimation of aquifer characteristics: fracture connectivity in consolidated sediments, stochastic properties of the aquifers, well skin and local anisotropy through the use of tracers, and detection of trapped air. Possible directions of technical advancement of the DFT include test miniaturization and use in direct push techniques. Over the last ten years, the DFT has emerged as a distinct methodology for aquifer characterization in unconsolidated and consolidated sediments.

MULTI-TRACER EXPERIMENTS AS A MEANS TO DISCRIMINATE BETWEEN FRACTURE MODELS.

I. Lunati, S. Attinger, and W. Kinzelbach
Institute of Hydromechanics and Water Resources Management,
ETH Hönggerberg, CH-8093 Zürich
email: lunati@ihw.baug.ethz.ch

At the Grimsel Underground Laboratory multi-tracer experiments in a dipole flow field are performed in a single fracture. The simple idea is that different tracers explore different features of the medium, and restrict the choice of possible conceptual models by providing more information. We theoretically investigate the possibility of increasing information obtained by classical tracer tests in saturated fractures, and in particular the possibility of using additional data from two-phase experiments to discriminate between different models of correlation between pore space and transmissivity. Three models are considered: a heterogeneous fault gouge filled fracture with constant aperture, a rough fracture filled with a homogeneous fault gouge, and a rough empty fracture. All these fractures have an identical transmissivity field, but a different correlation between pore volume and transmissivity (i.e. no correlation, linear relationship, cubic law, respectively) and thus between entry pressure and transmissivity. Based on the correlation we refer to the three conceptual models as Uncorrelated Model (UM), Completely Correlated Model (CCM), and Partially Correlated Model (PCM), respectively.

SOLUTE TRACER TESTS

A tracer test in a dipole flow field is simulated. We study the evolution of a tracer pulse due to instantaneous injection of a mass M_0 of an ideal tracer at the recharging well. We require that the three models have the same mean tracer arrival time and the same mass input per unit of volume. Despite of being hydraulically equivalent the three models differ dramatically with regard to transport phenomena as can be seen in Figs. 1. It shows a more irregular spreading in the UM than in the CCM. The PCM represents somehow an intermediate situation.

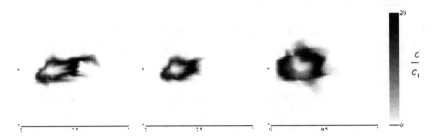

Figure 1. Dipole oriented along the x-axis: Dimensionless tracer concentration distribution for the different models (from left to right: UM, PCM, CCM)

It is desirable to discriminate among the conceptual models in order to identify the correct one and simulate the behaviour of the solute cloud adequately. Thus, we concentrate on the breakthrough curves (Fig. 2) that represent the only available information in most applications. The CCM shows a different breakthrough curve and recovery curve compared to the other two models. Nevertheless, our numerical simulations suggest, in accordance with theoreti-

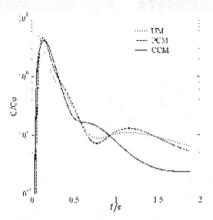

Figure 2. Normalized breakthrough curves for different models.

cal arguments, that the possibility of discriminating among these models by means of solute breakthrough curves recorded at the sink is subject to many constraints. Differences can be observed, but several causes can reduce or even destroy their evidence, and as local variability, very long or very short correlation lengths, relatively small Peclet number (i.e. non-negligible dispersion).

TWO-PHASE FLOW AND GAS-TRACER TESTS

We concentrate on the CCM and UM. On the basis of microscopic considerations the entry pressure p_d can be related to the conductivity k via Leverett's model ($p_d \sim 1/\sqrt{k}$), which has a strong influence on the macroscopic scale the gas saturation, S_G. In the CCM (homogeneous fault gouge) that yields a gas phase distributed quite uniformly and broadly throughout the domain (Fig. 3). In contrast, in the UM the space variability of p_d yields a higher saturation in the most permeable regions (Fig. 3).

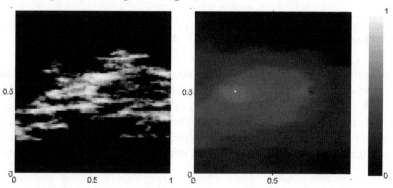

Figure 3. Quasi steady state gas saturation distribution for the UM (left) and CCM (right)

Once a quasi steady state saturation field is established (Fig. 3), a Gas Tracer Test is performed using tracers with different water solubility. For simplicity we neglect any dynamics and assume instantaneous equilibrium, within a cell, between the two phases. Thus, dissolution is simply described by a retardation factor $R_i = 1 + (S_G^{-1} - 1)\gamma_i$. ($\gamma_i$ depends on tracer solubility and on the temperature).

The CCM shows a more pronounced retardation, due to the fact that the tracer experiences a lower gas saturation. In the UM most of the tracer flows in channels characterized by a high gas saturation and only the H_2S is sensitively retarded (Fig. 4); the slope of the H_2S recovery curve is smaller than that

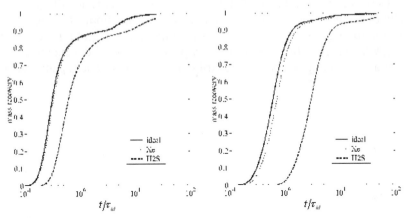

Figure 4. Mass recovery curves for gas tracers with different water solubility. UM (left) and CCM (right).

of the ideal tracer; that means that the effective retardation (averaged along the streamline) increases with the traveled time.

CONCLUSIONS

A pore volume-transmissivity correlation yields a smoother tracer distribution, since it diminishes the variability of the pore velocity. Despite of these strong differences in the tracer cloud behaviour, in situ discrimination among the models is subject to many constraints due to the scarce and averaged information provided by tracer breakthrough curves at the extraction wells. In two-phase flow experiments, the relative permeability is strongly determined by the capillary entry pressure distribution, which accentuates the differences among the models. In the CCM the capillary entry pressure is constant (homogeneous fault gouge), which yields a very smooth saturation distribution. In the UM the regions with the highest transmissivity are the most gas saturated and have the highest gas relative permeability. Channeling is enhanced if compared to solute tracer tests and gas flow takes place only through few preferential paths characterized by high gas saturation. A tracer test performed with gas of different water solubility provides an interesting tool to estimate the gas saturation. Indeed, assuming instantaneous equilibrium at the microscopic scale, the effect of dissolution can be described by a retardation coefficient that depends on gas saturation. By comparison among the recovery curves, one can infer whether the gas saturation distribution in the fracture is highly heterogeneous or not. In the former case, the recovery curves of soluble gas tracers plotted in a log-time scale is not simply translated with respect to an ideal tracer, but distorted. That implies a long correlation length of gas saturation along a streamline and a large transverse variability, which is possible only if the entry pressure is space dependent and produces an irregular gas saturation distribution, thus preferential paths, as in the UM.

STOCHASTIC ANALYSIS OF PUMPING TEST DRAWDOWN DATA IN HETEROGENEOUS GEOLOGIC FORMATIONS

Nadim K. Copty[1] and Angelos N. Findikakis[2]

[1] *Institute of Environmental Sciences, Bogazici University, Istanbul, Turkey;*
email: ncopty@boun.edu.tr
[2] *Bechtel Systems and Infrastructure Inc., San Francisco, California, USA;*
email: anfindik@bechtel.com

Pumping tests are often used to estimate effective values of the transmissivity and the storativity of the perturbed aquifer portion surrounding the pumping well and observation points. A number of methods are available to interpret the time-drawdown data depending on the existing flow conditions (such as confined/unconfined aquifers, leaky aquifers, presence of nearby flow boundaries). These methods are primarily based on the analytic method derived by Theis in 1935 for transient flow towards a well in a homogenous isotropic formation. However, this assumption of homogeneity within the zone of influence of a well, on which the Theis solution is based, is not always satisfied.

If a sufficient number of pumping test data are available, the effect of large-scale heterogeneity and parametric uncertainty can be accounted for by formulating the groundwater flow problem in a stochastic framework. In a stochastic formulation, the flow parameters, such as the transmissivity, are treated as random variables whose spatial structure is identified from the available data. Such an approach allows for the representation of the heterogeneity of the hydraulic conductivity at scales representative of the separation distances between pumping tests, which typically is appropriate for modeling at the regional scale. However, for many small and medium size groundwater contamination applications, contamination exists at scales that are comparable to the length scale of a single pumping test. No more than a few pumping tests are typically available in such applications. Consequently, by estimating an effective hydraulic conductivity from a pumping test, the small-scale heterogeneity that may play an important role in the fate and transport of a contaminant plume is averaged out.

The purpose of this study is to investigate numerically the impact of heterogeneity in the transmissivity field on the transient drawdown due to a pumping test. Specifically, we consider heterogeneity length scales that are smaller than the radius of influence of the pumping test: $I < R_i$ where I is the transmissivity integral scale and R_i is the radius of influence of the pumping test.

APPROACH

This study considers two-dimensional flow in heterogeneous confined aquifers. The natural logarithm transform of the transmissivity, $Y = \ln[T]$, is assumed to be multivariate Gaussian. The second statistical moment of the log-transmissivity is assumed to be stationary defined in terms of an exponential semi-variogram. Consequently, the log-transmissivity field is fully defined in terms of the first and second statistical moments which are defined in terms of three statistical parameters: the log-transmissivity mean, m_y, variance, σ^2, and integral scale, I. Storativity is assumed to be uniform.

Using Monte Carlo simulations, multiple realizations of the transmissivity are generated for various values of σ^2 and I. Based on these realizations, the transient drawdown rate at the pumping and observation wells is simulated and compared to the drawdown rate of an equivalent homogeneous system. Deviations in the drawdown rates of the heterogeneous and equivalent homogeneous aquifer are analyzed and related to the statistical spatial structure of the log-transmissivity field.

RESULTS AND DISCUSSION

The dependence of the drawdown rate on the log-transmissivity variance is shown in Figures 1a and 1b. The drawdown rate is normalized by the drawdown rate in a homogeneous system with transmissivity equal to ensemble geometric mean of the transmissivity field. The normalized drawdown is plotted as a function of time and radial distance: $r/I=0$ (i.e., at the pumping well) and 0.5. Analysis of the early time drawdown (of the order of the first 1 hr = 0.04 days) indicates that the drawdown rate in heterogeneous aquifers is dependent on the log-transmissivity variance. At very early times, the normalized drawdown at the pumping well is approximately equal to:

$$E\left[\frac{ds(\underline{x},t)}{dt}\right]_{normalized} \approx 1 + \frac{\sigma^2}{2} \qquad (1)$$

which is also equal to the ratio of the ensemble arithmetic mean to the ensemble geometric mean of the transmissivity, T_d/T_g, of multi-variate lognormal distributions.

The dependence of the normalized drawdown rate on the integral scale is shown in Figures 2a and 2b. These simulations assume a log-transmissivity variance $\sigma_2 = 1$. Similar to Figure 1, the results are also shown as a function of time and radial distance $r/I=0$ and 0.5

The main influence of the integral scale is on the time needed for the heterogeneous system to respond similarly to the equivalent homogeneous system. Analysis of these results shows that the drawdown rate for heterogeneous conditions approaches that of the equivalent homogeneous system when the non-dimensional time

$$\frac{tT_g}{SI^2} \approx 15$$

where T_g is the ensemble geometric mean of the transmissivity and S is storativity. This suggests that the integral scale may be inferred from the time needed for the drawdown rate of the heterogeneous system to approach the drawdown rate of the equivalent homogeneous system through the following relationship:

$$I \approx \sqrt{\frac{t_h T_{eff}}{15 S_{eff}}} \approx \frac{1}{4}\sqrt{\frac{t_h T_{eff}}{S_{eff}}} \qquad (2)$$

where t_h is the time for the drawdown rate to approach that of the equivalent homogeneous system, and T_{eff} and S_{eff} are the effective transmissivity and storativity, respectively, as determined from conventional pumping test analysis methods, such as the Jacob-Cooper method.

The main significance of the results of this study is that the log-transmissivity semi-variogram, which is defined in terms of the log-transmissivity variance and integral scale, can potentially be determined from the transient drawdown rate of the heterogeneous system. The variance can be inferred from the early time drawdown (within the first few minutes or tens of minutes of pumping), particularly from the drawdown at the pumping well or very close to the pumping well, because the influence of the variance on the drawdown rate decreases, and becomes more complex, with radial distance from the pumping test. The influence of the integral scale on the other hand extends further in time, and can be inferred from the time needed for the drawdown rate to approach that of the equivalent homogeneous aquifer..

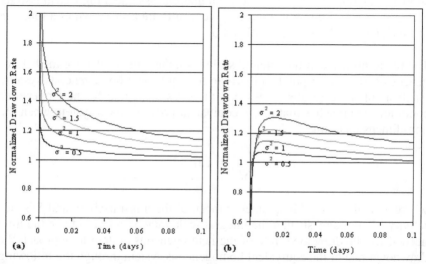

Figure 1: Impact of the log-transmissivity variance on the drawdown rate. The normalized drawdown is defined as the expected value of the drawdown rate for the heterogeneous aquifer, divided by drawdown rate in a homogeneous aquifer with transmissivity equal to the ensemble geometric mean. Figures (a) and (b) are for r/I=0 and 0.5, respectively.

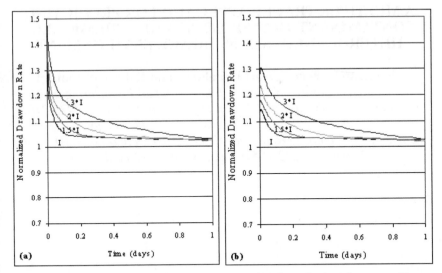

Figure 2: The impact of the log-transmissivity integral scale on the drawdown rate. The normalized drawdown is defined as the expected value of the drawdown rate for the heterogeneous aquifer, divided by drawdown rate in a homogeneous aquifer with transmissivity equal to the ensemble geometric mean. Figures (a) and (b) are for r/I=0 and 0.5, respectively.

A MULTIPLE TRACER APPROACH FOR PREDICTING CONTAMINANT TRANSPORT IN A GEOCHEMICALLY HETEROGENEOUS SUBSURFACE ENVIRONMENT

Jonathan R. Ferris[1], Carl D. Palmer[1] and Robert W. Smith[2]
[1] Geosciences Research Dept., Idaho National Engineering and Environmental Laboratory, P.O. Box 1625, Idaho Fall, ID 83425-2107; Phone: 208-526-4478; email: palmcd@inel.gov
[2] University of Idaho, 1776 Science Center Drive, Idaho Falls, ID 83402 Phone: 208-282-7954; email: smithbob@uidaho.edu

Heterogeneity in aquifers has long been recognized as an important factor controlling the migration of microbes, colloids, dissolved contaminants, and other solutes in groundwater. Much of this work has focused on hydraulic conductivity and dispersive processes on the transport of non-reactive, conservative tracers in aquifers (e.g. Lake,1981). Average values of hydraulic conductivity in heterogeneous materials often exhibit anisotropic behavior.

However, most contaminants do not behave as conservative tracers, but are involved in chemical reactions such as partitioning, sorption, coprecipitation, redox transformations, and hydrolysis. Some of these processes can be described by equilibrium equations whilst others require kinetic equations. Therefore, modeling of these contaminants requires additional parameters such as the fraction of organic matter, effective surface area, and pseudo-rate coefficients. These parameters are also spatially distributed and may or may not be correlated with hydraulic conductivity.

In principle, one could obtain many samples and measure the relevant parameters for each sample and then apply an appropriate averaging process to obtain a representative average that can be used in predictive and parametric models. But, there are inherent difficulties in obtaining detailed information on subsurface hydrogeochemical heterogeneity. Using simple arithmetic averages of laboratory-measured parameters may not be adequately represent bulk biogeochemical properties. In addition, some average hydrogeochemical properties may exhibit anisotropy. In most field situations, the difficulty and expense in obtaining and analyzing sufficient samples to find meaningful averages is prohibitive. Thus, the prediction of solute transport in heterogeneous porous media is difficult to achieve and more cost-effective methods of obtaining average hydrogeochemical parameters are needed.

One technique by which we can obtain useful and practical field parameters is by injecting into the subsurface, tracers for which the chemical processes are well known. These tracers act as probes for measuring average hydrogeochemical parameters that can be utilized in models to predict the transport of contaminants of concern.

To test this hypothesis, we have constructed a two-dimensional "column" and have filled it with a layered system. The benefit of this two-dimensional column is that a solution containing non-reactive and reactive tracers can be introduced in a layered system in the directions perpendicular to and parallel to the layers without repacking the cell. We are using a conservative (Cl^-) and slightly reactive tracers (F^-, Sr^{2+}) to assess the biogeochemical properties of a heterogeneous system with alternating layers of fine-grained, quartz-rich sand that contains differing amounts of Fe- and Al-hydroxides. The column was packed with alternating layers of sand with eight total layers.

The conservative tracer breakthrough curves for flow perpendicular to the layers and parallel to the layers are very different (Figure 1). When flow is perpendicular to the layering, breakthrough occurs at 1 pore volume and there is relatively little dispersion. In contrast, when flow is parallel to the layers, there is an initial breakthrough that occurs at approximately half a pore volume and a long "tail". Unit concentration is not attained until approximately 5 pore volumes have been flushed through the column.

	PERPENDICULAR-DYE	PARALLEL-DYE	PARALLEL-CL⁻
1st Moment(cm^3)	270	380	370
2nd Moment(cm^6)	720	9.6E4	1.1E5
3rd Moment(cm^9)	240	7200	6300

Table 1. Moment values for conservative tracers in the two-dimensional column with Ottawa sands calculated from the cumulative volume of tracer passed through the column.

The 1st, 2nd, and 3rd moments of the breakthrough curve were calculated (Table 1) using the method described by Palmer, (1988). These moments are reported with respect to the absolute volumes of injected fluid. The ratio of the values of the 1st moments (parallel/perpendicular) is 1.4. The second moment for parallel flow (96377 cm^6) is 135 times the second moment for perpendicular flow (715 cm^6) whilst the third moment parallel to flow (7180 cm^9) is 30 times greater than the value when flow in perpendicular to the layers.

Hydraulic conductivities of the two sands were measured in a constant head permeameter. Based on these values, the anisotropy of hydraulic conductivity in the column (K_H/K_V) = 2.2.

The breakthrough coincides with the arrival at the end of the column of the tracer in the high permeability layers that occupy half the pore space in the column and is confirmed by observation of the dye through the clear Plexiglas. The average concentration at the end of the column after the tracer has arrived in the high permeability layers but before it has arrived in the low permeability layers is estimated from the mass balance of the tracer to be 0.87 which is slightly higher than what is observed in Figure 1.

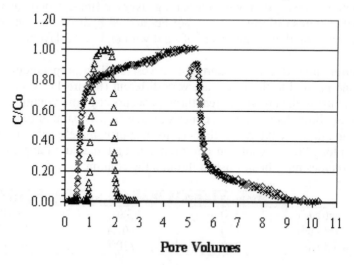

◇ Parallel-Dye △ Perpendicular-Dye × Parallel-Cl-

Figure 1. Breakthrough curves for conservative tracers through a hydraulically heterogeneous system.

The long "tail" on the breakthrough curve reflects the arrival of the tracer in the lower permeability layers. The mass of tracer in these layers comes not only from the source at the influent ends of the layers but also from diffusion from the higher permeability layers. Again, this is confirmed by visual observations of the distribution of the dyes that are seen migrating into the lower permeability layers from the edges. This transverse diffusion accounts for most of the dispersion in the latter portion of the breakthrough curve.

Breakthrough of strontium in a layered system, with flow in the direction perpendicular to the layers, resulted in a retardation factor of 50 based on the 1st moments (Figure 2 and Table 1). The second and third moments are even greater than that obtained from the one-dimensional columns for Oyster sand 2 (Table 1). Chloride breakthrough occurred at one pore volume although with much greater dispersion than the Oyster sands in the one-dimensional column. The retardation factor for flow perpendicular to the layers (R_z) can be estimated using the following equations

$$R_z = \frac{\sum_{i=1}^{n} d_i \theta_i R_i}{d\overline{\theta}} \quad (1) \qquad \overline{\theta} = \sum_{i=1}^{n} \left(\frac{d_i}{d}\right)\theta_i \quad (2)$$

where d_i, θ_i and, R_i are the thickness, porosity and retardation factor of layer i, d is the total thickness, and   is the average porosity.

The retardation factor for flow perpendicular to the layers calculated from data collected from the one-dimensional columns using the Eqs. (3) and (4) is 39. The difference between this value and the value calculated from the 1st moments is most likely due to either experimental uncertainty or variability in iron hydroxide amounts. Experimental uncertainty consists largely of differences in packing between the one-dimensional and two-dimensional

	SAND 1		SAND 2		LAYERED-PERPENDICULAR	
	Cl⁻	Sr²⁺	Cl⁻	Sr²⁺	Cl⁻	Sr²⁺
1st Moment(cm³)	36.4	170	33.0	2500	260	13000
2nd Moment(cm⁶)	63	20500	180	6.4E6	9200	1.8E8
3rd Moment(cm⁹)	25	1900	140	1.3E5	3050	1.7E6
Retardation Factor	1	4.7	1	76	1	50

Table 2. Moment values and retardation values for transport of tracers in the one-dimensional columns with Oyster sands. Moment values were calculated from the cumulative volume passed through the column.

columns (different porosity or bulk density), differences in pore-water velo- cities in the columns, differences in design between the one-dimensional and two-dimensional columns, and to a lesser extent uncertainty in the analytical measurement.

REFERENCES

BRUNAUER, S., EMMETT, P.H. and TELLER, E., 1938. Adsorption of gases in multimolecular layers. J. Am. Chem. Soc., 60: 309-319.

BURGER, R.L. and BELITZ, K., 1997. Measurement of anisotropic hydraulic conductivity in unconsolidated sands: A case study from a shoreface deposit, Oyster, Virginia. Water Resour. Res., 33(6): 1515-1522.

KUNZE, G.W. and DIXON, J.B., 1986. Pretreatment for mineralogical analysis. In: A. Klute (Editor), Methods of Soil Analysis, Part 1. Physical and Mineralogical Methods. Agronomy Monograph. American Society of Agronomy-Soil Science Society of America, Madison, WI.

LAKE, L.W., 1981. Taylor's dispersion in statified porous media. Society of Petroleum Engineers Journal, :459-468.

PALMER, C.D., 1988. The Effect of Monitoring Well Storage on the Shape of Breakthrough Curves - a Theoretical-Study. J. Hydrol., 97(1-2): 45-57.

PARSONS, B.S. and SWIFT, D.J.P., 1995. Stratigraphy of the Oyster, Virginia, site: A preli- minary report., Contribution No. 9 of the Sediment Dynamics Laboratory, Dep. of Ocenogr., Old Dominion Univ., Norfolk, Va.

ROESENTRETER, J.J. SMITH, R.W., HARRIS, R. and BUNDE, R.L., In preparation. Strontium sorption onto natural sands as a function of sediment characteristics and solution pH.

A UNIQUE APPROACH TO ESTIMATING LATERAL ANISOTROPY IN COMPLEX GEOHYDROLOGIC ENVIRONMENTS

Keith J. Halford[1] and Bruce Campbell[2]
[1] *USGS, 333 W Nye Ln, Carson City, NV, 89706, USA,*
e-mail: khalford@usgs.gov
[2] *USGS, American Emabassy Nicosia, Cyprus, PSC 845, FPO AE 09836*

Aquifers in fractured rock or karstic settings are likely to have anisotropic transmissivity distributions. Aquifer tests that are performed in these settings also are frequently affected by leakage from adjacent confining units. Finite-difference models such as MODFLOW are convenient tools for estimating the hydraulic characteristics of the stressed aquifer and adjacent confining units but are poor tools for the estimation of lateral anisotropy. This limitation of finite-difference methods can be overcome by application of the spin method, a technique whereby the positions of the observation wells are rotated about the production well to estimate anisotropy and orientation. Formal parameter estimation is necessary to analyze aquifer tests because of the number of parameters that are estimated. As a test, transmissivity, anisotropy, and orientation were successfully estimated for a simple hypothetical problem with known properties.

The technique also was applied to estimate hydraulic properties of the Santee Limestone/Black Mingo (SL/BM) aquifer and a leaky confining unit beneath Charleston, South Carolina. A nine-day aquifer test with an average discharge of 644 L/min was analyzed numerically. Drawdowns in the SL/BM aquifer and confining unit were simulated with a 12-layer MODFLOW model that was discretized into 81 rows of 81 columns. Simulated drawdowns at seven observation wells that ranged from 23 to 2700 m from the production well were matched to measured drawdowns. Transmissivity estimated along the minor axis ranged from 10 to 15 m^2/d and along the major axis ranged from 80 to 100 m^2/d. The major axis of transmissivity was oriented along compass heading 116° (degrees clockwise from north), which agrees with geologic interpretations. Vertical hydraulic conductivity and specific storage estimates for the overlying confining unit were 4×10^{-5} m/d and 2×10^{-4} 1/m, respectively.

GROUNDWATER FLOW TO HORIZONTAL WELLS IN WATER TABLE AQUIFERS: FIELD EXPERIMENTS AND THEORY

Hongbin Zhan

Department of Geology and Geophysics, Texas A&M University, College Station, TX 77843-3115, (979) 862-7961, zhan@hydrog.tamu.edu

Horizontal wells have screened sections parallel with the horizontal planes. They generate significant interests among groundwater hydrologists and engineers in recent years. This is attributed to several advantages of horizontal wells such as: large influence areas with groundwater bodies; operation in sites where direct site-access is forbidden; and recovery of thin layers of contaminated groundwater. Petroleum engineers have used horizontal wells for oil and gas productions in the past two decades and the interpretation of the pressure data is often challenging. The studies in petroleum engineering regarding horizontal wells may be extended for studying groundwater flow in aquifers. However, there are several limitations in that extension. First, petroleum reservoirs are often confined, similar to confined aquifers, but very different from water table aquifers, which are often to be the cases for shallow horizontal well applications. Second, it is usually too expensive to drill additional monitoring wells besides the production wells in petroleum engineering. It means that the recorded information, including fluid pressure, is often collected from the production well itself in petroleum engineering. However, aquifer responses can be recorded by various means such as by monitoring wells, monitoring piezometers, and the production wells themselves in groundwater hydrology. Therefore, groundwater flow to a horizontal well in a shallow water table aquifer remains to be a very different research subject from that studied in petroleum engineering.

Many present studies on horizontal wells are mostly theoretical works. Field experimental studies are very rare. At present, many horizontal wells are drilled and operated by environmental and engineering consulting firms with primary focuses on removing contaminated vapor or groundwater with the fastest speed and the lowest cost. Little effort is put on recording the important pressure data that are critical for validating the flow theory. Studies combining well-instrumented field experiments with theories do not exist. It is the purpose of this paper to integrate a recent field experiment and theory and to provide insights on flow to a horizontal well in a water table aquifer.

Horizontal well pumping test data are very scarce in hydrological practice. One recent test was conducted by Arthur D. Little (ADL), Inc. in the South Plants area of the Rocky Mountain Arsenal (RMA) located in Commerce City, Colorado. This field test data will be compared herein with the analytical solutions. Two parallel horizontal wells 301 and 302, each of 150 m in length with 76.2 m of horizontal screen, were installed at 24.6 m apart and 12.2 m below ground surface in the WBZ–1 zone. A series of aquifer tests were conducted on the horizontal wells and drawdowns were monitored by pressure transducers at the pumping well itself and at other monitoring wells. Vertical pumping tests were previously conducted. Therefore, it is possible to compare the horizontal and vertical well pumping test results. Similar analysis can be done for any other monitoring wells. A 48.5 hours pumping test with a rate Q=8.75 gpm was conducted in well 301 from 11:30AM, July 27, 1995, to 12:00PM, July 29, 1995. These test results will be interpreted using the theory described below.

A horizontal well pumping in a horizontally–infinite aquifer may go through three stages. For the initial stages of pumping, the influences of the top water table boundary and bottom no-flow boundaries are not perceptible. This stage of pumping is equivalent to a fully penetrating vertical well. At the end of the early flow stage, the aquifer boundaries and well end-effect influence the pressure behavior, and the drawdown curve enters the intermediate stage. The drawdown curves during this stage is the most sophisticated and the most difficult to interpret. After the intermediate stage, the equipotential surfaces in the far field are similar to right cylinders whose symmetric axes are parallel to the vertical axis in an isotropic medium. At this late stage, the horizontal well is like a large diameter vertical well. An adequate theory of flow to a horizontal well should honor these three stages of flow. Three methods will be explained below and the advantages and disadvantages of those methods will be discussed.

A weighted–distance method was proposed by Arthur D. Little, Inc to interpret horizontal well pumping tests. A horizontal well is treated as a uniform–head boundary with a nonuniform flux distribution in this method,. The well is further divided into numerous small segments, each of which is treated as a vertical well.

Although flow to a horizontal well at the intermediate stage is complicated, the early and late stage flows have quite simple drawdown formulae. Thus, we are able to employ the semi-log plot of drawdown versus time to determine the aquifer parameters. The procedures of using the semi-log plot are similar to that used in vertical well analysis. The success of the semi-log method relies on distinguishable early– and/or late–stage straight lines in a semi-log drawdown–time plot, which in turn depend on well screen length, distances to boundaries, aquifer parameters, and pumping test duration.

Since WBZ–1 is an unconfined aquifer, the drawdown needs to be corrected in order to use the semi-log method that is designed for a confined aquifer. Provided that drawdown is much smaller than the initial saturated thickness (<25%), the corrected drawdown is $s'=s-s^2/2B$, where s and B are the real drawdown and the initial saturated thickness, respectively. This correction procedure is commonly used for vertical well pumping tests. Using the semi-log analysis, we find the horizontal hydraulic conductivity $K_h=1.4$ m/day, and transmissivity $=17.1$ (m²/day). This K_h is consistent, in an order–of–magnitude manner, with previous vertical pumping tests, which showed K_h between 0.86 m/day and 5.18 m/day. The obtained K_h also agree with the results derived by the weighted–distance method proposed by ADL, which reported $K_h=1.13$ m/day when using the drawdown data at well 088.

To overcome the disadvantages of the weighted-distance method and semi-log method, we develop type curves of horizontal-wells, which honor the drawdown during the entire pumping time. The type curve plots the dimensionless drawdown s_D versus t_D/r_D^2 in a log-log paper, where $r_D^2 = x_D^2 + y_D^2$ is the square of the dimensionless horizontal distance from the observation well to the center of the horizontal-well. The type curve of a fully penetrating vertical-well in a confined aquifer only has one changing parameter t_D/r_D^2, while the type curve of a horizontal-well has six changing parameters t_D, L_D, z_{wD}, x_D, y_D, and z_D.

The type curve analysis can provide three aquifer parameters: hydraulic conductivity, specific yield, and specific storativity. However, comparison of the theory with the real data indicates that the present theory should be advanced to consider wellbore storage in order to understand the early pumping data better. Meanwhile, graphically integrated software for horizontal well pumping test interpretation is needed to accelerate the interpretative procedures.

This paper shows that the analysis of horizontal-well pumping tests is difficult to interpret because of many parameters affecting the drawdown near a pumping horizontal well. A field experiment of horizontal-well pumping tests in a water table aquifer at the Rocky Mountain Arsenal site near Denver, Colorado is analyzed using three different interpretative methods: the weighted-distance method, the semi-log method, and the type curve method.

The weighted-distance method is only suitable for dealing with the late-time drawdown because it treats the horizontal well as many pieces of fully penetrating vertical wells. This method is also difficult to use because the pumping rate distribution along the horizontal well must be a priori determined.

The semi-log method can be used to find the hydraulic conductivity if a linear segment corresponding either to the early or to the late pumping stage can be identified from the semi-log plot. We have shown that this method provides the hydraulic conductivity that agrees with the results of previous vertical pumping tests. However, this method cannot be used to find the storativity. It is also difficult to use this method to find the specific yield.

The type curve method honors the drawdown data during the entire pumping period thus appears to be the most suitable method for interpreting the pumping tests. We have shown that this method indeed can provide the hydraulic conductivity, storativity, and specific yield that are consistent with previous vertical-well test. However, it is also a time consuming procedure to use this method because type curves depend on the locations of the monitoring wells, thus must be generated for each monitoring well. It appears that a fully graphically integrated software package that can generate the type curves quickly can greatly accelerate the interpretive procedures and should be pursued in the near future. Present theory should also be advanced to include the wellbore storage effect, which substantially masks the early pumping data.

WELL TESTING IN FRACTURED MEDIA:
FLOW DIMENSIONS AND REVS

Richard L. Beauheim[1], Randall M. Roberts[1] and John D. Avis[2]
[1] Sandia National Laboratories
[2] Duke Engineering and Services

[handwritten annotations:]

- important to plot 1st derivative of pressure (drawdown).

$$n = -2 \frac{d \log(p')}{d \log(t)} + 2 \quad \longrightarrow \; \frac{1}{p'} d \frac{dp}{dt} + 2$$

Can also do this for 2nd derivative.

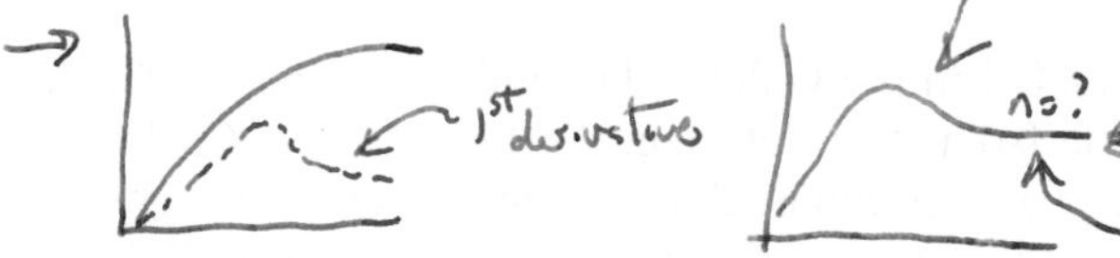

1st derivative   n=?   n

Plot late time gives flow dimension. Shows REV exists. If no REV, no analytical soln exists!

Hydraulic tests in heterogeneous media, particularly fractured media, are notoriously difficult to analyze. One reason for this difficulty is that most well-test analysis techniques were derived for conditions in which flow is radially symmetric around a well, which occurs only under homogeneous conditions. In highly heterogeneous media, pressure transients propagating from well tests encounter different hydraulic properties with both distance and direction from the source well, causing flow to be distinctly nonradial. The resulting pressure responses often fail to display the horizontal derivatives (or semilog straight lines) on which radial well-test interpretations rely.

In 1988, Barker introduced the theory of flow dimensions and derived the "generalized radial flow" equation, providing a method of analyzing tests in non-radial systems. However, except for a few nuclear waste repository programs around the world, little use seems to be made of the flow-dimension approach to well-test analysis. One factor contributing to the apparent lack of interest in flow dimensions may be that no easily applied method has been presented for determining, at the initial stage of an analysis, if a flow-dimension approach is needed (i.e., flow is not radial). In addition, any well-test-analysis method requires that hydraulic properties be stable on some scale, which might be termed the representative elementary volume (REV), before those properties can be uniquely quantified. Determining whether or not an

REV exists should, therefore, be one of the first steps in any well-test analysis. We propose a method for simultaneously determining, first, if an REV exists, and second, if so, what the flow dimension is within the REV.

Roberts and Beauheim (in press) developed what they term "flow-dimension diagnostic plots" for each of the three common types of hydraulic test (constant-rate, constant-pressure, and slug/pulse). These diagnostic plots display a scaled first or second derivative of the pressure or flow-rate response. If an REV is encountered during a test, the scaled derivative will exhibit a constant value, and that value will be equal to the flow dimension. We suggest that this constant value persist for at least one log cycle of time to have confidence in it. If the scaled derivative does not stabilize at a constant value, then no REV exists (on the scale of the test) and no unique hydraulic properties can be inferred from the test.

A pumping test conducted in the Culebra Dolomite Member of the Rustler Formation at the Waste Isolation Pilot Plant (WIPP) site near Carlsbad, NM, provides an example of a fractured medium exhibiting an REV. The WQSP-4 pumping test consisted of a 53.1-hr period of pumping at 0.26 L/s, followed by a 48.6-hr period of pumping at 0.14 L/s, followed by a 900-hr recovery period. Figure 1 shows the log-log diagnostic plot of the recovery data from this test. The late-time pressure derivative is not horizontal as it would be in a radial flow system, but instead has a positive log-log slope. The flow-

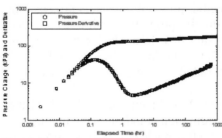

Figure 1. Log-log plot of WQSP-4 pumping test recovery

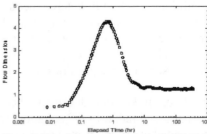

Figure 2. Flow-dimension diagnostic plot for WQSP-4 pumping-test recovery showing presence of an REV with a flow dimension of 1.2

dimension diagnostic plot for the recovery is shown in Figure 2, and shows clear indications of an REV between approximately 10 and 300 elapsed hours with a flow dimension of approximately 1.2. Thus, this test is interpretable. A second example is provided by a slug test conducted in another well into the Culebra, H-11b4, approximately 3 km from WQSP-4. Figure 3 shows the log-log Ramey B plot of the data from this test. The flow-dimension diagnostic plot (Figure 4) shows the late-time derivative oscillating between approximately 0.8 and 1.2, without stabilizing at a constant value. Hence, no REV appears to have been reached in this test.

The differences between these tests are informative. The 1.6-hr slug test interrogated a much smaller volume of rock than the 102-hr pumping test, and failed to reach an REV. For the pumping test, on the other hand, an REV was reached after approximately 10 hr of recovery. If the scale of underlying interest is close to that of the slug test, then well testing may be futile; heterogeneity on this scale cannot be represented by a single dimension. If the scale of interest is larger, then pumping tests might provide useful information.

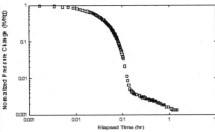

Figure 3. Log-log plot of H-11b4 slugtest

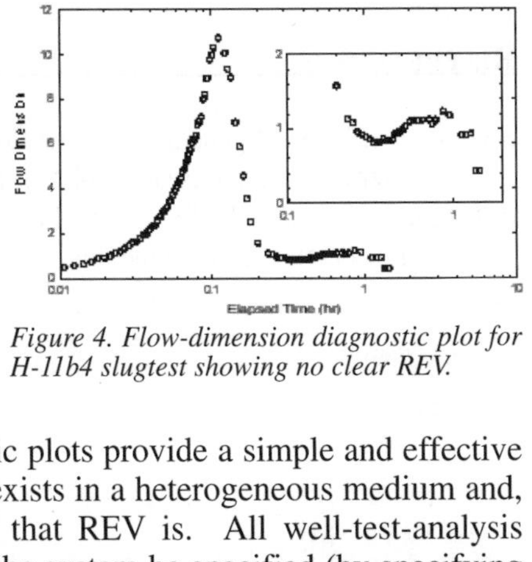

Figure 4. Flow-dimension diagnostic plot for H-11b4 slugtest showing no clear REV.

In summary, flow-dimension diagnostic plots provide a simple and effective means of evaluating, first, if an REV exists in a heterogeneous medium and, second, what the flow dimension of that REV is. All well-test-analysis methods require that the geometry of the system be specified (by specifying the flow dimension), and then provide estimates of the hydraulic properties given that geometry. If a constant geometry cannot be specified, that is, if there is no REV over which the flow dimension does not change, then no unique hydraulic properties can be inferred.

The examples given in this paper highlight the importance of scale. If an REV is present in a heterogeneous system at all, the method of testing must be appropriate to assess the scale at which the REV exists. A slug test, which typically has a smaller radius of influence than a pumping test, may not necessarily reveal the flow dimension shown by a pumping test if that dimension does not exist at the smaller scale. Conversely, if an REV has an upper limit on its size, a slug test might show it while a pumping test might not.

Thus, two factors need to be balanced in any investigation: the scale of interest and the scale of testing. Testing should always be performed at the same scale as the features or processes of underlying interest. Information obtained on flow dimension at one scale cannot be assumed to be valid at a different scale. As this method gains wider acceptance and use, the technical community will be able to see if fractured media commonly, or rarely, have REVs, which should have implications for future hydraulic-testing strategies.

ACKNOWLEDGEMENT

Sandia is a multiprogram laboratory operated by Sandia Corporation, a Lockheed Martin Company, for the United States Department of Energy under Contract DE-AC04-94AL85000.

REFERENCES

BARKER, J.A. 1988. "A generalized radial-flow model for hydraulic tests in fractured rock," Water Resources Research, 24(10), 1796-1804.
ROBERTS, R.M., and R.L. BEAUHEIM. In press. "Hydraulic-test interpretation in systems with complex flow geometries," Water Resources Research.

USING THE HURST EXPONENT TO DETERMINE FRACTURED ROCK NON-INTEGER FLOW DIMENSIONS FROM PUMPING TESTS

Ingrid van der Voort and Gerrit van Tonder
Institute for Groundwater Studies, University of the Free State, South Africa

Groundwater is becoming a very important water resource. In order to manage this resource correctly the hydrogeologist has to understand the groundwater system. Pumping tests can aid the hydrogeologist in this process. A major objective in cost-effective groundwater protection and management is to focus on obtaining optimal value from information from such tests.

Pumping test analysis methods have been developed primarily to investigate and characterise flow within idealised confined radial flow systems. Unfortunately these assumptions are usually invalid in the shallow fractured rock aquifers in South Africa. Notable attempts have been made to expand pumping test methodologies. A worthwhile method to consider when analysing a pumping test was developed by Barker (1988), where he generalised the Theis equation by including a term called the non-integer flow dimension, making it applicable in an arbitrary fractured confined aquifer.

The Hurst exponent was defined by a hydrologist, Hurst, while working on studies of the Nile River. The exponent is also widely used in stock market predictions. This paper presents a method to determine the non-integer flow dimension, using the Hurst exponent and pumping test data.

STANDARDISATION OF HYDRAULIC TESTS FOR DETERMINING HYDRAULIC CONDUCTIVITY

W.G. Coldewey[1], P. Göbel[1] and K.-H. Striegel[2]

[1] *Geological-Palaeontological Institute and Museum, University of Muenster, Muenster, Germany*
[2] *Landesumweltamt NRW, Düsseldorf, Germany*

INTRODUCTION

Hydraulic tests give important information that can be used to determine hydraulic conductivity of sub-surface materials, and more specifically:

- to estimate the hydraulic properties of groundwater flow systems
- to determine groundwater flow and solute transport parameters used in modeling
- by measuring the properties of materials of low conductivity to confirm their suitability for insulation (in form of surface insulation, or rather as geological barrier)
- to plan water supply and seepage installations

Up to now no standardised method exists to allow the determination of the hydraulic conductivity. Depending on the purpose and the location of investigation, several methods can be used, e.g. pumping tests (long-term and short-term), openendtests, pulsetests, packertests, slug and bailtests, drillstemtests, transient response method or squeeze injection, each with specific advantages and disadvantages (Coldewey & Krahn 1991) (see Table 1).

HIDRAULIC TESTS

In accordance with test design, test execution and test analysis differences can result when their results are compared. These differences in the estimated values for instance depend on the following aspects.

Test design:
• investigated hydrogeology (saturated / unsaturated, confined / unconfined, 2-phase-flow, homogeneous / heterogeneous, consolidated / unconsolidated, continuum or discrete fractured, dual porosity flow, boundary effects)
• construction of the test location (exploratory excavation, borehole, developed well, groundwater observation well, etc.)
• test zones (different depth, length or level)
• drilling methods
• experience of the test designer

Test execution:
• methods of the single test (caused by the technical conditions)
• specific borehole effects (skin effect, well bore storage)
• steady or unsteady state
• weather effects (e.g. precipitation, wind, isolation)
• alteration of structure and texture of subsurface material
• leaky test equipment (packer systems, clay barrier)
• method of data logging (electric sounder, data logger, etc.)
• knowledge of the operator

Test analysis:
• curve-fitting method, straight line method, manual or digital modeling, etc. (observe objectivity)
• consideration of specific borehole effects
• flow model (e.g. radial cylindrical)
• finishing plausibility control
• knowledge of the analyst

STANDARDISATION

For these reasons a direct comparison of results from different methods should be done with circumspection. By using two or more methods at the same location differences resulting from the test method can be excluded. But even a comparison of the results from the same method, used at several locations, may show differences.

For standardised comparable execution and analyses of hydraulic tests to determine the hydraulic conductivity, it is desirable to fix certain test methods and test analyses. In Germany the „German standard committee" („Deutscher Normenausschuss Bauwesen, Arbeitsausschuss 05.03.00 "Baugrund, Versuche und Versuchsgeräte" DIN 18130-2: Baugrund, Untersuchung von Bodenproben – Bestimmung des Wasserdurchlässigkeitsbeiwerts – Feldversuche") has lately made some efforts to determine hydraulic conductivity by field testing.

To make an objective, transparent, comprehensive and acceptable decision, each user needs a unequivocal guideline – even if it is only a criterion by convention – to weight single results in a realistic way.

A first step to develop guidelines for collecting realistic hydraulic conductivity data was the compilation and representation of necessary requirements, boundary conditions, and methods to run a test and do the analysis (Deutsche Montan Technologie 1993). Following this first step, a comparison of several test methods was made at a characteristic test location. First results show that attempts of standardisation must be assessed in a differentiated way. The need for a standardisation becomes more and more evident, especially regarding the development of new and highly technological test processes.

REFERENCES

COLDEWEY, W.G. & KRAHN, L. 1991. Leitfaden zur Grundwasseruntersuchung in Festgesteinen bei Altablagerungen und Altstandorten. Im Auftrag des MURL-NRW und LAWA. Düsseldorf.

Deutsche Montan Technologie 1993. Durchführung von methodischen Geländeuntersuchungen zur Feststellung der Durchlässigkeit von Festgesteinen und wechselfesten Gesteinen bei der Planung von Deponien. Im Auftrag des Landesamt für Wasser und Abfall NRW. Essen.

DIN 18130-2. Baugrund, Versuche und Versuchsgeräte – Bestimmung des Wasserdurchlässigkeitsbeiwerts - Feldversuche. – [in press]

TESTS	ADVANTAGES	DISADVANTAGES	APPLICATION
pump test long-term	specifications of hydraulic conductivity for greater areas; exact specification of hydraulic conductivity	great time exposure; increased costs	aquifer
short-term	acute exposure; low costs; exact specification of hydraulic conductivity	specifications of hydraulic conductivity only for small areas	aquifer aquitard
open-end-test	acute exposure; low costs; minimum of test equipment	only approximate specifications of hydraulic conductivity; only selective specifications of hydraulic conductivity depending on the depth	aquifer aquitard
pulse-test	definite pressure measurement applicably for zones of low hydraulic conductivity; acute exposure; low costs	only approximate specifications of hydraulic conductivity; specifications of hydraulic conductivity valid only in proximity of the borehole; specifications of hydraulic conductivity only apply to the selective testing range depending on the depth; outsize pressure impulses entail deformation of the borehole wall and crack the ground; destruction of the casing packer in jointed rock	aquitard
packer-test	acute exposure; low costs; definite logging of loosening zones applicably above and below the groundwater table	only approximate specifications of hydraulic conductivity; specifications of hydraulic conductivity valid only in proximity of the borehole; outsize pressure impulses entail cracking and purification of joints, water creeping along the casing packer is possible; difficulties by specific measures of the pressure; destruction of the casing packer in jointed rock	aquifer aquitard
slug-test/ bail-test	slight technical expenditure; acute exposure; low costs; no changes in hydraulic conditions	only approximate specifications of hydraulic conductivity; specifications of hydraulic conductivity valid only in proximity of the borehole	aquifer aquitard
drill-stem-test	low pressure in the testing range entailing a purification of artificial plugged fracture cleavages	only approximate specifications of hydraulic conductivity; specifications of hydraulic conductivity valid only in proximity of the borehole; borehole exposure; increased costs; high hydrostatic pressure necessary; destruction of the casing packer in jointed rock	confined aquifer aquitard
transient response test	acute exposure; low costs; definite logging of loosening zones; no changes in hydraulic conditions	only approximate specifications of hydraulic conductivity; specifications of hydraulic conductivity valid only in proximity of the borehole; results depending on the construction of the groundwater measuring station (a small diameter is more effective)	aquifer aquitard

WELLBORE STORAGE AND SKIN EFFECT ON HORIZONTAL WELL PUMPING TESTS IN FRACTURED AQUIFERS

Eungyu Park and Hongbin Zhan
Department of Geology & Geophysics, Texas A&M University, College Station, TX77843-3115. Tel: (979) 845-9683, Fax: (979) 845-6162, e-mail: park@hydrog.tamu.edu

Horizontal wells have screen sections parallel to the horizontal directions. They have advantages that are irreplaceable by vertical wells at some circumstances. For instance, they can be used at sites where ground surfaces are obstructed by permanent structures; they also can have great contact areas with the ground water aquifers; they can be effective in recovering thin layer contaminants; and they can perform better recovery in vertically fractured aquifers.

Hantush and Papadopulos (1962) have initially investigated the hydraulics of a collector well, which is a series of horizontal wells distributed in a horizontal plane. Petroleum engineers have studied fluid flow to horizontal wells in oil and gas reservoirs. In recent years, hydrogeologists have studied hydraulics of horizontal wells in shallow ground water aquifers. In most of these studies, the horizontal well is treated as a line source and the well storage and skin effect are not included.

Extensive studies on hydraulics of finite or large diameter vertical wells, including the wellbore storage and skin effect, have been reported before. The analytical solution for the drawdown produced by a large-diameter vertical well including fluid storage capacity was introduced by Papadopulos and Cooper (1967) in groundwater literature.

The concept of double-porosity for a fractured aquifer was first introduced by Barenblatt et al. (1960). Later on, this concept is developed in a transient model by Kazemi (1969). Double-porosity concept is widely applied in petroleum and groundwater literature on flow to vertical wells. But the concept is rarely used in analytical studies of a finite horizontal well with the consideration of wellbore storage and skin effect, except in a few petroleum studies, albeit horizontal wells have good environmental applications in vertically fractured aquifers.

The exact hydraulics of a finite-diameter horizontal well, including the wellbore storage and skin effect, has rarely been studied before. The available references in this field include an analytical study for horizontal wells with wellbore storage and skin in a layered petroleum reservoir (Kucuk and Habashy, 1996); and an analysis of horizontal wells in a bounded naturally fractured reservoir (Ozkan and Raghavan, 1991). More general studies of finite-diameter horizontal wells in three-dimensionally anisotropic fractured confined aquifers, including wellbore storage and skin effect, have not been done yet.

Through this study, the analytical solution for finite-diameter horizontal well in fractured confined aquifer including wellbore storage and skin effects, is derived. Our solution can be expressed as a convolution of source and kernel functions and has analytical form in Laplace domain. The numerical evaluation of the drawdown is accomplished using FINHOW_DP, a MATLAB© program, developed by the authors. This program is available by individual contact. These solutions offer better physical insights into the hydraulics of horizontal well in three-dimensionally anisotropic naturally fractured aquifers than previous line source solutions. They are more useful for describing the near field or early time drawdown behavior.

We test several relative hydraulic conductivity ratios. Our test shows that the higher water conductance of the matrix results in lower drawdown at given time and this is confined by later time solution in certain range of the time. When the hydraulic conductivity of the matrix is much lower than that of the fracture, the drawdown coincides with the single porosity solution derived. In contrast, when the hydraulic conductivity of the matrix is closer to that of the fracture, the drawdown departs much earlier from early single porosity solution and converges to later time solution very quickly. According to this analysis, we generally cannot ignore the amount of flow from the matrix to fracture system except for the case with extremely large contrast of hydraulic conductivity between fracture system and matrix system. A dual porosity model is closer to reality for most of naturally fractured aquifers.

We test several relative specific storativity ratios. This test shows that after certain amount of time, i.e. when drawdown curves start to depart from the early single porosity curve, one can see the dependency of the departing time on specific storativity ratios. Even when the departing times from the early time solution are almost the same, the converging times to late single porosity solutions are all different. In general, a lower specific storativity ratio means a slower converging rate. Our analysis shows that when the specific storativity of the matrix is extremely low, dual porosity model can be replaced by the single porosity model because the separation of the early and later time solution also converges to zero. But, in most real cases, matrix system has a much higher specific storativity than fracture system and we cannot ignore the capability of water storage of the matrix system.

We tested different dimensionless matrix block sizes. Larger size of the matrix block means low frequency of the fracture. The frequency of the fracture is closely related to the actual hydraulic conductivity of the total fracture-matrix system. Through our analysis, we find that the aquifer response is very sensitive to the size of matrix block.

Finally, we test different dimensionless wellbore radii. Given the same skin conductance, a different well radius means a different wellbore storage. If the effect of wellbore storage is included, water withdrawn in the initial pumping is mostly from the wellbore storage and less from the aquifer storage. Such a wellbore storage effect will distort and mask the early time drawdown data resulting in a drawdown much smaller than that excluding wellbore storage effect at the early time. With increasing pumping time, the wellbore storage is gradually depleted and more water is withdrawn from the aquifer. Then, we should observe a rapid increase of drawdown. Thus, compared to the case excluding the wellbore storage, it seems that the influence of the horizontal well diameter on the drawdown is delayed by a period of time during which the wellbore storage supplies more water to the pumping than the aquifer. The largest well diameter has the longest delay. The masked section of the drawdown curve has almost a straight line with a unit slope when most of the water is deduced from wellbore. This agrees with previous works. The effect of wellbore storage cannot be ignored in horizontal well pumping simulation due to its extraordinarily long wellbore in most of the applications.

REFERENCES

BARENBLATT, G.I., ZHELTOV I.P., and KOCINA I.N., 1960. Basic concepts in the theory of seepage of homogeneous liquids in fissured rocks, J Appl. Math. Mech. Engl. Transl., 24, 1286-1303.

HANTUSH, M.S., and PAPADOPULOS, I.S., 1962. Flow of ground water to collector wells. J. Hydraulics Division, Proc. Am. Soc. Civil Engrs, HY 5, 221-244.

KAZEMI, H., 1969. Pressure transient analysis of naturally fractured reservoirs with uniform fracture distribution, Trans. Soc. Pet. Eng. AIME, 246, 451-462.

KUCUK, F. J., and HABASHY, T., 1996. Pressure behavior of horizontal wells in multiplayer reservoirs with crossflow. SPE Formation Evaluation, 11(1), 55-64.

OZKAN, E., and RAGHAVAN, R., September 1991. New solutions for well-test-analysis problems: Part 1-Analytical consideration. SPE Formation Evaluation, 359-368.

PAPADOPULOS, I.S., and COOPER, H.H., 1967. Drawdown in a well of large diameter. Water Resour. Res., 3(1), 241-244.

ANALYSIS OF SLUG TESTS USING THE CONCEPT OF INSTANTANEOUS FLOW

A. C. Thilo[1] and W. Milne- Home[2]
[1] Civil and Environmental Engineering Studies Sydney Institute of Technology, TAFE NSW, Australia
[2] National Centre for Groundwater Management University of Technology, Sydney, Australia

A method that extends the Hvorslev solution for a 'Slug Test' to the case of a rapidly recovering well in either, a confined, or unconfined, saturated aquifer is described. The procedure utilizes an orifice to regulate the sand face flow and pressure regime, requiring the simultaneous measurement of the standpipe and sand face pressures. The basics of the required equipment are given with details of the analytical procedure. System capacitance is treated as 'Transportation Lag', and the sand face pressure to flow relationship is determined throughout the test using the concept of the 'Instantaneous Flow Derivative'. That the flow regime in a recovering well is not always continuous is demonstrated, and four types of well response are identified. The result of the hydraulic conductivity for a well obtained using the described, equipment, and analytical procedure, is compared to that obtained using other recognized analytical procedures.

GENERAL REVIEW

The 'Slug Test' is a relatively simple and cheap test used to determine the hydraulic conductivity of an aquifer. With today's technology all that is requi-red is, a single piezometer set in the aquifer, one or two pressure transducers in watertight housings, and a data gathering system. The test requires a rapid, pulse or instantaneous impulse, change in the aquifers ambient hydrostatic pressure, and the measurement of the decay of that change. There are two commonly used analytical procedures for, unconfined or confined, saturated aquifers using a single piezometer whose screen is set below the standing water level. The first procedure, developed by Hvorslev (1951), and later extended by, Bouwer and Rice (1976), and Dax (1987), is based on the simple first order exponential decay $H_t = H_{t=0} e^{-\beta t}$ where H is the displacement head, t is the lapsed time after the application of the impulse, and β is the exponential decay constant. Hvorslev expresses β as its reciprocal, "The basic time lag" T_o. This form of analysis assumes the 'capacitance' of the aquifer to be insignificant. The second procedure, developed by Cooper et al (1967), takes into account any system capacitance. These analytical procedures work well for all cases of wells except for the case of a 'rapidly' recovering well, where the acceleration and dynamic effects of the moving column of water in the piezometer affect the well's response, Van de Kamp (1976), McElwee and Zenner (1998), and Butler (1999). The application of the equations that lead to these author's solutions are relatively complex and often involve the selection of the correct values for a series of constants. However all of these methods of analysis are predicated on the assumption that the hydraulic parameters and functions that determine the sand face pressure to flow relationship are constant throughout the recovery. We have taken a different approach. We introduce an orifice between the sand face and the piezometer standpipe allowing us to break the nexus between the sand face and standpipe pressure disturbances, resulting in the apparent inapplicability of the direct application of either the Hvorslev or Copper procedure of solution. We show by determining the value of â, $(1/T_o)$, from the plot of piezometer pressure disturbance – time derivative against the sand face pressure, (the instantaneous flow derivative), the Hvorslev solution can be applied directly, and any significant change in the sand face flow to pressure relationship observed. By altering the severity of the orifice we can regulate the sand face pressure disturbance partially independent to the piezometer's pressure disturbance. This requires the simultaneous determination of both the sand face and piezometer pressure disturbance by calculation, calibration, or direct measurement. We selected direct measurement, using two or three down-hole pressure transducers whose slopes are linear and identical so we do not have to calibrate our transducers. Our circuit boards are hand built and designed to enable the interchange of transducers with different working ranges in the field.

BASIC EQUIPMENT

Our original design was to adapt a 50mm 'plumbers plug'. The plug could be expanded to provide a sliding fit in the casing, and the whole assembly pushed below the standing water table using a string of rods. Any small variable leakage around the seal is of no consequence. The equipment used for the work described in the paper is more complex as we wished to have the ability to carry out a variety of testing and sampling procedures using either, the full or partial length of the screened zone of a bore, Figure 1.

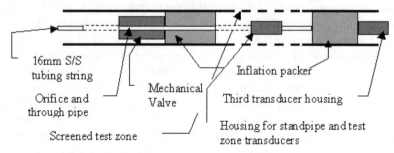

16mm S/S
tubing string

Orifice and
through pipe

Screened test zone

Mechanical
Valve

Inflation packer

Third transducer housing

Housing for standpipe and test
zone transducers

Figure1. Schematic of the equipment used for the work reported in this paper.

SYNOPSIS OF FIELD WORK FINDINGS

We have also found the assumption of the continuity of the sand face flow to pressure relationship may not always be valid for either fast or slow recovering wells.

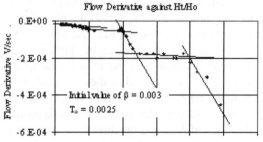

Figure 3. Slow recovering well in Deeply weathered Granite

FINDINGS

A comparison of the values of hydraulic conductivity obtained using the instantaneous flow derivative procedure with those obtained using other industry recognised procedures exposed no significant difference in the values obtained. We have demonstrated the importance of using the instanta-

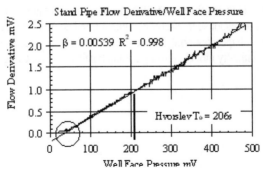

Figure 4. the instantaneous flow derivative plot showing a typical 'tail end' flow, circled

neous flow derivative procedure in the determination of the exponential decay constant β, or Hvorslev's $1/T_o$ as in many of the tests we have analysed there appears a significant period of 'tail end' flow, which indicates an order of magnitude change in the sand face flow to pressure relationship. This might be related to the behaviour of the clays when subjected to hydraulic stresses, which are abnormally high during the early part of the test with respect to those naturally occurring in the ground. This aspect can be investigated as the introduction of an orifice allows the regulation of the pressure disturbance without loss of total quantity of flow across the sand face.

REFERENCES

Hvorslev M.J. 1951. Time lag and soil permeability in groundwater observations. Waterways   Experimental Station, Corps of Engineers, US Army. Bull no 36.

Bouwer H., & Rice R.C. 1976. A slug test for determining hydraulic conductivity of unconfined aquifers with completely or partially penetrating wells. Water resource Research 12 no 3:423-428

Dax A. 1987. A note on the analysis of slug tests. Journ. Of Hydrology 91, 153-177

Cooper H.H., Bredehoeft J.D., & Papadopulos I.S. 1967. Response of a finite diameter well to an instantaneous charge of water

Van de Kamp G. 1976. Determining aquifer transmissivity by means of well response tests: The underdamped case. Water Resource Research 12 no 1:71-77

McElwee C.D. & Zenner M.A. (1998) A non-linear model for analysis of slug-test data. Water Resources Research 34 no1: 55-66

Butler J.J. 1999. The design, performance, and analysis of slug tests. Boca Raton, Lewis Publishers.

D. R. Coughanowr 1991 Process Systems Analysis and Control, McGraw-Hill, ISBN 0-07-100807-1

By breaking the nexus between the piezometer and sand face pressures we have been able to measure the pressure response in a saturated unconfined aquifer with depth, and found this response has the shape commonly associated with system 'Transportation Delay', which can be mathematically modelled using a Padé type two curve, Coughanowr (1991)[8]

SUMMARY OF FLOW DIMENSIONS CORRESPONDING TO HYDROGEOLOGIC CONDITIONS

Douglas D. Walker[1], Randall M. Roberts[2]

[1] *Illinois State Water Survey, 2204 Griffith Dr., Champaign, IL 61820, USA, ddwalker@uiuc.edu, (217) 333-1724*
[2] *Sandia National Laboratories, 4100 National Parks Highway, Carlsbad, NM 88220, USA, rmrober@sandia.gov (505) 234-0073*

One method for interpreting borehole hydraulic tests is the Generalized Radial Flow (GRF) approach, which uses the flow dimension to describe the cross-sectional area of flow within the tested media. The flow dimension, n, also has been shown to be a function of boundary conditions and heterogeneity, so that the interpreted flow dimension of a hydraulic test may reflect several characteristics of the hydrogeologic system. We have derived analytical and semi-analytical solutions for the flow dimension of common hydrogeologic conditions in domains with spatial dimensions of two. We show that imposing a linear, constant head boundary on the Theis solution yields a late-time flow dimension of four, while a linear, no-flow boundary has a late-time flow dimension of two. The Hantush solution for a leaky aquifer yields a flow dimension that is a function of time and the leakage factor. Semi-analytical solutions for heterogeneous transmissivity fields show that the flow dimension of a stationary field stabilizes at $n = 2$, while the flow dimension of nonstationary fields depends on the form and magnitude of the nonstationarity.

STUDY OF SEAWATER INTRUSION IN COASTAL AQUIFER OF MINJUR AREA, CHENNAI (INDIA)

Md. Abdul Hameed[1], Deepak Kashyap[2] & D.C. Singhal[2]
[1] Public Works Deptt., Govt. of Tamilnadu
[2] Indian Institute of Technology, Roorkee – 247 667 (INDIA)

Coastal aquifers are at high risk of contamination due to seawater encroachment. Thus, planning for sustainable ground water development in the coastal aquifers is very essential. Minjur aquifer on the coast of Tamil Nadu, North of Chennai, in India is a confined aquifer, which has been subjected to indiscriminate pumping for irrigation and for augmenting the city's water supply. The large scale pumping has resulted in progressive lowering of the piezometric level, much below the mean sea level and the hydraulic gradient has been created towards land. Consequently, seawater has intruded into aquifer. In the present study, the ground water quality data has been used to study the spatial and temporal variation of salinity in the Minjur confined aquifer and to study the movement of freshwater-seawater interface. The ground water flow in the Study Area has been modeled to simulate the piezometric heads distribution under different pumping strategies. A grid of 12 x 24 cells has been designed and the model has been calibrated under transient conditions in two stages (i.e. for nonmonsoon period and monsoon period of 1988). The model has been verified using data of periods Feb. to Sept. 1997 and Oct. to Dec. 1997. Subsequently, projection runs have been performed with various stipulated pumping patterns.

From the simulation results, it is inferred that if the present extractions are allowed to continue, complete salinization of the aquifer is inevitable. If the pumping is reduced to 1 mgd or less, the piezometric heads would rise above sea level and the groundwater flow will occur from aquifer to sea.

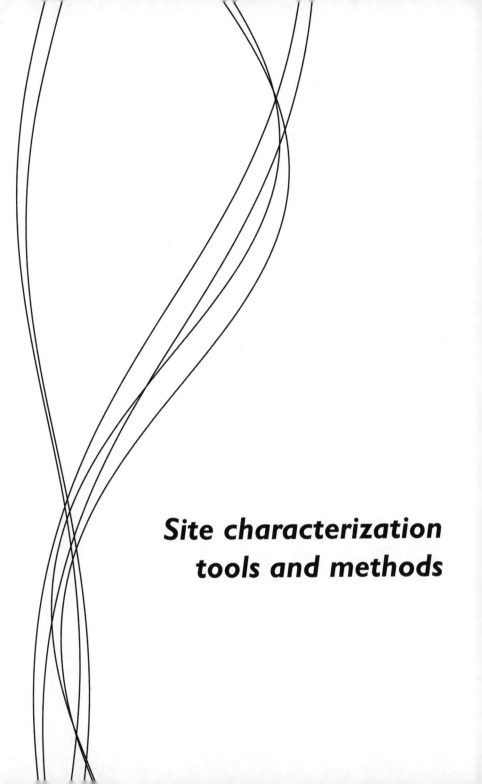

*Site characterization
tools and methods*

Streamline simulation —
- assumes streamline production & no mixing.
1) determine streamline
2) calculate travel time along stream lines.
  - makes calculation into 1D equation.
    - decoupled from grid.

Invert to get K.
① start with heterogeneous K.
② match travel time of tracer
③ match amplitudes.

Partitioning Tracer Test →
         Annable et al 1994
  - gives NAPL concentration.

PARAMETER ESTIMATION IN SUBSURFACE FLOW AND TRANSPORT USING STREAMLINE MODELS

Akhil Datta-Gupta[1] and D. W. Vasco[2]

[1] *Department of Petroleum Engineering, Texas A&M University, College Station, TX 77843*
[2] *Earth Sciences Division, Lawrence Berkeley National Laboratory, Berkeley, CA 94720*

GET THESE PAPERS!!

Subsurface models derived from static data such as geologic, well, and seismic data, will often result in fluid flow predictions that do not match the observed field response. The models then need to be further conditioned to dynamic data such as transient pressure, tracer response and multiphase production history. Reconciling static and dynamic data from a petroleum reservoir or an aquifer is an important challenge for the industry as it typically requires the solution of an inverse problem. Such inverse modeling is computationally intensive, often requiring orders of magnitude more computational efforts compared to forward modeling or flow simulation. Recently, streamline models have shown significant potential in this respect (Datta-Gupta, 2000). Streamline models are advantageous primarily in two ways. First, streamline simulators offer an efficient approach to modeling fluid flow and transport in the reservoir. Second and more importantly, sensitivities of the production response with respect parameters such as porosity, permeability and fluid saturation can be computed analytically using a single streamline simulation. In particular, an asymptotic approach leads to an extremely efficient formalism for imaging reservoir or aquifer properties based on dynamic field response such as transient pressure or tracer data (Vasco and Datta-Gupta, 1999; 2001). Using the asymptotic formalism, large-scale three-dimensional subsurface imaging problems may be solved in hours on a workstation, rather than days or weeks. Another reason for pursuing the asymptotic formulation is the valuable insight it offers when studying reservoir flow and transport. For example, applying asymptotic methods to study subsurface flow and transport, we find that an eikonal equation governs the propagation of the fluid front. Its analytical form clearly indicates the particular combination of flow properties (saturation, pressure, porosity, permeability, relative permeability) that influences the front arrival time. Such insight is essential for understanding the trade-offs and uncertainties inherent in using dynamic data to image reservoir flow properties.

Using streamline models and the asymptotic approach we exploit an analogy between a propagating wave front and a propagating fluid front to develop an efficient formalism for subsurface characterization akin to geophysical tomography. In particular, we can partition the production history matching problem into two sub-problems: an arrival time inversion and an amplitude inversion. The benefits are identical to waveform inversion in seismology: the arrival time matching is quasilinear whereas the amplitude matching is strongly non-linear. The two-step approach substantially speeds-up the computation, makes the solution relatively insensitive to the starting model and also prevents the solutions from being trapped by secondary peaks in the production response. Another key advantage of the asymptotic approach is that parameter sensitivities required for solving inverse problems can be expressed in terms of 1-D integrals along streamlines and evaluated using a single streamline simulation. In addition, the approach is very versatile and the production data can be in the form of transient pressure response, tracer response, or multiphase production history (Vasco and Datta-Gupta, 2001). We illustrate the power and versatility of our approach using field examples involving characterization of NAPL distribution from partitioning tracer tests at the Hill Airforce Base and fracture zone identification from pressure interference tests at the Conoco Borehole Test Facility in Kay County, OK.

REFERENCES

DATTA-GUPTA, A., "Streamline Simulation: A Technology Update," SPE Distinguished Author Series, Journal of Petroleum Technology, 68-73 (December 2000).

VASCO, D. W. and DATTA-GUPTA, A., "Asymptotic Solutions for Solute Transport: A Formalism for Tracer Tomography," Water Resources Research, 35 (1), 1-16 (1999).

VASCO, D. W. and DATTA-GUPTA, A., "Asymptotics, Streamlines and Reservoir Modeling: A Pathway to Production Tomography," The Leading Edge, Special Issue on Reservoir Engineering, October 2001.

A FRACTURED ROCK DECISION TOOL: THE USE OF FUZZY LOGIC IN GROUNDWATER RISK ASSESSMENTS

Ingrid van der Voort and Gerrit van Tonder
Institute for Groundwater Studies, University of the Free State, South Africa

The Constitution of South Africa states that everyone has the right to an environment that is not harmful to his or her wellbeing. It also states that everyone has the right to have the environment protected, for the benefit of present and future generations, through legislation that prevents pollution and ecological degradation, promotes conservation; and secures ecologically sustainable development and use of natural resources while promoting justifiable economic and social development. However as surface water resources are limited emphasis is being placed on groundwater.

Risk assessment is becoming an increasingly important tool in groundwater management and decision-making. Risk assessment is a qualitative or quantitative approach to examining dangers (for example to groundwater and human health). The risk assessment methodology consists of three interactive phases: problem formulation, analysis and risk characterisation. Problem formulation establishes whether there are potential hazards and considers the consequences of the hazard. Analysis calculates the magnitude and probability of consequences. Risk characterisation evaluates the risk or determines the significance of the risk. One of the tools that can be used in groundwater risk assessment is fuzzy logic. Fuzzy logic provides a simple way to arrive at a definite conclusion based upon vague, ambiguous, imprecise, noisy, or missing input information. Fuzzy logic can be defined as a superset of conventional (Boolean) logic that has been extended to handle the concept of 'partial memberships'.

In classical set theory, an element either is or is not in a set. Fuzzy set theory addresses this type of problem by allowing one to define the degree of membership of an element in a set by means of a membership function. For classical sets, the membership function only takes 2 values: 0 (non-membership) and 1 (membership). In fuzzy sets the membership function can take any value from the interval [0,1]. The value 0 represents complete non-membership, the value 1 represents complete membership and the values in-between are used to represent partial membership (transitional zone). The shape of the membership function is determined by the knowledge of experts. However, it has been found that sine-shaped functions provide smooth variations of values.

The decision tool discussed in this paper has been developed to aid groundwater resource managers in the task of optimising the utilisation of fractured aquifer groundwater. Therefore the following are included in the tool:

- *A framework for risk assessments:* the project introduces fuzzy logic based tools to assist in decision making while systematically considering all possibilities.
- *Methods to make cost-effective decisions:* Negative impacts can place heavy burdens on society and economics. Cost-benefit assessments are therefore considered to define, compare and measure benefits and costs with regards to an impact.
- *Possibilities of remediation:* Remediation forms an important component of many groundwater investigations, therefore experiments were conducted, the results of which were included in the decision tool. The results can give the groundwater manager an indication of the possible success of a remediation project.

To align the decision tool with South African legislation a tiered approach was followed. The first tier is a rapid assessment in which only existing data is required and it produces low confidence results. It is intended to give the assessor a guideline of what the risks, cost implications and possibilities of remediation are going to be. The next tier is an intermediate assessment. The first step in the intermediate assessment is to collect all relevant data. Data requirements include recharge values, aquifer and contaminant parameters, health and ecological information. Most of the general information will be obtained from the database included in the decision tool software, however it is sometimes necessary to have site-specific data. The confidence attached to the results is low to medium. Finally a comprehensive assessment requires extensive field investigations and specialist studies. Once all necessary data have been collected, the data must be analysed to develop a conceptual model for the area. At this point, depending on the required outcomes of the assessment it might be necessary to set up a numerical flow and/or mass transport model to be able to make future predictions. As South Africa is mostly underlain by fractured rock aquifer systems, the models will have to account for fractures.

For each of the tiers the following risk assessments can be performed:

- A groundwater risk assessment can be defined as the probability of an adverse effect or effects on the sustainability and/or quality of groundwater associated with measured or predicted hazards. Examples of hazards can be overpumping, drought conditions and chemical spills.
- A groundwater health risk assessment can be defined as a qualitative or quantitative process to characterise the probability of adverse health effects associated with measured or predicted levels of hazardous agents in groundwater. The health risk assessment is divided into a carcinogenic and a non-carcinogenic or toxic assessments.
- Ecological risks of interest differ qualitatively between different stresses, ecosystem types, and locations. A groundwater ecological risk assessment quantifies the impacts of groundwater quantity and quality on ecosystems.

GROUNDWATER MODELLING IN AQUIFERS WITH HIGHLY KARSTIC AND HETEROGENEOUS CHARACTERISTICS (KHC) IN PALESTINE

Dr. Luay J. Froukh
Millennium Engineering, Al Tibi Building , Beit Hanina–Jerusalem
Froukh@meg.palnet.com

Groundwater modelling is hindered by the lack of adequate information about the groundwater system and hence the need for an interactive and efficient system for data preparation and results analysis. Such a lack of information usually necessitates the use of tedious iterative methodology within a sensitivity analysis scheme. The heterogeneous aquifer systems complicate the issue since more data is required to simulate the system. This study demonstrates the integrated approach to bridge the gap between data handling and modelling. The karst cretaceous aquifer system (complex aquifer system) of the Eastern Basin in the West Bank is used to illustrate this approach.

The groundwater modelling approach integrates the outputs from different programs for data preparation and analysis. These include (1) Groundwater Database (GWW) (2) Geographic Information System (GIS) (3) Groundwater Modelling System (GMS).

In addition, the paper will summarize the data collection efforts, problems faced and experience gained working with heterogeneous media. This involves linking the results from various field investigations for groundwater development programs in the West Bank.

EFFECTS OF FLUID DISTRIBUTION AND SUBSURFACE STRUCTURAL HETEROGENEITY ON GROUND-PENETRATING RADAR

Michael B. Kowalsky[1], Yoram Rubin[1] and Peter Dietrich[2]

[1] Dept. of Civil and Environmental Engineering, U. of California, Berkeley, CA 94720; MBKowalsky@lbl.gov
[2] Dept. of Applied Geology, U. of Tuebingen, 72076 Tuebingen, Germany

INTRODUCTION

There is a great need for improved shallow subsurface characterization tools, with the motivation being, for example, to monitor water content in agricultural applications, or to predict the transport of contaminants through the vadose zone and into the groundwater. In the right conditions geophysical tools, such as ground-penetrating radar (GPR), can be helpful to assist in characterizing sedimentary environments and constructing contaminant transport models. Through outcrop analog studies, it has also been noted that the electrical parameters that govern GPR wave propagation depend not only on sedimentological units but are also highly sensitive to the presence of water (Kowalsky et al., 2001), the amount and location of which of course varies with time. GPR images are then expected to vary significantly with the state of water saturation.

In the present study we simulate unsaturated flow and GPR surveys simultaneously using an outcrop analog model to investigate the response of GPR during various hydrologic events such as wetting and drying cycles in the subsurface. This enables the investigation of time-lapsed GPR data for an improved characterization of the subsurface. The simulation of different GPR acquisition techniques during different stages of water saturation will allow for the evaluation of GPR for different goals including the construction of contaminant transport models, the monitoring of water content for agriculture, and the overall characterization of sedimentary environments.

OUTCROP MODELING STUDY

The field site being modeled in this study is at a gravel quarry in the city of Herten, Germany. Sedimentary deposits in this region were formed in a braided river environment and consist mainly of layers of poorly to well-sorted sand and gravel with no silt or clay. During the summer of 1999, an outcrop analog project was performed in which geophysical data were first collected, and the site was then excavated in increments of 1-2 meters such that photographs of the advancing outcrop face could be taken and later converted to lithologic maps (Bayer, 2000). In the present study, TOUGH2 (Pruess, 1991) is used to simulate ponding infiltration at the Herten site using an outcrop model. For several times during infiltration, GPR is simulated using a finite-difference code, and the impact of non-uniform time-varying water saturation on GPR data is investigated.

Simulating infiltration

In order to simulate infiltration in the vadose zone, hydrogeological parameters typical for course sands were chosen. A grid size of 5 cm was used for a model extending 6 meters in depth. Atmospheric conditions were held at the top of the model. And since the water table is known to have been below the bottom of the outcrop, water saturation was held constant at the bottom of the model at a value of 0.7. After obtaining 'natural' conditions (i.e., gravity-capillary equilibrium) by simulating flow with appropriate boundary conditions until the system was approximately at steady state, a ponding infiltration experiment was simulated by placing a constant water head of 5 cm at the upper boundary for 30 minutes. Following this, atmospheric conditions were returned to the surface and the water distribution was observed for increasing times.

The distribution of water within a modeled 1D column is shown for several times in Figure 1a. The well known phenomenon of water ponding is observed above the partially saturated open frame-work gravel layers, which are indicated by regions of gray shading (Figure 1-2). In contrast, water content below these gravel layers is much lower and drains more quickly with time. This trend forms the basis for understanding the time-varying change in electrical properties and as will be shown, might allow for the delineation of such open frame-work gravel layers with geophysical methods. It is also useful to note that the location of such capillary barriers is important (i.e., the distance to underlying capillary barrier affects rate of drainage). The relative change in water content is shown in Figure 1b, and the model permeability distribution is shown in Figure 1c. 2D flow modeling was also performed and additional variations in water content associated with 2D flow phenomena were observed. For example, the inclination of the gravel layers affects the rate of ponding/drainage and directs water laterally.

Simulating GPR during infiltration

In order to simulate GPR, the electrical properties were estimated for each lithological unit using petrophysical models (see Kowalsky et al. [2001] for a more detailed description). The EM velocity distribution for three times after the simulated infiltration is shown in Figure 2a, and the relative change in velocity from 1 week to 6 months after infiltration is shown in Figure 2b. Among other factors, EM velocity is inversely proportional to water content (Figure 1a) and proportional to porosity (Figure 1c). This explains why the high porosity open-framework gravel (at low saturation) have higher velocity, whereas, the regions above gravel layers with increased water content due to ponding have lower velocity. Changes in velocity with time above the open frame-work gravel layers are small, whereas changes in velocity below are relatively large. One instance where this trend is not apparent is between the first two gravel layers (both located between 1 and 2 m depth); the second gravel layer is so close to the first that ponding above the second layer is already occurring directly below the first layer. A finite difference time-domain (FDTD) code was next used to simulate GPR for various data acquisition geometries and frequencies at different times during drainage. The relative changes in travel time and amplitude observed for this case are small for surface reflection data. But these changes are more pronounced when the infiltration front is passing through the model (i.e., at earlier times). For crosshole tomography, however, preliminary results indicate that time-lapsed tomographic data is sensitive to changes in velocity which are caused by differential draining above and below open frame-work gravel layers.

CONCLUSIONS AND FUTURE RESEARCH

It is well known that GPR is sensitive to water content, and that water content is often non uniform (between and within lithologic units). This should be considered while interpreting GPR data. In addition to being related to soil type, water content in the vadose zone is of course also related to the sequence of hydrogeological properties such as the permeability. During transient flow events like infiltration and drying cycles, the distribution of water content in the subsurface also varies with time. We present some forward modeling results in which the sensitivity of GPR to transient fluid flow in an outcrop model is investigated. In this manner, we aim to better understand the relation between fluid flow processes and GPR data. Since GPR has the potential, as shown, to measure changes in water saturation, which are related to permeability structure, we aim to use GPR data to infer permeability structure in the subsurface (e.g., using time-lapsed GPR data in conjunction with hydraulic data for hydraulic parameter inversion).

ACKNOWLEDGEMENTS

The authors would like to thank Stefan Finsterle for assistance with the TOUGH2 modeling. This research was supported by NSF grant EAR 9628306 and USDA Grant 2001-35102-09866.

REFERENCES

BAYER, P., Aquifer-Anolog-Studie in grobklastischen 'braided river' Ablagerungen: Sedimentaere/ hydrogeologische Wandkartierung und Kalibrierung von Georadarmessungen, Diplomkartierung, Universitaet Tuebingen, 2000.

KOWALSKY, M. B., P. DIETRICH, G. TEUTSCH, and Y. RUBIN, Forward modeling of ground-penetrating radar data using digitized outcrop images and multiple scenarios of water saturation, Water Resour. Res., 37(6), 1615-1625, 2001.

PRUESS, K., TOUGH2—A general purpose numerical simulator for multiphase fluid and heat flow. Report No. LBL-29400, Lawrence Berkeley National Laboratory, Berkeley, CA, May, 1991.

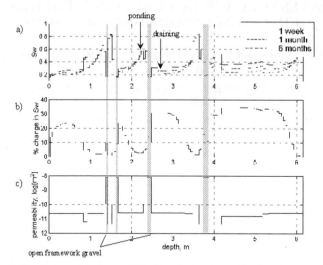

Figure 1: 1D Simulation of drainage (following infiltration). The distribution of water satura-tion (Sw) with depth is shown (a) with increasing time after an infiltration event (5cm ponding infiltration for 30 minutes). The relative change in Sw from 1 week to 6 months is shown in (b). The infiltration simulation is based on the permeability distribution shown in (c).

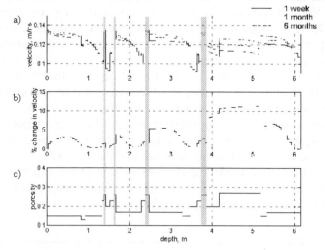

Figure 2: Electromagnetic (EM) wave velocity during drainage are shown (a) for increasing times during drainage. The relative change in EM velocity from 1 week to 6 months is shown in (b). The porosity values shown in (c) and the Sw values (Figure 1a) were used to calculate the EM velocity values in (a).

INVESTIGATION OF FRACTURED POROUS MEDIA -NEW LABORATORY METHODS

Leven, C.[1*], McDermott, C.I.[1], Dietrich, P.[1], Lield, R.[1], Sauter, M.2 and Teutsch, G.[1]

[1] *University of Tuebingen, Applied Geology, Center for Applied Geosciences*
[2] *University of Jena, Institute of Geoscience, Dept. of Hydrogeology*

In this paper an investigation of flow and transport processes in a fractured sandstone block of approximately 1 m_ is presented using new experimental methods. The investigation is based on the aquifer analogue concept. Two different types of experiments were used, point-to-point measurements and borehole to point measurements for diffusivity tests. Both investigation methods show similar results. The experiments indicate that the flow will be dominated by fractures only if they are directly connected, while pure matrix connections do not show any influence of the fracture network. The diffusivity tests are found to be an appropriate tool for the investigation of fractured porous systems and can provide detailed information for distinguishing between properties of the fracture network and the matrix.

For important details considering the presentation of the experiments, their preparation, setup and results as wells as quantitative procedures and references, we refer to the extended proceeding version of this paper.

INTRODUCTION

The investigation of flow and transport processes in confined fractured porous aquifers under natural conditions can be difficult due to the hydraulic contrasts between fractures and the porous matrix. However, for the understanding of the coherence between the flow and transport processes and the parameter distributions, the detailed investigation of the processes is an essential prerequisite. The approach of aquifer analogue and new experimental techniques can contribute to improve the understanding and can allow the detailed investigation of particular flow and transport paths, as it is required e.g. for contaminant site remediation or the exploration of nuclear waste repositories.

THE AQUIFER ANALOGUE APPROACH

The aquifer analogue approach was mainly used in the petroleum exploration and in the field of the investigation of potential nuclear waste repositories. Within the aquifer analogue concept, the investigations of an aquifer, which is mostly inaccessible or only accessible by some few boreholes, take place at an outcrop area, whose lithological and sedimentological properties are considered to be analogous to the fractured porous aquifer. This approach allows by the use of appropriate methods an easy examination and characterization of the fractured porous media. This leads to high resolution and precise data sets, which contain geometrical information of the fracture network and detailed information on the porous matrix, as well as characteristic values, which are relevant for flow and transport processes. The aquifer analogue approach further permits experiments under fully controllable boundary conditions at different scales (laboratory, technical, or field scale). In this paper, we focus on laboratory-scale experiments, which have been conducted to investigate flow and transport processes in a water-unsaturated fractured sandstone block.

PREPARATION OF THE FRACTURED SANDSTONE BLOCK

A block of approximately 1 m^3 was cut out of fractured sandstone from Triassic sandstone, which is quarried in the southern part of Germany near Tübingen. The preparation of an absolute regular block with same edge length failed because of the highly fractured nature of the material, so the block was cut to approximately 0.9 x 0.9 x 0.8 m^3.

To acquire an absolute airtight coating the complete fractured sandstone block was covered by epoxy resin of 5 mm thickness. To be able to conduct flow and transport experiments, on each block side 16 connections of 3 cm diameter were drilled in a 4 x 4-matrix through the resin cover and sealed by so-called "ports". These ports are plastic plugs, which allow access to a controlled area on the block surface. The advantage of individual ports is that tomographic measuring configurations can then easily be applied to determine the characteristics of the block.

EXPERIMENTAL METHODS

For the flow and transport experiments a multi-purpose-measuring device was developed. This measuring device is automated and can be used for an online data acquisition.

In this paper, two different measuring configurations based on the multi-purpose-measuring device are described. Firstly, a pneumatic flow and tracer tomography was conducted to the fractured sandstone block using the above-described measuring device combined with a setup for tracer injection and detection. Secondly, after the completion of the flow and tracer tomography, a vertical borehole was drilled through the center of the sandstone block. Through this central borehole, a constant pressure was applied and the pressure change at the outside of the block was recorded at each port to gain information of the diffusivity of the fractured sandstone block.

Flow and tracer tomography

For flow and tracer tomography, the setup shown in the extended proceeding version was utilized. Pressure regulated compressed air is injected into the sandstone block through the ports optional for different measuring configuration. The release of the air at the outlet of the fractured sandstone block is realized by simple outflow to atmosphere. Steady state conditions are applied to determine the characteristic values of gas flow. For the transport experiments a definite volume of helium (as conservative tracer gas) is injected using a bypass loop thus preventing disturbances of the stable flow field. At the outlet, the breakthrough of helium is detected with a mass spectrometer. All gas and tracer tomographical experiments described in this paper were performed by using one port for the injection and one port for the withdrawal (port-to-port), each on opposite block sides to create a three-dimensional flow field pattern within the block.

Diffusivity tests

The setup for the diffusivity tests is also shown in the extended proceeding version. Here compressed air is injected at a constant pressure over a central borehole, which is closed tightly at the top and bottom by simple packers. All ports at the outside were closed so that the block is airtight. Simultaneously, the pressure build up at the single ports at the outside of the fractured sandstone block is recorded.

RESULTS

Flow and tracer tomography

The analysis of the results of the flow and tracer tomography indicate that fracture dominated flow occurs only in cases of direct fracture connections. At connections to the matrix, the influence of the fracture network strongly decreases. Details considering the quantification can be found in the extended proceeding version.

Breakthrough curves detected at matrix dominated port connections can be characterized by flat curves with a smooth concentration increase due to lowered transport velocities. Therefore, distinctive dispersive and diffusive effects become apparent. Some of these curves show strongly delayed tracer recovery, which corresponds to tailing, caused by matrix diffusion effects or differential advection (transport occurs on pathways with varying lengths). In contrast, breakthrough curves recorded at the outlet of direct fracture connections show a steep increase of the curve and the injected mass will be withdrawn relatively quickly at the exit port. Further, those configurations for which the flow rate is highest and therefore the hydraulic conductivity, the residence time of the tracer in the system is lowest. Additionally, the initial breakthrough occurs at significantly earlier times with a sharp concentration increase for direct fracture connections.

To quantify the anisotropy of the parameters reflecting the transport processes within the fractured sandstone block, the measured breakthrough of the tracer with respect to time was compared to the response of the numerical simulation.

Diffusivity tests

The analysis of the recorded temporal pressure build up indicates that the pressure-time curves recorded at matrix dominated ports gather at late times, while the pressure curves recorded at direct fracture connections gather at early times. Also the fracture dominated ports indicate a very quick responses within the first logarithmic cycles, while the first response of the matrix dominated connections occurs two time orders later followed by a very steep increase in pressure.

These phenomena can be attributed to particular conductive and storative effects: The response of direct fracture connection indicates that the pressure buildup arises very fast along the interconnected fracture network. Storage effects are small immediately after starting the pressure injection. However, with time the further buildup will be retarded due to compression of the gas, while the last branch is mostly influenced by the elastic decompression of the matrix due to storage. Vice versa, for matrix-dominated connections, the pressure buildup is strongly dominated by the compression of the gas and the storage. Nevertheless, after this time of compression and elastic matrix decompression, the pressure buildup occurs very quickly up to the applied pressure.

Contrary, there are some direct fracture connections as well as matrix dominated ones that behave vice versa as described above. The pressure buildup responses interrelate with the spatial position of the connection. Those matrix dominated connections, which response very quickly, are situated in close vicinity to fractures. Direct fracture connections, which react with significant retardation, are found for fractures, which are assumed to have no interconnection with the fracture network, thus the response is limited by the properties of the matrix.

SUMMARY AND CONCLUSIONS

The application of new experimental methods for the investigation of flow and transport processes in fractured porous media can be based on the aquifer analogue concept. The presented investigations were performed on laboratory macro-scale to a fractured sandstone block of approximately 1 m_. For the investigation, two different types of experimental setup were used, point-to-point measurements and borehole to point measurements for diffusivity tests. The high-resolution point-to-point measurements indicate that the flow will be dominated by fractures only if they are directly connected. Connections to the sandstone matrix hardly show fracture-induced effects. Similar results are found for the tomographical tracer experiments, which show in most cases an impact of the matrix. Pure matrix connections do not show any influence of the fracture network. The diffusivity tests are found to be an appropriate tool for the investigation of fractured porous systems and can provide detailed information allowing to distinguish between properties of the fracture network and the matrix.

MODELING FLOW AND TRANSPORT IN SATURATED FRACTURED ROCK TO EVALUATE SITE CHARACTERIZATION NEEDS

Christine Doughty and Kenzi Karasaki
Earth Sciences Division
E.O. Lawrence Berkeley National Laboratory

Using regional geographic, geologic, hydrologic, geophysical, and meteorological data for the Tono area in Gifu, Japan, we developed an effective continuum model to simulate regional groundwater flow and the transport of radionuclides away from a hypothetical repository in a 4 km by 6 km by 3 km thick fractured granite rock mass overlain by sedimentary layers. Individual fractures are not modeled explicitly. Rather, continuum permeability and porosity distributions are assigned stochastically, based on well-test data and fracture density measurements. Large-scale features such as lithologic layering and major fault zones are assigned deterministically.

We start with a regular 3D grid with a basic grid block size of 100 m by 100 m by 100 m. Grid block thickness is decreased to 50 m near the top of the model, to enable better representation of surface topography changes. Grid block thickness is gradually increased near the bottom of the model since no data are available and flow variability is expected to be gradual at depth. The bottom of the model is a closed boundary. Next, we trim the grid laterally to reproduce the irregular 4 by 6 km model boundary that follows natural topographic boundaries such as ridgelines (closed boundaries) and rivers (open boundaries). Finally, we trim the grid vertically to match surface topography. The top of the model is held at a head value equal to the surface elevation, to represent a near-surface water table. Flow from the constant head boundary into the model represents subsurface recharge. This configuration eliminates the need to model percolation through the vadose zone, which is a highly non-linear process and hence computationally intensive.

We include the following features of interest deterministically:

• The Tsukiyoshi fault, a major east-west, subvertical fault is represented as a plane with location and orientation inferred from the surface trace, borehole occurrences, and seismic profiles. Several smaller surface lineaments identified from satellite or aerial images that are also identified in boreholes are modeled explicitly as well.
• Lithofacies changes observed in boreholes are kriged to form surfaces. These surfaces provide the boundaries between different material types in the model.
• The sediment/bedrock boundary inferred from an electrical resistivity survey is used as the boundary between the uppermost granite (Biotite) and the lowermost sedimentary rock (Toki-lignite bearing rock).

The resulting model is shown in Figure 1 and Table 1 summarizes the various types of surface and subsurface data used to construct it.

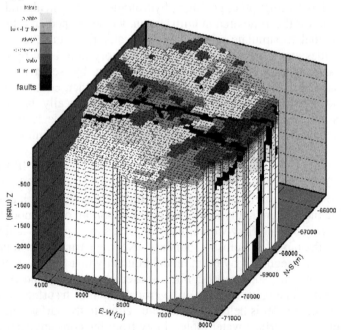

Figure 1. 3D perspective view of the model

DATA TYPE	ACTUAL USE	POTENTIAL USE
Landsat images	Qualitative understanding of regional surface topography	Improve lateral model boundaries at great depths
Surface topography	Provide detailed topography that impacts shallow groundwater flow	
Seismic profiles	Locate faults in 2-D sections	
Electrical resistance	Provide spatially extensive image of the sediment/bedrock boundary	
Surface geological map	Verify granite outcrop locations in model	Improve assignment of shallow material types, especially among sedimentary rocks
Water balance data	Estimate average surface recharge into the model	Identify locations of especially large or small recharge
Wellbore lithologies	Assign material types	
Wellbore fracture identification	Determine stochastic distribution of fracture density for use in calculation of model porosity	
Well tests	Provide distributions of conductivity values for model	Use in inversion to determine conductivity of specific regions
Multi-packer monitoring	Investigate connectivity and flow barriers	Same as well tests
Drillers' notes		Identify high flow zones
Flow and temperature logs		Investigate regional groundwater flow

Table 1. Summary of data used to develop the 4x6 km model

Each grid block represents an effective fractured continuum with permeability and porosity assigned stochastically based on field measurements. Permeability is proportional to hydraulic conductivity K, which is determined from slug tests and pumping tests conducted using packed-off intervals in boreholes. Because many of the intervals used for the tests are of the same order as the grid block size, we assume that there is no need to scale up or scale down K values measured during well tests, and that they directly represent effective continuum conductivities. Grid block K values are drawn from random distributions for each material type, constructed by resampling field measurements, unless there are not enough measurements for a given material type to make resampling viable, in which case a log-normal distribution is used. Table 2 summarizes the material types and conductivity distributions used for the model.

Material Type	Number. of conductivity measurements	$\log_{10}K$ (m/s)		Type of distribution used for $\log_{10}K$
		Mean	S.D.	
Alluvium	0	−7.9	1.6	Normal
Seto group	0	−7.9	1.6	Normal
Oidawara	1	−8.7	1.6	Normal
Akeyo	11	−7.9	0.8	Resampled
Toki lignite-bearing	21	−7.0	0.9	Resampled
Biotite granite	192	−7.1	1.7	Resampled
Felsic granite	46	−6.9	1.1	Resampled
Faults	12	−7.7	1.0	Tsukiyoshi resampled; other faults normal

Material Type	Number. of fracture density measurements	Fracture density (m⁻¹)		Model Porosity	
		Mean	S.D.	Mean	S.D.
Biotite granite	57	7.7	4.2	3.9E-4	5.9E-4
Felsic granite	4	10.8	4.2	3.5E-4	2.7E-4
Overall	67	7.9	5.0	3.2E-4	4.2E-4

Table 2. Summary of material properties used in the model. For materials with no data, use average for all materials.

Porosity ϕ is calculated as the product of fracture aperture w and fracture density d, with aperture determined from K and d using the cubic law:

$$\phi = w\,d = (12\,K\,\mu\,/\,d)^{1/3}\,d = (12\,K\,\mu\,d^2)^{1/3} \qquad (1)$$

Fracture density measurements are sparse and there is no obvious correlation between fracture density and conductivity, so fracture density measurements from all lithological layers are combined to determine a mean fracture density of 7.95 m⁻¹ and a standard deviation of 5 m⁻¹. For most of the lithological layers, fracture densities are drawn from a normal distribution with these moments, which is truncated at a small positive number (0.01 m⁻¹) to ensure that fracture density is always positive.

For each grid block, after K and d have been drawn from the appropriate distribution, Equation (1) is applied to determine ϕ. The resulting model porosity statistics are summarized in Table 2. Model porosity is considered to be less well constrained than model conductivity for several reasons. First, basing porosity estimates on fracture density measurements is problematic because a high percentage of observed fractures may not contribute to flow at all. Moreover, the cubic law can greatly misrepresent the relationship between fracture aperture and conductivity, and even if it is valid, the hydraulic aperture used in the cubic law tends to underestimate the volumetric aperture relevant for transport. Finally, there are very few fracture density measurements available for materials other than the Biotite granite.

The numerical simulator TOUGH2 simulates the steady-state groundwater flow through the site, then streamline tracing analysis is used to calculate travel times to the model boundary from specified monitoring points that represent leakage from a hypothetical nuclear waste repository. These travel times consider transport due to advection only; no diffusion or dispersion is included.

The base case simulation was conducted for 10 realizations of the stochastic permeability and porosity distributions. For all realizations, the modeled water balance is reasonable, with the modeled recharge about a factor of two smaller than the value inferred from rainfall, evaporation, and streamflow data. Most of the outflow is to or below the Toki River, which constitutes the southern boundary of the model. Predicted travel times from the repository site to the model boundaries range from 1 to 25 years, with a mean of 7 years. Observed heads above and below the Tsukiyoshi fault suggest that it may act as a low-permeability barrier to flow. To test this hypothesis, we consider a case in which the permeability of grid blocks representing the Tsukiyoshi fault is decreased by a factor of ten. Figure 2 shows head profiles for several realizations of the two cases. The effect of assigning lower permeability to the Tsukiyoshi fault results in an obvious increase in head below the fault depth that is consistent with field observations. In addition, the average travel time increases slightly, from 7 to 9 years.

There is significant variability among the different stochastic realizations in terms of the details of the streamtrace patterns, including model exit locations. However, if only average results such as the mean travel time or mean path length are considered, then variability among realizations is relatively small. Greater variability arises from imposing different boundary conditions or assigning low permeabilities to the Tsukiyoshi fault, emphasizing the need to establish a sound basis for determining these model properties.

Several other research groups also developed models based on the same data set, and a key feature of the work is a comparison between different models'

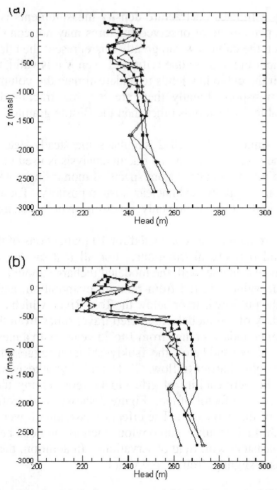

Figure 2. Head profiles for (a) the base case; and (b) the low-permeability Tsukiyoshi fault case.

results to highlight which aspects of site characterization need to be improved in order to increase confidence in model predictions. Because a field investigation program is ongoing, model results can potentially have a significant impact on future characterization activities. The effective porosity of the fracture network is the least well-constrained parameter of our model, and a wide range in travel times obtained by the different research groups (1 to 1,000,000 years) can be attributed to orders of magnitude differences in the effective porosities used. This underscores the importance of improved porosity estimates as a key component of future site characterization.

This work was supported by Japan Nuclear Fuel Cycle Corporation (JNC) and Taisei Corporation of Japan. through the U.S. Department of Energy Contract No. DE-AC03-76SF00098.

SIMULATING INFILTRATION IN UNSATURATED BASALT FOR THE LARGE-SCALE AQUIFER PUMPING AND INFILTRATION TEST AT INEEL

André J.A. Unger, Ardyth M. Simmons and Gudmundur S. Bodvarsson
Earth Sciences Division, Lawrence Berkeley National Laboratory, Berkeley, CA, USA

The Idaho National Engineering and Environmental Laboratory (INEEL) contains one of the largest subsurface disposal facilities for plutonium-contaminated waste. This waste resides in the 144,100 m2 Subsurface Disposal Area (SDA) within the Radioactive Waste Management Complex (RWMC) and was placed in unlined pits, soil vaults and trenches in surficial sediments. The INEEL waste burial site is underlain by undulating basaltic lava flows containing interbedded fluvial, lacustrine and eolian deposits of clay, silt, gravel and sand with the water table located approximately 170m below ground surface beneath the SDA. The purpose of the Large-Scale Aquifer Pumping and Infiltration Test (LPIT) was to mimic the intermittent flood events observed at the SDA and was located approximately 1.43km south of the RWMC within the same geological units.

The purpose of this modeling effort was to simulate the highly transient water infiltration and ponding conditions that existed during the LPIT. The modeling approach used here involved determining parameters controlling unsaturated and saturated flow in the fractured basalt using a dual-permeability representation of the basalt fracture and matrix continua. These parameters were determined by simultaneous calibration to multiple hydrographs measured during the LPIT and reflect large-scale properties of the lithological units affected by the field-scale LPIT test as used in the dual-permeability approach. In the context of this work, the INEEL site provides an anthropogenic analog for testing models describing unsaturated flow through both fractured and non-fractured stratigraphic layers at the proposed high-level waste repository at Yucca Mountain

The LPIT consists of a 183m diameter infiltration pond constructed by removing surficial soil to build a 1.5m high earthen berm. Figure 1 shows a vertical E-W cross-section cut through the center of the model. This figure shows the undulating thickness of the A and B basalts as well as the BC interbed. Unsaturated flow due to the impact of the infiltration pond was simulated using TOUGH2 using the EOS9 module which solves Richards equation.

Perched water hydrograph data were collected at 17 locations at the B basalt—BC interbed interface. Of the 17 hydrographs, six were selected for the calibration effort. Numerical tests indicated that inversion using the full 3-D LPIT model containing all 17 hydrographs was too computationally extensive; therefore, a wedge of nodes on radial spokes of 342°–0°–18°–32° was extracted in order to simultaneously calibrate to hydrographs in wells B04N11, C04C11, B06N11 and C06C11.

Initial manual calibration indicated that the six most sensitive parameters controlling the calibration of the LPIT model to the hydrographs were the constant scaling factor used to reduce the interfacial area between the basalt fracture and matrix continua A_{BFM}, the basalt fracture continuum permeability k_{BF}, the basalt matrix continuum permeability k_{BM}, the BC interbed matrix continuum permeability k_{BCM}, the BC interbed van Genuchten capillary pressure α_{BCM} and m_{BCM}. The basalt fracture and matrix continua porosities were not sensitive parameters controlling calibration. This is due to the fact that imbibition of the infiltration front from the basalt fracture continuum to the matrix continuum controlled its downward advection rate rather than the porosity due to the initial dry conditions present at the site.

Figure 2 shows simultaneous calibration results to hydrographs B04N11, C04C11, B06N11 and C06C11 using the 342°–0°–18°–32° submodel extracted from the full 3–D LPIT model. This model will be referred to hereafter as the "2–D model" while the entire LPIT model will be referred to as the "3–D model". The symbols on Figure 2 represent water pressure and indicate ponded water elevation within the fracture continuum of the B basalt on top of the BC interbed where reference atmospheric gas–phase pressure is 85kPa. Calibration parameters were obtained by setting $A_{BFM} = 0.01$ while the sensitivity of the other five calibration parameters to A_{BFM} was determined by doubling it to $A_{BFM} = 0.02$ and then by halving it to $ABFM = 0.005$. Parameters obtained from the ITOUGH2 calibration are provided on Table 1.

Comparison of calibrated parameters obtained with $A_{BFM} = 0.01$ indicate that the estimated basalt matrix permeability is almost equal to the mean value estimated from field samples, the BC interbed permeability is just above the minimum observed value while the BC interbed van Genuchten parameters are also near the mean of the field estimated values. Although the field samples were not obtained from the LPIT site, their close correspondence to the estimated parameters does build confidence in the ability of the LPIT model to yield a spatially averaged set of hydrological parameters to fit the hydrographs.

The basalt fracture continuum permeability was the most sensitive parameter in reducing residuals to the hydrograph data and was least correlated to the other concurrently estimated parameters. The basalt matrix and BC interbed permeability exhibited equal sensitivity in reducing residuals. Furthermore, they exhibited a strong inverse correlation indicating that imbibition of water into either the basalt matrix continuum or BC interbed could equally control the fit of the calibrated hydrographs to the observed data. Successful calibration of the LPIT model helps to build confidence in the ability of the dual-permeability approach to simulate transient unsaturated flow in fractured-porous media. This is especially significant to the site-scale Yucca Mountain model where the dual-permeability approach is used extensively to simulate both unsaturated flow and transport in fractured tuff.

Param.	$A_{BFM} = 0.01$		$A_{BFM} = 0.005$		$A_{BFM} = 0.02$	
	mean	std. dev.	mean	std. dev.	mean	std. dev.
$^{\dagger}k_{BF}$	3.27×10^{-10}	0.0701	3.13×10^{-10}	0.0553	3.44×10^{-10}	0.0759
$^{\dagger}k_{BM}$	2.51×10^{-15}	0.395	6.31×10^{-15}	0.197	1×10^{-15}	0.381
$^{\dagger}k_{BCM}$	5.01×10^{-17}	1.51	6.31×10^{-17}	0.538	1.26×10^{-16}	0.848
$^{\ddagger}\alpha_{BCM}$	1×10^{-4}	1.23	4.07×10^{-6}	0.465	1×10^{-4}	0.852
m_{BCM}	0.28	0.341	0.86	0.718	0.67	1.08

†*mean permeability values are in $[m^2]$ while standard deviation is in $[\log_{10} m^2]$*
‡*mean α_{BCM} values are in $[Pa^{-1}]$ while standard deviation is in $[\log_{10} Pa^{-1}]$*

Table 1: *Parameters estimated during calibration to hydrographs B04N11, C04C11, B06N11 and C06C11.*

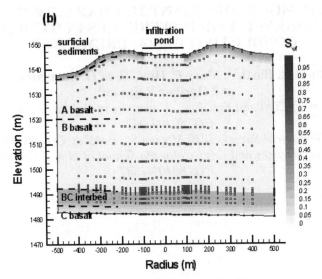

Figure 1: East-West cross-sectional view with the centroids of the elements as well as the steady-state water saturation in the fracture continuum.

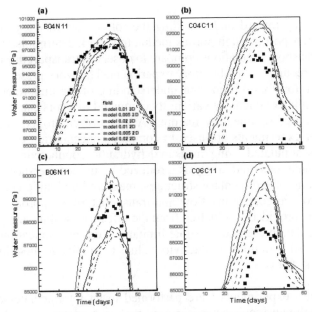

Figure 2: Ponded water hydrographs in wells B04N11, C04C11, B06N11 and C06C11. Symbols represent field data with reference atmoshperic gas phase pressure equal to 85 kPa. Lines represent calibration results using the 2–D submodel as well as the full 3–D LPIT model.

IS IT MORE IMPORTANT TO CHARACTERIZE HETEROGENEITY OR DIFFERENCES IN HYDRAULIC CONDUCTIVITY MEASUREMENTS?

Gilbert R. Barth[1,2], Mary C. Hill[2], Tissa H. Illangasekare[3] and Harihar Rajaram[1]

[1] *Dept. of Civil and Env. Eng., University of Colorado,Boulder, CO 80309-0428*
[2] *U.S. Geological Survey, 3215 Marine St., Boulder, CO 80303-1066*
[3] *Env. Sciences and Eng., Colorado School of Mines, Golden, CO 80401-1887*

As a first step toward understanding the role of sedimentary structures in flow and transport through porous media, this work deterministically examines how transport simulations compare to observed transport through simple, artificial structures in a laboratory experiment. The work presented here is a critical step towards refining our understanding of the importance of measured hydraulic-conductivity variability compared to errors caused by inaccurate zonation of sedimentary features. A series of controlled, intermediate-scale tracer experiments are used to compare concentration observations to predictions simulated using measured hydraulic conductivity. The experiments, simulations and analysis produced a unique perspective on our understanding of sedimentary structures, measured hydraulic conductivities, and their role in controlling flow and transport through porous media. The experiments provided results free from the effects of scaling and parameterization. The data presented illustrate limitations on the application of laboratory-measured hydraulic-conductivity values to predictive modeling of heterogeneous systems.

The transport experiments were performed in an intermediate-scale (10-m long), two-dimensional, heterogeneous porous medium (σ^2_{lnK}=1.26, μ_{lnK} = 4.18, where K is cm hr^{-1}). Permeameter and column experiments produced laboratory measurements of hydraulic conductivity for each of the five sands used to create the intermediate-scale, heterogeneous porous medium. The experiments provide a complex, explicitly characterized system, that is simple enough to be controlled, definitive, and allow explicit numerical representation, yet complex enough to be relevant to field-site heterogeneity. Results were judged based on how well the simulated transport matched observed transport through the tank. Despite explicit numerical representation of the heterogeneity, predictions using the laboratory-measured values under-estimated the mean arrival time by as much as 35%. The significance of differences between simulated and observed mean arrival time was investigated by comparing variability of transport predictions using the different measurement methods to that produced by 150 realizations of the heterogeneous distribution. Results indicate that the variations in measured hydraulic conductivity were more important to transport than variations between realizations of the heterogeneous distribution of hydraulic conductivity.

Typically, the reported mean and variance of a heterogeneous distribution represent the magnitude and variability of sedimentary structures but do not represent the variations that occur for either repeated measurements or use of alternate measurement methods on a single sedimentary structure. Even under the ideal conditions of the reported experiments the variability of transport predictions, as a function of the hydraulic conductivity measurement methods, was significant compared with that produced between realizations of a heterogeneous distribution of hydraulic conductivity. The results show that the variability in measured values of hydraulic conductivity contributes as much or more to the uncertainty in transport simulations as the random variations between realizations of the heterogeneous distribution. This suggests that the statistical parameters summarizing a heterogeneous distribution should be reported with confidence intervals that reflect the variability of hydraulic-conductivity measurements.

- Knowing K for sands, perfect distribution of sands, still didn't get model to work.

A MODEL FOR WATER FLOW AND PARTICLE TRANSPORT IN FRACTURED MEDIA

Doohyun Lim, Joonhong Ahn, and Paul L. Chambré
Department of Nuclear Engineering, University of California
Berkeley, CA 94720-1730

The effects of the heterogeneity in the fractured near-field rock (NFR) on the particle residence time are investigated for a water-saturated repository for high-level radioactive wastes (HLW). A model is developed to analyze the water flow through the NFR around one waste canister by assuming time-independent, incompressible, Darcy's flow. Water-flowing regions in the NFR are transformed into a heterogeneous continuum by applying local homogenization. The Kozeny-Carman equation is used to obtain the space-dependent permeability including a tortuosity correction. If fractures are distributed isotropically, local (scalar) tortuosity distributes with a median of 0.5. The tortuosity is incorporated also into the molecular diffusivity. The residence times of 10^4 particles are obtained by observing the detailed tracks of each particle. A wide distribution ($10^{-3} \sim 10^4$ years) of the residence time is observed due to extremely small values of tortuosity ($\sim 10^{-8}$) in a limited region of the water-flowing region. The water-stagnant region (i.e. non-FBC region) is important for the residence time determination.

OPTIMAL MODEL STRUCTURES
IN GROUNDWATER SYSTEM IDEN TIFICATION

Aristotelis Mantoglou
National Technical University of Athens, Greece
Laboratory of Reclamation Works and Water Resources Management
Iroon Politechneiou 9, Zografos, 15780 Greece
e-mail: mantog@central.ntua.gr

For wise management of groundwater systems we need good and reliable models. Often the available measurements regarding the system response are limited and contaminated by noise. A model calibrated based on such data may exhibit a good calibration performance but possibly a poor prediction (generalization) performance when used for predicting new information not used in the course of calibration. A model with too few parameters may not have enough flexibility to track the real system dynamics. A model with too many parameters on the other hand may possibly learn insignificant details and the errors included in the measurements rather than the essential system dynamics. Therefore a good model of the system should be neither too simple nor too complex and is anticipated that depending on the real system complexity and the quality of measurements there exists a model structure with optimal generalization characteristics. The objective is to determine such optimal model structure and its dependence on the system complexity and the quality of measurements.

A two-dimensional aquifer is selected for demonstration. It is assumed that the aquifer transmissivity is a realization of a two-dimensional random field. By varying the random field pa-rameters (such as the correlation length) it is possible to generate multiple realizations of aquifers of various characteristics and complexities and thus investigate the dependence of the optimal model structure on aquifer complexity and the quality of measurements. The direct problem is solved using finite differences and the head measurements, contaminated with noise, are recorded at specific locations. It is assumed that there is no prior information or direct measurements of transmissivity available; therefore the estimation process relies solely on head measurements. The number of pa-rameters is reduced using zonation with fixed zone geometries for all realizations. Thus each model structure is completely characterized by the number of zones and the objective becomes to deter-mine the number of zones so that the model has good calibration as well as prediction (generaliza-tion) performance.

For each simulation run several model structures with various numbers of zones are cali-brated by minimizing the mean squared calibration error bet-ween the measurements and the model predictions. In order to evaluate the model prediction performance (generalization) a new prediction error crite-rion that specifies how well the model predicts the true heads in the whole extend of the aquifer is defined. A number of simulations were performed for various system complexities (quantified by the correlation ratios R/L of the underlying random fields of ln$T$) and qualities of measurements (quantified by the standard deviation of the measurement error σ_m), in order to in-vestigate the dependence of the calibration and prediction errors on the model structure (quantified by the number of zones).

Figure 1 plots the calibration error as a function of the number of zones for 20 realizations for R/L =0.1 and σ_m=0.2m. The thick line represents the mean for the 20 realizations. It is ob-served that the calibration error generally decreases as the number of zones increases. Figure 2 plots the prediction error for the same realizations and shows that the prediction error is not decreasing monotonically but there is a minimum prediction error for 5-8 zones, i.e. a model with 5-8 zones has optimum prediction (generalization) performance despite the better calibration performance of models with more parameters. Therefore, in this case, a model with 5-8 parameters is the opti-mal model structure since it has better generalization properties.

The dependence of the optimal model structure on the system complexity is investigated in Figure 3 by varying the correlation ratios R/L. For small correlation lengths (R/L=0.01-0.02), the optimal model is a single-zone model and the estimated homogeneous hydraulic conductivity is approxima-tely equal to the geometric mean. This result is anticipated from stationary stochastic theories where one effective parameter (the geometric mean) is used to describe the whole aquifer. For larger correlation lengths however, (R/L=0.1-1), the optimal model structure has more zones (5 and 8 respectively). This is because in this case the system exhibits a more complex behaviour with large-scale features that cannot be adequately described with a simple uniform parameter model.

Figure 4 examines the dependence of the generalization error on the meas-

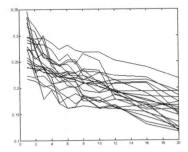

Figure 1. Calibration error as a function of the number of zones for 20 realizations.

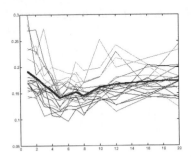

Figure 2. Prediction error as a function of the number of zones for 20 realizations.

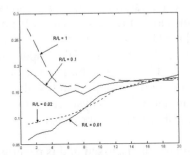

Figure 3. Mean head prediction error as a function of the number of zones for various correlation ratios R/L for fixed measurement error $\sigma_m=0.2m$.

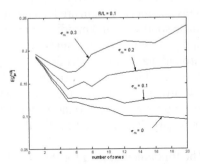

Figure 4. Dependence of mean prediction error on the measurement error σ_m, for fixed R/L=0.1.

urement error. As the measurement error increases the optimal model becomes simpler with fewer parameters. This result is intuitively anticipated since the reduced flexibility of a model with fewer parameters pro-tects it from learning the errors that are present in the measurements.

A MODEL COUPLING DISCRETE AND CONTINUUM FRACTURE DOMAINS FOR GROUNDWATER FLOW IN FRACTURED MEDIA

Hongtao Wang[1], Enzhi Wang[2] and Fusheng Zhou[2]

[1] Dept of Environmental Science & Engineering, Tsinghua University, Beijing, 100084, China
[2] School of Civil and Hydraulic Engineering, Tsinghua University, Beijing, 100084, China

China has been constructing many giant high-head hydroelectric power stations and most of them are located in the "V" shape valleys in the bedrock areas in the southwest and middle south regions, such as Xiaowan Arch Dam (286 m high), Goupitan Arch Dam (236 m high), Three Gorges Dam (175m high) etc. Ground water flow analysis in such projects has become one of the important issues for the safety construction and operation of the projects for two reasons: (1) Ground water flow may have a great impact on the slope stability after a reservoir starts to impound water, and (2) Ground water analysis can provide necessary data required for the designing of leakage control measures.

The fundamental idea for the two domain approach discussed in this paper is to use the distinct medium method to describe fluid flow in the dominant fracture system and to use the continuum medium method in the network fracture system. It is assumed that the continuum medium fills the entire studied domain while the distinct medium is embedded in the continuum medium domain, according to the locations and orientations of the dominant fractures. This method has some distinctive features over the traditional ones[1-2]. It simulates one-by-one the fluid flow of dominant fractures that are of the major water transport conduits. Meanwhile, it avoids calculating the fluid flow of individual network fractures that are numerous but treats them as a whole. In this way, the approach can not only describe the individual contribution of dominant fractures in the transport of ground water but can also be applied to a large-sized simulation domain.

If dominant fractures inside are not considered, the rock mass can be regarded as a continuum medium domain (CMD), in which the ground water flow can be described by

$$\mu_{sm} \frac{\partial h}{\partial t} = \text{div}(K_m \text{grad} h) + W_m \qquad (1)$$

$$(x, y, z) \in D_m, \quad t > 0$$

where subscript m and f represent the matrix and fracture domain respectively; $h(x,y,z,t)$ is hydraulic head in the continuum medium domain; μ_{sm} is specific storativity; W_m is source/sink term; K_m is hydraulic conductivity; Dm is continuum domain. The equation can be solved with proper initial and boundary conditions. The coupling conditions to the fracture domain is $h(x,y,z,t)|_{(x,y,z) \in Dfi} = H_i(x,y,z,t)$, $i=1,2...,N_f$ in which $H_i(x,y,z,t)$ is hydraulic head in fracture i; N_f is number of dominant fractures; D_{fi} is domain of fracture i.

Dominant fractures are embedded in the CMD, according to their locations and orientations. Suppose that the fluid flow along a dominant fracture plane is two dimensional in a local coordinate owned by that fracture. Fractures exchange water with one another through intersected slits between them and exchange water with the continuum medium domain through fracture walls.

In a local coordinate system of dominant fracture i, the differential equation for the fluid flow along the fracture plane in distinct medium domain (DMD) is

$$\mu_{fi}^* \frac{\partial H_i}{\partial t} = \text{div}(T_{fi} \text{grad} H_i) + W_{fi} + F_i \qquad (2)$$

$$(x, y) \in D_{fi}, \quad t > 0$$

where μ_{fi}^* is coefficient of storage; T_{fi} is fracture transmissibility: $T_{fi}=K_{fi}b_i$, K_{fi} is fracture hydraulic conductivity; b_i is fracture hydraulic opening; W_{fi} is source/sink item; F_i is coupling item with CMD, defined as the flow flux from the continuum to fracture i in a unit fracture area: $F_i=K_{m1}dh/dn_1+K_{m2}dh/dn_2$, in which Km_1, Km_2 and n_1, n_2 are respectively the hydraulic conductivity and outer normal vector of the two fracture walls.

The paper discussed also the sources and sinks in reservoir regions, including pipe drainage systems, pumping/ injection wells, infiltration recharge either from rainfall or from discharge atomization and evaporation. The coupled model is solved by the finite element method (FEM) with an iterative approximation approach. A test problem is used to compare the calculation results of the model in this paper with the Theis well flow solution. Calculation shows that the numerical results fit the analytical solutions well.

Wujiang Goupitan Hydroelectric Power Station is located in Guizhou province, China. Its hyperbola arch dam is 536.7 m long, 231 m high, and 639 m at top elevation. The power station can generate the electricity of some 8.9~9.2 billion KW.h. The purpose of study is to simulate the ground water flow under the flood discharge conditions for leakage prevention design and slope stability analysis. Principle lithology is Permian carbonate rocks, which strike 30∞~45∞, perpendicular to the direction of Wujiang River valley, and dip 45∞~55∞ to northwest. Major geological structures incorporate stratum faults, bedding faults, joints and fractures. Below the carbonate rock formations are shale and sandstone (see Fig. 1).

The calculation domain is divided into two parts from the impervious screen. The upstream part is simplified as a pure continuum medium because it is unnecessary to concern this part in detail, and the downstream part as a coupling discrete and continuum medium. Big faults identified by field exploration are considered as dominant fractures. The hydraulic conductivity values are determined primarily by field water injection tests.

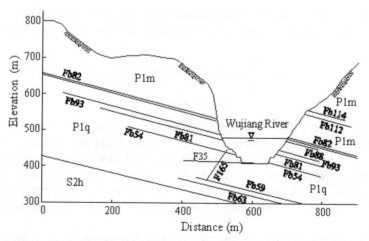

Fig. 1. Profile of geology. P_{2w}, P_{1m}, P_{1q}: carbonate rocks; P_{2s}, P_{1sh}: shale; Imp scr: impervious screen.

The FEM discretization is such: for CMD, 4599 nodes and 4034 elements are divided based on the properties of rocks and their relationship with fractures; for DMD, 1560 nodes and 1395 elements are divided based on the fracture sizes and their intersection relationship.

Three cases of ground water flow are simulated: 1) reservoir water level Z_u=630 m, stilling basin water level Z_d=463.76 m, no rainfall; 2) Z_u=630 m, Z_d=480 m, 1% of flood frequency with rainfall recharge from flood discharge; 3) Z_u=632.17 m, Z_d=483.23 m, 0.2% of flood frequency with rainfall recharge from flood discharge. As an example, here we will just briefly discuss the results of case 2).

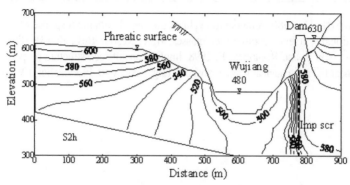

Fig. 2. Profile contours of simulated hydraulic head at the end of flood discharge, in meter.

Steady state ground water flow field calculated for case 1) is used as the initial condition for case 2). The profile head contour calculated at the end of the 3 days flood discharge for case 2) is shown in Fig. 2. After flood discharge through the dam, the recharge to ground water from flood discharge rainfall causes a rapid rise of ground water level along dominant fractures on both sides of the stilling basin. The responses of rock matrixes are relatively slow. They get recharge both from direct infiltration of discharge rainfall and from the dominant fractures. This phenomenon indicates that the fracture domain has a quick response to the change of external conditions while the response of rock matrixes is stagnant. Since many bedding faults pass almost perpendicularly through Wujiang River, which connects hydraulically the rock mass and the River, ground water discharges quickly to Wujiang River along the faults while rising. After flood discharge stops, the fractures head decreases quickly because their quick flow to Wujiang River. Head of fractures becomes lower than the matrix head gradually from the River to the mountains at both sides. Ground water reaches its steady state flow 4-5 months after flood discharge stops.

In summary, theoretical application and practical case study indicate that the approach presented in this paper is an effective and practical method for the fluid flow calculation in a fractured rock mass in reservoir regions.

Key words: mathematical model, dominant fractures, network fractures, groundwater flow, computer simulation, hydroelectric engineering

REFERENCES

[1] ELSWORTH, D., 1986. A model to evaluate transient hydraulic response of three dimensional sparsely fractured rock masses. Water Resour. Res., 22(13), 1809-1819.
[2] ANDERSSON, J. and ROBINSON, P., 1998. Implications of rock structure on performance in near field of a nuclear waste repository. Eng. Geol., v 49, Elsevier Sci B.V.,pp. 195-200.

CHARACTERIZING LITHOFACIES FROM GEOPHYSICAL DATA USING THE BAYESIAN MODEL COUPLED WITH A FUZZY NEURAL NETWORK

Jinsong Chen and Yoram Rubin
Department of Civil and Environmental Engineering
University of California at Berkeley

A Bayesian model coupled with a fuzzy neural network (BFNN) is developed to alleviate the difficulty of using geophysical data in lithofacies estimation when cross correlation between lithofacies and geophysical attributes is nonlinear. The prior estimate is inferred from borehole lithofacies measurements using indicator kriging based on spatial correlation, and the posterior estimate is obtained from updating of the prior using the geophysical data. The novelty of the study lies in the use of a fuzzy neural network for the inference of likelihood function. This allows incorporating spatial correlation as well as a nonlinear cross correlation into lithofacies estimation. The effectiveness of the BFNN is demonstrated using synthetic data generated from measurements at the Lawrence Livemore National Laboratory (LLNL) site.

INTRODUCTION

Heterogeneity of lithofacies has an important effect on the determination of hydrogeological parameters. Since traditional methods for characterizing lithofacies rely on expensive and invasive lithofacies core measurements, many efforts have been made to integrate geophysical data into lithofacies estimation. The crucial part of the integration is to connect geophysical attributes to lithofacies through a possibly complex cross correlation.

Several models have been used to estimate lithofacies from lithofacies measurements and geophysical data, such as indicator kriging, indicator cokriging, and neural networks or fuzzy neural networks. Indicator kriging uses only borehole lithofacies measurements, whereas neural networks or fuzzy neural networks (FNN) use only geophysical information. Indicator cokriging combines lithofacies measurements with geophysical data, but it is limited when cross correlation between lithofacies and geophysical attributes is highly nonlinear. This study develops an innovative model to integrate geophysical data into lithofacies estimation using spatial correlation of lithofacies as well as a nonlinear cross correlation between lithofacies and geophysical attributes.

BAYESIAN MODEL

The developed model integrates geophysical data into lithofacies estimation using a Bayesian framework. Let $Z(x)$ be a categorical random variable at location x defined on $K=\{1,2...,d\}$, where d is the total number of lithofacies. Let $Z(x_i)$ be a lithofacies measurement at location $x_i, i \in \{1,2,...,n\}$, and $g_1(x)$ and $g_2(x)$ be the geophysical data at location . Consider the Markov assumption, the Bayesian model is given by

$$f_{post}(Z(x) = k) = CL(Z(x) = k \mid g_1(x), g_2(x)) f_{prior}(Z(x) = k),$$

where C is a normalizing constant and $L(\cdot)$ is a likelihood function. $f_{prior}(Z(x)=k)$ is the prior probability estimated from lithofacies measurements using indicator kriging, and $f_{post}(Z(x)=k)$ is the posterior probability obtained from updating of the prior using collocated geophysical data through the likelihood function.

The key to using this model is to infer the likelihood function using a fuzzy neural network with several inference rules, which is similar to the one given by Takagi and Sugeno [1985]. The input of the system is the geophysical data, and the output is the log likelihood with the normalizing constant. All the rules will be applied to a given input, and the final result is a combination of the outputs from each rule. The learning of the fuzzy neural network includes determining the number of inference rules using the fuzzy cluster analysis method and estimating the parameters associated with those rules using a hybrid algorithm combining the least squares estimation and the Levenberg-Marquart method.

CASE STUDY

This case study demonstrates the efficiency of the BFNN in lithofacies estimation using synthetic data generated from measurements at the LLNL site by comparing it with indicator kriging, indicator cokriging and the fuzzy neural network without using lithofacies measurements (FNN). We generate a lithofacies field with sand and silt from borehole lithofacies measurements using the sequential indicator simulation (SIS), a gamma-ray shaliness field conditioned to the previously generated collocated lithofacies and borehole gamma-ray shaliness using the sequential Gaussian simulation (SGS), and a resistivity field conditioned to the collocated lithofacies and gamma-ray shaliness using the parameters given by Ezzedine et al. [1999].

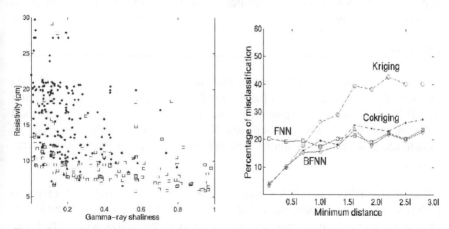

Figure 1: (a) Cross-plot based on data at the boreholes (dots—sand and squares—silt). (b) Model comparison in terms of misclassification, where I=10m is the integral length of sand at the LLNL site. The horizontal coordinate is the minimum distance of a testing location from the boreholes.

The generated lithofacies and geophysical data will be used to evaluate performances of each model. We first randomly select eight columns from each field to mimic boreholes in a real situation and then use the data at those boreholes to train each model. The trained models are used to estimate lithofacies at any testing location, and the total numbers of misclassification are counted according to the minimum distances of testing locations from the boreholes for each model. Figure 1(a) shows cross correlation between gamma-ray shaliness and electrical resistivity according to the data at the boreholes, and it is nonlinear and non-unique. Figure 1(b) compares performances of indicator kriging, indicator cokriging, FNN and the BFNN in terms of percentages of misclassification. It is evident that spatial correlation is important as the testing location is in the short vicinity of the boreholes and cross correlation is important as the testing location is in the region far away from the boreholes. Otherwise, both spatial correlation and cross correlation are important for lithofacies estimation.

The effects of nonlinearity of cross correlation between lithofacies and geophysical attributes on the performances of the BFNN and indicator cokriging were also demonstrated using a similar method. Results show that when there are two lithofacies, the BFNN and indicator cokriging have similar performances; however, the difference between BFNN and indicator cokriging becomes more obvious as the number of lithofacies or nonlinearity of cross correlation increases.

DISCUSSION

The BFNN is the most effective model for incorporating geophysical data into lithofacies estimation compared to indicator kriging, indicator cokriging and FNN in terms of the previous case study. This is because the method takes advantages of the Bayesian model for combining different types of information and the fuzzy neural network for fitting a nonlinear cross correlation.

Although the BFNN is oriented toward the LLNL project where we have two different geophysical attributes that have been shown most informative to lithofacies estimation, it can be directly used to the cases where there are more than two geophysical data.

The limitation of the fuzzy neural network lies in the assumption that each variable is approximately parallel or perpendicular to axes, which is valid for many applications. In other cases, we need either rotate coordinates using the principal component analysis or develop a more general neural network to estimate likelihood functions.

ACKNOWLEDGEMENT

This study was support by NSF Grant EAR-9628306.

REFERENCES

EZZEDINE, SOUHEIL, YORAM RUBIN and JINSONG CHEN (1999), Hydrological-geophysical Bayesian method for subsurface site characterization: theory and application to the LLNL superfund site. Water Resources Research, 35(9).

TAKAGI, TOMOHIRO and MICHIO SUGENO (1985), Fuzzy identification of systems and its applications to modeling and control. IEEE Transaction on Systems, Man, and Cybernetics, SMC-15(1), 1985.

GIS-BASED INTEGRATION, COMPARISON AND SPATIAL ANALYSIS OF MULTIPLE GEODATA SOURCES: A KEY ISSUE FOR BETTER CHARACTERIZATION OF DEEP GROUND WATER AQUIFERS

Gernot Paulus

School of Geoinformation, Carinthia Tech Institute, Europastr. 4,
A-9524 Villach, Austria. E-mail: g.paulus@cti.ac.at

Knowledge about the 3D spatial distribution of faults at basin scale is a key issue to build up a reliable conceptual hydrogeological model and important for hydrogeological investigations, hydrocarbon migration studies or site investigations for radioactive waste disposals.

Digital Terrain Models (DTM) are broadly used to enhance visualization of the landscape. Little research is undertaken to develop analytical models for interpreting these data sets, partly because of the difficulties obtaining ground data with which to validate the model outputs. Analysis of a Digital Terrain model (DTM) is an appropriate tool for detecting superficially fault traces. By combining 2.5 D DTM data and 2D subsurface fault data, a qualitative 3D information set for conceptual hydrogeological modeling of fluid flow can be generated. It was possible to determine locally information about the duration of fault activity by using this technique. Another goal was the detection of potential vertical fault-related hydraulic windows where an aquifer is connected by a fault to the surface. Depending on the hydraulic properties and the geometric architecture of a fault, such windows may act as possible recharge zones for deep groundwater aquifers in a sedimentary basin. The knowledge about the spatial distribution of any fault-related hydraulic windows is important information for building better conceptual hydrogeological models. Furthermore, first results from the Molasse basin indicate that it is possible to map traces of subsurface strike-slip faults by analyzing a DTM. These faults have a high horizontal and low vertical displacement and can conventionally only be detected by expensive 3D seismic techniques.

A DTM was used for a topographic quality check of existing satellite lineaments. This is important especially in areas with high vegetation cover like the Molasse basin. Topographic lineaments mapped by DTM analysis have been compared to published LANDSAT satellite lineament data. Results from the Molasse basin suggest a strong need for a re-evaluation of the existing LANDSAT satellite lineament data for the study area because of the nearly overall missing spatial correlation between topographic lineaments and existing satellite lineaments.

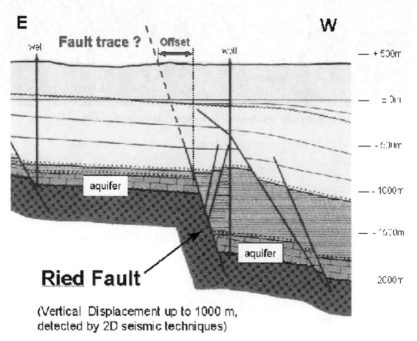

Fig. 1: Can major subsurface faults be traced at the topographic surface? The expected offset at the surface between corresponding fault traces depends on the fault geometry. E-W cross section Ried fault. All published faults terminates subsurface within the basin. (after Wessely et.al, 1993).

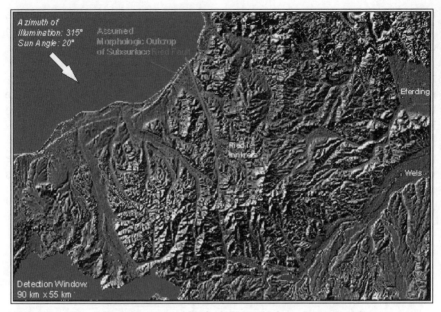

Fig. 2: Principle of detecting topographic lineaments, Molasse Basin, Austria.

3-D GROUNDWATER FLOW MODELING FOR THE OAK RIDGE RESERVATION (ORR): FINITE-VOLUME METHOD ON AN UNSTRUCTURED GRID SYSTEM

Jian Luo, Michael N. Fienen and Peter K. Kitanidis
Department of Civil & Environmental Engineering, Stanford University, CA94305

In the design of in-situ bioremediation schemes, the flow near injection-extraction well pairs must be well understood. Finite-volume methods (FVM) have two main advantages in modeling flow. First, they ensure mass conservation. Second, finite-volume methods do not require a coordinate transformation in order to be applied on irregular meshes. Most FVM schemes for unstructured grids are either two-dimensional or assume horizontal layers. Those that assume horizontal layers may be in serious error if the dipping is more than 10 degrees.

We are dealing with the flow near wells in a formation where the bedding is 45 degrees. The study site is located in the Natural and Accelerated Bioremediation Research (NABIR) Field Research Center (FRC) at the Oak Ridge Reservation (ORR) in the Appalachian Valley and Ridge geomorphic province of eastern Tennessee, U.S.A.

We describe a computationally efficient 3-dimensional finite-volume model for groundwater flow in a heterogeneous layered anisotropic porous medium with dipping beds. This algorithm is developed applying the cell-centered finite volume method on an unstructured triangular grid system with fully implicit time discretization. The hydraulic conductivity is isotropic on a plane parallel to the layers, while the third principal axis, the one with the lowest value, is normal to the layers. The domain is discretized into parallel dipping layers and each layer is discretized into triangles, the same at every level. The triangles are chosen using Delaunay triangulation techniques. The use of triangles and adaptive technique makes this scheme more flexible and able to accurately represent a domain with wells and other small- or large-scale features. In this scheme the total flux crossing each interface between neighboring control volume is approximated by a one-point integration rule based on the specific discharge at the midpoint. The wells are vertical. At wells, realistic boundary conditions are used. Hydraulic conductivities are derived from well tests using inverse methods. We show the flow regime near wells and compare with the results from a numerical model that assumes horizontal flow.

ISOTOPE CHARACTERISTICS OF GROUNDWATERS IN THE PINGTUNG PLAIN, SOUTHERN TAIWAN

Chung-Ho Wang[1], Ching-Huei Kuo[1], Tsung-Ren Peng[2], Wen-Fu Chen[3], Tsung-Kwei Liu4 and Chung-Jung Chiang[5]

[1] *Institute of Earth Sciences, Academia Sinica, Taiwan*
[2] *Department of Soil and Environmental Sciences, National Chung Hsing University, Taiwan*
[3] *Center of Groundwater Development and Conservation, Taiwan Sugar Corporation, Ministry of Economic Affairs, Taiwan*
[4] *Department of Geological Sciences, National Taiwan University, Taiwan*
[5] *Central Geological Survey, Ministry of Economic Affairs, Taiwan*

The isotope compositions (δD, $\delta^{18}O$, T, ^{14}C) of groundwater have been measured for samples collected from monitoring wells in the Pingtung Plain, one of the most important groundwater regions in southern Taiwan. Based on recent proposed hydrogeology framework, isotope characteristics are reported for unconfined and confined aquifers. The stable hydrogen and oxygen isotopic compositions of groundwater samples show distinct signals for unconfined and confined aquifers, indicating that they are recharged from different altitudes. The tritium contents of unconfined groundwaters suggest an active exchange with surface waters, whereas the confined one exhibits very low values. The ^{14}C compositions of tritium-free confined groundwaters reflect an age span from modern to late Pleistocene period. Due to inappropriate overdraft of groundwaters in the coastal zone since 1980, seawater encroachment has been a serious problem and has caused a substantial loss of local freshwater resources. Hydrogen and oxygen isotope compositions from monitoring wells surrounding the seawater salinization zone show an alarming enrichment trend during recent analyses when compared with previous values, implying active expansion of the seawater intrusion zone. The isotope signals collected thus far provide a valuable field database and lay solid groundwork for further modeling.

INTRODUCTION

The Pingtung Plain covers a rectangular area of 1210 km^2 located in southwestern Taiwan. The plain consists of unconsolidated sediments of late Pleistocene and Holocene periods. It is bounded by low hills of Quaternary sediments on the north and west, by the Tertiary Central Mountain Range on the east, and by the Taiwan Strait on the south. Since 1992, the Groundwater Monitoring Program in Taiwan has established an important hydrogeological database in the studied area using a network of 51 evenly distributed stations, including 127 monitoring wells drilled to depths ranging from 10 to 260 m. The proximal, mid and distal sections of the plain are distinguished for their alluvial-fan nature according to the subsurface lithology and hydraulic conductivity. Generally, there is one major aquitard and two aquifers (upper unconfined and lower confined) in the central mid- and southern distal fans of the Pingtung Plain. In this report, we present environmental isotope characteristics (δD, $\delta^{18}O$, T, ^{14}C) for the groundwaters of various aquifer sections in the Pingtung Plain. These isotope signals not only reveal some unique features for the recharge and flow pattern of the groundwaters, but also provide a primary basis for further modeling work in the studied area.

DATA AND METHODS

More than of 200 groundwater samples were collected from stations of Groundwater Monitoring Program in the Pingtung Plain between 1995 and 2000 for stable isotope analyses. Water samples were prepared and analyzed for hydrogen and oxygen isotope compositions at the Institute of Earth Sciences, Academia Sinica according to well-established methods and expressed as per mill (‰) notation relative to SMOW standards. Tritium and radiocarbon data are retrieved from previous studies.

RESULTS AND DISCUSSION

The foothill terrains along the Central Range are the main and primary recharge source area for nine groundwater regions in Taiwan. For the Pingtung Plain, the Quaternary low hills in the north and west are also potential source regions for groundwater recharging. Isotope compositions of unconfined groundwaters with modern tritium values (TU = 2.8) show that for the north and northeastern area, the modern recharge gives the most depleted isotope values. The input isotope values get enriched progressively from north toward south along both the eastern (from -10.2‰ to -8.6‰) and western foothills (from -10.2‰ to -7.9‰). This feature is consistent with the geomorphological setting of the Pingtung Plain, where the altitudes lessen from north toward south, and the eastern mountain range lies at a relatively higher altitude than that of western hills.

The isotope signals along a transect from the eastern hilly proximal to the western coastal distal regions demonstrate that the groundwater flow lines have two distinctive paths. One flow route is through the upper unconfined layer with $\delta^{18}O$ values ranging from -8.4‰ to -7.0‰. The other is through the lower confined aquifer with $\delta^{18}O$ values ranging from -9.0‰ to -9.9‰, significantly depleted relative to the upper unconfined groundwaters. The discrepancy suggests that groundwaters of the upper unconfined aquifer have been derived from a relatively lower altitude and mixed with surface waters along its flow course. On the other hand, in the lower confined aquifer the more depleted isotope values, indicate recharge from a higher altitude and no mixing with surface waters, consistent with the existence of a thick aquitard.

For the benefit of further modeling work, the mean isotope values (δD, $\delta^{18}O$, ^{14}C and tritium) of groundwaters in various aquifers from proximal to distal regions in the Pingtung Plain are grouped and listed accordingly in Table 1, as well as the coastal area which has been encroached by seawater since 1980. Generally, the hydrogen and oxygen isotopes in the unconfined aquifers show relatively enriched values relative to those in the confined ones. The main sections of the mid- and distal regions in the Pingtung Plain are consistent with this general pattern, having mean hydrogen and oxygen isotope values that differ greatly between groundwaters of the unconfined (δD: -50‰ ~ -59‰; $\delta^{18}O$: -7.8‰ ~ -8.7‰) and confined (δD: -62‰; $\delta^{18}O$: -9.3‰) aquifers, indicating that the recharging sources and flow paths of these two groundwaters are indeed quite different. However, there is virtually no deviation between isotope values for groundwaters of unconfined and confined aquifers (δD: -51‰; $\delta^{18}O$: -7.8‰) in the west section, suggesting a common origin of groundwater recharge.

The mean radiocarbon values exhibit a general decreasing pattern along the flow course of the confined groundwaters (PMC: 74%~15%). The lowest value is found in the west section of the distal region and expresses a reduction of more than two half lives to the modern mean value (=79%), implying an age of late Pleistocene for the distal deep groundwaters. The tritium (as TU) values display a trend similar to the radiocarbon data. High values are detected for unconfined groundwaters (3.2~2.9), except the west section of the distal region (2.0~0.7), reflecting the active exchange with surface waters during intensive agriculture irrigation and evaporation effect. The deep confined groundwaters bear relative low values (2.0~0.1) as expected.

Due to inadequate over drafting of the groundwaters in the Pingtung Plain, seawater has encroached the aquifers through outcrops along the offshore canyon of the Kaoping Chi river at an estimated rate of 400-500 m/year since 1980. The net loss of freshwater resource due to this groundwater salinization is estimated to exceed $3x10^9$ M^3. Though many measures have been proposed and carried out to alleviate the salinization problem of the coastal groundwaters, the seawater intrusion remains a pressing and developing problem. Compared with the values of December 1998, our two most recent analyzed isotope compositions of five groundwater samples that proximate the seawater intrusion area show a consistent enrichment trend. This observation certainly raises a warning signal and heralds the active inland expansion of seawater through the aquifers. Thus, in addition to suitable remediable actions, a thorough and close isotope monitoring programs should be initiated for these wells to oversee future migration of seawater into the coastal Pingtung Plain.

		δD	$\delta^{18}O$	PMC	TU
Proximal	Upper (<150m)	-59	-8,7	72	2,9
	Lower (>150m)	-62	-9,3	22	0,7
Middle (Main)	Unconfined	-56	-8,3	69	3,2
	Confined	-62	-9,2	44	2,0
Distal (Main)	Unconfined	-50	-7,8	95	2,9
	Aquitard	-54	-8,0	46	0,9
	Confined	-62	-9,3	32	0,1
Middle (West)	Unconfined	-52	-7,9	81	2,0
	Confined	-51	-7,8	74	0,1
Distal (West)	Unconfined	-50	-7,6	52	0,7
	Confined	-51	-7,7	15	0,1
Seawater Intursion area		-19	-3,0	34	0,5

Table 1. Isotope mean values of groundwaters in the Pingtung Plain.

WATER MOVEMENT IN THE ZONE OF INTERACTION BETWEEN GROUNDWATER AND THE COLUMBIA RIVER, HANFORD SITE, WASHINGTON

R. E. Peterson[1] and M. P. Connelly[2]

[1] *Battelle-PNNL, P.O. Box 999, Mail Stop K6-96, Richland, WA 99352;*
(509) 373-9020; robert.peterson@pnl.gov
[2] *HydroGeoLogic, Inc., 1201 Jadwin Ave., Suite 204, Richland, WA 99352;*
(509) 943-1711; mconnelly@hgl.com

INTRODUCTION

The groundwater flow system beneath the Hanford Site represents the primary environmental pathway for contaminant movement away from source areas. This path-way ultimately discharges into the Columbia River. Information developed for the Hanford Site suggests that physical processes are the predominant influence on contami-nant concentrations and fluxes at locations of discharge into the free-flowing stream of the river. Physical processes include (a) layering and mixing of groundwater and river water, which infiltrates the banks and riverbed sediment, and (b) variable hydraulic gradients caused by river stage fluctuations. Flow patterns beneath the shoreline region are influenced by the infiltration of a significant volume of river water during high river stage and up-to complete reversal of hydraulic gradients. The resulting flow patterns have implications for strategies involving environmental monitoring and restoration activities. Because of these implications, investigations have been undertaken to develop a better understanding of the zone of interaction and the various interfaces with the free-flowing stream of the river.*

* Support for this project was provided by the U.S. Department of Energy through the Groundwater/ Vadose Zone Inte-gration Project, Hanford Site, Washington.

Two-Dimensional Flow Simulation

A spatial model of the Hanford Site's 100-H Area was prepared that included land-surface and river-bottom topography, along with the dimensions of sub-surface hydrogeologic units. The uppermost hydrologic unit is comprised of loosely consolidated sands and gravels. These fluvial deposits are heterogeneous with respect to hydraulic properties and can be generally characterized as very transmissive. Immediately below the uppermost unit is a fine-grained sequence that is an aquitard. In the river channel, the bed sediment is primarily well-rounded gravels and cobbles.

The simulation was developed using Pacific Northwest National Laboratory's code "Subsurface Transport Over Multiple Phases" (STOMP). This code solves transient flow and transport problems in the subsurface environment in one, two, or three dimensions using an integral-volume, finite-difference approach. Principal assumptions made for the simulation include: single hydrologic unit; no impediment to flow at the river channel interface; an anisotropy ratio of 1:10 for vertical-to-horizontal hydraulic conductivity; and transmissivity of the underlying aquitard is 0.01 that of the unconfined aquifer. Hydraulic conductivity was set at 107 meters per day and effective porosity at 20%. Hourly water level data for 1998 from the aquifer and adjacent river were used for the simulation.

Model Output

The following param-eters were computed and saved in 1-hour time steps: pressure head, hydraulic head, moisture content, percent saturation, and pore water velocities in the horizontal and vertical directions. The simulation output was animated using the computer program FRAMER™ (Amtec Engineering, Bellevue, Washington). A single time-step frame for May 31, 1998, at 11:00 p.m. is shown in Figure 1 to illustrate the graphical display for the various types of information generated by the model.

Panel 1 is the basic display for water movement patterns. The Columbia River (1a) rises and falls during the simulation. The colored zones (1b) indicate pore water velocities. Small white triangles (1c) indicate instantaneous gradient direction. Red pathlines (1d) show the progression of a water parcel, with red squares at one-week intervals. Values in white boxes are the hydraulic head in meters. Light gray lines show the position of various planes across which water volume flux is calculated. The date and time for each hourly frame is shown in the lower left of the panel (1e). Contours showing partial saturation above the water table are shown as cyan lines (1f). Panel 2 shows the region beneath the shoreline with greater vertical exaggeration than Panel 1. Color coding is used to illustrate elapsed time along the pathlines. Panel 3 is a table that keeps track of cumulative water volume flux across the various flux planes shown in Panel 1. Panel 4 provides elevations for the river level (4a) and the water table (4b) at a monitoring well at the inland boundary for the model. The vertical green line (4c) identifies the current time frame that is displayed in the other three panels.

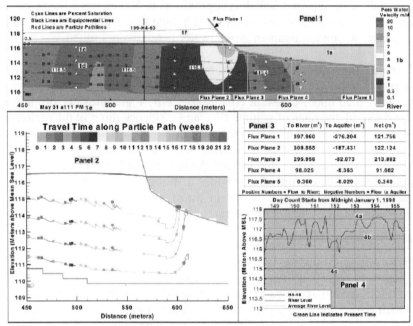

Figure 1. Example Graphical Display of Model Output

RESULTS

Pathlines for groundwater moving toward the river are deflected downward beneath the shoreline by the infiltration of river water during high stage conditions. Infiltrating river water mixes with approaching groundwater in this region, thus reducing the concentration of contaminants that may be present in the groundwater. Evidence from the model that supports this idea includes (a) flow patterns revealed by the com-puted pathlines and (b) the larger net volume flux across a vertical plane located toward the river side of the shoreline (Flux Plane 3), as compared to the flux across a plane located inland of the shoreline (Flux Plane 2).

A second important result pertains to where groundwater dis-charge is focused at the riverbed. Pathlines tend to converge relatively close to the shoreline, i.e., within 30 to 40 meters, and slightly offshore of a region that appears to be constantly influenced by infiltrating river water. Discharge from the unconfined aquifer to the channel is not spread evenly across the Hanford Site half of the channel, which is approximately 500 meters wide at this location. Thus, the areal extent of riverbed habitat that is potentially at risk from exposure to contaminants in groundwater is relatively limited.

Running the model under the assumption of steady-state river stage conditions (a simplifying assumption) produces significantly different movement patterns than under transient conditions. Where groundwater discharges to the riverbed, the rates of volume flux, and residence times in the region beneath the shoreline are all portrayed very differently. These differences could lead to improper design of monitoring networks and subsequent collection of biased monitoring data that are not the best possible for representing actual conditions. The comparison provides a strong argument for including transient river boundary con-ditions in transport models for groundwater and contaminant movement into the river environment.

The model was also run to simulate the movement pattern for two parcels of water whose origin was near the shoreline (in contrast to the inland locations adopted to represent three seasonal periods). This was done to illustrate the path followed by river water that infiltrates the bank during May 1 to July 31, which covers the spring peak runoff and the gradual decline in discharge as the seasonal cycle progresses into summer. The initial motion is downward and slightly inland, reflecting the high river stage at the beginning of the simulation. As the river stage falls after approxi-mately 6 weeks, the parcels stop their downward movement and reverse course back toward the river, with subsequent discharge through the riverbed relatively close to shore. These pathlines represent in a very general way the area within which dilution of ground-water by infiltrating river water is likely to be the greatest during a seasonal cycle.

THE USE OF SUBJECTIVE INFORMATION FOR SELECTING GROUNDWATER REMEDIATION DESIGN IN A HETEROGENEOUS AQUIFER

Minoru Yoneda[1], Shinsuke Morisawa[1], Koji Nakau[2], Yushi Ota[1], Yoriteru Inoue[1] and Masaru Tanaka[3]

[1] Kyoto University, [2] Hokkaido University, [3] Okayama University

INTRODUCTION

Many investigations of layouts of pump-up wells for groundwater remediation have considered uncertainty. Most of these investigations assumed a statistical structure of the ground and pollutant leakage probability but it is often difficult to obtain sufficient information to produce an appropriate stochastic model for such problems. It is sometimes necessary and effective to use subjective information. In this study, factors that require attention when utilizing subjective information using Bayes estimation theory are compiled. Then, a technique is proposed for applying Bayes estimation method using a Monte Carlo simulation to an uncertain aquifer problem. A simulated problem of optimal allocation of pump-up wells for groundwater remediation in which uncertainty of a field is considered using conditional simulation and subjective information is used in the estimation of the period of pollutant leakage is presented to verify the applicability of the proposed technique.

THE USE OF SUBJECTIVE INFORMATION

Probability distribution functions are often estimated from subjective information. However, it has been suggested that human beings commit unexpected errors due to biased estimation of probability in the estimation of subjective probability distribution functions. When estimating probability distribution functions of the break-down of an impervious sheet in a waste disposal site, the following should be considered:

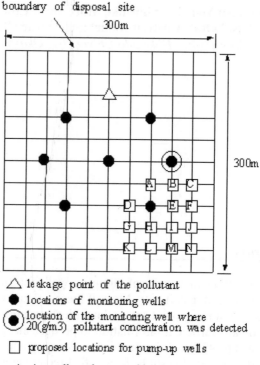

Figure 1. Locations of monitoring wells and proposed locations for pump-up wells.

1) Items of information used for a decision of prior distribution should be investigated and carefully considered before gathering. The execution of a fault tree analysis is recommended.

2) Persons judging prior distribution should have no knowledge of pollutant leakage to avoid the feedback of the posterior distribution.

3) Care is necessary to avoid subjective prejudice when the estimated manner of a prior distribution is changed once the posterior distribution is calculated using the prior distribution.

4) Development of a probability information system for waste disposal site is desirable.

ASSUMED GROUNDWATER REMEDIATION PROBLEM

The following groundwater remediation problem is assumed. A pollutant of 20 g/m3 was detected in one of seven monitoring wells in the landfill site shown in Figure 1, suggesting leakage of the pollutant to the groundwater. The pollutant was not detected in other monitoring wells and an emergency investigation showed that the pollutant did not cross the boundary of the disposal site. It was confirmed from trial pits that the location of the leaking was the white triangle of Figure 1 and that a known amount of the pollutant leaked at one time. The time of leakage, however, could not be determined. Therefore, the use of subjective information to estimate the time of leakage was considered. Groundwater transmissivity had been measured at each well. A decision-maker estimates the transmissivity field and groundwater flow field of the site and formulates a plan to purify the groundwater by pumping followed by purification procedures on the surface. The pump-up wells extract groundwater at a constant rate and the water is not returned underground.

It is planned to install two pump-up wells with an extraction rate of 10 m3/hour. The possible positions are shown as white squares in Figure 1. The decision-maker must select two positions from the fourteen choices. The expectation of the value of the following objective function reflecting expected cost of purification and risk of remediation failure is adopted as a selection criterion. The option that satisfies the expectation of the function (1) minimum is selected.

$$\Phi_j = C_e \times M_j + C_O \times M_j \times T_j + \sum_i C_{ri} \times P_{ij} \qquad (1)$$

where, Φ_j is the objective function of alternative j, C_e is the installation cost, M_j is the number of pump-up wells in alternative j, C_o is the monthly operational cost, T_j is the period of time needed to complete remediation, C_{ri} is the cost of failure i, and P_{ij} is a random variable with a value of 1 when failure i occurs in alternative j and 0 when it does not occur.

It is assumed that the remediation is completed when 98% of the leaked pollutant is collected. Two failure cases are considered. The first is when 2% of the leaked pollutant crosses the boundary of the disposal site. This is case i=1 and a compensation must be paid to local residents. The other is when the purification period exceeds 6 years. This is case i=2 in which remediation by groundwater pump-up will be abandoned and soil will be removed on a massive scale.

ANALYSIS CONDITIONS

The spatial transmissivity distribution is assumed to be lognormal. Spatial ergodicity, isotropy, and stationarity are also assumed, and the covariance of log-transmissivity Y between point i and j is assumed to be as follows:

$$cov(Y_i, Y_j) = \sigma_Y^2 \exp(-r_{ij}/\lambda_Y) \qquad (2)$$

where σ_Y is the standard deviation of log-transmissivity, r_{ij} is the distance between point i and j, λ_Y is a constant called a correlation scale. A transmissivity field with the stochastic structure of equation (2) is created by an unconditional simulation and it is assumed to be the real transmissivity field, which is unknown. Only the values of transmissivity at the points of monitoring wells are given as known values. Other parameters necessary for pollutant movement are assumed to be known. The waste site was filled one year prior to identification of the leakage.

BAYES ESTIMATION USING PRIOR DISTRIBUTION OF LEAKAGE TIME AND MONTE CARLO METHOD

The time of leakage is unknown and hence estimated from subjective information. The subjective probability distribution of leakage time is also the prior distribution of break-down of the impervious sheet. It is assumed that the probability density function of break-down of the impervious sheet is estimated from the experience of the engineers. It is expressed as the following function:

$$f(t) = 0.1 \times \delta(t) + 0.9 \times 0.1 \times \frac{\{1 + \exp(-3)\}\exp(0.1t - 3)}{\{1 + \exp[(0.1t - 3)]\}^2} \qquad (3)$$

where, t is time (years) and $\delta(t)$ is Dirac's delta function.

The posterior distribution of leakage time is calculated using the prior distribution represented in equation (3) and information of the detection of the pollutant at the monitoring well. The optimum alternative is selected according to the evaluation criterion, which is the expectation of equation (1). The result is compared with the result of the case that the uniform distribution function is adopted as a prior distribution assuming that no information pertaining to leakage time is given. The posterior distribution of leakage time and conditional expectation of criterion function were deduced approximately using the conditional simulation and the Monte Carlo method.

RESULTS AND DISCUSSION

Evaluation criteria (expected cost), probability of success of remediation, and the probability of case 1 and 2 failures of the 12 installation alternatives were compared for the case of no prior information and for the case of using subjective information. Although the optmimum alternative is the same for the both cases, that is DH, the expected cost when using subjective information is smaller than that when no prior information is used and the probability of success of remediation when using subjective information is larger than that when using no prior information for all alternatives. This suggests that the use of no prior information may result in the overestimation of the probability of remediation failure. There may be some cases in which the optimum alternative will change when using subjective information because the ranks of DE and BG or CH and GJ are different in the two cases. This means that using the no information prior distribution in case of the existence of effective subjective information may lead to the overestimation of the uncertainty of a problem and the failure to select the optimum alternative. Therefore, using the no information prior distribution is not necessarily desirable for the selection of the optimum alternative. It is thought that subjective information such as experience should be used in the proper frame of Bayes' estimation, when the appropriateness and reliability of the information is high.

PERIODIC RESPONSE OF HETEROGENEOUS, ANISOTROPIC AQUIFER TO PERIODIC FORCING

Hailong Li[1,2] and Qichang Yang[1]

[1] *Institute of Biomathematics, Anshan Normal College, Anshan 114005, Liaoning, P. R. China*
[2] *Department of Earth Sciences, The University of Hong Kong, Hong Kong, P. R. China*
Tel: +852 2857 8278; Fax: +852 2517 6912; e-mail: hlica@hkusua.hku.hk

This paper presents an efficient method analyzing the aquifer response to periodic forcing, based on the use of complex transformation. It is shown that the groundwater flow in a confined aquifer will be periodic if the forcing such as boundary conditions and source terms (e.g., precipitation, recharge etc.) is periodic, even if the aquifer is heterogeneous and anisotropic. Based on this method, the unsteady-state governing differential equation with respect to the unknown, time-dependent hydraulic head subject to time-dependent, periodic boundary conditions is transformed into equivalent steady-state governing differential equation of an introduced unknown complex function of the aquifer's spatial variable(s) subject to time-independent boundary conditions. The time-independent unknown complex function can be treated much more easily than the time-dependent hydraulic head of the aquifer. In case that the aquifer comprises different homogeneous layers less than 4 and has simple boundary geometry, analytical solutions can be derived; in other more complicated cases, a semi-analytical numerical method is proposed. The semi-analytical numerical method includes two steps. First, the derived time-independent equations with respect to the unknown complex function are solved numerically to determine the spatial distribution of the complex function in the aquifer. Then the inverse complex transform is implemented to obtain the hydraulic head at any time and spatial point in the aquifer. To overcome the difficulties in solving the unknown complex functions, the complex differential equation is changed into an equivalent real system comprising two real governing differential equations of two unknown real functions. An effective iterative method is used to solve the system.

SITE CHARACTERIZATION OF A CHROMIUM SOURCE AREA AT THE USCG SUPPORT CENTER, ELIZABETH CITY, NC

Cynthia J. Paul[1], Faruque A. Khan[2] and Robert W. Puls[1]
[1] U.S. Environmental Protection Agency, Office of Research and Development, National Risk Management Research Laboratory, 919 Kerr Lab Drive, Ada, OK 74820.
[2] U.S. Environmental Protection Agency, 1200 Pennsylvania Avenue, N.W., Washington, DC 20460

The chrome source area is located beneath an old electroplating shop at the United States Coast Guard Support Center near Elizabeth City, NC . This electroplating shop was in use for approximately 30 years until 1984 and was the source of discharges of chromic and sulfuric acid wastes though a hole in the concrete floor of the plating shop. These wastes infiltrated into the soils and ground water beneath the shop. Initial site characterization was conducted beneath the plating shop by the National Risk Management Research Laboratory (NRMRL), U.S. EPA, in 1990 and 1991 to determine the extent of soil and aquifer contamination. In general, the highest concentrations of total chromium in the soils beneath the shop were detected in the shallow soils 0.91 - 1.22 m above the water table, with a maximum concentration of 14,500 mg/kg at 0.91 m below land surface (bls). It was initially felt the chromium in the soils would remain immobile and did not present potential risk; therefore, initial remedial efforts focused on treating the diffuse chromium plume which was moving toward the Pasquotank River by installing a permeable reactive barrier (PRB) in 1996.

However, a subsequent rupture of a subsurface fire suppression water line adjacent to the former electroplating shop occurred in 1994. Chromate salts were discovered and identified on the surface rocks within the shop in August 1995. This water main break is suspected to have caused an artificial rise in the water table which likely solubilized some of the chromate in the remaining soils/sediments and redistributed contaminants into the fill material, gravel and ground water below the shop. Historical data for monitoring well MW12 (installed in 1991) inside the plating shop shows Cr(VI) concentrations increased from 1.41 mg/L in June 1993 to 28.0 and 27.0 mg/L in June 1994 and May 1995 respectively (Table 1). Sulfate levels also increased from 86 mg/L to 140 and 120 mg/L during the same time period. Although Cr(VI) levels subsequently decreased, levels still remained approximately three times greater than before the water main break. This suggested a continual release of Cr(VI) into the mobile contaminant plume being treated by the PRB.

	Feb. 1991	April 1992	June 1993	June 1994	May 1995	June 1997	June 1998	June 1998
Cr(VI)	1.60	0.800	1.41	28.0	27.0	4.40	3.00	3.00
SO_4^{2-}	82.0	87.0	86.0	140	121	143	128	128

Table 1. Historical Cr(VI) and SO_4^{2-} ground water concentrations (mg/L) for MW12 inside the plating shop.

In an effort to re-characterize the extent of chromium contamination, soil cores were collected from 35 locations beneath the shop (Figure 1). The cores were cut into six-inch intervals, resulting in more than 500 discrete samples for vertical and horizontal delineation of the chromium. An array of ten moni-

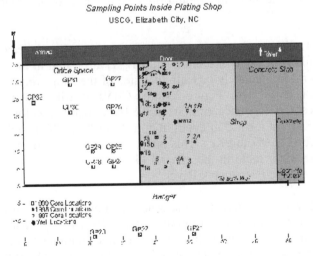

Figure 1. Locations of soil cores and monitoring wells inside the plating shop.

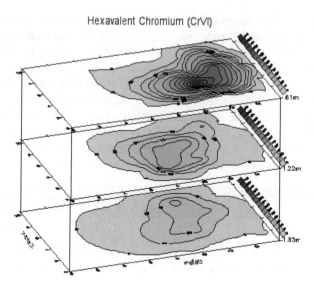

Figure 2. Spatial distribution of Cr(VI) (mg/Kg) in soils and sediments beneath the plating shop.

toring wells (Figure 1) were installed in determine contaminant concentrations and geochemical parameter values in the ground water beneath the shop and provide injection and monitoring wells for a future field-scale pilot study.

Results of selective laboratory extractions on the soils indicate the highest concentrations of total chromium and Cr(VI) are found in the shallow soils (0.5 - 0.6 m) immediately beneath that area of the shop where chromic acid tanks had been located. Figure 2 shows Cr(VI) distribution at three depths. The highest Cr(VI) concentrations at the 0.6 m depth was found in core 15 (625 mg/Kg), at the 1.2 m depth in core 11 (120 mg/Kg), and at the 1.8 m depth in core 12 (87 mg/Kg). This indicates downward movement of Cr(VI) toward the water table in the general direction of groundwater flow to the North toward the Pasquotank River.

Results of this study show that the water main break in 1994 resulted in significant re-distribution of chromium in the soils and sediments beneath the chrome plating shop, providing a continual contaminant source into the plume which is currently being treated by the PRB. While PRB treatment has proven effective for remediating the contaminant plume, its long-term effectiveness is unknown, therefore the chromium source must be treated in order to meet remedial performance objectives. The results of this study have provided chemical speciation and distribution of the total chromium and Cr(VI) as a part of site characterization for the source area. This information was crucial to developing an effective remedial design for the site.

DISCLAIMER

Although the research described in this article has been funded wholly or in part by the U.S. EPA, it has not been subjected to the Agency's peer and administrative review and therefore may not necessarily reflect the views of the Agency; no official endorsement may be inferred

METHODOLOGY FOR MODELLING OF FUTURE HYDROGEOLOGICAL CONDITIONS AT THE SFR NUCLEAR WASTE REPOSITORY

J. G. Holmén[1], M. Stigsson and J-O. Selroos[2]
[1] Golder Associates AB, Stockholm, Sweden.
[2] Swedish nuclear fuel and waste management Co., Stockholm, Sweden.

The Swedish Nuclear Fuel and Waste Management Co. (SKB) operates a repository for low- and intermediate-level nuclear waste, known as SFR (see Figure 1). As part of a renewed safety analysis of the operating repository, the future hydrogeological conditions at SFR have been predicted using ground-water flow models on regional, local and detailed scales. The models are based on the continuum approach, and include a detailed description of the tunnel system in the local and detailed models.

Modelling the groundwater flow at the SFR repository involves the analysis of a large flow system for which the amount of information available regarding the properties of the system varies, both in space and time. By using a chain of models of different sizes and resolutions we have combined models based on different levels of information. By building the models from the local domain outwards we have included the calibration of the local model in the properties of the larger models, and by using an order of simulation from the regional model to the smaller models we have included the regional flow in the smaller models. By giving the regional model effective properties that depend on the equivalent properties of the local model, we have ensured close agreement in flow between the local and regional models.

For the system studied, it is possible to identify three different types of flow media: (i) the rock mass between fracture zones, (ii) the fracture zones and (iii) the tunnels. The following approach was used considering the continuity and the conductivity of the different identified flow media. The rock mass between large fracture zones was defined as continuous, having either: a homogeneous conductivity by use of representative average values of conductivity or a heterogeneous conductivity by use of the stochastic continuum approach. Fracture zones were defined as continuous structures, by use of an implicit formulation regarding the conductivity of the different blocks defining the geometry of the models. The conductivity of the zones was defined as being homogeneous by use of representative average values of conductivity. The tunnels were defined as separate continuous structures by use of an explicit formulation regarding the conductivity of the different blocks defining the geometry of the models.

Conductivity values for the local properties have been derived through a calibration procedure, based on (i) a structural geological interpretation and (ii) measured conductivity values, as well as (iii) measured inflow to the drained tunnels. The local conductivity values were scaled up to an equivalent conductivity by calculating a single conductivity value for the whole of the calibrated local model considering the flow direction (determined by the regional topography) that will dominate after approximately 5000 AD. This value was set as the effective conductivity of the rock mass of the regional scale stochastic continuum model. The varying stochastic conductivity values of the cells of the regional model were based on scaling down from this effective value.

Considering the length of the period studied (several thousands of years), the shore level displacement needs to be included in the models (see Figure 2). It follows that the models must be time-dependent to be able to reproduce the changing flow pattern of the groundwater caused by shore level displacement. In the models, the shore level displacement will be simulated as a lowering of the level of the seawater table, in relation to a fixed reference system. The period studied starts with an initial condition in the year 0 AD (at this time the topography studied was below the sea water table) and continues until steady-state-like conditions are reached for the groundwater system at SFR, which means until about 5 000 AD – 7 000 AD (at this time the topography will be above the sea).

The regional model was used for fully time-dependent simulations, whereas the local model was not. The local model was instead given boundary conditions from the regional model representing different moments in time. For these moments the local model was solved without considering internal storage or release of water. The advantage of this approach is close control of the accuracy of the numerical solution of the local model. The local model contains a complicated three-dimensional system of permeable tunnels and fracture zones, and it is very important to ensure an accurate numerical solution for such a complex system.

The total flow through the local domain in the regional model and the flow through the same domain in the local model are very close. A good match, as in this case, might partly be caused by differences between the models that equal out when comparing the total flow. Nevertheless, the good match between regional and local flow for the presented case is probably a result of the method that we used for estimating the effective conductivity of the regional model (see above). This method will produce a good match considering the correspondence of flow between local and regional models at the boundary of the local model.

Figure 1. The fracture zones of the local structural geological interpretation, and the general layout of the tunnel system at SFR.
TUNNELS: Grey= Access, Red= Silo, Blue= BTF1, Light-Blue= BTF2, Green= BLA, Yellow= BMA
ZONES: Purple= ZH2, Dark. Blue= Z3, Dark-Red= Z6, Yellow= Z8, Green= Z9, Light-Blue= Singö-zone

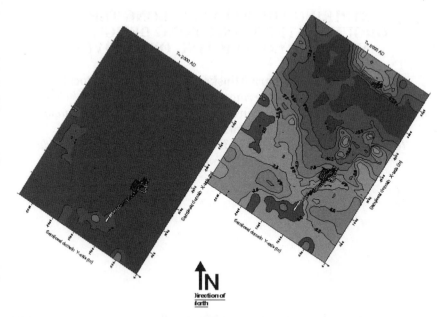

Figure 2. The position of the SFR repository and the topography of its surroundings as well as the retreat of the shoreline. The figure on the left represents 2000 AD, the figure on the right represents 5000 AD.

STRIKING THE BALANCE: LONG TERM GROUNDWATER MONITORING DESIGN FOR MULTIPLE CONFLICTING OBJECTIVES

Patrick Reed[1], Barbara Minsker[2] and Albert J. Valocchi[2]
[1] *3230 Newmark Civil Engineering Laboratory, Department of Civil and Environmental Engineering, University of Illinois at Urbana-Champaign (UIUC), 205 N. Mathews Ave., Urbana, IL, 61801,*
Tel (217) 333-6979; Fax (217) 333-6968; email: preed@uiuc.edu
[2] *Department of Civil and Environmental Engineering, UIUC*

The National Research Council (NRC) (1997) estimates that between 300,000 and 400,000 contaminated sites within the United States will require a potential remedial cost of up to a trillion dollars. The tremendous magnitude of these costs has motivated a shift in the environmental industry toward risk-based approaches to remedial design. Risk-based approaches often involve leaving some contamination in place, which can require significant long-term monitoring (LTM). Long-term monitoring at many sites can involve decades of expensive sampling at tens or even hundreds of existing monitoring wells, resulting in hundreds of thousands or millions of dollars for sampling and data management per year.

Developing efficient and effective LTM sampling plans can be difficult when numerous options exist. In any given monitoring period, the number of possible sampling plans is 2n, where n is the product of the number of wells and the number of possible constituents to be measured. A site with 10 wells where up to 3 constituents can be measured (n = 30) requires the decision maker to identify a sampling plan among the more than one billion that exist while also trying to balance the cost and other performance objectives for each sampling scheme. Assume that the practitioner can eliminate 99 percent of these designs using intuition and further assume that it only takes him or her 1 second to evaluate each of the remaining designs. A comprehensive analysis of the remaining designs would still require more than a full work year.

This study utilizes the Non-Dominated Sorted Genetic Algorithm (NSGA) to efficiently search large numbers of possible LTM designs while quantifying the optimal tradeoff among multiple objectives, in this case minimizing cost and estimation error. The test case developed in this study uses data drawn from a 50 million-node flow-and-transport simulation performed by Maxwell et al. (2000). The simulation provided realistic historical data for the migration of a hypothetical perchloroethylene (PCE) plume in a highly heterogeneous alluvial aquifer. The hydrogeology of the test case is based on an actual site located at the Lawrence Livermore National Laboratory (LLNL) in Livermore, California. Data were provided for a total of 58 hypothetical sampling locations within a 29-well multi-level monitoring network. The data represent a snapshot in time, 8 years after an underground storage tank has continuously released contamination into the aquifer system. The monitoring wells can sample from 1 to 3 locations along their vertical axis and have a minimum spacing of 10 m between wells in the horizontal plane.

The site is assumed to be undergoing long-term monitoring, in which groundwater samples are used to assess the effectiveness of current remediation strategies. During this long-term monitoring phase of a remediation, sampling and laboratory analysis can be a controlling factor in the costs of remediating a site. Quarterly sampling of the entire network has a potential cost of over $85,000 annually for PCE testing alone, which could translate into millions of dollars if the site had a typical life span of 20 to 30 years.

In this study, the NSGA successfully searched the decision space of more than 500,000,000 potential sampling plans to identify 33 non-dominated solutions in approximately 20 minutes on a Pentium III personal computer. These solutions compose the optimal tradeoff between cost and error (i.e. the Pareto front). Recall, a design dominates another design if and only if it performs as well as in all objectives and better in at least one. A plot of these 33 solutions provides the stakeholder with a direct representation of the reduction in estimation error she or he can attain for a given level of cost.

Loaiciga et al. (1992) state "[o]ne of the key difficulties in the design of ground water monitoring networks via mathematical models is to choose objective functions that faithfully represent a [stakeholder's] objective". The modeling approach presented in this work addresses this difficulty by enabling stakeholders and regulators to isolate and visualize a small number of sampling strategies that are optimal with respect to multiple objectives. This allows both modeled and non-modeled fiscal, technical, and social objectives for a given site to be addressed.

EXPLORATION FOR MODELING OF PESTICIDES DECOMPOSITION IN MINERAL WATERS OF THE TRANSCARPATHIAN REGION

N.P. Osokina, V.M. Shestopalov, I.P. Onischenko
Institute of Geological Sciences National Academy of Science of Ukraine
55-B, O.Gonchara St., Kyiv 01054, Ukraine
tel. 216 07 81; fax (044) 216 93 34;
e-mail:ony@rc.kiev.ua

The Transcarpathian region is the richest province of Ukraine, its main recreation resources being mineral waters, climate and landscape. About 50 fields with mineral waters of different types are known, among those the most widespread and valuable are carbonic waters. In 1989 and 1997 the Institute of Geological Sciences National Academy of Science of Ukraine (IGS NASU), carried out examinations of mineral water fields for the content of strong organochloric pesticides (DDT and its metabolites, HCCH and its isomers, aldrin, heptachlor, dilor); organophosphoric pesticides (methaphos, carbophos); fluorine-containing pesticide (trephlane). In 1989 sixteen fields were examined, and three fields in 1997. Analytical experiments were performed using two gas chromatographs "Tsvet-500M" (Models 550 and 570). It was established that in the same sample there could be present up to eight substances and their metabolites, derivatives of chemical compounds of different groups in concentrations lower than MPC (maximal permissible concentration) for potable water.

NUMERICAL MODELING AS A TOOL IN UNDERSTANDING TH (THERMO-HYDRODYNAMIC) PROCESSES IN GEOTHERMAL SYSTEMS (KAMCHATKA AND KURILE ISLANDS EXAMPLES)

Alexey V. Kiryukhin
Lawrence Berkeley National Laboratory
1 Cyclotron Rd , MS 90-1116 , Berkeley CA 94720

INTRODUCTION

The current conceptual understanding of TH (thermal-hydrodynamic) processes in hydrothermal systems may be expressed in the following lumped parameter pipe model (Fig.1).Cold meteoric water from a recharge area (M1) descend through sub-vertical channels (such as permeable faults or sub-vertical intrusive body contacts) to a deep heat exchange high-temperature zone (B1) (such as permeable sub-horizontal basement/sedimentary basin boundaries or hot intrusive body boundaries). Cold meteoric water converts to high temperature fluid through heat exchange and the fluid ascends through   relatively narrow high permeability zone (R1 reservoir, "root feeding channels") into a wider high permeability zone (R2 reservoir, "geothermal reservoir"), and finely discharges at the earth surface in the form of hot springs and fumaroles (D1). Discharge may also take place into shallow groundwater reservoirs and mixing with fresh meteoric waters. Flows from recharge to discharge areas are driven by pressure and fluid density differences (forced and free convection).

Application of numerical models (TOUGH2; K.Pruess 1987,1991) to herein targeted mainly geothermal reservoirs R1 and R2 , specifying numerical grids for them , that correspond to local structural , geological and hydrogeological conditions. Numerical modeling is further employed in : 1. Modeling natural state conditions , 2. Flowtests matches , 3.Modeling of different exploitation scenarios - and yields specific understanding for each geothermal system.

PARATUNSKY GEOTHERMAL FIELD

"Well by well 110 elements" model used . Seasonal variations of natural hotwater flow , permeability distribution and «seepage type» boundary conditions were studied. Anually averaged natural hotwater mass flowrate is estimated as 283 kg/s with enthalpy 360-400 kJ/kg and reservoir permeability values 50-90 mD .

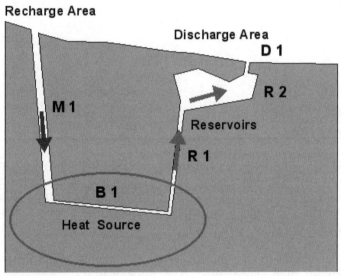

Fig.1 Conceptual understanding of the thermo-hydrodynamic processes in hydrothermal systems (see text above)

NORTH-KURILE GEOTHERMAL FIELD (PARAMUSHIR ISL., KURILES)

«1-D radial 33-elements model» used. Natural hotwater mass flow rate estimated as more than 40 kg/s with temperature more than 110°C. Modeling of exploitation (well P2) is used to understand mechanism of cycling pulses ,caused by high fluid conductivity of the well, given low permeability-thickness (1.65 D*m) and compressibility (2.4 10^{-8} Pa^{-1}) of reservoir.

MALKINSKY GEOTHERMAL FIELD

3-D numerical rectangular model (5 layers and 350 elements) was developed. Based on modeling studies the hotwater upflow rate is 59 kg/s in reservoir with permeability 300 mD.The most interesting thing of this modeling study is a flexure type tube shaped form of the permeable zone in reservoir, derived from modeling studies (natural state modeling). There was not any geological indications (such as fault intersections or so on) for this tube.

MUTNOVSKY GEOTHERMAL FIELD

3-D Numerical rectangular model (5 layers, 500 elements) was developed in 1991-1996 . Modeling of the natural state conditions indicated the following reservoir parameters: permeability of 3-5 mD within the 240°C temperature zone; estimated total mass upflow rate of 54 kg/s with enthalpy of 1270 – 1390 kJ/kg . Based on modeling of the flow tests matches double porosity parameters of two-phase production zones estimated as 0.45 - 9 mD with fracture void 0.01 – 0.0002 ,and fracture spacing 25 – 200 m. Based on modeling of five scenarious , total steam production of exploitation wells by the end of the 20 year exploitation period should be no less than 87.9 kg/s (that is equivalent of 44.0 MWe). Small-scale models of well-fracture interactions were investigated to explain pressure cycling in a two-phase geothermal reservoir.

OCEANSKY GEOTHERMAL FIELD (ITURUP ISL., KURILES)

A 3-D Numerical rectangular model (4 layers , 168 elements) was developed. Based on modeling natural state conditions the following reservoir parameters were estimated: production zone permeability is 15-30 mD, vertical and horizontal extension are more than 1500 m. Total natural high temperature flowrate estimated as 35 kg/s with enthalpy 1470 kJ/kg. Modeling of the flowtests matches yield the following double-porosity parameters of production zone: fracture void 0.0002 - 0.02 , fracture permeability 3.6 – 30 mD, fracture spacing 2 – 100 m.

PAUZHETSKY GEOTHERMAL FIELD

Numerical «well-by-well model» (135 elements) was developed. Based on modeling natural state conditions the following parameters of the natural high temperature upflow was estimated: mass flowrate - 330 kg/s, enthalpy 830 – 920 kJ/kg .

CONCLUSIONS

Numerical modeling (TOUGH2) of the six Kamchatka and Kurile Islands geo-thermal fields (Paratunsky, North-Kurilsky, Malkinsky, Mutnovsky, Oceansky and Pauzhetsky), targeted to basic validation of conceptual models of fields through TH (thermo-hydrodynamic) processes understanding and estimations, including: 1. Natural thermal fluid upflow rate and enthalpy; 2. Space bounda-ries and permeability distributions in reservoir; 3. Hydro-dynamic boundary con-ditions of reservoir (for single-phase reservoirs); 4. Double-porosity properties of reservoir (two-phase reservoirs); 5.Forecast of different exploitation scenarios.

In most cases numerical modeling of TH processes is an effective tool to estimate reservoir parameters mentioned above , if background conceptual models are properly defined. In some cases numerical modeling may be used as independent tool to understand permeability distributions and mass flows in geothermal systems .

GEOSTATISTICAL ANALYSIS OF WATER LEVEL IN A FRACTURED AQUIFER AND OPTIMIZATION OF THE MONITORING NETWORK

Shakeel Ahmed, Dewashish Kumar and J.C. Maréchal
Indo-French Centre for Groundwater Research
National Geophysical Research Institute, Hyderabad-500007, India
Ph: +9140 7158090, fax: +9140 7170491,
email: shakeelahmed@satyam.net.in

Appropriate and adequate data are essential for the success of any scientific study. Scarcity of data and their collection on isolated location mainly in the field of hydrogeology makes it necessary to adopt special procedures or an estimation technique for bridging the gap between field measurements and data requirements. Numerical simulation of flow and transport processes in an aquifer necessitates, dividing and discretizing the natural heterogeneous system into a number of small volumes called mesh which are assumed to be uniform with almost no variation of the aquifer properties over it. To satisfy this condition, it is necessary to discretize the system into much finer and hence more number of grids. Although with the availability of more powerful computers, computation with large number of grids/mesh is not a difficulty but the data preparation that is to assign the aquifer parameters to each grid/mesh becomes cumbersome. Thus an appropriate estimation procedure is required to provide an unbiased, minimum variance and with unique value over the entire area of the mesh.

Geostatistics based on the theory of regionalized variables has found more and more applications in the field of groundwater hydrology. Now Geostatistics has found applications in almost all domain of Hydrogeology from parameter estimation to predictive modeling for Groundwater Management e.g., designing an optimal groundwater monitoring network, estimating parameters at unmeasured locations, groundwater model fabrication (optimal discretization), unbiased model calibration using estimation errors and in deciding the best models for prediction. Geostatistical estimation variance reduction, cross-validation techniques etc. are a few procedures that could study adequacy of a given monitoring network and could evolve an optimal monitoring network with some given constraints. The advantage of the geostatistical estimation technique is that the variance of the estimation error could be calculated at any point without having the actual measurement on that point (well). Thus the benefits to be accrued from an additional measurement could be studied prior to its measurement.

A few new procedures have been developed using geostatistical technique so that the number of monitoring wells was reduced without loosing the monitoring benefits. The objectives of the geostatistical optimization of the monitoring network has been that the monitored parameter should (a) represent the true variability of the parameter and (b) provide its estimate on unmeasured locations with a desired accuracy in the form of the variance of the estimation error.

A small watershed with a semi-confined aquifer in a fractured granite rocks of a semi-arid region having an area of 60 km^2 have been studied. A number of bore wells (32 plus 25) based on geomorphology, land use and other variations were decided to have a first hand network for measurement of water-levels and water quality. The existing network consisted of 57 bore-wells out of which 25 were specially drilled for monitoring the water levels and 32 were selected from the existing irrigation wells. The values of water levels (amsl) of the aquifer from the given network of monitoring wells have been geostatistically analyzed to study the variability of the head data. A few common variograms were tried to use and tested through cross-validation tests to arrive at a variability during the monsoon periods but a different variability for the non-monsoon periods.

The analysis of the variance of the estimation error obtained using kriging technique on a suitably finer grid in the entire area has been the basis to discard some of the private irrigation wells. The wells were discarded such a way that the variance of the estimation error does not exceed a pre-decided value. Thus after a few iterations, a network of 40 monitoring wells have been evolved consisting of 25 specially drilled observation wells and 15 private irrigation wells keeping the variance of the estimation error within the desired limit.

Monitoring through an optimal network can reduce the amount of data requi-red while providing the desired accuracy and a few simple procedures have been developed for a geostatistical optimization of the monitoring network in this study. Also the use of common variogram reduces the half of the estima-tion procedure for estimating water levels for various time periods.

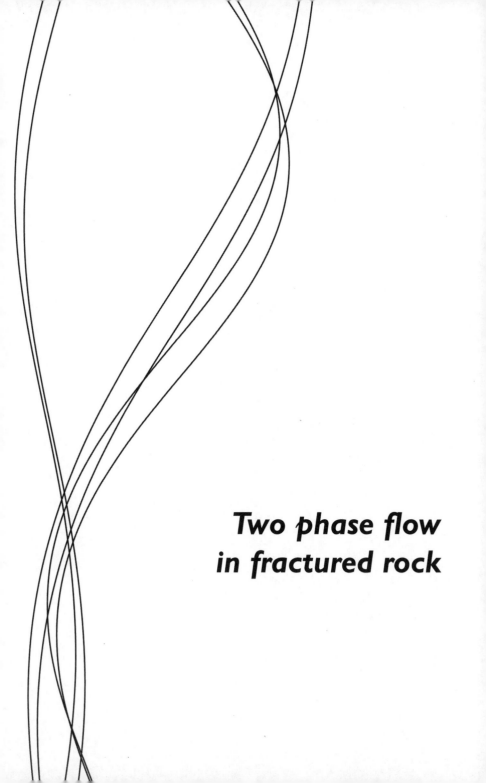

*Two phase flow
in fractured rock*

DENSITY DRIVEN FLOW IN POROUS MEDIA: HOW ACCURATE ARE OUR MODELS?

W. Kinzelbach, R. Held, K. Johannsen[1], S. Oswald[2], C. Schwarz[3]
Institute of Hydromechanics and Water Resources Management (IHW)
Swiss Federal Institute of Technology, Zurich, Switzerland
[1] IWR, University of Heidelberg, Germany
[2] formerly IHW now Groundwater Protection and Restoration Group,
University of Sheffield, Great Britain
[3] formerly IHW now UBS Warburg, Zurich, Switzerland

Density driven flow in porous media occurs in a number of field situations. Among those are flows around salt domes, which are relevant in nuclear waste disposal, salt water intrusion and saltwater upconing both near the coast and inland, flows occurring in geothermal problems, the disposal of heavy brines in aquifers and many others. In the prediction of those phenomena numerical models are necessary. Due to the non-linear nature of the density flow equations their solution is more difficult than that of the passive tracer transport equations. The flow is truly rotational and naturally unstable situations are possible. For these reasons, numerical schemes and discretization must be chosen carefully to control both numerical dispersion and numerical instability in the solution.

The equations of density flow consist of an equation for the conservation of total mass usually written in pressure as a variable and an equation for the conservation of solute mass usually written in the mass fraction of solute as variable. Several formulations are possible and often the Boussinesq approximation is used. In the definition of a problem care must be taken to use consistent boundary conditions in order to avoid model artefacts. The parameters may be scale dependent, e.g. the dispersion parameters will have to be upscaled if density variance is averaged out due to low resolution. The driving force of fingers in an unstable situation will be strongly reduced if fingers are averaged out by inadequate resolution. It might even be that finger propagation on the scale of the pores is of importance for fingering dynamics. These phenomena would never be adequately represented by the continuum model approach and its validity may be put into doubt. The investigation of processes at higher resolution scales provides further information on the scaling behaviour of relevant parameters. Of special interest are the short temporal scales up to the onset of density driven flow instabilities, and their representation in the continuum equations or auxiliary conditions.

Once one accepts the generally used form of the density flow equations, a number of codes are available for their solution. When testing the reliability of those codes, basically 5 methods are available: Comparison to analytical solutions, comparison to exact solutions, establishment of grid convergence, inter-model comparison and comparison to experiments. All have their strong points as well as their flaws and shortcomings.

Analytical solutions are rather narrowly limited as actually only very few solutions are known and they require simplifying assumptions such as the Boussinesq approximation or a spatially constant dispersion coefficient. Exact solutions can always be found by inserting functions for pressure and mass fraction into the equations and interpreting the mismatch as a source or sink density both for total mass and solute mass. The corresponding boundary conditions are then given by the function values at the boundary of the domain as Dirichlet type boundary conditions. The problem is that the required sources and sinks may be so large that they dominate the problem and the solution does not test the code but only reflect the dominating sources and sinks. If one manages however to find a function for which the source sink terms are small compared to other terms the technique is actually the best available to test a code for errors. One such a solution for steady state is presented. It is inspired by the salt dome problem. In principle one can calculate solutions for any type of problem to the required accuracy if a code is available which allows for arbitrary grid refinement until grid convergence is reached. An example is presented for a strong density contrast flow, where 18 million nodes are required to reach grid convergence. It is to be suspected that usually model discretization is determined by computing power rather than be grid convergence criteria. Basically a new generation of models must contain error estimators and automatic refinement according to the error estimate so that the user can be sure that the model gives a solution of the required degree of accuracy. Of course this check concerns the local error only. An intercomparison of codes cannot determine the absolute accuracy of a solution. It can, however, help to test codes. This works especially well in the case that the two compared codes use a completely different solution method e.g. a Lagrangian particle tracking method versus a standard finite element or finite difference method.

The comparison with a careful laboratory experiment can also help to check a model. However, this procedure combines two issues, checking of the validity of the equations as well as the reliability of the numerical solution. Still, if we believe in the correctness of the basic equations one can still learn a lot from the comparison with experiments. Two basic situations could be exploited: A situation starting out from stable conditions or a situation starting out from an unstable situation, in which generic properties could be compared such as finger growth rates, finger frequency etc. One situation often used in benchmarking is the buoyant plume experiment by Elder. But also the falling plume by Schincariol et al. 1997 has been used. In 3 dimensions the experiments by Oswald (1998) and Ackerer and Younes (1999) are available. In the experiments by Oswald, the 3D salt distribution and its evolution in time are measured in high spatial resolution by NMR using the copper ion as NMR tracer. In the first type of experiment, salt water is injected below freshwater in a cubic box, leading to a stable initial situation after some equilibration. Then a flow is induced with injection and pumping at two wells opposed to each other diagonally on the top side of the cube. The stable situation can be computed to the required accuracy - easily in the case of low concentration and after much higher discretization in the case of high solute concentration. In the first case solute is simply displaced while in the second case a different mode of flow arises with streamlines running on top of the saline fluid. By turning the box after the initial solute injection, an unstable situation is created, which leads to fingering. This situation is not easily modelled. The finger growth rate can be reproduced but the onset of fingering is very much delayed in the computation. Obviously this is due to an inadequate representation of the initial perturbances. Also the issue of resolution of initial fingers plays a role. These microscale aspects are looked into by micromodels both in the experiment as well as in theory.

REFERENCES:

P. ACKERER, et al. 1999. On the modelling of density driven flow. In: Stauffer et al. (eds.), Calibration and Reliability in Groundwater Modelling, p. 13-21, IAHS Publications Nr. 265.

J. W. ELDER, 1967. Transient convection in a porous medium. Journal of Fluid Mechanics, 27, 3, p. 609ff.

K. JOHANNSEN, et al.2002. Numerical simulation of density driven flow in porous media, Advances in Water Resources, in press.

S. OSWALD, 1998. Dichteströmungen in porösen Medien: Dreidimensionale Experimente und Modellierung, Ph. D. Thesis ETH Zurich.

SCHINCARIOL, et al. 1997. Instabilities in variable density flow: Stability and sensitivity analyses for homogeneous and heterogeneous media. Water Resources Research, 33, 1 p. 31 ff.

C. SCHWARZ, 1999. Dichteabhängige Strömungen in homogenen und heterogenen porösen Medien, Ph D. Thesis ETH Zurich.

COMPARISON OF FIELD-SCALE EFFECTIVE PROPERTIES OF TWO-PHASE FLOW IN HETEROGENEOUS POROUS MEDIA OBTAINED BY STOCHASTIC ANALYSIS AND NUMERICAL EXPERIMENTS

Quanlin Zhou[1], Lynn W. Gelhar[2] and Bruce Jacobs[3]

[1] *Earth Sciences Division, Lawrence Berkeley National Laboratory, Berkeley, California*
[2] *Department of Civil & Environmental Engineering, Massachusetts Institute of Technology, Cambridge, Massachusetts*
[3] *Jacobs Consulting Services, Boston, Massachusetts*

INTRODUCTION

The spectral perturbation technique has been applied to investigating the field-scale effective properties of two-phase flow. These effective properties include effective capillary pressure and relative permeability functions with respect to mean saturation. The difference between effective properties and their counterparts in homogeneous formations represents the effect of subsurface heterogeneity at the field scale. In this study, the effective properties of two-phase flow in a heterogeneous system were estimated using numerical simulations. The heterogeneous system with random fields of intrinsic permeability and two capillary parameters was generated, and a number of two-phase flow situations with different mean saturations were simulated. The effective properties were derived from the simulation results and were compared with those obtained by stochastic analysis.

RANDOM FIELDS OF PERMEABILITY AND CAPILLARY PARAMETERS

A statistical scaling technique was used to generate a heterogeneous system consisting of random fields of intrinsic permeability and two capillary pressure parameters (α^{-1} and m in the van Genuchten formulation). In this scaling, both the deterministic correlation between capillary pressure parameters and intrinsic permeability k and random perturbations are considered:

$$F = \overline{F} + f \qquad B = \overline{B} + b_B f + g_B \qquad L = \overline{L} + b_L f + g_L$$

with the definition of

$$F = \ln k \qquad B = \ln\alpha^{-1} \qquad L = -\ln(1/m - 1)$$

where f, g_B, g_L are the statistically independent perturbations of zero mean, b_B and b_L are the correlation parameters, and the bar over a variable indicates its mean value. The statistic properties representing the Borden Aquifer were used to generate the random fields. The correlation scales (λ_x and λ_z) are 2.8 m and 0.12 m in the horizontal and vertical directions, respectively; other related parameters are: $\overline{F}$=-9.5114(lnm/s), $\overline{B}$=-1.0937(lnm), $\overline{L}$=1.50, σ_f=0.351, b_B=-1.03, σ_{g_B}=0.113, b_L=-0.83 and σ_{g_L}=0.174, where σ indicates the standard deviation of a random variable of interest. The heterogeneous domain is $8\lambda_x$ long and $16\lambda_z$ high in the two-dimensional vertical cross-section. The uniform spatial discretizations in the horizontal and vertical directions are $\lambda_x/16$ (Δ_x=0.175m) and $\lambda_z/4$ (Δ_z=0.03m).

EFFECTIVE RELATIVE PERMEABILITY AND CAPILLARY PRESSURE FUNCTIONS

The first step in determining the field-scale effective relative permeability in heterogeneous formations is to estimate the field-scale effective saturated hydraulic conductivity tensor. We simulated steady-state single-phase flow in the generated heterogeneous system for two different sets of boundary conditions, and estimated each component of the tensor on the basis of the mean Darcy law. Excellent agreement was obtained between the estimated effective saturated conductivity tensor and the generalized spectral-perturbation approximation.

In the second step, the transient process of two-phase (water and DNAPL) flow from a uniform initial DNAPL saturation field to a quasi-steady highly heterogeneous one in the generated heterogeneous system was simulated using the FEAS-MPFlow written in C++. Both vertical boundaries are impervious to water and DNAPL flow. A constant rate of DNAPL is injected on the top with no-flow condition for the wetting phase. On the bottom boundary, a constant water head is specified and a solution-dependent DNAPL flux is specified to allow for DNAPL outflow. Nine flow situations with different infiltration rates (5000, 2000, 1000, 500, 200, 50, 20, 10, 1<->$10^{-8}m/s$) on the top boundary were simulated to obtain the effective relative permeability and capillary pressure functions with respect to mean effective saturation (μ_{Se}).

For each flow situation or infiltration rate, a quasi-steady NAPL saturation field with large variation was obtained, representing the overall influence of variability of the intrinsic permeability and capillary parameters. The NAPL saturation fields show (1) the standard deviation of NAPL saturation varies with μ_{Se}, with its maximum at $\mu_{Se}=0.5$; (2) the NAPL saturation field is positively correlated with intrinsic permeability. This positive correlation mainly comes from the negative correlation between the characteristic capillary pressure α^{-1} and intrinsic permeability.

Figure 1 shows the vertical effective relative permeability (k_{rz}^{en}) obtained by numerical simulation, in comparison with the approximation of spectral-perturbation analysis (k_{rz}^{nS}) and the homogeneous one ($k_m(\overline{m})$) with mean capillary parameters. The ratio of $k_{rz}^{en}/k_m(\overline{m})$ gradually decreases from 1.0 at $\mu_{Se}=0$ to the value of 0.068 at $\mu_{Se}=0.970$. The large difference is mainly due to positive correlation between the local-scale DNAPL relative permeability and intrinsic permeability, leading to a large variance of actual permeability (combination of relative permeability and intrinsic one), as shown in Figure 2b. The agreement between k_{rz}^{en} and k_{rz}^{nS} is reasonably good. Figure 2 shows very good agreement between the effective capillary head functions obtained by numerical and spectral analysis. The deviation in the effective capillary head from the homogeneous one is not significant, in particular for a high μ_{Se}. This small deviation may be due to the small variance of capillary head field shown in Figure 2b.

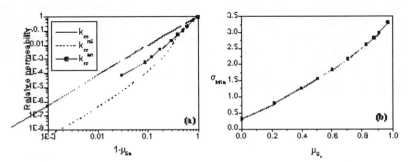

Figure 1. (a) Comparison of the vertical effective relative permeability obtained by numerical and spectral analysis, and (b) standard deviation of log actual conductivity.

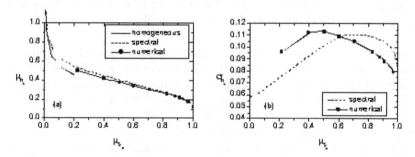

Figure 2. Comparison of (a) effective capillary head function and (b) standard deviation of capillary head obtained by numerical and spectral analysis.

CONCLUSION

The field-scale effective relative permeability and capillary pressure function (with respect to mean saturation) of two-phase flow were obtained for a heterogeneous system with properties representing the Borden Aquifer, using numerical and stochastic analysis. The vertical effective relative permeability is significantly lower than the homogeneous one found using mean capillary parameters, particularly at low mean DNAPL saturation (low mean capillary pressure). The significant difference is mainly due to the large variance of actual DNAPL permeability (combination of intrinsic permeability and its positively correlated relative permeability). On the other hand, the effective capillary pressure function differs only slightly from the homogeneous case. This deviation results from the small variance of capillary pressure, which is smaller than that of the characteristic capillary pressure. By comparison, the effective properties of two-phase flow obtained by the numerical simulation and stochastic analysis are in good agreement. The numerical analysis can be used for any highly heterogeneous formations, whereas the stochastic analysis can give us insight into the internal correlations between output and input variability in mildly heterogeneous systems.

MEASURING AND MODELING FLOW IN WELDED FRACTURED TUFFS

Rohit Salve, Christine Doughty, and Joseph S.Y. Wang
Earth Sciences Division
E.O. Lawrence Berkeley National Laboratory

INTRODUCTION

We have carried out a series of in situ liquid-release experiments in conjunction with a numerical modeling study to examine the effect of the rock matrix on liquid flow and transport occurring primarily through the fracture network. Field experiments were conducted in the highly fractured Topopah Spring welded tuff at a site accessed from the Exploratory Studies Facility (ESFS), an underground laboratory in the unsaturated zone at Yucca Mountain, Nevada. During the experiment, wetting-front movement, flow-field evolution, and drainage of fracture flow paths were evaluated. Modeling was used to aid in experimental design, predict experimental results, and study the physical processes accompanying liquid flow through unsaturated fractured welded tuff.

This paper presents the results of the field investigation and numerical modeling study. Field experiments and modeling suggest that it may not be sufficient to conceptualize the fractured tuff as consisting of a single network of high-permeability fractures embedded in a low-permeability matrix. The need to include a secondary fracture network is demonstrated by comparison to the liquid flow observed in the field.

METHODS

Field experiments were conducted over a period of six weeks starting in late July 1998. The test bed is located approximately ~210 m below the surface of the mountain in an Alcove, within the middle nonlithophysal portion of the TSw. The rock is visibly fractured with predominantly vertical fractures and few subhorizontal fractures. Relatively wide fracture spacing (on the order of tens of centimeters) facilitated the choice of injection zones, allowing discrete fractures and well-characterized fracture networks to be isolated by packers for localized flow testing.

Four horizontal boreholes (located within the test bed) and a horizontal slot (located immediately below the test bed) are the distinct features of the test bed (Figure 1). Borehole A was used for fluid injection while boreholes B, C, and D were monitored for changes in moisture conditions. The field experiments included multiple releases of tracer-laced water in one low-permeability zone (LPZ) and one high-permeability zone (HPZ) along the horizontal injection borehole. During and following liquid release events, changes in saturation and water potential in the fractured rock were measured in the three monitoring boreholes using psychrometers and electrical resistance probes (ERP).The slot was used to collect water seeping from the fractured rocks above. This seepage was quantified for volumes and rates, and analyzed for tracers.

The modeling approach assumes that the multiphase extension of Darcy's law governs fluid flow in both fractures and rock matrix. Space is discretized into a regular rectangular grid composed of cubic gridblocks, or elements, that is fine enough to represent individual fractures and their intersections deterministically. Within the rectangular grid, fractures are modeled as disks with a one-element thickness. Figure 2 shows the 3-D model constructed using this approach. These elements are assigned properties of a fracture continuum rather than properties of an individual fracture, to account for actual fracture aperture (~10^{-4} m) being much less than element thickness (0.15 m). Any element that is not part of a fracture disk is assigned properties of the intact rock matrix. Fracture-matrix interactions (i.e., imbibition, drainage, chemical diffusion) potentially occur wherever fracture elements are connected to matrix elements. The present modeling approach is considered a quasi-explicit fracture-network representation, in that the fractures are individually resolved, but not modeled using element dimensions commensurate with actual fracture apertures. The high-permeability fracture disks are located deterministically.

OBSERVATIONS

The liquid-release tests conducted in two zones only one meter apart demonstrate significant variability in hydrologic response. The formation response to liquid releases in the LPZ suggests a conceptual flow model consisting of a strongly heterogeneous fracture network in which the high-permeability fractures are not extensive or are poorly connected. The closed-end features tend to wet up early and remain saturated throughout the remainder of the test.

In contrast to the liquid-release rates observed in the LPZ, the HPZ did not show large decreases in release rates as additional water was introduced into the formation. Further, the rates fluctuated significantly during the entire duration of the liquid releases at constant head. Slot seepage rates also fluctuated strongly, whether liquid was injected under constant-head or constant-rate conditions. Flow between the injection interval and the underlying slot occurred quickly (1.6 m in 3 to 7 minutes) unless the injection rate was low. These features are consistent with a conceptual model dominated by high-conductivity, well-connected fracture flow paths.

Simulations with the fracture-network model yield reasonably good matches to the basic results of the liquid-release tests: breakthrough time at the slot, the fraction of injected water that is captured by the slot, and temporal variations of capillary pressure measurements made at observation boreholes

CONCLUSIONS

The key finding of this work concerns the nature of the fracture network in the welded tuff at the test site. It has become common practice to conceptualize the fractured tuffs at Yucca Mountain as consisting of a network of high-permeability fractures embedded in a very low-permeability rock matrix. This conceptualization does not work well for the present liquid-release tests. If such a model matched the LPZ behavior, then HPZ breakthrough times would be much too slow. Conversely, if the model reproduced the HPZ behavior, then the LPZ tests would either incorrectly show breakthrough (if the injection interval intersected the fracture network) or incorrectly show a huge pressure increase (if the injection interval did not intersect the fracture network). We find that a model containing two fracture networks with different characteristics works much better to explain the observed data. In this model, much of the flow occurs quickly through the primary fracture network (fractures large enough and extensive enough to be mapped on the alcove walls and ceiling). However, a secondary fracture network also exists, consisting of lower-permeability, less-continuous fractures that span a range of sizes. With such a network, the LPZ tests can accept a large volume of water (with a declining intake rate) without showing breakthrough at the slot, and the HPZ tests show a lower fraction of water recovered at the slot than can be explained by imbibition into an intact rock matrix. Moreover, borehole capillary-pressure measurements suggest that while the secondary fracture network is not just localized around the primary fractures, neither does it uniformly pervade the rock.

The existence of two scales of fracture networks and the inferred heterogeneity at both scales are consistent with conceptual models that regard heterogeneity as having a hierarchical or fractal nature, in which features such as fractures occur at a range of scales. Accordingly, our modeling approach should prove useful in interpreting data from a variety of geological settings.

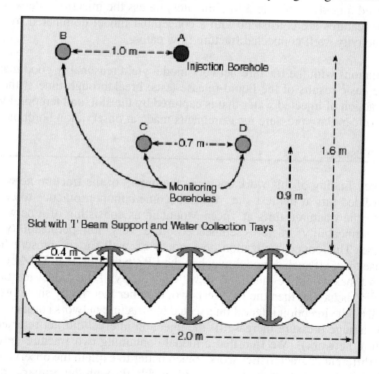

Figure 1. Vertical view of test bed layout.

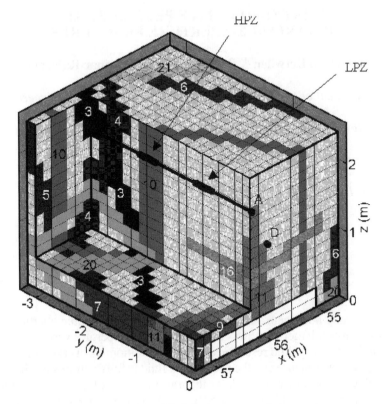

Figure 2. The 3-D fracture-network model of the fracture-matrix interaction test site.

SATIATED RELATIVE PERMEABILITY OF VARIABLE-APERTURE FRACTURES

Russell L. Detwiler[1,4], Robert J. Glass[2], Harihar Rajaram[1] and Michael J. Nicholl[3]

[1] *Department of Civil, Environmental and Architectural Engineering, University of Colorado, Boulder, Colorado.*
[2] *Flow Visualization and Processes Laboratory, Sandia National Laboratories, Albuquerque, New Mexico.*
[3] *Department of Materials, Metallurgical, Mining, and Geological Engineering, University of Idaho, Moscow, Idaho.*
[4] *Now at: Division of Geophysics and Global Security, Lawrence Livermore Naitonal Laboratory, Livermore, California.*

In a statistically homogeneous, horizontal, initially dry, variable-aperture fracture that is much larger than the correlation scale of aperture variability, slow invasion of a wetting fluid results in a satiated condition: the wetting fluid completely spans the fracture and the nonwetting fluid is fully entrapped. The satiated relative permeability (k_{rw}) relates the transmissivity of the wetting fluid in the satiated fracture to the fully saturated transmissivity of the fracture. Nicholl et al. [2000] compared experimental measurements of flow through a satiated fracture to flow simulations (based on the depth-averaged Reynolds equation) in measured aperture and phase-distribution fields demonstrating that simulated estimates of satiated relative permeability closely matched the corresponding experimental measurements. They also presented a conceptual model for k_{rw} that suggested that increased tortuosity and decreased wetting phase saturation induced by the entrapped phase are the primary contributions to reduction in k_{rw}. In this paper, we use the modified invasion percolation (MIP) algorithm developed by Glass et al. [1998] to systematically investigate the combined influence of capillary forces and aperture variability on entrapped-phase structure. Subsequent simulations of flow of the wetting phase provide measures of satiated relative permeability, which we compare to predictions from the conceptual model presented by Nicholl et al. [2000].

Under quasi-static flow conditions, capillary forces will control phase structure in a horizontal fracture; in general, the nonwetting phase will be found in large apertures and the wetting phase in small ones. The Laplace-Young equation, which form the basis for the MIP algorithm, relates surface tension (ϕ) and interfacial curvature, as quantified by the two principle radii of curvature, r_1 and r_2, to the pressure jump across the curved interface (P_c):

$$P_c = \phi\left(\frac{1}{r_1} + \frac{1}{r_2}\right) \tag{1}$$

Following Glass et al. [1998], we define the radius of out-of-plane curvature as $r_1 = -a/2\cos(\alpha+\beta)$ and the radius of in-plane curvature as $r_2 = <r_2>\tan(\gamma/2)$ where a is the local aperture, α is the fluid/fluid/solid contact angle, β is the convergence/divergence angle of the fracture surfaces, $<r_2>$, the mean in-plane radius of curvature, is estimated as $\lambda/2$, and g is a weighted measure of the local included angle of the interface [Glass et al., 1998, 2000]. Rewriting (1) in terms of its mean and perturbations along the air-water interface and nondimensionalizing yields a dimensionless perturbation equation for P_c:

$$P_c^{'*} = -a'^* sign(\cos\alpha) + C'\frac{1}{r_2^*} \tag{2}$$

with:

$$P_c^{'*} = \frac{\langle a\rangle^2}{2\sigma_a\phi|\cos\alpha|}P_c \qquad a'^* = \frac{a'}{\sigma_a} \qquad r_2^* = \tan\left(\frac{\gamma}{2}\right) \qquad C' = \frac{\langle a\rangle^2}{\lambda\sigma_a|\cos\alpha|}$$

where $<a>$ is the mean aperture and C' is the dimensionless perturbation curvature number, which is equal to $C/(\sigma_a/<a>)$, where C is the curvature number presented by Glass et al. [1998, 2000]. Equation (2) suggests that the entrapped phase structures resulting from invasion of an immiscible fluid into a fracture will be a function of C'. Thus, for a given invasion process with any values of $<a>$, σ_a, λ, and α that yield the same value of C', the resulting entrapped phase structure should be identical.

To evaluate the influence of C' on entrapped-phase distribution and the resulting relative permeability, we simulated invasion and subsequent flow of the satiated wetting phase in four synthetic aperture fields with $\sigma_a/<a> = 0.0625$, 0.125, 0.25, and 0.5, $<a> = 0.02$ cm, and $\lambda=0.075$ cm. In each of the four aperture fields, we simulated invasion of a wetting phase into the initially non-wetting-phase-filled fracture for C' ranging from 0 to 8.58. $C' = 0$ corresponds to a standard invasion percolation model (i.e. Pc depends only on local aperture because r_2 is assumed infinite), so the distribution of the entrapped phase should be identical regardless of $\sigma_d/\langle a \rangle$ and for C' of 8.58 and larger, nonwetting phase fluid did not become entrapped within any of the aperture fields. Figure 1 shows measurements of the areal portion of the fracture occupied by the flowing phase plotted against C' for each value of $\sigma_d/\langle a \rangle$. For the range $0<C'<0.5$, the entrapped area is insensitive to   , and depends only on C'. However, for larger values of C' there is an additional dependence on $\sigma_d/\langle a \rangle$, except at small $\sigma_d/\langle a \rangle$ (see the curves for $\sigma_d/\langle a \rangle=0.0625$ and 0.125). The additional dependence on $\sigma_d/\langle a \rangle$ for large $\sigma_d/\langle a \rangle$ is because the assumption of small local aperture perturbations required in deriving (5) is violated.

Flow of the satiated wetting phase can be simulated using the Reynolds equation, a depth-averaged approximation to the three-dimensional Stokes equations. The ratio of the simulated flow-rate in the satiated fracture to that in the saturated fracture provides an estimate of the satiated relative permeability (k_{rw}) of a fracture occupied by a specific phase distribution. Plots of k_{rw} versus S_f for all of the simulated entrapped-phase distributions (Figure 2) exhibit similar behavior regardless of $\sigma_d/\langle a \rangle$. The only significant scatter occurs at the smallest values of S_f, or for the entrapped-phase distributions corresponding to $C'=0$. S_f measures only the fractional volume of the entrapped phase and provides no information about the entrapped-phase structure. However, C' is intrinsically linked to the entrapped-phase structure and thus may provide a better parameter for estimating k_{rw}. Plotting krw against C' (Figure 3) demonstrates that for small values of C', C' provides a more reliable single parameter than S_f for estimating krw. However, for larger values of C' (smaller S_f), particularly for $\sigma_d/\langle a \rangle=0.5$, Sf is an effective single parameter for estimating k_{rw}.

We compared the simulated estimates of k_{rw} to a conceptual model presented by Nicholl et al. [2000]:

$$k_{rw} = \tau \, s_f \underbrace{\left[\frac{\langle a_f \rangle^2}{\langle a \rangle^2} \right]}_{A} \underbrace{\left[\left(1 + \frac{9\sigma_a^2}{\langle b \rangle^2} \right)^{1/2} \left(1 + \frac{9\sigma_{a_f}^2}{\langle b_f \rangle^2} \right)^{-1/2} \right]}_{B} \tag{3}$$

where τ is a tortuosity factor that quantifies the lengthening of flow paths through the fracture due to the entrapped phase, S_f is the saturation of the flowing fluid, part A quantifies the change in effective mean aperture available to the flowing phase, and part B quantifies the influence of changes in aperture variability due to the entrapped phase. As observed by Nicholl et al. [2000], t had the most significant influence on estimates of k_{rw}, with S_t having a secondary influence. As $\sigma_a/<a>$ increases, the role of part A in (3) increases, especially for small C', and changes in aperture variability (quantified by part B) have a negligible influence on predicted krw for all values of $\sigma_a/<a>$ and C'. Furthermore, across the ranges of $\sigma_a/<a>$ and C' investigated here, (3) provides very good estimates of the simulated values of k_{rw}.

REFERENCES

GLASS, R.J., L. YARRINGTON, and M.J. NICHOLL, A modified invasion percolation model for low capillary number immiscible displacements in horizontal rough walled fractures: Influence of local in-plane curvature, Water Resour. Res., 34, 3215-34, 1998.

NICHOLL, M.J., H. RAJARAM, and R.J. GLASS, Factors controlling satiated relative permeability in a partially-saturated horizontal fracture, Geophys. Res. Lett., 27, 393-396, 2000.

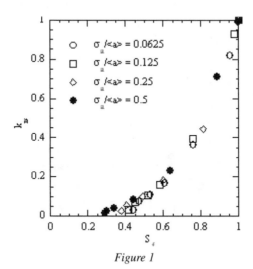

Figure 1

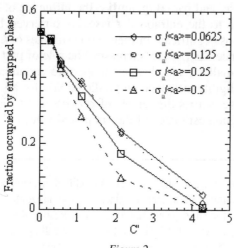

Figure 2

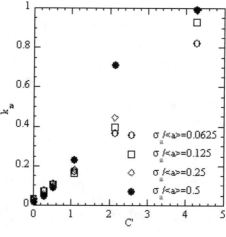

Figure 3

UNSATURATED FLOW THROUGH A FRACTURE-MATRIX-NETWORK: A FIRST EXPERIMENT

RJ Glass[1], MJ Nicholl[2] and SE Pringle[1]
*[1] Flow Visualization and Processes Laboratory
Sandia National Laboratories
[2] Department of Materials, Metallurgical, Mining, and Geological
Engineering, University of Idaho*

Unsaturated flow through a fractured rock mass remains a topic of considerable uncertainty. We designed a laboratory-scale fracture-matrix-network to explore the assembly of single-fracture and single-fracture-matrix processes. A thin, uncemented wall of porous bricks was constructed within a two-dimensional load frame. Water, chemically equilibrated with the bricks, was supplied to a fracture in the middle of the top of the initially dry system, and subsequent system behavior was followed photographically over a 71 day period. While our experiment was quite rudimentary, our results are the first of their kind, and yield a number of significant observations. In retrospect, most of our observations were hypothesized earlier by Glass et al. [1995]. Flow pathways evolved that were heavily controlled by processes acting within the fracture network, demonstrating the schizophrenic roles of fractures as both flow conductors and capillary barriers. Additionally, evaporation-precipitation processes led to a varied behavior that included: pathway starvation and flow shifting, flow field narrowing/constraining, and the development of tertiary pathways. We enumerate and briefly discuss our critical observations below.

1) Flow pathways evolved that remained primarily within the fractures: Our fracture-matrix network was designed to have tight fractures and a matrix with both significant storage capacity and capillary gradient (dry and small

pores). Yet flow occurred primarily in the fractures with only occasional flow thru the matrix. The matrix flow was presumably due to either the local tightening (lowered permeability) or loosening (capillary barrier) of the fracture network, and/or variability in the properties of the bricks across the network. When in the fractures, flow was predominantly gravity-driven with obvious indications of gravity driven fingering. Fracture intersections played an interesting role, in that flow sometimes crossed the intersection and sometimes turned 90 degrees.

2) Lateral interaction was minimal within the fracture-matrix network: Vertical fractures acted as capillary barriers, constraining pathways to be essentially two bricks wide. The primary pathway that spanned our network in two days, did not widen significantly in the next 7. The slow growing secondary pathway also showed the same growth structure as the primary, but in 'slow motion'. By day 9, the composite plume indeed looked diffuse and one is tempted to suggest that it could be represented by continuum approaches as outlined in the introduction. However, wetted structure at the bottom of the network is clear evidence that it contained discrete pathways with limited matrix communication.

3) Multiple pathways formed: An offset in the primary pathway at a fracture intersection eventually led to the formation of secondary pathway at later time. This observation is very similar to what has been seen in unstable flow fields within both individual fractures [Nicholl et al., 1993a] and sands [Glass et al., 1989] where slow growing dendrites form from appendages along fingers under steady supply. Multiple pathway formation has also been documented in nonwetting invasion experiments within heterogeneous sands where it was attributed to locations of pulsation [Glass et al., 2000]. While pulsation was documented within two vertical fractures and used as our designator for the occurrence of gravity driven fingering, it could also be associated with fracture intersections.

4) Evaporation-precipitation processes greatly influenced long term pathway evolution: Evaporation of matrix equilibrated fluid led to a gradual change in the flow field. The extent of the flow field reduced, all flow shifted into the secondary pathway starving the primary, and outflow at the bottom of the network retracted to a single fracture. On subsequent reduction of evaporation, the wetted structure swelled and two additional 'tertiary' pathways formed, one of which was eventually starved, the other was still growing at the end of the test. There is significant evidence that within networks, complexities due

to fracture coatings and the erosion and mobilization of fillings arise to create situations where the physical and chemical domain of the network may be changing in time (Weisbrod et al 1998). Our experiment further emphasizes this important point.

ACKNOWLEDGEMENTS

This experiment was conducted in 1995 at the Flow Visualization and Processes Laboratory, Sandia National Laboratories with funds from the U.S. Department of Energy's Basic Energy Sciences Geoscience Research Program under contract DE-AC04-94AL85000. The authors wish to thank Stephanie Pankretz and David Lopez for their help in constructing and maintaining the experiment. Additionally, RJG and SEP gratefully acknowledge support from the Office of Environmental Management, U. S. Department of Energy under Contract DE-AC07-99ID13727 to the Idaho National
Engineering and Environmental Laboratory that allowed the analysis of experimental results and the writing of this manuscript.

REFERENCES

GLASS, R.J., T.S. STEENHUIS and J-Y. PARLANGE, Mechanism for finger persistence in homogeneous unsaturated porous media: Theory and verification, Soil Science, 148, 60-70, 1989.

GLASS, R.J., S.H. CONRAD, and W. PEPLINSKI, Gravity destabilized non-wetting phase invasion in macroheterogneous porous media: Experimental observations of invasion dynamics and scale analysis, Water Resources Research, 36(11), 3121-3137, 2000.

GLASS, R.J., M.J. NICHOLL, and V.C. TIDWELL, Challenging models for flow in unsaturated, fractured rock through exploration of small scale flow processes, Geophysical Research Letters, 22(11), 1457-60, 1995.

NICHOLL, M.J., R.J. GLASS, and H.A. NGUYEN, Small-scale behavior of single gravity-driven fingers in an initially dry fracture, Proc. of the Fourth Ann. Int. Conf. on High Level Rad. Waste Mgmt., 2023-2032, Am. Nuclear Soc., Las Vegas, Nevada, April 26-30, 1993a.

WEISBROD, N., R. NATIV, D. RONEN, and E. ADAR, On the variability of fracture surfaces in unsaturated chalk, Water Resources Research, 34(8), 1881-1887, 1998.

CREATING AND EXPLICITLY CHARACTERIZING HETEROGENEITY AND NAPL MACRO-SCALE ENTRAPMENT AT THE INTERMEDIATE SCALE

Gilbert R. Barth[1,3], Tissa H. Illangasekare[2], Harihar Rajaram[1] and Mary C. Hill[3],

[1] Civil and Environmental Engineering, University of Colorado, Boulder, CO 80309-0428
[2] Env. Sciences and Eng., Colorado School of Mines, Golden, CO 80401-1887
[3] U.S. Geological Survey, 3215 Marine St., Boulder, CO 80303-1066

The pervasive use of non-aqueous phase liquid (NAPL) has inevitably lead to a considerable number of sites contaminated by NAPLs. Unfortunately, there has been only limited work assessing the behavior of NAPLs for heterogeneous field sites and laboratory experiments. These investigations were forced to deal with different scales of heterogeneity and a more limited heterogeneous system, respectively. However, such work has illustrated the preference of NAPL for certain materials and the propensity for NAPL to be distributed almost exclusively in such materials, at high levels of saturation. This work presents a series of intermediate-scale laboratory experiments that recreate aspects of a field-site dense-NAPL (DNAPL) spill to examine the propensity for distribution and saturation under controlled conditions.

Two sequential, non-aqueous phase liquid (NAPL) injection experiments, performed in an intermediate-scale heterogeneous porous medium, provided the unique opportunity to explicitly characterize NAPL migration and high-saturation entrapment. A 10-meter long two-dimensional tank was filled with a heterogeneous packing using five different sands. The heterogeneity approximated a log normal distribution of hydraulic conductivity (K) with a mean $\ln K$ value of 4.18 ($\mu_{\ln K}$), where K has units of cm/hr, a variance of 1.22 ($\sigma^2_{\ln K} = 1.22$) and an anisotropic exponential covariance structure. The horizontal (λ_h) and vertical (λ_v) correlation scales of $\ln K$ were 50.8 and 5.08 cm, respectively, leading to an anisotropy ratio, $\lambda_v / \lambda_h = 0.1$. A light NAPL was injected into the bottom of the water-saturated heterogeneity. NAPL migration proceeded according to buoyancy and capillary forces, jumping vertically to coarse lenses and then following them laterally for large distances. The rate of NAPL redistribution was monitored at several locations during infiltration, and its distribution mapped at quasi steady state, using a gamma system. Modified ln$K$ distributions were estimated using gamma-system-measured NAPL saturations and the Brooks-Corey relative-permeability function. Variograms of the modified ln$K$ distributions reflect the NAPL's tendency to occupy coarse sand regions, resulting in a large increase in $\sigma^2_{\ln K}$. Variogram structure indicates that differences between the pre-spill and post-spill ln$K$ distribution occur at smaller separations: at separations greater than the spill extent, the post-spill variograms approach the pre-spill variogram. The results provide, (1) unique insight to the migration of NAPL in heterogeneous material, (2) demonstrate extreme contrasts in NAPL saturation and the influence of heterogeneity on NAPL distribution, and (3) provide considerable motivation for using integrated, as opposed to point, methods of NAPL spill characterization.

Although the experimental studies presented here were carried out in a two-dimensional system, similar behavior is plausible in three-dimensional field systems. The most important feature of the entrapped NAPL distribution, macroscale entrapment within coarse lenses, has been observed in the field. With large spill volumes in field settings macroscale entrapment can be expected. For example, using the Borden site parameters, if we consider the dimensions of a typical coarse lens to be of the order of a correlation length in each direction, the pore volume inside such a lens is only about 0.75 m^3. Thus, a large spill can readily lead to macroscale entrapment and local NAPL saturations that are much larger than residual.

This study produced quantitative estimates of the NAPL saturation distribution in an intermediate-scale heterogeneous porous medium. A review of the literature did not reveal any previous experiments involving NAPL spills in a realization of a random field at the scale of the experiments presented, with fine-scale resolution of the heterogeneity. The experimental data on NAPL saturations are potentially useful for evaluating models of NAPL migration in heterogeneous porous media. In particular, it appears that models based on the continuum multiphase flow equations are not capable of predicting the pore-scale fingering which seems to have produced the discontinuous distribution of NAPL saturation. However, recently developed models based on percolation theory appear promising. The dataset produced should serve as a useful, high-quality dataset for testing and improving models of NAPL migration.

ANOMALOUS DIFFUSION IN REGULARLY NON-UNIFORM MEDIA

A.M. Dykhne, I.L. Dranikov, P. S. Kondratenko and A.V. Popov
Nuclear Safety Institute, Russian Academy of Sciences,
52 Bolshaya Tul'skaya St., Moscow 113191, Russia
Phone: (095) 955 2291, Fax: (095) 958 0040, E-mail: kondrat@ibrae.ac.ru

Over the last decades studies of contaminant migration processes in irregular media have experienced the period of intensive development (see, for example, Isichenko (1992) and references therein). In many respects, the reason is in the fact that, for most of the systems under consideration, time dependences of migrant dispersion prove to be anomalous with asymptotic power indexes other than one. Such systems cannot be described by the ordinary transport equation with regular and piecewise differentiable coordinate dependence of parameters, in other words, they have stochastic or fractal structure.

In this study we analyze an example of a very simple system, consisting of two regions with constant parameters in each of them, which exhibits anomalous diffusion properties in extremely wide time range that covers many orders of magnitude.

The problem formulation consists in the following. Classical diffusion in a system consisting of two regions is considered. A region *I*, corresponding to a plane-parallel layer of thickness *a* or a straight cylinder (does not need to be circular) with the same value of characteristic diameter, is filled by a media characterized by diffusivity *D*. A media with diffusivity *d* fills the rest of the space, which is a region *II*. It is supposed that diffusivity of a medium in the first region is significantly higher than a corresponding value for the second region:

$$D >> d \qquad (1)$$

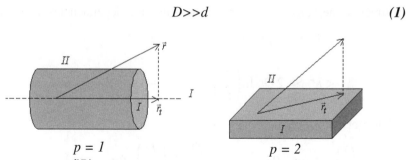

Fig. 1. Geometry of the problem.

At the initial moment of time, contaminant particles are concentrated in the region I, occupying a finite section with characteristic dimension $\geq a$. The aim of the study is to find the time dependence of contaminant dispersion $<r_t^{-2}>$ defined by the relation:

$$< \vec{r}_t^2 > = \frac{\int\limits_{(I)} d\vec{r}\; \vec{r}_t^2\; n(\vec{r},t)}{\int\limits_{(I)} d\vec{r}\; n(\vec{r},t)} \qquad (2)$$

Here, $n(\vec{r},t)$ is contaminant concentration depending on spatial coordinates and time, $\vec{r}_t^2 = (\vec{r}_t \cdot \vec{r}_t)$, where $\vec{r}_t$ is the projection of the radius vector $\vec{r}$ on the boundary plane if the area corresponds to a plane parallel layer (in this case $\vec{r}_t$ has dimensionality $p=2$) or on the generatrix if the region I is a straight cylinder (then the dimensionality of $\vec{r}_t$ is $p=2$). An illustration of the type of media arrangement is presented in Fig. 1. The integrals in Eq. (2) are taken over the region I.

The analysis, based upon the solution of the diffusion equation with the appropriate matching conditions, shows that the processes of contaminant migration are described by radically different regularities depending on a time range. When $t_0 << t << t_1$, where characteristic times t_0 and t_1 are defined as

$$t_0 = a^2 / 4D \qquad\qquad t_1 = a^2 / 4d \qquad (3)$$

contaminant dispersion is given by an the expression:

$$< \vec{r}_t^2 > \cong 2 p D t \qquad (4)$$

For times in the range of $t_1 \ll t \ll t_2$, the following dependencies take place

$$< \vec{r}_t^2 > \cong 4D\sqrt{\pi t t_1} \qquad p = 2 \tag{5}$$

$$< \vec{r}_t^2 > = 2Dt_1 \ln\left(\frac{t}{t_1}\right) \qquad p = 1 \tag{6}$$

And at times $t \gg t_2$ with

$$t_2 \sim \left(\frac{D}{d}\right)^2 t_1 \quad \text{for} \quad p = 2 \qquad t_2 \sim \frac{D}{d}t_1 \ln\left(\frac{D}{d}\right) \quad \text{for} \quad p = 1 \tag{7}$$

we have

$$< \vec{r}_t^2 > \sim 2pdt \tag{8}$$

One can see that for very short ($t \ll t_1$) and very long ($t \gg t_2$) times, t_2 being much greater than t_1, classical diffusion with high (D) and low (d) diffusivities takes place, respectively. In the intermediate range ($t_1 \ll t \ll t_2$), the anomalous diffusion regime (subdiffusion) occurs with dispersion characterized by square root time dependence for a plane parallel layer and by a logarithmic plateau for a straight cylinder. It should be stressed that at very large ratio D/d the limits of this range can be spread over many orders of magnitude and the upper limit t_2 can be virtually inaccessible. In this case, similar to irregular media, the anomalous diffusion mode plays the role of the asymptotic one.

The dispersion behavior is schematically depicted on Fig. 2.

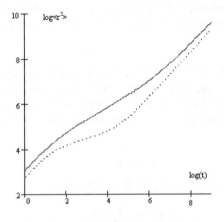

Fig. 2.   Log-log time dependence of dispersion at   (dash line) and at   (solid line).

Diffusion processes in non-uniform media are of special interest in connection with the problem of radioactive waste storage. Fractured rock massifs are a promising place for the waste disposal. Therefore, studies of contaminant particle migration in a unit crack (a region I in our problem), surrounded by a medium of a low permeability (a region II), may be helpful for development of the methods of radioactive waste storage reliability assessments. As applied to this problem, the established in this paper anomalous diffusion regime can be considered as the effect of suppression of the dispersion in fractures.

ACKNOWLEDGMENT

The authors would like to express their deep gratitude to Professor S.A. Rybak for interesting and fruitful discussions.

REFERENCES

ISICHENKO, M.B., Percolation, statistical topography, and transport in random media, Reviews of modern physics, 64, 961-1043, 1992.

EXACTLY AVERAGED EQUATIONS FOR FLOW
AND TRANSPORT IN RANDOM MEDIA

Mark Shvidler and Kenzi Karasaki
*Earth Sciences Division, Lawrence Berkeley National Laboratory, 1
Cyclotron Rd, MS 90-1116, Berkeley, CA 94720; Mshvidler@lbl.gov,
Kkarasaki@lbl.gov*

Recently the methods of analysis for the flow and transport in random media
are finding ever-widening applications in science and technology of various
physical processes. Effective description of flow and transport in irregular
porous media involves interpretation of the porosity and permeability fields
as random functions of the spatial coordinates and the flow velocity as a random function of the spatial coordinates and time. It also involves averaging
of the stochastic system of flow and transport equations containing these
functions (conservation laws, Darcy`s law and closing relations). The avera-
ging problem consists of finding the relations between the non-random functionals of the unknown and the given fields – means, variations, distributions,
densities, etc, or a closed set of equations that contain these functionals. The
greatest interest attaches to the description in which the equations for the averaged functionals are the laws of conservation of mass, momentum, and
energy that are invariant with respect to a certain set of conditions that uniquely determine the process (for example, the initial and boundary conditions). It is apparent that in general this splitting is impossible and thus an
averaged description is used for computing the nonrandom characteristics
(functionals) of the random flow and transport processes for estimating the
uncertainty of these processes. It is possible to select an investigation strategy
from the following three approaches.

1. Exact analytical approach: It is well known that the exact analytical averaging of the equations of flow and transport in random porous media can be realized only for a small number of special, occasionally exotic, fields.

2. Numerical approach: Numerically solve appropriate equations for representative sets of realizations of random fields. This approach is so-called the Monte Carlo technique. The information obtained in this way makes it possible to find the highest moments together with the computation of the local and mean fields of pressure, velocity, etc. However, the exceptionally large volume of calculation and the difficulty for generalizing the results and finding the relations between the known and unknown functionals restrict the significance of this approach.

3. Perturbation theory approach: The methods of averaging are basically approximate. It should be noted that the approximate methods of averaging and derivation of the averaged equations of transport, using either Lagrangian or Eulerian approach, are related to the method of perturbation in one way or another. Every so often one can use the series expansion of small parameters, which specifies the deviation of some fields from their mean values. This approach usually utilizes analytical techniques. Although it is possible to find many results, it should be pointed out that it involves significant difficulties. Even in problems of comparatively simple structures one can usually find only the first terms of the expansion, because the analytical difficulties grow very quickly with the number of terms. Moreover, the convergence of the expansion is not very well studied, especially when the deviation is not very small. One approach utilizes a distinctive space scale for a fast oscillating field as the small parameter. This approach, so-called "homogenization", was largely developed to investigate processes with periodical structures. Many rigorous results were obtained that justify the method, although the computation of the results is highly laborious. For random structures, which is the focus of the present paper, some results have been obtained but the constructive theory is still absent.

Generally speaking, direct averaging and defining the functionals and the relations between them are exceptionally complicated. However, the fundamental information contained in the local equations and their structure has not been sufficiently utilized.

In this context it is difficult to overstate the value of the exact results obtained by using the averaging theory. These results can be exactly averaged flow and transport equations or the exact asymptotic estimation of an averaged concentration field for small and large times. In the latter case it must be remembered that the notation of small and large times for the fields with time dependent sources of solute needs some refinement, because the particles of solute that are inserted in the field at different times have different ages, hence they can have significantly different parameters of dispersion.

Here it is also appropriate to point out the basic difficulty associated with the exact averaging of the transport equations. Even in a simplest case of averaging the stochastic differential equation of transport one needs to compute the correlation moment between the random flow-velocity and the random concentration that is a non-linear functional of flow-velocity. The structure of this functional is not known a priori. We show that an investigation in this direction leads to, for example, finding the forms for the relations between the averaged fields. We demonstrate that this is possible in some cases without actually solving the appropriate equations but only by presupposing the existence of the solutions and using their general properties.

The following question has for a long time stimulated attempts to find the answer: Are there in existence some exact general and sufficiently universal forms of averaged equations for transport of mass, moment, energy, etc? If the answer is positive, then there arises a quest to construct the equations and to analyze them. Many publications can be found related to this subject that discuss different applications. They include hydrodynamics, flow and transport in porous media, theory of elasticity, acoustic and electromagnetic waves in random fields (Batchelor, 1953; Monin and Yaglom, 1965 and 1967; Tatarsky, 1967; Saffman, 1971; Klyatskin, 1975 and 1980; Shermergor, 1979; Shvidler, 1985; Dagan, 1989; Bakhvalov and Panasenko, 1989; Zhikov et all, 1993; Neuman and Orr , 1993; Indelman and Abramovich, 1994; Indelman, 1996; Teodorovich, 1997; Shvidler and Karasaki, 1999).

We present a method of finding the general form of exactly averaged equations by using (1) an assumption of the existence of random Green's functions for appropriate stochastic problems, (2) some general properties of the Green's functions, and (3) the information about the random fields of the conductivity, porosity and flow velocity. We present a general form of the exactly averaged non-local equations for the following cases:

1. Steady-state flow with sources in porous media with random conductivity,

2. Transient flow with sources in compressible media with random conductivity and porosity.

3. Non-reactive solute transport in random porous media.

In this paper we discuss the properties of the non-local averaged equations. We present the results for the case 1 in detail and only the basic results for the other two cases. We discuss the problem of uniqueness and the properties of the non-local averaged equations for the cases with some type of symmetry (isotropic, transversally isotropic and orthotropic). We also present and analyze the hypothesis used to develop the non-local equations in a general case of stochastically homogeneous fields.

HYDRAULIC PROPERTIES OF PARTIALLY SATURATED FRACTURED POROUS MEDIA

Markus Tuller[1] and Dani Or[2]

[1] *Department of Plant, Soil & Entomological Sciences, University of Idaho, Moscow, Idaho 83844. Email: mtuller@uidaho.edu*
[2] *Department of Plants, Soils & Biometeorology, Utah State University, Logan, Utah 84322. E-mail: dani@tmendel.usu.edu*

Fractured porous media (FPM) consist of interconnected fracture and pore networks forming two (or more) distinct pore spaces. Typically, voids of sizes in the order of 10^{-4} to 10^{-2} m are associated with fractures, whereas the porous matrix contains smaller pore sizes in the range of 10^{-7} to 10^{-5} m. The resulting large disparity in hydraulic behavior between fractures and matrix in unsaturated FPM presents practical and theoretical challenges to modeling of total system response. In contrast to relatively well-developed theory and experiment-al data for flow behavior in saturated FPM, theory and measurements for unsaturated FPM are limited. Most modeling approaches employ macroscopic continuum representation where parameterization schemes and constitutive relationships developed for homogeneous porous media are extended to FPM. Such approaches often fail to capture localized and time-varying flow phenomena, and may result in inconsistencies due to the lack of a physical basis for their effective hydraulic parameters. In the absence of consensus regarding the spatial scales, flow behavior, and types of pore space heterogeneity amenable to continuum representation, there is a clear need for physically sound constitutive relationships between matric potential, liquid retention, and hydraulic conductivity. We propose to assemble these relationships for simplified pore space geometry using fundamental solid-liquid physical interactions and basic flow behavior. Such an approach could bridge some gaps between volume-averaged macroscopic representation of flow properties and discrete fracture representation of the FPM, and offer a framework that builds total system response from fundamental physical processes (instead of nonphysical extension of standard porous media parameters).

Progress in modeling equilibrium liquid-vapor interfacial configurations in angular pore space of homogeneous porous media [Tuller et al., 1999; Or and Tuller, 1999] offers a means for derivation of liquid retention characteristics and hydraulic conductivity functions of fractured porous media. The FPM pore space is represented by a bimodal statistical distribution of angular pores and fracture apertures, reflecting the two disparate populations of small matrix pores and larger apertures. Additionally, fracture surfaces roughness is represented by a distribution of angular pits and grooves. Three parallel laminar flow regimes are considered: (1) flow in completely filled pore spaces; (2) corner flow in partially filled pores and grooves; and (3) film flow on surfaces. A key assumption is that equilibrium liquid-vapor interfaces remain stable under slow laminar flow conditions. This assumption enables solutions of the Navier-Stokes equations for flow in thin liquid films and in corners bounded by liquid-vapor interfaces. Liquid-vapor interfacial configurations for different matric potentials are used to derive unsaturated hydraulic conductivity functions from velocity expressions weighted by associated flow cross-sectional areas (these are defined by relative saturation and by liquid configuration in a given pore geometry). The statistical representation of pore space forms the basis for an upscaling scheme that yields analytical expressions for sample-scale hydraulic functions.

In this study we focus on derivation of fracture domain hydraulic conductivity, for details on matrix hydraulic conductivity we refer interested readers to a companion study by Tuller and Or [2001]. Unlike the relatively small role of the fracture domain in determining overall liquid retention behavior of the rock mass, this domain dominates the hydraulic conductivity of the FPM near saturation. The composite unsaturated hydraulic conductivity function contains multiple "humps" representing at least three processes: (1) fracture flow (dominates under wet conditions); (2) matrix capillary flow (controls conductivity for intermediate wetness range); and (3) matrix film flow (important under dry conditions). Presently, the biggest obstacle to model application is the lack of definitive data sets. The 2-D analysis presented in this study relies on some measure of fracture aperture distribution, which may be derived from image analysis, due to the limited information contained in fracture domain liquid retention. However, considering evidence suggesting that less than 20% of the fractures are water conducting [Chiles and de Marsily, 1993], this casts some doubts on the direct use of such image-based geometrical information. We are thus left with limited options with respect to reliable input data for the model, and the most robust input variable is a direct measurement of FPM saturated permeability. Critical path analysis offers an additional avenue for considerations of potential 3-D effects using fracture aperture distribution (rather than the detailed 3-D network). The results reduce the problem to calculation of the saturated permeability of a "critical" unit fracture element. First order approximations for inclusion of 3-D network effects, either based on direct measurements of saturated hydraulic conductivity, or from theoretical considerations applying critical path analysis are proposed. Effects of non-equilibrium conditions between matrix and fracture domains on the hydraulic conductivity function are discussed.

The model is applied to two datasets with different pore and fracture characteristics. Datasets containing information on matrix and fracture liquid retention and unsaturated permeability, as well as other physical properties of the two domains, are virtually non-existent. A comprehensive search of relevant literature spanning the last few decades yielded only a few incomplete datasets suitable to test the proposed model. In the following, we use data for Tiva Canyon welded tuff reported by Wang and Narasimhan [1993] to illustrate

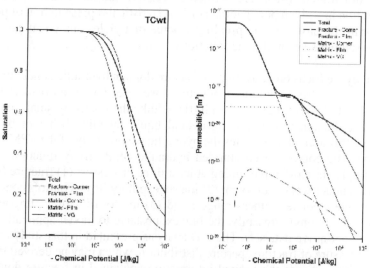

Figure 1. Calculated saturation and predicted permeability curves for the Tiva Canyon welded tuff unit. Note the corner and film flow contributions within the matrix and fracture domains.

the primary features of the proposed model, and a dataset for crystalline rock reported by researchers at the Swiss Federal Institute of Technology (SFIT) [Fischer et al., 1998; Gimmi et al., 1997] for model applications. While the results depicted in Figs.1 and 2 are encouraging, they point to a critical need for definitive data sets for unsaturated FPM.

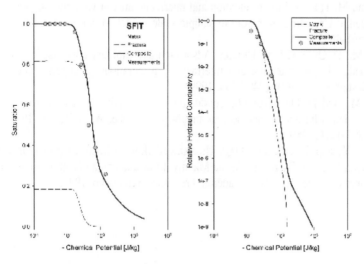

Figure 2. Calculated saturation and predicted permeability curves for the SFIT granodiorite. Note the corner and film flow contributions within the matrix and fracture domains.

ACKNOWLEDGEMENTS

The authors gratefully acknowledge the partial support the USDA-NRI under grant 2001-35107-10181, and the Nuclear Regulatory Commission (NRC) under Contract No. NRC-02-97-009 to the Center for Nuclear Waste Regulatory Analysis (CNWRA). This study is an independent product of a contract to the CNWRA and does not necessarily reflect the view or regulatory position of the NRC.

REFERENCES

CHILES, J.P., and G. DE MARSILY, Stochastic models of fracture systems and their use in flow and transport modeling, In: Bear, J., Ch.-F. Tsang, and G. de Marsily, Flow and contaminant transport in fractured rock, pp. 169-236, Academic Press Inc., San Diego, 1993.

FISCHER, U., B. KULLI, and H. FLÜHLER, Constitutive relationships and pore structure of undisturbed fracture zone samples with cohesionless fault gauge layers, Water Resour. Res., 34(7), 1695-1701, 1998.

GIMMI, T., M. SCHNEEBELI, H. FLÜHLER, H. WYDLER, and T. BAER, Field-scale transport in unsaturated crystalline rock, Water Resour. Res., 33(4), 589-598, 1997.

OR, D. and M. TULLER, Liquid retention and interfacial area in variably saturated porous media: Upscaling from pore to sample scale model, Water Resour. Res., 35(12), 3591-3605, 1999.

TULLER, M., D. OR, and L.M. DUDLEY, Adsorption and capillary condensation in porous media: Liquid retention and interfacial configurations in angular pores, Water Resour. Res., 35(7), 1949-1964, 1999.

TULLER, M., and D. OR, Hydraulic conductivity of variably saturated porous media - Laminar film and corner flow in angular pore space, Water Resour. Res., 37(5), 1257-1276, 2001.

WANG, J.S.Y., and T.N. NARASIMHAN, Unsaturated flow in fractured porous media, In: Bear, J., Ch.-F. Tsang, and G. de Marsily, Flow and contaminant transport in fractured rock, pp. 325- 394, Academic Press Inc., San Diego, 1993.

ANALYTICAL SOLUTIONS FOR COLLOID TRANSPORT IN FRACTURED MEDIA USING EFFECTIVE PARAMETERS AND COMPARISON WITH INNOVATIVE PARTICLE TRACKING ALGORITHMS

Scott C. James[1] and Constantinos V. Chrysikopoulos[2]

[1] *Department of Civil and Environmental Engineering, University of California, Irvine, CA 92697–2175, sjames@eng.uci.edu, (949) 824--7711*

[2] *Department of Civil and Environmental Engineering, University of California, Irvine, CA 92697–2175, costas@eng.uci.edu, (949) 824–8661*

Analytical solutions are derived in this work that describe the transport of finitely sized monodisperse and polydisperse particles of neutral buoyancy within a semi–infinite, uniform aperture fracture subject to several boundary and initial conditions. The transport of one monodisperse and three polydisperse particle plumes composed of spherical particles with equivalent mean but different log–normally distributed diameters are investigated. Instantaneous as well as continuous particle injections are examined. Both reversible and irreversible particle–wall interactions are considered. We derive expressions for the effective velocity and effective dispersion coefficient for spherical particles, and it is shown that both the finite particle size and the characteristics of the particle diameter distribution significantly affect the shape of particle concentration breakthrough curves. Because the finite size of a particle excludes it from the slowest moving portion of the velocity profile, the effective particle velocity is increased, while the overall particle dispersion is reduced. Furthermore, increasing the standard deviation of the particle diameter distributions enhances particle spreading and increases the number of sorbed particles when particle–wall interactions are taken into account. Both constant spatial step and constant time step particle tracking techniques are employed to examine the breakthrough curves of instantaneous releases of polydisperse colloids. Excellent agreement between the analytical solution and both particle tracking algorithms is observed.

Characterization of chemical heterogneeity and reactions and ramifications for field-scale fate

MODELING OF REACTIVE CONTAMINANT TRANSPORT IN HYDRAULICALLY AND HYDROGEOCHEMICALLY HETEROGENEOUS AQUIFERS USING AN UPSCALING APPROACH BASED ON SEDIMENTOLOGICAL FACIES

Thomas Ptak, Rudolf Liedl

*Applied Environmental Geoscience, University of Tuebingen,
Sigwartstrasse 10, 72076 Tuebingen, Germany
Phone: +49-7071-2976991, Fax: +49-7071-5059,
e-mail: thomas.ptak@uni-tuebingen.de*

INTRODUCTION

It is well known that aquifer structural properties and the resulting heterogeneous distribution of hydraulic conductivity and porosity significantly control groundwater flow and spreading of solutes. In addition to this, physicochemical aquifer heterogeneity, i.e. different sorption and desorption properties for different source rocks of the aquifer material (lithological components) grouped in different grain size fractions, influence the interaction of reactive solutes with the aquifer material, and may tend to enhance tailing of reactive solutes, compared to non-reactive ones.

To be able to consider both the physical (hydraulic conductivity, porosity) and the hydrogeochemical aquifer heterogeneities (different sorption and desorption parameters for different lithological components of the aquifer material and the different grain size fractions), a three-dimensional finite-difference solute transport modeling approach was developed. This approach is based on a sedimentological facies characterization using categorical variables and allows for upscaling of small-scale hydraulic and hydrogeochemical parameters, measured at laboratory scale, to field-scale scenarios.

THE THREE-DIMENSIONAL REACTIVE TRANSPORT MODELING APPROACH

The concept and the basic steps of the reactive transport simulation approach are summarized in Figure 1.

For an application of the modeling approach, the aquifer is represented by a three-dimensional finite-difference model grid. Due to the hydraulic and hydrogeochemical aquifer heterogeneity, the lithological composition and the grain size distribution may differ from one model cell to another. The data needed are introduced into each model cell following a facies-based categorical variable approach (Fig. 1). Since it is known that aquifer hydraulic properties are closely linked to the sedimentary lithofacies (for example well sorted sand, gravel with fine grain matrix etc., e.g. Kleineidam et al. 1999), the aquifer body is at first classified at the model cell scale (order of tens of cm) into typical lithofacies types (Ptak 1997), which may be interpreted as aquifer material categories.

Then, for each lithofacies (aquifer material category, cluster of grain size distribution curves), characteristic sediment samples are collected, and a sediment material decomposition and analysis / batch experiment procedure is applied (Fig. 1) to obtain the lithofacies-specific hydraulic parameters, mass fraction of (j,k)-grains (here j = index denoting a lithological component and k = index denoting a grain size class) and the lithocomponent-specific hydrogeochemical parameters, which are described below. Herfort (2000) has shown that each facies exhibits different hydraulic and hydrogeochemical parameters. Of course, depending on the aquifer genesis, the facies properties may be site specific.

In the next step, a facies type has to be assigned to each finite-difference model cell within the simulation domain. For the facies-based approach, the three-dimen-sional condi-tional sequenti-al indicator simulation method (SIS) for categori-cal variables (Deutsch and Journel, 1992), which represent the different facies types respective aquifer material categories, is applied to generate conditioned equi-probable three-dimensio-nal realiza-tions of the facies fields. The indicator-based geostatistical simulation technique was improved by imposing directional trends on the anisotropy axes of indicator variogram models and merging of different stochastic facies images (Vert et al. 1999). With this approach a much more realistic image of the subsurface is obtained as compared to conventional geostatistical approaches.

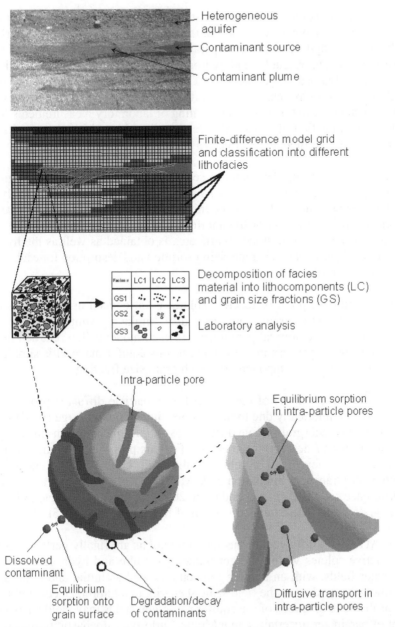

Figure 1. Concept and basic steps of the three-dimensional reactive transport modeling approach.

Since, as an outcome of the geostatistical generation step, a facies type is assigned to each model cell, and since each facies exhibits characteristic hydraulic and hydrogeochemical parameters as shown by Herfort (2000), three-dimensional hydraulic and hydrogeochemical aquifer parameter distributions are obtained simultaneously. These parameter distributions are then used in a next step for reactive transport simulations at field scale, employing a numerical code. In this way, an upscaling of laboratory measurements for a numerical simulation of field-scale scenarios is achieved implicitly, without the need to define field-scale effective parameter values.

As a result of the aquifer material separation into individual lithologi-cal components j and grain size fractions k, and subsequent laboratory analyses and batch experi-ments (Fig. 1), the lithological composition of each characteristic grain size fraction of the aquifer material, i.e. the percentage of, for instance, sandstone, limestone, quartz etc., is obtained as well as the hydrogeochemical parameters characterizing sorption and desorption for each individual lithocomponent.

Sorption and desorption of reactive solutes is introduced using a diffusion-based formulation at grain scale, instead of employing simple transfer rate models involving empirical parameters. In each model cell, a retarded intra-particle diffusion process in the heterogeneous aquifer material is simulated for each lithological component and each grain size fraction.

The mathematical model of the retarded intra-particle diffusion process has to be solved numerically due to the complex interaction of large (field) scale transport and local (grain) scale diffusion as well as linear or non-linear equilibrium sorption / desorption processes. For this purpose, a solution technique has been developed combining the well known three-dimensional groundwater transport simulation code MT3D (Zheng 1990) and a new finite-difference code IPD (Jaeger and Liedl 2000) for the intra-particle diffusion at the grain scale. The extended version of MT3D is called MT3D-IPD.

Using MT3D-IPD, flow and transport simulations are finally perfor-med for the reactive solutes within the generated hy-draulic and hydrogeochemical parameter fields, with an aquifer geometry as well as initial and boun-dary conditions accor-ding to the field scale scenario. In addition, an en-semble of equiprobable realizations of the aquifer parameter fields may yield an assessment of parameter uncertainty in a Monte-Carlo-type stochastic framework.

EXAMPLE OF APPLICATION

In order to demonstrate the applicability of the modeling approach, and to emphasize the importance of a correct representation of aquifer material lithology in reactive transport simulations, a simple one-dimensional example scenario has been selected, representing flow and transport during a column experiment. In this first example, the focus is on hydrogeochemical heterogeneity only. Therefore a hydraulically homogeneous column was chosen.

The first modeling results emphasize the strong impact of the lithological aquifer material composition and confirm the need for a complex process-based reactive transport modeling approach with spatially variable hydraulic and hydrogeochemical aquifer parameters.

REFERENCES

DEUTSCH, C.V. and JOURNEL, A.G. (1992): GSLIB Geostatistical software library and user's guide. Oxford University Press, New York, 340 pp.

HERFORT, M. (2000): Reactive transport of organic compounds within a heterogeneous porous aquifer. Ph. D. Thesis, C54, University of Tübingen, Center for Applied Geoscience, Tübingen, 59 pp.

JAEGER, R. and LIEDL, R. (2000): Prognose der Sorptionskinetik organischer Schadstoffe in heterogenem Aquifermaterial (Predicting sorption kinetics of organic contaminants in heterogeneous aquifer material). Grundwasser 5(2): 57-66.

KLEINEIDAM, S., RÜGNER, H. and GRATHWOHL, P. (1999): Impact of grain scale heterogeneity on slow sorption kinetics. Environ. Toxic. Chem. 18(8): 1673-1678.

PTAK, T. (1997): Evaluation of reactive transport processes in a heterogene-ous porous aquifer within a non-parame-tric numerical stocha-stic transport model-ling framework based on sequenti-al indicator simulation of categorical variables. In A. Soares et al. (eds.), geoENV I - Geostatistics for Environmental Applications, Kluwer: 153-164.

VERT, M., PTAK, T., BIVER, P. and VITTORI, J. (1999): Geostatistical generation of three-dimensional aquifer realizations using the conditional SIS approach with direction trends imposed on variogram models. In J. J. Gomez-Hernandez et al. (eds.), geoENV II - Geostatistics for Environmental Applications, Kluwer: 343-354.

ZHENG, C. (1990): MT3D – A modular three-dimensional transport model for simulation of advection, dispersion and chemical reactions of contaminants in groundwater systems. S. S. Papadopoulos and Associates, Inc.

CHARACTERIZATION OF GEOCHEMICAL PROPERTIES AND POTENTIAL REACTIVITY OF FLUVIAL DEPOSITS USING A FACIES BASED APPROACH

Pieter-Jan van Helvoort, Peter A. Burrough and Pauline F.M. van Gaans,
*Centre for Geo-ecological Research, Department of Physical Geography,
Utrecht University, P.O. Box 80115, 3508 TC Utrecht, The Netherlands*

INTRODUCTION

Characterization of heterogeneity in sedimentary deposits is essential for a sound prediction of ground water movement and solute transport. Koltermann & Gorelick (1996) categorized methods for hydraulic property characterization and estimation in three groups: deterministic, stochastic and mixed. The advantage of the mixed approach is that the incorporation of geologic observations stratifies the heterogeneity problem and enables us to focus on the characterization of more homogeneous sedimentologic facies units. Complex fluvial deposits comprise systematic alterations of sandy and clayey facies, each related to a specific depositional environment. The combination of a sedimentary facies model and the characterization of hydraulic properties of the facies can predict spatial variation of hydraulic conductivity of fluvial deposits more effectively than pure deterministic and stochastic methods. Therefore, many authors believe the facies-based approach is useful for the spatial characterization of aquifer heterogeneity in fluvial districts (Allen-King, 1998; Anderson, 1989, 1997; Bierkens et al., 1994).

In addition to the characterization of hydraulic properties, solute transport models also require geochemical characterization of sediment properties to enable the prediction of sediment water-interaction and reactive plume movement in the subsurface (e.g. Allen-King, 1998; Davis, 1997). Johnsson (1993) mentioned four main factors that control the chemical composition of clastic sediments: (1) source rock composition, (2) chemical weathering processes acting on source rock, (3) transport, sorting and depositional processes, (4) diagenesis after burial. Due to sorting and diagenetic processes, different compositions result in sediments even if they have a common source. Hence, it is expected that geochemistry and facies are related, because both are affected by syn- and post depositional environment.

In this research, we identify eight key parameters that describe the geochemical variation of unconsolidated Holocene fluviatile deposits in the Rhine-Muese delta (Netherlands). We apply this set of parameters to characterize the geochemical properties of six sedimentary facies defined after a depositional model, which was developed earlier for this area (Törnqvist, 1993b; Weerts, 1996). Finally, the geochemical characterization is used to assess potential reactive properties of the facies, which should be considered for reactive solute transport modelling. The characterization presented is a first step in schematizing aquifer/aquitard heterogeneity for fluvial deposits using the facies-based method.

CHARACTERIZATION OF THE GEOCHEMICAL AND GRAIN SIZE DATA

A set of 110 sediment samples taken from six different sedimentary facies occurring in the delta was analysed for bulk chemistry and grain size. A principal components analysis performed on the geochemical data showed that six components explained 95% of the total variance. Eight geochemical key parameters with factor scores > 0.4 for any of the extracted components were used to describe geochemical variation of the sample population. The selected key parameters were divided into two groups of non-reactive and reactive fractions (Table 1), according to their supposed capability to interact with ground water. A second division was made to separate key parameters with a clear relation with grain size from those that were not, by calculating significant correlations of the key parameters with grain size.

The four key parameters that have significant correlations with grain size explain 45% of total variance. Among these are non-reactive contituents embedded in clay mineral lattices (Al_2O_3 and Fe_2O_3) and Na-bearing feldspars (Na_2O). The only reactive fraction directly related to grainb size is the CEC, associated with clay mineral surface. The other part of the variance (50%) is explained by parameters that are no part of the clastic matrix. They

GROUP	KEY PARAMETERS		RELATED SEDIMENT FRACTION
	grain-size related	not related to grain size	
non-reactive	Al_2O_3		clay minerals (clay fraction)
	Fe_2O_3		clay minerals (clay fraction)
	Na_2O		feldspars (silt fraction)
reactive	CEC*		surface exchanger clay
		CEC	surface exchanger OM**
		OM	organic matter
		$CaCO_3$	carbonate
		Fe_2O_3 - MnO	Fe/Mn oxides
		Fe_2O_3 - P_2O_5	Fe-phosphates

*CEC = cation exchange capacity   **OM = organic matter

Table 1. Grouping of key parameters and related sediment fractions

represent a reactive fraction and do not have a direct relation with grain size. Note that CEC is related to both classes, because it is also related to OM content. Fe_2O_3 occurs as reactive contituent in Fe-oxides or reduced Fe-minerals and as non-reactive species in clay mineral lattice.

CHARACTERIZATION OF SIX SEDIMENTARY FACIES UNITS

The classification of Holocene deposits in the Dutch deltaic plain into six facies units (see Table 2) is a simplification of the facies model earlier developed for this area (Törnqvist, 1993b; Weerts, 1996). In a strict sense, the depositional architecture consists of architectural elements recognized at the 100-1000m scale, such as channels belts or floodplains. Each architectural element comprises a set of facies with different grain size or structure at a much smaller scale (Miall, 1996) like foresets or lateral accretion planes in channel deposits. Regarding the scale of property characterization that matches with regional solute transport modelling, the architectural elements are possibly the appropriate scale for this purpose. Therefore, we will use the most dominant facies unit of the architectural elements in the characterization.

Facies code	Architectural element	Lithology	Reactive properties	Potential
CHS	channel belts	fine-coarse sand	carbonate	low
ES	inland dunes	fine- medium sand	organic matter	low
CHC	natural levees, crevasse splays	sandy clay	CEC, carbonate, Fe/Mn oxides	medium to high
LB	loam beds (early Holocene)	sandy clay, organi[c]	CEC, OM	medium
FPC	overbank deposits	massive clay	CEC, Fe-phosphates	high
FPO	organic deposits	peat	CEC, OM, Fe-phosphates	high

Table 2. Facies codes, architectural elements, lithology, reactive properties and potential.

Figure 1 is indicative for the results of the geochemical characterization of the six facies units. The box plots of the two selected key parameters Al_2O_3 and $CaCO_3$ show that the facies are chemically different, having different means and ranges. Also, the key parameters show different patterns across the facies, indicating that grain size can not be the only source of chemical heterogeneity in these deposits. Different carbonate contents in two sandy facies with comparable grain size (CHS and ES) resulted from carbonate lea-ching in inland dunes (ES) that had a longer exposure time than channel deposits (CHS) before burial. Thus, the results suggest that facies units are more than grain-size units alone and that facies-bound diagenetic processes such as carbonate leaching also have a clear imprint on bulk chemistry.

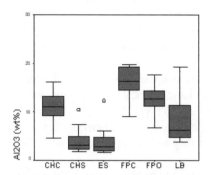 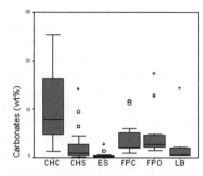

Figure 1. Box plots of Al2O3 and carbonate content in six sedimentary facies. Boxes include interquartile range with median (horizontal line), whiskers show the range of samples within 1.5 times the interquartile range of the box. Circles represent samples that are higher than 1.5 interquartile ranges, and asterisks greater than 3 times the range. See Table 2 for facies codes explanation.

Table 2 lists for each facies the most important reactive fractions based on the interpretation of the complete set of eight key parameters per facies. The relative potential indicates how much of the reactive fraction mentioned is present in a facies. The CEC is the only reactive parameter with a significant correlation with grain size (Table 1). However, most reactive fractions are also associated with finely textured facies occurring in floodplains, natural levees and crevasse splays. This suggests that there also exists an indirect relation between reactive properties of facies and its texture. Alternatively stated, grain size imposes a clear effect on the hydrologic regime. Local hydrology is the driving force in regulating diagenetic and solute transport processes that determine the occurrence of reactive constituents within a facies.

REFERENCES

ALLEN KING R. M. et al. (1998) Characterizing the heterogeneity and correlation of perchloroethene sorption and hydraulic conductivity using a facies-based approach. Water Resources Research 34, 385-396.

ANDERSON M. P. (1989) Hydrogeologic facies models to delineate large-scale spatial trends in glacial and glacio-fluvial sediments. Geological Society of America Bulletin 101, 501-511.

ANDERSON M. P. (1997) In Subsurface Flow and Transport (ed. G. Dagan and S. P. Neuman). Chap. 1, pp. 23-43. Cambridge University Press.

BIERKENS, M.F.P., WEERTS, H.J.T. and BURROUGH, P.A. (1994). Geostatistical characterization of a semi-permeable layer. In Engeneering Geology of Quartary Sediments (ed. N. Rengers) Rotterdam, Balkema. pp.73-92.

DAVIS, J.A. (1997). Spatial heterogeneity of geochemical and hydrologic parameters affecting metal transport in ground water. EPA Environmetal Research Brief. Reportnr. EPA/600/S-92/006, pp. 1-22.

JOHNSSON, M.J. (1993). The system controlling the composition of clastic sediments. In Processes controlling the compositionn of clastic sediments (ed. Johnsson, M.J. and Basu, A.) Geological Society of America Special Paper 284, 1-19.

KOLTERMAN, C.E. and GORELICK, S.M. (1996). Heterogeneity in sedimentary deposits: A review of structure-imitating, process imitating and descriptive approaches. Water Resources Research 32, 2617-2658.

MIALL, A.D. (1996). The geology of Fluvial Deposits. Sedimentary Facies, Basin Analysis, and Petroleum Geology. New York. pp. 582.

TÖRNQVIST, T.E. (1993b). Fluvial sedimentary geology and chronology of the Holocen Rhine-Meuse delta, The Netherlands. Nederlands Geografische Studies 166, pp. 1-169. PhD. thesis.

WEERTS H.J.T. (1996) Complex Confining Layers. Architecture and hydraulic properties of Holocene and Late Wechselian deposits in the fluvial Rhine-Meuse delta, The Netherlands. NGS 213, pp. 1-187. PhD. thesis.

A REACTIVE TRANSPORT INVESTIGATION OF A SEAWATER INTRUSION EXPERIMENT IN A MILDLY PHYSICAL AND GEOCHEMICAL HETEROGENEOUS AQUIFER

F. D. Christensen and P. Engesgaard
Environment & Resources DTU, Technical University of Denmark
Flemming Damgaard Christensen, Technical University of Denmark,
Environment & Resources, 2800 Kgs. Lyngby, Denmark.
Email: fdc@er.dtu.dk

Previous investigations on seawater intrusion have mainly focused on either the physical density flow system with transport of a single non-reactive species or on the geochemical aspects neglec-ting density effects. The current study focuses on both the physical and geochemical aspects of seawater intrusion and their interaction during a small-scale intrusion experiment in a shallow coastal aquifer in Denmark. This paper presents preliminary mode-ling results of the effects of the forced seawater intrusion in the mildly physical and geochemical heterogeneous aquifer.

INTRODUCTION

The field site experiment consisted of three steps: (1) monitor the natural physical and biogeochemical conditions, (2) create a forced intrusion by pumping and monitor the inward movement of the seawater interface and biogeochemical changes, and (3) stop pumping, and monitor the outward movement of the interface.

Seawater intrusion is accompanied by cation exchange processes and by degradation of organic matter due to the large sulfate source in the intruding seawater. Degradation increases alkalinity and thus affects calcite saturation. Cation exchange, degradation, and mineral reactions are therefore strongly interdependent. These sets of reactions are trigged to various degrees in the mildly heterogeneous aquifer.

A new 3D numerical model PHASTD has been developed that can simulate density flow and transport with biogeochemical reactions. The code was developed by coupling the single-species variable density transport code HST3D with the geochemical reaction code PHREEQC.

PHYSICAL AND CHEMICAL HETEROGENEITY

The experiment is modelled in a cross-section located along a transect of wells and Figure 1 shows the two-dimensional hydrogeological model used in the modelling of the experiment. The following biogeochemical reactions were included: (1) cation exchange, (2) calcite dissolution and precipitation, (3) secondary redox processes and (4) biodegradation. Reactions (1-3) were assumed at equilibrium, while biodegradation was assumed kinetically controlled.

The aquifer is anoxic and contains reactive organic matter in varying amounts. The distribution of the organic matter is believed to be correlated with zones of lower or higher hydraulic conduc-tivity. A mixed sand and peat layer is located above an impermeable peat layer and has a smaller hydraulic conduc-tivity than the main sand aquifer. Within the main sand aquifer there are six lenses (type 4-9 in Figure 1), where the sand is mixed with peat, which results in a lower hydraulic conductivity. Different hydraulic conductivities, Cation Exchange Capacities (CEC) and degradation rates were used for the different layers and lenses. The CEC was measured mainly in the sand aquifer, with a mean value of 0.51 meq/100g. For the peat lenses (type 4-9) larger CEC were used and for the two sand layers (type 10-11) a smaller value were used.

PHYSICAL NATURAL AND FORCED INTRUSIONS

First the natural situation is simulated by running the model for a long period to get the initial conditions for the forced intrusion. Figure 2 shows the relative chloride concentration together with flow velocity vectors for the first 70-meter. The wedge shaped form of the intrusion is created due to the density difference between seawater and freshwater. The wedge shaped form is kept during the forced intrusion (Figure 3).

Figure 3 shows the 50 % seawater fraction at different times after pumping started. The groundwater table and velocity distribution are after 180 days of

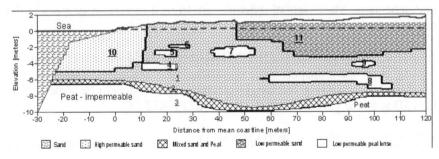

Figure 1: The hydrogeological model setup. The numbers refer to sediment type.

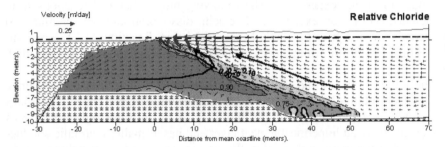

Figure 2: Results from the natural situation (simulation period of 40 years with constant boundaries conditions). Only the first part of the aquifer that is affected by seawater intrusion is shown.

pumping. The movement of the interface does not seem to be largely affected by physical heterogeneity within the first 150 days of pumping. At later times lens 8 and the change in elevation of the sand and peat layer noticeably affect the movement of the interface. After 210 days of pumping the flow is divided up in two flow paths around lens 8, 60-70 meters from the coast line.

The heterogeneity also is visual on the biogeochemical evolvement during the seawater intrusion. Figure 4 shows the enrichment of calcium (DCa positive) after 180 days of pumping, which is due exchange of calcium from the cation exchanger with sodium from the intruded seawater. The effects of the high CEC for lens 7 and the mixed sand and peat layer is noticeably due to a high release of calcium. For more figures with the biogeochemistry, see the CD with the full manuscript.

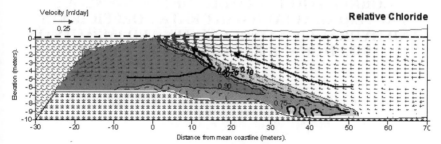

Figure 3: The movement of the interface illustrated by the 50% seawater fraction at 0, 90,120, 150, 180, 210, 240 and 270 days after start of pumping. The velocity map and groundwater table is after 180 days after pump start.

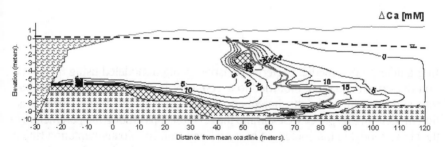

Figure 4: Results from the forced situation after 180 days of pumping. The thick solid line is the 0.5 seawater fraction, the mean sea/freshwater interface. The fill represents more than 30 mM for ΔCa.

CORRELATION BETWEEN HETEROGENEOUS BACTERIAL ATTACHMENT RATE COEFFICIENTS AND HYDRAULIC CONDUCTIVITY AND IMPACTS ON FIELD-SCALE BACTERIAL TRANSPORT

Timothy D. Scheibe

Pacific Northwest National Laboratory, tim.scheibe@pnl.gov Richland, WA, USA

In granular porous media, bacterial transport is often modeled using the advection-dispersion equation, modified to account for interactions between the bacteria and grain surfaces (attachment and detachment) using a linear kinetic reaction model. In this paper we examine the relationships among the parameters of the above model in the context of bacterial transport for bioaugmentation (injection of bacteria into the subsurface to augment the existing population for purposes of enhancing in situ bioremediation). In this context, we wish to quantify the distance to which significant concentrations of bacteria can be transported, as well as the uniformity with which they can be distributed within the subsurface. Because kinetic detachment rates (Kr) are typically much smaller than corresponding attachment rates (Kf), the attachment rate exerts primary control on the distance of bacterial transport. Hydraulic conductivity (K) also plays a significant role in bacterial transport because of its direct relationship to the advective velocity and its typically high degree of spatial variability at field scales. Because Kf is related to the velocity, grain size, and porosity of the medium, as is K, it is reasonable to expect that there exists correlation between these two parameters. Previous investigators have assumed a form of correlation between Kf and $\ln(K)$ based in part on reparameterization of clean-bed filtration equations in terms of published relations between grain size, effective porosity, and $\ln(K)$. The hypotheses examined here are that (1) field-scale relationships between K and Kf can be developed by combining a number of theoretical and empirical results in the context of a heterogeneous aquifer flow model (following a similar approach to previous investigators with some extensions), and (2) correlation between K and Kf will enhance the distance of field-scale bacterial transport in granular aquifers. We test these hypotheses using detailed numerical models and observations of field-scale bacterial transport in a shallow sandy aquifer within the South Oyster Site near Oyster, Virginia, USA.

QUANTIFYING THE EFFECTS OF CHEMICAL HETEROGENEITY BY COMBINING LAGRANGEAN TRANSPORT AND THE EXPOSURE-TIME CONCEPT

U. Seeboonruang, T.R. Ginn, and C.T. Green
University of California, Davis

Many dissolved subsurface contaminants undergo transport with heterogeneous reactions. In such cases, the fate of a contaminant depends on physical and chemical properties of the aquifer. While the physical properties of subsurface porous media govern transport of solutes, fate often depends on contact times of the solutes with spatially variable reactive mineral and organic surfaces. The total time that the solute contacts these reactive zones is known "cumulative reactivity" or "reaction time." This parameter may be used to predict the amount of transformation of a solute without having to simulate transport through multiple, heterogeneous reactive zones. Thus, the objectives of this study are 1) to develop a Lagrangean transport model with the exposure time concept to characterize the cumulative reactivity as a distribution function, 2) to use the distribution in scaling, or averaging, spatially-dependent reactive transport, and 3) to investigate the effects of the correlation between physical and chemical heterogeneity on reactive transport using the Lagrangean description of travel time and cumulative reactivity in the form of a joint distribution function. The ultimate goal is a predictive model of solute breakthrough curves observed at arrival locations in physically and chemically heterogeneous flow fields in the natural subsurface.

The newly developed Lagrangean method, called the modified stochastic convective reactive method (mSCR), is based on the conventional streamtube stochastic convective reactive technique (SCR), which addresses the problem of transport and fate in heterogeneous aquifers using the concept of variations in travel times within an ensemble of streamtubes characterizing heterogeneity in physical properties. The main advantages of the streamtube method over direct Eulerian simulation of reactive fate and transport with heterogeneous properties are that the reliance on perfect characterization of the heterogeneous subsurface is replaced by the reliance on functions describing how solute flux is distributed over travel time and cumulative reactivity. This advantage is obtained by focusing the modeling on solute arrival distributions instead of the plume characterization.

The streamtube method treats transport as divided among macroscale one-dimensional convective-dispersive paths that do not exchange mass. The streamtube ensemble can be approximated with a corresponding ensemble of effective streamtubes each with a constant effective velocity. Given a distribution of solute flux over travel time, a flux-averaged solute concentration at a given location can be calculated by weighting particular breakthrough curve solutions corresponding to ith streamtube, c_i, with the corresponding fractional flux of the discrete travel time distribution,

$$p_i, \ \langle c \rangle (t;x) = \sum_{i=1}^{I} c_i(t) p_i \ .$$

However, the standard streamtube method has been limited by the invariance condition requiring uniformity of chemical reactions over the flow domain. The modified streamtube approach amends the ability of the previously developed streamtube method to handle solid-phase reactive heterogeneity occurring within a transport domain. The technique is based on the following concepts: the exposure time concept, the random walk particle tracking method, and the streamtube method.

Firstly we restrict the analysis to reaction kinetic expressions that can be factored into spatially dependent and concentration-dependent terms. Using the concept of exposure time, the spatially dependent term is first transformed into a spatially invariant mass transfer model involving a constant effective reactivity rate. This constant effective reactivity rate represents the global density of reaction sites along the streamtube's path, and it can be expressed as the ratio of cumulative reactivity to travel time for the solute parcels within the streamtube. Because each solute parcel experiences varying degrees of reactivity within a streamtube that is defined by physical properties (e.g., travel-time) alone, a single value of an effective reaction parameter cannot capture complexities of the reactions. Rather, a constant reactivity ensemble, (i.e. an ensemble of constant effective velocities and an ensemble of cumulative reactivity) is required to approximate the chemical heterogeneity.

Analogous to the distributing flux over travel times within a single streamtube, in the mSCR method we approximate the effects of chemical heterogeneity by additionally distributing flux also over cumulative reactivity. To do this, the flux in a given streamtube is redistributed into a subensemble of streamtubes all with the same travel time but each with a different cumulative reactivity and different corresponding flux. Thus, solute flux in the mSCR is distributed jointly over both travel time and cumulative reactivity, $p_{i,j}$. One way to obtain an explicit estimate of this joint distribution is to perform particle tracking with the knowledge of spatially dependent information and to record particle travel time and cumulative reactivity during transport and at breakthrough. Given a discrete joint distribution over travel time and exposure time $p_{i,j}$, the flux-averaged reactive solute breakthrough can then be approximated with the flux weighting method,

$$\langle c \rangle (t;x) = \sum_{i=1}^{I} \sum_{j=1}^{J} c_{i,j}(t) p_{i,j}$$

The flux-weighted distribution is used in the mSCR method to generate breakthrough curves of the reactive solutes.

An intermediate-scale flow experiment designed to study the effect of bimodal physical heterogeneity on biodegradation as described in Murphy et al. (1997) is used as a basis for this study. The two-dimensionally heterogeneous porous medium is constructed of sand with low conductivity inclusions distributed within. In this modeling extension, we hypothesize a negative correlation between the hydraulic conductivity and reactivity, such that reactions occur only within the inclusions. We simulate the breakthrough curves resulting from the injection of 10-hour unit pulses of passive and reactive tracers at the inlet. First-order kinetic sorption/desorption is used in this analysis. Breakthrough curves of the passive and reactive tracers obtained with the deterministic numerical code, RAFT, [Chilakapati, 1995] are used as baselines for comparison to the simulated breakthrough curves obtained with the mSCR method.

The results of the mSCR simulations are as follows. The passive tracer breakthrough curve comparison implies that the discrete travel time distribution acquired by performing particle tracking may serve as a useful representation of the Eulerian physical parameters, (i.e. hydraulic conductivity and boundary conditions). Moreover, the comparison of the reactive breakthrough curves suggests that the mSCR approach can estimate fate and transport for particular kinetic reactions in a physically and chemically heterogeneous field.

In summary, the Lagrangean method together with the exposure time technique is used to approximate the effects of physical and chemical heterogeneity on reactive transport. The mSCR method is a novel way to visualize the connection between the physical and chemical properties and the consequences of these properties in reactive transport. The correlation between the Eulerian physical and chemical properties has been applied to several numerical models for subsurface transport, but to our knowledge none has used in a deterministic, Lagrangean description.

RANDOM WALK PARTICLE TRACKING FOR SIMULATING REACTIVE TRANSPORT IN HETEROGENEOUS AQUIFERS: EFFECTS OF CONCENTRATION AVERAGING.

Christopher T. Green, Eric M. LaBolle and Graham E. Fogg
Hydrologic Sciences, University of California, Davis, CA

INTRODUCTION

The random walk particle method (RWPM) has been applied to problems of mass and energy transfer as well as problems of solute transport in porous media. RWPM has also been used for problems of non-conservative reactive transport with linear and non-linear reactions. However, technical barriers remain for the use of RWPM for non-conservative transport in field scale, heterogeneous 3-D aquifers. In this paper, we present particle tracking methods to efficiently model biodegradation in such scenarios, and we use the techniques to study effects of dilution and grid scale averaging on reaction rates.

One advantage of the particle tracking method is that run times do not change greatly as the number of grid cells increases. Rather, the number of particles used to represent solute mass dictates the speed of RWPM computation. Furthermore, in the particle-based approach more information is available on local spatial variability of concentration. Such information is potentially very important for an accurate solution of a reactive flow problem. Local-scale cross-correlation in concentrations of electron donors and electron acceptors typically controls the rate of biodegradation. Local concentration information is unavailable in grid based methods that use macro-dispersion coefficients and average concentrations on the grid scale. In the case of particle tracking, concentrations are based on particle distributions, which do not depend on the grid dimensions.

METHODS

For this study, two RWPM methods were developed: (1) a particle-in-grid approach, in which reaction rates are calculated on grid-scale concentrations, and (2) a particle based reaction scheme, in which reaction rates are calculated for each particle and are unaffected by the grid. Both approaches were applied to a single data set from an LLNL aquifer system. Results were compared to illustrate the potential range in decay under different assumptions of concentration averaging in a heterogeneous 3-D aquifer system.

Changes were made to improve the efficiency of the RWPM method. Electron acceptor concentrations were modeled using "deficit particles" that represent depletion of the otherwise uniform concentration. This greatly reduced the number of particles needed. In addition, reactants were assumed to have identical transport properties and to occur on a single particle type. This is necessary in the particle based scheme, which does not have interaction between particles. The same convention was used in the grid based scheme, for purposes of comparison.

The two schemes represent opposite extremes of concentration averaging. In the particle based scheme, each particle is assigned a constant volume, based on particle density at the source. The plume does not dilute, or change in volume. In the grid based scheme, mass is assumed to be evenly distributed within each grid cell. Therefore, as particles move into previously empty cells, the plume volume expands and captures additional electron acceptor.

Identical reaction kinetics were used for both scenarios. The solute of concern was assumed to be an electron donating hydrocarbon, undergoing a microbially mediated reaction described by Monod kinetics. The decay of electron donor is described by:

$$\frac{\partial C_D}{\partial t} = -v_{max} M \left[\frac{C_D}{K_D + C_D} \right] \left[\frac{C_A}{K_A + C_A} \right] \qquad (1)$$

where t is time; C_D is the electron donor concentration; C_A is the electron acceptor (e.g. oxygen) concentration; v_{max} is the maximum specific rate of utilization of electron donor; M is the microbial concentration; K_D and K_A are half-saturation coefficients for electron donor and acceptor, respectively. Likewise, the consumption of electron acceptor is described by:

$$\frac{\partial C_A}{\partial t} = R_A \frac{\partial C_D}{\partial t} \qquad (2)$$

where R_A is the stoichiometric mass ratio of electron acceptor per electron donor consumed. Microbial growth is described by

$$\frac{\partial M}{\partial t} = -Y \frac{\partial C_D}{\partial t} \qquad (3)$$

where Y is the cell yield coefficient.

The reaction kinetics were implemented in the reactive transport algorithm by solving equations 1, 2, and 3 with the explicit finite difference approach at the end of each transport step. In the grid based scheme, the proportion of mass change assigned to each particle in a cell was set equal to the proportion of cell mass contained in the particle prior to the reaction step.

The kinetic algorithms were validated using an analytical solution for the concentration of a solute undergoing Monod-type decay. This implicit solution has been solved explicitly using the Lambert W function. We compared analytical results to numerical simulations. The numerical approximation matches the analytical solution very closely.

The overall simulation procedure consisted of (1) simulation of geologic variability in the LLNL aquifer system (2) specifying hydraulic characteristics for each sediment type (3) simulation of groundwater flow velocities, and (4) simulation of reactive transport of a non-sorbing hydrocarbon.

We ran three scenarios: two reactive transport scenarios using the previously described algorithms and one, non-reactive scenario. Results of the three simulation scenarios were compared to illustrate the effects of plume dilution on reaction rates and total mass reduction in 3-D heterogeneous systems. In the reactive transport scenarios, particle locations and reaction kinetics were identical to ensure that differences in mass distribution resulted only from differences in the methods used to calculate concentrations.

RESULTS AND DISCUSSION

Results of the reactive transport simulations demonstrated that spreading versus dilution is an important consideration in the LLNL aquifer system. Maps of particle distributions showed multiple branches of the plume in the x (dip) and z (vertical) directions. Such branches represent increased spreading of plume mass, but do not necessarily imply increased dilution. However, grid-based concentration averaging will predict increased dilution due to a greater number of occupied cells.

For each of the three scenarios, we compared total mass of electron donor degraded over time (Figure 1). As shown, dilution on the grid scale results in an eventual three-fold increase in total mass loss. In the particle-based approach, the plume becomes oxygen depleted at 2000 days and bioremediation ceases. The increased decay in the grid-based approximation stems from capture of electron acceptor via growth of the plume volume. The actual amount of mass loss in a natural system could range anywhere between the values for zero dilution or grid-scale dilution and would depend on local scale mixing phenomena controlled by small-scale geologic heterogeneity,

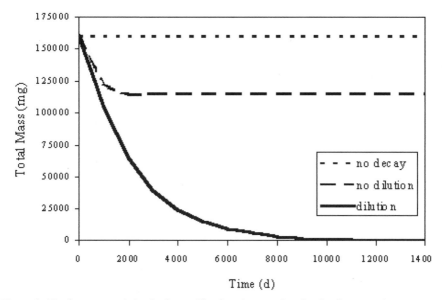

Figure 1. Total mass remaining in the aquifer domain over time for the three reaction scenarios.

diffusion, and local-dispersivity. This is a source of considerable uncertainty in numerical models of field scale bioremediation.

CONCLUSIONS

Results confirm that concentration averaging is an essential consideration for simulating reactive transport in 3-D heterogeneous systems. For typical grid-based approaches, the resolution of the reaction grid determines the plume volume, which controls the amount of electron donor available for reactions. As shown in this work, the extent of dilution can cause a wide range of results in bioremediation simulations. More work needs to be done to determine appropriate scales for volume averaging of concentrations in such heterogeneous 3-D systems.

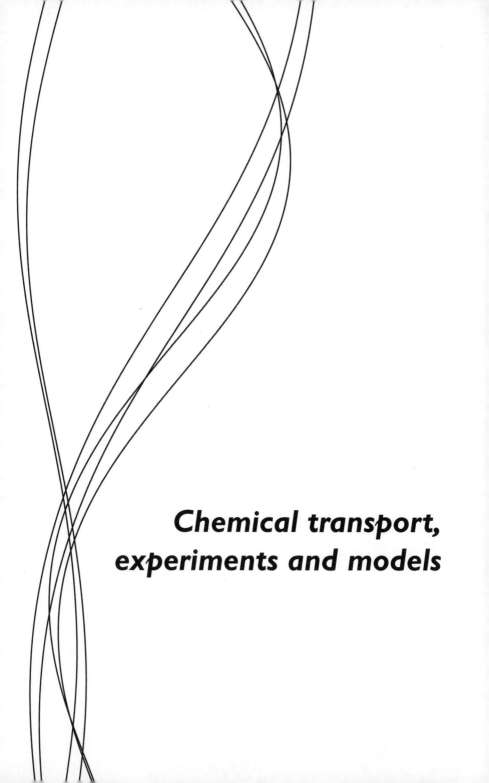

*Chemical transport,
experiments and models*

MASS-FLUX VS. CONCENTRATION MEASUREMENTS: CONCEPTS AND FIELD APPLICATIONS

Georg Teutsch

Centre for Applied Geoscience, University of Tuebingen, Sigwartstrasse 10, D-72076 Tuebingen, Germany, e-mail: teutsch@uni-tuebingen.de

Groundwater risk assessment is generally performed on the basis of contaminant concentration measurements either from soil (elution tests) or form groundwater samples in or downstream the contaminant source area. Recent protocols however (LfU, 1996; EPA OSWER Directive, 1999) propose to take into account also the (mobile) contaminant mass in addition to MCLs. This information might be more useful in assessing the impact of a contaminated site on the groundwater flow within a catchment. However, so far no field method existed for the direct quantification of the mass flow-rates.

The other challenge in groundwater risk assessment is that of adequate plume characterisation. Today, it is generally accepted that groundwater plumes can be very irregular in shape showing high concentration gradients. Therefore, point concentration measurements obtained from a sparse well network can be very misleading in plume delineation.

This paper therefore presents an alternative approach, the so called integral pumping, which can solve the two problems described above. At first, the conceptual advantage of using the total mass-flow rates, respectively the (spatially integrated) flux-averaged contaminant concentration as an additional (robust) metrics in the evaluation of contaminated sites will be discussed for the various fields of application will be discussed. These are:

- the assessment of contaminant source strengths
- the localisation of contaminant sources
- the measurement of source remediation performance
- the quantification of Natural Attenuation Rates

Then the field implementation of the new method will be described. One or more pumping wells are used along a control plane downst-ream of a potential contaminant source zone perpendicular to the mean groundwater flow direction and operated simulta-neous-ly or sequentially. Well positions, pumping rates and pumping times are optimized to allow the well capture zones to cover the entire groundwater flow downstream of the contaminant site. During well operation, the concentrations of the target substances are measured as a function of time in the well discharge of each of the pumping wells. The figure below shows the setup with one well and one contaminant plume before and during (steady-state) pumping.

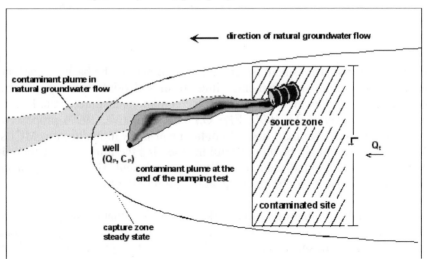

The total mass-flow rate M_t is then simply determined as the product of Q_p, the well pumping rate and C_p, the contaminant concentration in the pumped water.

$$M_t = Q_p \, C_p \qquad [M/T]$$

The flux-averaged mean concentration C_{av} across the control plane downstream of the contaminated site is obtained deviding the total mass-flow rate M_t by the (natural, i.e. unpumped) flow rate Q_t.

$$C_{av} = M_t/Q_t \quad [M/L^3]$$

It should be noted that both, the total mass-flow rate Mt as well as the flux-averaged mean concentration Cav can be quantified without the need to know the number or position of the (irregular) contaminant plumes.

In practice, the time required to reach steady-state is often too long to be acceptable and therefore, an unsteady-state version of the method has been developed and applied at more than 40 sites so far. For some simple initial and boundary conditions, an analytical solution was developed too.

Finally, some of the results obtained under field conditions will be presented and the advantages and disadvantages of the approach will be critically discussed.

MULTIPHASE FLUID FLOW AND MULTICOMPONENT REACTIVE TRANSPORT AT THE HANFORD SX TANK FARM

Steve Yabusaki
Pacific Northwest National Laboratory, P.O. Box 999. Richland, WA 99352
Phone (509)372-6095, Fax (509)372-6089, Email yabusaki@pnl.gov

On the Hanford Site, the high-level radioactive waste (HLW) in the SX Tank Farm was among the highest in temperature, density, radioactivity, pH, and ionic strength. 10 of the 15 subsurface single-shelled carbon steel tanks in this tank farm were known or suspected leakers, and all are now well past their design lifetimes (Gephart and Lundgren 1998). The future disposition of the waste contained in these tanks will be based, in part, on a predictive understanding of contaminant behavior in the Hanford vadose zone. In addition to the typical challenges of inadequate data and spatially varying vadose zone properties, a key impediment is the lack of a definitive conceptual model describing how the extreme physical and chemical properties of the SX Tank Farm wastes affect(ed) contaminant transport and fate in vadose zone sediments.

Modeling analyses were performed by a team of scientists from Pacific Northwest National Laboratory (PNNL), Lawrence Livermore National Laboratory (LLNL), Lawrence Berkeley National Laboratory (LBNL), and Los Alamos National Laboratory (LANL) that was assembled in 1999 by the Hanford Groundwater/Vadose Zone Integration Project Science and Technology (S&T). Historical events were modeled to points in time and space where observed data is available to compare with the simulations. Three cases from the S&T modeling studies of the SX tank farm investigation are presented:

- interpretation of the contemporary temperature peak 10 meters below the SX-108 tank,
- interpretation of the SX-108 tank leak speciation in the context of cesium mobility, and
- interpretation of the SX-115 tank leak and speciation in the context of ion exchange behavior.

THERMAL HYDROLOGIC MODELING

From 1955 to 1967, tank SX-108 was "self-boiling;" i.e., radiolytic heating by the HLW raised tank temperatures sufficiently to exceed the boiling point of the supernatant (~110°C). Peak sludge temperatures were around 150°C. Thirty-three years later in 2000, temperature measurements beneath the SX-108 tank identified a peak of 74°C, 10 meters below the bottom of the tank (Gardner and Reynolds, 2000). The depth of the observed temperature peak coincided with the highest cesium-137 concentrations. Pruess et al (2002) found that a 2500 watt cesium-137 heat source 30 m below ground could approximately account for the temperature peak; but without additional thermal source terms/boundary conditions or radical changes to the flow field, the character of the temperature distribution, especially in the shallower sediments was not reproducible.

Historical temperature measurements were subsequently discovered for tank SX-108 (David Myers, personal communication) that revealed a large temperature range (>40°C in 1981) in SX-108 that was strongly dependent on whether the sensor was in the sludge, supernatant, or head space. Incorporating the updated thermal boundary condition for the tank (Pruess et al 2002) into the entire operational history of tank SX-108 resulted in a simulated result in the year 2000 (Figure 1) that agrees well with both the magnitude and character of the temperature distribution, without introducing a heat generation source outside of the tank.

TANK SOURCE SPECIATION

Zachara et al (2001) performed batch experiments demonstrating that sodium in sufficiently high concentrations could mobilize cesium. The critical issue was whether the supernatant that leaked from tank SX-108 had sodium concentrations that could mobilize cesium to the degree observed. In the absence of analytical chemistry on the tank wastes at the time of the leaks, reconstructed tank compositions (Agnew 1997) based on process sheet monitoring and tank transfer records were used. These estimated compositions did not distinguish between solid and liquid phases or species. Our interest in liquid phase species concentrations (e.g., Na^+) required that a high-temperature, high-ionic strength speciation calculation be performed that included the formation of secondary minerals. Jones and Maclean (2000) used the Agnew (1997) estimated SX-108 compositions as a starting point with the exception of fixing OH- at 0.1 M and using Na+ for charge balancing. These assumptions were consistent with an 11 M limit (Doud and Stivers 1959) on total sodium concentrations that was designed to keep densities sufficiently low (specific gravity less than 1.6) to prevent tank design loads from being exceeded. Free sodium (Na^+) in the resulting speciation at 100°C (Table 1) was predicted to be 4.54 M, which was not high enough to attain the depth of cesium transport observed (Lichtner et al 2002).

Lichtner and Felmy (2002) chose to use the total sodium from the reconstructed SX-108 inventory and charge balanced with OH- (Table 1). This approach yielded a free sodium concentration of 10.9 M (17.2 m) that was capable of mobilizing cesium-137 to the extent observed by the position of the cesium-137 center of mass beneath SX-108. However, the total sodium concentration of 19.5 M significantly violated the 11 M sodium guideline for tank waste. The issue was resolved with the discovery of a document (Smith and Tomlinson, 1967) that recommended maximizing sodium concentrations in tank waste to enhance the precipitation of sodium minerals, which were thought to self-seal chronic tank leaks.

MULTICOMPONENT ION EXCHANGE

Building on the batch experimental cesium ion exchange studies by Zachara et al (2001), a series of saturated column studies were performed (Steefel et al 2002) to investigate the migration of exchangeable cations through a composite sediment representative of the Hanford formation beneath the SX Tank Farm. Parameters for a 3-site multicomponent ion exchange model were identified for selectivity coefficients and cation exchange capacity for the Ca^{++}, Mg^{++}, K^+, Na^+, Cs^+ system (Steefel et al 2002). The key issue was whether this multicomponent ion exchange model developed in the laboratory, could be adapted for use in the field situation.

We chose to use the SX-115 tank leak, a relatively well-characterized 57,000 gallon leak over a 1 week period in 1965 (Raymond and Shdo 1966). Furthermore, a comprehensive geochemical characterization of samples from a borehole (299-W23-19) 2 meters from the southwestern edge of the tank in 1999 (Serne et al 2001) provided a unique snapshot of the chromatographic behavior of the exchangeable cations from ground surface to the water table. The SX-115 operational history beginning in 1958 with the leak event in 1965 and the intervening 34 years was simulated using a three-dimensional model of thermohydrologic and geochemical processes with 5 stratigraphic material zones (Steefel and Yabusaki 2001). The source term for the SX-115 leak was based on a high-ionic strength Pitzer speciation (Lichtner and Felmy 2002) of the Agnew (1997) reconstructed tank composition at the time of the leak. While the initial Ca^{++}, Mg^{++}, and K^+ concentrations on exchange sites were adjusted to match the field-mobilized values, all laboratory fitted parameters for selectivity coefficients and cation exchange capacity remained unchanged for the field application.

The initial modeling results reproduced the observed trends of elevated Ca^{++}, Mg^{++}, and K^+ at the leading edge of the tank leak pulse and retarded Na^+. However, it was clear that the speciated concentrations introduced with the simulated leak were much higher than indicated by the field data. Consequently, the simulation was repeated with a dilution that honored the observed concentration and distribution. Simulation results with the new leak source term resulted in an excellent match (Figure 2) with the field observations for potassium, magnesium, calcium, and sodium.

CONCLUSIONS

With limited historical records, reconstructing the behavior of wastes in the sediments beneath the SX tanks is a daunting task, especially with the extreme physical and chemical conditions that were present during the leak events. Our mechanistic subsurface simulators were particularly useful in these situations because they provided a systematic and quantitative framework for 1) incorporating knowledge gained from experiments, 2) evaluating the consistency of assumptions with the available data, 3) advancing the understanding of dominant processes and their interactions, and 4) building quantitative process model representations that honor the new knowledge.

REFERENCES

AGNEW, S.F. (1997), Hanford tank chemical and radionuclide inventories: HDW Model. Rev. 4, LA-UR-96-3800, Los Alamos National Laboratory, Los Alamos, NM.

DOUD, E. and H.W. STIVERS, "Limitations for Existing Storage Tanks for Radioactive

Wastes from Separations Plants", HW-59919, October 1959, General Electric Richland, Washington.

GARDNER, M.G. and K.D. REYNOLDS (2000), "SX-108 Slant Borehole Completion Report," RPP-6917, Rev. 0, Prepared for CH2M-Hill Hanford Group, Inc by Waste Management Technical Services, Richland, Washington.

GEPHART, R.E. and R.E. LUNDGREN (1998), "Hanford Tank Clean up: A Guide to Understanding the Technical Issues, " Battelle Press, Columbus, Ohio.

JONES, T.E. and G.T. MACLEAN (2000), Inventory estimates for single-shell tank leaks in S and SX tank farms. RPP-6285, Rev. 0.

LICHTNER, P.C. and A.R. FELMY (2002). "Estimation of Hanford SX Tank Waste Compositions from Historically Derived Inventories," (submitted)

LICHTNER, P.C., D.L. BISH, S.B. YABUSAKI, K. PRUESS, and C.I. STEEFEL (2001) Cesium Migration Beneath the Hanford SX Tank Farm: Role of Super-High Ionic Strength Fluids on Chromatographic Displacement (submitted for publication)

PRUESS, K. (2001), "Fluid Flow, Heat Transfer, and Solute Transport at Tank SX-108; A Summary Report on Modeling Studies," in S-SX Tank Farms Field Investigation Report. U.S. Department of Energy, Richland, Washington. (in press)

PRUESS, K., S.B. YABUSAKI, C.I. STEEFEL, and P.C. LICHTNER (2002), Fluid Flow, Heat Transfer, and Solute Transport at Nuclear Waste Storage Tanks in the Hanford Vadose Zone. Vadose Zone Journal (submitted).

RAYMOND, J. R., and E. D. SHDO (1966), "Characterization of Subsurface Contamination in the SX Tank Farm," BNWl-CC-701, Richland, WA.

SERNE, RJ, HT SCHAEF, BN BJORNSTAD, DC LANIGAN, GW GEE, CW LINDENMEIER, RE CLAYTON, VL LEGORE, MJ O'HARA, CF BROWN, RD ORR, GV LAST, IV KUTNYAKOV, DS BURKE, TC WILSON, and BA WILLIAMS (2001), "Geologic and geochemical data collected from vadose zone sediments from borehole 299 W23-19 [SX -115] in the S/SX waste management area and preliminary interpretations." PNNL-2001-3, Pacific Northwest National Laboratory, Richland, Washington.

SMITH, P.W. and R.E. TOMLINSON (1967), "Hanford High-Level Waste Reevaluation Study", ISO-981, August 1967, Richland, Washington.

STEEFEL, C.I., CARROLL, S.A., ZHAO, P., ROBERTS, S.(2002). "Cesium Migration in Hanford Sediment: A Multi-Site Cation Exchange Model Based on Laboratory Transport Experiments." Submitted to the Journal of Contaminant Hydrology.

STEEFEL, C.I. and YABUSAKI, S.B. (2001), "Evaluation of the field exchange capacity of Hanford sediments with implications for ^{137}Cs migration." In: Appendix D: Digest of S&T Program Evaluations, RPP-7884, (Knepp, A. J., ed.), CH2M HILL Hanford Group, Inc., Richland, WA.

ZACHARA, J. M., S. C. SMITH, J. P. MCKINLEY, R. J. SERNE, and P. L. GASSMAN, 2001, "Sorption of Cs+ to Micaceous Subsurface Sediments from the Hanford Site," Geochimica et Cosmochimica Acta (Accepted).

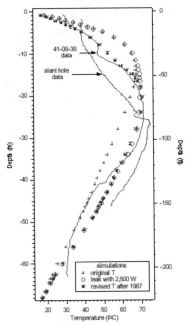

Figure 1. Predicted Temperature Distributions Beneath SX-108 (after Pruess et al 2002)

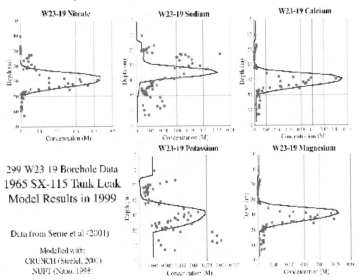

Figure 2. Comparison of Predicted and Observed Cation Concentrations Beneath SX-115 (after Steefel et al 2002)

BIOENHANCED IN-WELL VAPOR STRIPPING TREATMENT OF TCE CONTAMINATION SOURCE AT EDWARDS AIR FORCE BASE

Perry L. McCarty[1], Steven M. Gorelick[1], Mark N. Goltz[2], Gary D. Hopkins[1], Brian Timmins[1], Laurence Smith[1], Rahul K. Gandhi[1] and Freddi-Jo Eisenberg[1]

[1] Stanford University and [2] Air Force Institute of Technology, USA

Two innovative technologies in combination, cometabolic bioremediation (McCarty et al., 1998) and in-well vapor stripping (Gvirtzman and Gorelick, 1993; Pinto et al., 1997), are in operation for the removal of TCE from groundwater at a contaminant source area at Edwards Air Force Base in southern California. The site was contaminated with TCE used to maintain the X-15 rocket plane during the 1950s and 1960s. Contaminated TCE was sent to a waste pit, and a pipeline from there discharged an unknown amount of TCE to the ground surface, where it percolated to the groundwater below. This has created a plume of TCE that extends several hundred meters from the source. In the source area where the treatment system has been installed, the groundwater lies about 8 m below the ground surface and the aquifer is about 10 meters thick. Underneath the aquifer lies fractured bedrock. Whether the TCE source has penetrated into the bedrock is not clear.

The bioenhanced in-well vapor stripping (BEHIVS) system includes three treatment wells; an upgradient vapor stripping well to reduce the TCE source concentrations to levels that enable two bioremediation wells, located about 10 m downgradient, to efficiently remove TCE to near regulatory levels. There is no need to pump contaminated groundwater to the surface for treatment. About 16 m separates the biotreatment wells. Groundwater passes through the vapor stripping well in an upward direction, flows through the aquifer, and is pumped through the biotreatment wells in a downward direction, causing circulation between the vapor stripping and biotreatment wells, effecting high TCE removal efficiencies. TCE removal is being monitored using an automated system that collects and analyzes samples around the clock at 64 points, providing shallow and deep coverage over an area of approximately 43 m by 50 m. The TCE concentration in the aquifer in this area was monitored over a 10 month period, during which 2330 samples were processed prior to the start of the treatment system. This represents about 40 samples at each location. While the TCE concentrations varied broadly between sampling locations throughout the study area, they varied little at any given sampling location over the 10 month period. The average coefficient of variation for 61 different sampling locations was less than 20%. The concentration in the deeper regions of the aquifer was found to be significantly higher than in the shallow regions. The 26 deep aquifer sampling locations had an average TCE concentration of 4,600 µg/l, with a range between 2,500 and 8,300 µg/l. The lower concentrations occurred at the northern and southern borders of the study area, and the highest concentration was found in the middle of the study area, about 10 m upgradient from the in-well vapor stripper. Thus, the treatment system appears to have been well situated in the middle of the source area. The TCE concentrations in the upper aquifer averaged 1,200 µg/l and ranged between 460 and 2,900 µg/l.

The evaluation is proceeding in four stages. During the first stage, which began in August 2001, the vapor stripping well was operated in order to reduce the TCE concentration reaching the biotreatment wells to less than 1,000 µg/l in order to reduce the potential for TCE transformation product toxicity to the microorganisms. This was accomplished through one month of vapor stripper operation with liquid flowrate of about 30 liters/min and air injection rate of 74 standard cubic feet per minute (2,100 standard liters/min), giving an air to water ratio of 70. The 1.9 cm diameter air line injected air 8.5 m below water surface. The in-well vapor stripper removed about 96% of the TCE from groundwater passing through it, much higher than the 90% removal originally anticipated. The groundwater and air are separated in the well at an elevation that is within the vadose zone, with the groundwater being returned to the upper aquifer and the air passing to an above ground activated carbon system for TCE removal. The cleaned air is then recycled back to the air injection line after the addition of sufficient carbon dioxide to maintain the pH in the groundwater being treated at between 6.9 and 7.1, or that of the native groundwater. The purpose of pH control is to prevent system clogging through calcium carbonate precipitation.

During the second phase, toluene injection at the biotreatment wells has begun in order to establish an active population of toluene degrading bacteria. Once established, these organisms are expected to degrade about 85% of the TCE through cometabolism. The establishment of the bacterial population is being accomplished in several steps. For one week, pure oxygen was added to the biotreatment wells while pumping at each with a groundwater flowrate of 7.5 liters/min in the downward direction, This resulted in sufficient dissolved oxygen in the aquifer to begin toluene as well as oxygen addition. Initially, about 4 mg/l toluene was added over a few days, and then the system was shut off to allow the population to develop, requiring about 2 weeks. This toluene addition was then repeated.

After an additional two weeks, when the population was established, the third phase of continuous operation of the biotreatment wells and vapor stripping wells began. Pulsed toluene injection is being used to maintain an average injected toluene concentration of 4 mg/l initially, and this will be increased gradually to 12 mg/l and the biotreatment flowrate to 15 liters/min. Hydrogen peroxide was also added up to 40 mg/l to prevent biofouling near the treatment wells as well as to supply extra oxygen to satisfy the need at higher toluene concentrations. A series of three bromide tracer tests is being conducted to help define the recirculatory flow system.

Full operation will continue for 2 months. The system will then be shut down and the groundwater will be monitored for three months (ending March 31, 2002) to determine the rate, extent, and location of a likely rebound in TCE concentrations. This will help to determine the residual contamination source as well as to help plan for future cleanup strategy. A three-dimensional numerical model of the technology was used to help design the system and to predict performance. The model will subsequently be modified to take into consideration aquifer heterogeneity as evaluated from pump and tracer tests, and will be used to analyze the extensive data base that is being obtained. The modified model will be used to help determine optimum operational strategies for further site cleanup.

REFERENCES

GVIRTZMAN, H. and S.M. GORELICK, "Using Air-lift Pumping as an In-Situ Aquifer Remediation Technique," Water Science Technology, 27(7-8), 195-201 (1993).

McCARTY, P. L., M. N. GOLTZ, G. D. HOPKINS, M. E. DOLAN, J. P. ALLAN, B. T. KAWAKAMI, and CARROTHERS, T. J., "Full-Scale Evaluation of In Situ Cometabolic Degradation of Trichloroethylene in Groundwater through Toluene Injection," Environmental Science and Technology, 32(1), 88-100 (1998).

PINTO, M. J., H. GVITRZMAN, and S. M. GORELICK, "Laboratory-Scale Analysis of Aquifer Remediation by In-Well Vapor Stripping 2. Modeling Results," Journal of Contaminant Hydrology, 29 (1), 41-58 (1997).

CHARACTERIZING HETEROGENEOUS HYDROGEOLOGICAL SYSTEMS THROUGH INVERSE GROUNDWATER FLOW AND GEOCHEMICAL MODELING

Y.S. Yang[1], A.A. Cronin[2], T. Elliot[3] and R.M. Kalin[3]
[1] School of Civil Engineering, Queen's University Belfast, Belfast, BT9 5AG, UK
[2] Robens Centre for Public and Environmental Health, University of Surrey, Guildford, GU2 7XH, UK
[3] School of Civil Engineering, Queen's University Belfast, Belfast, BT9 5AG, UK

Characterization of heterogeneous hydrogeological systems plays an important role in groundwater protection and contaminated site remediation schemes. A good understanding and description of the hydrogeological system is essential for successful modeling results. However, uncertainty associated with sparse field observations and insufficient in-situ test results (particularly in fractured systems) hinders the modeling process. Thus, advanced modeling techniques can improve characterization of such complex hydrogeological systems. The nonlinear inverse optimization helped to understand the regional hydrogeology, while geochemical modeling provided further constraints to flow characterization. This demonstrates the importance of incorporating both flow and geochemical analysis techniques in a hydrogeological study.

A methodology was developed in the characterization of the regional hydrogeology and groundwater systems by using nonlinear inverse numerical modeling and geochemical modeling. A case study on the Triassic Sherwood Sandstone aquifer systems in the Lagan and Enler Valleys, Northern Ireland was carried out using this approach. Forward groundwater modeling and inverse optimization incorporated the Quaternary porous media aquifer and the fractured bedrock aquifer at regional scale. Hydraulic parameter, recharge and lateral flows of the heterogeneous complex were optimized to achieve best fits between modeled and observed water heads. Based on this flow modeling, geochemical sampling and analysis of groundwater samples were carried out to gain a more detailed knowledge of the groundwater geochemical evolution and residence times in the aquifer. Thus, the characteristics of the heterogeneous systems were validated by geochemical analyses and modeling. The integration between these approaches and the case study are outlined.

GROUNDWATER FLOW MODELING

Six solid geology layers (Greywackes, Permian Mudstone, Sandstone, Mercia Mudstone, Chalk and Basalt) and Quaternary drift (alluvium, sand/gravel and till) were represented in the regional conceptual model (Fig. 1). Considering the heterogeneous aperture and fracture development, two layers of Sandstone (50-120 m thick) were conceptualized to represent the permeability-depth profile. The River Lagan and the Enler are located in the center of the valley. A regional numerical groundwater model was built using MODFLOW based on the conceptual model. Regular finite difference grids of 500 meter were used. Extensive data were gathered to build the model. Effective recharge of 30 mm was initially taken for the valleys and urban areas. A higher value of 150-300 mm was used on areas where the till cover is thin or preferential flows exist. The aquifer property values were taken from various pumping tests results and previous reports carried out on the study area. Geological structures and intrusion dykes were taken into account when assigning permeability values (Fig. 1). Seasonal variations in the water head were examined. The ranges were low, 1-2 m, at most observation sites except some wells near boundaries of the

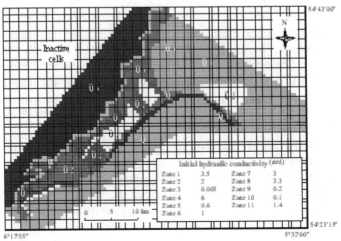

Fig. 1. Regional setting and model grids (with K zones)

Sandstone aquifer. Therefore, a steady-state flow model was chosen for the system characterization.

INVERSE CALIBRATIONS

The regional groundwater system was calibrated through nonlinear inverse numerical modeling. The complexity of geology and topography made this a complex modeling problem. Some major issues were dealt with by the inverse calibration: 1) heterogeneous distribution of hydraulic conductivities; 2) lateral flow into/out of the aquifer; 3) the relationships between the drift and bedrocks and 4) spatial recharge loading in the region. The observation data for the inverse optimization were taken from the means of 1971-1975 at 18 targets in the Lagan Valley and 4 more recent measurements in the Enler area. The hydraulic conductivity (K) was calibrated by the inverse modeling based on the forward model. Zonation of hydraulic conductivity was determined on the basis of the geology, structure, land use, topography, and hydrology (Fig. 1). The sensitivity analysis of K shows that the inversion of the regional model was sensitive to the K values of the sand/gravel, till and the Sherwood Sandstone in the middle part of the Lagan Valley, and then to the Basalt and Greywackes. System uncertainty exists due to the limited number of the observations and data quality.

To identify the boundary condition of the groundwater model at spatial and quantitative scales, several inverse scenarios were investigated to identify the lateral in/out flow rates and their spatial locations. The overall optimization shows that the model was only sensitive to the inflows in the lower layers along the Greywackes boundaries, and not to that in the Quaternary drift. This demonstrates groundwater from the Greywacke fractures interacts laterally with the Sandstone but little water flows to the drift. The low permeability clay till prevents groundwater from moving into the Quaternary sand/gravel aquifers. The lateral inflow to the Sandstone from the Greywackes in the northwestern area was optimized as 2 m3/d per meter of boundary. The model was not sensitive to the western boundary, suggesting that the lateral inflow recharge along these boundaries is insignificant in comparison with the Sandstone aquifer totals. This is identical to the regional hydrogeology: the Mudstone conformably overlying the Sandstone forms an aquiclude in the regional sense and prevents groundwater from penetrating it. The groundwater then comes out as springs and flows to the Sandstone as surface recharge.

The spatial distribution of the recharge was characterized with 11 recharge zones considering the land use, geology and topography. The calibrated recharge is 420 mm/a around the dyke in the Enler area and along the Chalk in the west of Belfast where springs are located. Actually most of the effective recharge comes out in the springs at the Basalt/Chalk escarpment to the west of the Lagan Valley. It is only 10 mm/a in the southern area. The value of some cells where the faults cross the boundary between the Chalk and Sandstone reaches as high as 970 mm/a. This demonstrates that this system is highly heterogeneous and the most recharge occurs along some preferential flow paths. There is little recharge in less permeable areas such as the Basalt, Greywackes and area of urban development.

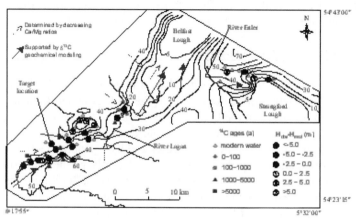

Fig. 2. Flow & geochemical modeling results

GEOCHEMICAL VALIDATION

To validate the inverse groundwater flow modeling results, geochemical analysis was carried out along with d13C analysis and radiocarbon dating. Geochemical evolution and flow paths in the aquifer were characterized with the inverse geochemical modeling. Hydro-geochemical evolution in this Sandstone aquifer is dominated by carbonate mineral dissolution and congruent dissolution of calcite, dolomite and gypsum may lead to the precipitation of calcite. This allowed delineation of flow paths through the aquifer using such techniques as Mg/Ca ratios. However, due to the multiple sources and sinks for these elements, d13C was used as a more reliable tracer to constrain the flow paths.

Groundwater sampling was carried out at 40 wells throughout the study area and analyzed for all the major and minor ions along with d13C and radiocarbon dating at selected wells. Based on the flow-paths from flow model, geochemical inverse modeling of d13C using the NETPATH model indicates a partly closed water evolution by decreased pCO2 values downgradient in the study area. Most, not all, of the flow lines from Ca/Mg ratios were supported by radiocarbon analysis (Fig. 2). The geochemical evolution along the flow paths through the Sandstone aquifer were constrained by d13C values within the range of ±2‰ which represented the uncertainty in soil CO2 d13C values. Once a plausible geochemical evolution model had been identified, radiocarbon dates were evaluated by the model correcting for all the sources and sinks of carbon along the flow paths. The corrected ages allowed a plot of residence times within the aquifer to be made (Fig. 2).

DISCUSSIONS AND CONCLUSIONS

The inverse calibration shows a good overall match and the lateral inflow estimates may contain uncertainty due to the lack of observations. The estimated higher K values of the Quaternaries (e.g. sand/gravel) may indicate an exaggeration phenomenon to the Quaternaries at the spatial scale (i.e. thickness). The K of the Sandstone is characterized by a general decrease, without surprise, from shallow layers to depth. It's relatively greater, horizontally, in north and middle of the study area, which features the high heterogeneity of the aquifer as a result of the structures. The boundary flow calibration and sensitivity analysis reveal the hydraulic interactions between the Sandstone and the surrounding strata. Highly heterogeneous recharge mechanisms exist in the groundwater systems.

The hydraulic conductivity was estimated as 49 m/d for the sand/gravel and 0.02-4.5 m/d for the Sandstone in this area. The lateral inflow was estimated as 2 m3/d per meter boundary in the northeast area. The recharge was mainly from the areas where preferential paths exist. The inverse model was sensitive to the K values of the sand/gravel, Sandstone in the middle part of the Lagan Valley, and then to the Basalt and Greywackes.

Geochemical and isotopic study provided validation to the flow modeling. The geochemical modeling provides accurately corrected residence times, which can be used to validate groundwater flow modeling output. This groundwater system has a long turnover time and the radiocarbon dating indicates some extremely old water, e.g. over 5000 years in the south of the

Lagan Valley (Fig. 2). However, modern water components occur where the local recharge was induced by well abstractions, or circuiting of the well (e.g. the Enler area in the east). The nonlinear inverse optimization proved to be a better way to understand regional hydrogeology and, when coupled with geochemical modeling, can provide further constraints/validations to flow characterization, which demonstrates the importance of incorporating both flow and geochemical analysis techniques in hydrogeology study.

MODELING REACTIVE GEOCHEMICAL TRANSPORT IN NATURAL FRACTURED ROCK SYSTEMS OVER GEOLOGICAL TIME

Tianfu Xu[1], Karsten Pruess[1], and George Brimhall[2]
[1] Earth Sciences Division, Lawrence Berkeley National Laboratory, University of California, Berkeley, CA 94720
[2] Department of Geology and Geophysics, University of California, Berkeley, CA 94720

Reactive fluid flow and geochemical transport in natural fractured rock systems has been of increasing interest to investigators in areas of geosciences such as mineral deposits, sedimentary diagenesis, and fluid-rock interactions in hydrothermal systems. Validation of numerical models for natural and anthropogenic (engineered) systems may differ markedly. In anthropogenic systems such as contaminant transport and nuclear waste repositories, models must be validated based on measurements of state variables such as pressure, water saturation, and chemical concentration, and the scientific relevance of modeling must be in prediction. For natural phenomena, the geological relevance of modeling often is in hypothesis testing, because natural processes and geochemical systems may involve too many complications and uncertainties to allow for quantitative prediction. Natural mineral systems are characterized by the abundance and distribution of primary and secondary mineral phases, and by the composition of fluid phases (aqueous, gas). Often it is the presence or absence of certain minerals that provides clues to the specific physical and chemical processes and conditions during the evolution of the system. In this sense empirical tests of the accuracy of geochemical modeling are of a more qualitative nature for natural systems. If modeling can find an unambiguous answer to a simple question which is well-posed, then something can be learned. The test of numerical results is by comparison with known patterns, sequences and processes from natural systems, which may be qualitative rather than quantitative in terms of mineral abundances. Therefore, in this paper we use the term "observation" instead of "measurement", and we intend to bridge the gap between observation and modeling.

Methods for modeling geochemical reactions during a complex interplay of physical and chemical processes are described in Xu and Pruess (2001a). The physical and chemical process model is embodied in a numerical simulator TOUGHREACT. The simulator was implemented by introducing reactive geochemistry into the framework of the existing non-isothermal multi-phase flow code TOUGH2 (Pruess, 1991). In this paper, we present two examples that use the TOUGHREACT simulator to test geochemical hypotheses based on petrologic observation, and to compare with field-observed patterns and sequences of mineral assemblage.

The first example is a modeling study on mineral alteration in fractured caprock of magmatic hydrothermal systems. The simulation study used water and gas chemistry data as well as caprock mineral composition from the hydrothermal system in Long Valley Caldera (LVC), California. The flow system studied is intended to capture realistic features of fractured magmatic hydrothermal systems of the LVC. Many hot springs in and around LVC occur along north to northwest trending normal faults, and are derived from hydro-thermal reservoirs. Hot water is transported upward along fault systems into shallow aquifers. In these aquifers, the hydrothermal fluids mix with varying proportions of cold meteoric water before discharging in the hot springs. The observed sequence of argillic alteration in the LVC consists of an upper zone with smectite and kaolinite (in the lower temperature region), a lower illite zone, and an intermediate mixed illite and smectite zone. The sequence is rea-sonably well reproduced in the numerical simulation. In addition, calcite and chlorite precipitation in the hot region coincides with the observations. More details on the problem setup and results are given in Xu and Pruess (2001b).

The second example is a study on a simplified supergene enrichment system. The system involves hydrochemical differentiation by near-surface weathe-ring processes in which water transports metals from a source region or lea-ched zone to a locus of an enrichment blanket zone where these ions are reprecipitated as secondary ore compounds. Oxidative weathering of pyrite (FeS_2) and chalcopyrite ($CuFeS_2$) causes acidification and mobilization of metals in the oxidizing zone and intense alteration of primary minerals, with subsequent formation of enriched secondary copper-bearing sulfide mineral deposits (enrichment blanket) in the reducing conditions below the water table. The numerical simulation offers confirmation of well-posed questions based upon field study and petrologic information. Specifically, it has been possible here to demonstrate that oxidation of primary pyrite and chalcopyrite drives supergene leaching and destroys wall rock mineral solution buffer assemblages which otherwise restrain redox conditions to a reducing level. Further details are given in Xu et al. (2001).

The results from the two problems have illustrated how by abstraction of a simplified set of relevant factors, certain natural processes can be effectively modeled and how model validity can be tested against qualitative field observations. In addition, our "numerical experiments" give a detailed view of the dynamical interplay between coupled hydrologic, thermal, and chemical processes. The modeling results can provide useful insight into process mechanisms such as fracture-matrix interaction, water-gas-rock interaction, and conditions and parameters controlling chemical evolution.

Acknowledgement. We thank Patrick Dobson and Keni Zhang for a review of the manuscript and suggestions for improvement. This work was supported by the Laboratory Directed Research and Development Program of the Ernest Orlando Lawrence Berkeley National Laboratory, and by the Assistant Secretary for Energy Efficiency and Renewable Energy, Office of Wind and Geothermal Technologies, of the U.S. Department of Energy, under Contract No. DE-AC03-76SF00098.

REFERENCES

PRUESS, K., TOUGH2: A general-purpose numerical simulator for multiphase fluid and heat flow, Lawrence Berkeley Laboratory Report LBL-29400, Berkeley, California, 37 pp., 1991.

XU, T., and K. PRUESS, Modeling multiphase non-isothermal fluid flow and reactive geochemical transport in variably saturated fractured rocks: 1. Methodology, American Journal of Science, v. 301, 16-33, 2001a.

XU, T., and K. PRUESS, On fluid flow and mineral alteration in fractured caprock of magmatic hydrothermal systems, J. Geophys. Res., v. 106 (B2), 2121-2138, 2001b.

XU, T., E. SONNENTHAL, N. SPYCHER, K. PRUESS, G. BRIMHALL, and J. APPS, 2001, Modeling multiphase non-isothermal fluid flow and reactive geochemical transport in variably saturated fractured rocks: 2. Applications to supergene copper enrichment and hydrothermal flows, American Journal of Science, v. 301, 34-59, 2001.

ANALYSIS OF TRACER TESTS IN HETEROGENEOUS POROUS MEDIA

Luis Moreno[1] and Chin-Fu Tsang[2]

[1] *Department of Chemical Engineering and Technology, Royal Institute of Technology, Stockholm, Sweden; E-mail: lm@ket.kth.se*
[2] *Earth Sciences Division, Ernest Orlando Lawrence Berkeley National Laboratory, Berkeley, USA*

Flow and solute transport through porous media with strongly varying hydraulic conductivity was studied by numerical simulations. Solute dispersion in a porous medium is caused mainly by the variability of the fluid velocities in it, which in turn are caused by the variation in the medium's hydraulic conductivity.

Heterogeneous porous media can be characterized by statistical distributions of the hydraulic conductivity, which may be described by its geometric mean, the standard deviation, and its correlation structure (if it exists). Solute transport through porous media depends on the variability of the medium permeability and the way this variability is distributed in the system. The highest fluid rates are found along the least-resistive pathways.

For large heterogeneity, the flow is highly channelized, with the solute transported through a few bundles of channels. This effect was studied for a converging radial flow, to simulate tracer tests in a production well. The results show that for large heterogeneities, the solute is indeed transported through a few channels, and breakthrough curves show a high peak at very early times, much shorter than the mean residence time.

Figure 1 shows breakthrough curves for different standard deviations in conductivity distribution for two different integral range. For an integral range of

0.40 of the flow domain. If the heterogeneities are extremely large (σ = 4 or 6), the curves present a clear peak, which occurs for very short travel times. This means that for large heterogeneities, a fraction of the solute is transported through channels with a large flow. When a small correlation length (integral scale of 0.10 of the flow domain) is used, no clear peak is observed for extreme large heterogeneities.

From the calculated tracer breakthrough curves, a measure of the spreading of the tracer may be calculated by using a dimensionless identity, an apparent Peclet number, Pe=L/α, where L the apparent (macroscopic) travel distance and á the dispersivity. We use the expression deduced by Robinson (1984) for Pe based on the moments of the inverse travel time is used, so that the Pe is not dominated by the long tail with large times.

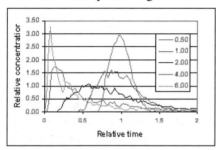 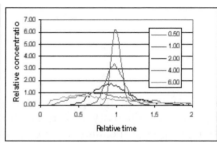

Figure 1 Breakthrough curves from a 3-D porous medium for integral scales of 0.40 (top) and 0.10 (bottom) of the flow domain.

A new procedure is proposed to analyze the results of experimental tracer tests performed with nonsorbing tracers. From the moments of the residence-time distribution, the heterogeneity and porosity of the porous medium may be determined. Figure 2 shows the spreading of the tracer expressed as the inverse of Pe plotted as a function of the product $\sigma^2\lambda$. A linear relationship exists for most of the interval, deviations are observed for large values of $\sigma^2\lambda$. This shows that the spreading of the tracer is directly related to the product $\sigma^2\lambda$ (i.e., the grade and range of the heterogeneities).

The results using 100% of the particles (Figure 2) are not useful from the practical point of view, since it is almost impossible to recover 100% of the injected tracer. Tracer tests with non-sorbing species carried out over short distances are usually stopped when 80-90% of the injected tracer is recovered. For tests performed over large distances the recovery of the tracer is usually much less. For this reason, we explore the possibility to determine the dispersivity using a smaller fraction of the tracer, e.g., when 50% of the tracer is recovered. The same type of problem is found in the determination of the mean residence time. In order to determine the actual mean residence time, the totality of the injected tracer would be recovered. For a porous medium with large heterogeneities, there is a large difference between the actual mean residence time and the time when the 50 % of the tracer is recovered. This shown in Figure 3, where the ratio between the time required to recovered the 50% of the tracer and the mean residence time is shown as a function of the product $\sigma^2\lambda$.

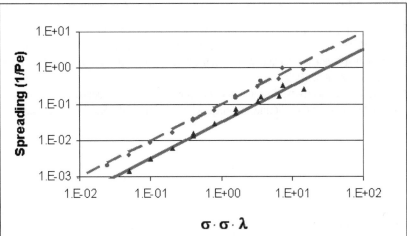

Figure 2. Spreading of the tracer (expressed as the inverse of Pe) as a function of the product $\sigma^2\lambda$ when 100% (circles / dashed line) and 50% (triangles / full line) of the tracer injected is recovered.

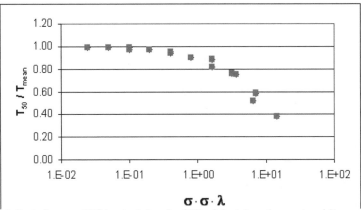

Figure 3. Ratio between T50 (arrival time for 50% of the injected tracer) and Tmean (mean residence time) as a function of the product $\sigma^2\lambda$.

The procedure described above was applied to three tracer tests with nonsorbing tracers (Amino G, iodide, and uranine) performed at Finnsjön by Andersson et al (1989). Spreading of the tracer at the pumping location was calculated using Equation (2) for 50% of the tracer recovered in the experiments. From the spreading of the tracers and using Figure 2, the value of the product $\sigma^2\lambda$ was determined. Mean residence time was calculated using the arrival time for 50% of the injected tracer and Figure 3.

REFERENCES

ANDERSSON, J.E., L. EKMAN, E. GUSTAFSSON, R. NORDQVIST, and S. TYRÉN, Hydraulic interference tests and tracer tests within the Brändan zone, Finnsjön study site, Swedish Nuclear Fuel and Waste Management Co., SKB Technical Report TR-89-12, Stockholm, 1989.

ROBINSON P.C., Connectivity, flow and and transport in network models of fractured media, Ph. D. Thesis, St. Catherine's College, Oxford University, Ref TP 1072, May 1984.

CHARACTERIZATION OF UNSATURATED FLUID FLOW AT DIFFERENT SCALES IN WASTE ROCK

Craig Nichol, Roger Beckie and Leslie Smith
Department of Earth and Ocean Sciences, University of British Columbia
6339 Stores Road, Vancouver, British Columbia, Canada, V6T 1Z4

Waste rock piles at mine sites can pose an environmental hazard when minerals such as pyrite are exposed to oxygen and release metals and acidity. The rate of mineral oxidation and metal loading to the environment is strongly coupled to fluid flow patterns through the largely unsaturated piles. The wide range of grain sizes in waste rock, from clay particles to meter-scale boulders, and unique stratigraphic structures, which may include matrix-free clast-supported zones, give rise a continuum of co-existing flow regimes during recharge events. Flow can be either rapid and channelized with relatively short water-rock contact times and relatively low metal concentrations, or slow and diffuse through the matrix, with long water-rock contact times and substantially higher metal concentrations. The challenge in waste rock is to determine the appropriate scale at which to characterize flow behaviors and to develop an appropriate conceptual framework for reliable predictions of metal loadings to the environment. We describe laboratory and field flow and tracer experiments through waste rock conducted at different scales. A large (1 m diameter x 2 m long) laboratory column study did not show evidence of the rapid flow observed at larger scales. We also present flow and transport results from an instrumented experimental pile, 8 m x 8 m x 5 m high. The experimental pile is built upon sixteen, 2 m x 2m contiguous lysimeters. We show how the outflow hydrographs from individual lysimeters display evidence for significant variability in both flow and transport behavior. We examine how this variability is averaged out by combining hydrographs from adjacent lysimeters and discuss the implications of this variability for the appropriate scale of characterization and modeling of flow through the piles.

EXPERIMENTAL DESIGNS

A 1 m in diameter by 2 m high reinforced fiberglass pipe was used for the laboratory column. It was manually loaded with waste rock using 20 L buckets. The column is instrumented with 20 time-domain-refectometry (TDR) probes to measure water content, 4 thermistors to record temperature, 16 tensiometers / soil water samplers to measure matrix suction and to collect pore fluids from the fine-grained matrix. The TDR probes are connected to a datalogger and polled every 15 minutes during experiments. Water is introduced at the top of the column at adjustable rates using a rainfall simulator. The column rests on a cement base, lined with impervious geomembrane that is sloped to a drain pipe located at the center. The presence of free water at the geomembrane creates a zero pressure head boundary. Outflow from the column is directed to a tipping-bucket rain gauge, which records outflow in ~5 ml increments. During extremely low outflow, the outflow is recorded gravimetricly.

The field experiment was constructed in 1998. It was designed to mimic the behavior of the upper 5m of a much larger unsaturated waste rock pile. Simplified plan and cross sectional views of the pile are shown in Figures 2. The instrumented core of the pile has a footprint of 8 m by 8 m and is 5 m high. Outflow from the base of the pile is collected in a contiguous grid of 16 lysimeters. Outflow from each 2 m by 2 m lysimeter is separately piped to an instrumentation hut where outflow is monitored using tipping-bucket rain gauges. The piping at the base of the pile is equipped with heat tracing to allow year round operation. Three instrument profiles were installed in the pile to measure water content, matric suction, temperature and matrix soil water chemistry. Application of simulated rainfall to the laboratory column began in 1998. To date, seven rainfall events have been applied, one dosed with a chloride tracer. The experimental pile was completed in September 1998 after 4 1/2 months of construction and data has been collected continuously since then. A lithium chloride tracer (2100 mg/l Cl-) was added to one such event in September 1999. The current data set includes 7000 water samples, 150,000 measurements of matric suction, 700,000 measurements of water content and 6.6 million measurements of flow.

DISCUSSION AND CONCLUSIONS

Our results have implications for characterization of flow and transport processes in waste rock. Ideally, one would like to quantify the average behavior of the pile, and the smaller-scale variability. The variability in observed responses of the individual and combined lysimeters in the field means that the laboratory column (1 m diameter) or a single 2 m X 2 m lysimeter is too small to provide a representative characterization of flow and transport behavior on the scale of a pile. The order of magnitude variability between flow issuing from individual lysimeters implies that a 2 m X 2 m area is not large enough to average out sufficient preferential flow paths. Predictions and designs based upon a single lysimeter have the potential to be in great error. However, at lower water contents, or at late times after rain events, the outflow response of the laboratory and individual field lysimeters are similar. Indeed, at the lowest flow rates, when flow is restricted to the finest grain size material, the responses become identical between meter scale, or 8m scale observations. The spatial scale of experiment required to characterize low flow rate water flow volumes will be smaller.

Our overall goal is to characterize flow processes to predict metals release from waste rock piles. The break through curve of the whole pile can be used to estimate travel times, and hence take a first step towards estimating water-rock interaction. The flux-averaged breakthrough curves and in-situ soil water sampling indicate in-situ water chemistry is not spatially uniform at field, or pore scales. The proportions of rapid flow and slower matrix flow on the scale of a pile will contribute to water chemistry, and must be understood to determine overall water chemistry. If the scale of characterization is too small, then there is a risk that rapid flow processes will not be observed, and biased predictions will result.

REFERENCES

NICHOL, C., L. SMITH and R. BECKIE, 2001a, Time domain reflectrometry measurements of water content in coarse waste rock, submitted to the Canadian Geotechnical Journal

NICHOL, C., L. SMITH and R. BECKIE, 2001b, Field evaluation of thermal conductivity sensors for the measurement of matric suction, submitted to the Canadian Geotechnical Journal

NICHOL, C., L. SMITH and R. BECKIE,, 2002a, Water flow in unsaturated heterogeneous porous media: A constructed mine waste rock pile, in preparation for Water Resources Research

NICHOL, C., L. SMITH and R. BECKIE, 2002b, Unsaturated transient transport in constructed heterogeneous media, in preparation for Water Resources Research

THE INVERSE PROBLEM OF MULTICOMPONENT REACTIVE SOLUTE TRANSPORT: APPLICATION TO THE AQUIA AQUIFER IN MARYLAND

Dai Zhenxue[2] and Javier Samper[1]

[1] *E.T.S. de Ingenieros de Caminos, Canales y Puertos. Universidad de La Coruña. Campus de Elviña s/n. 15192 La Coruña. Spain samper@iccp.udc.es; http://hydra.udc.es/*
[2] *now at Wright State University. zhenxue.dai@wright.edu*

A mathematical and numerical methodology for solving the inverse problem of water flow, heat transport and multicomponent reactive solute transport in variably saturated media has been developed. Its application to salt water leaching at the Aquia aquifer (Maryland, USA) is presented here.

INTRODUCTION

Coupled models accounting for complex hydrological and chemical processes have been developed with varying degrees of sophistication. Appelo and Postma (1993) used PHREEQM to model column experiments. They claimed that some deviations between measured and computed concentrations could be attributed to exchange coefficients which had not been optimized by inverse tools. The trial and error procedure for parameter estimation is time consuming and does not provide an accurate solution for the inverse problem. Dai (2000) developed an inverse methodology which uses the Gauss-Newton-Levenberg-Marquardt method to minimize a generalized least squares objective function. It was implemented in an inverse code, INVERSE-CORE$^{2D©}$ (Dai and Samper, 1999) which solves both the forward and inverse problems. The forward modeling part is based on CORE$^{2D©}$(Samper et al, 2000). INVERSE-CORE$^{2D©}$ provides error estimates and confidence intervals for the estimated parameters. It has been applied to the inverse analysis of: 1) diffusion experiments (García-Gutiérrez et al., 2001), 2) hydrochemical data from the Llobregat Delta aquitard (Dai and Samper, 1999) and 3) hydrochemical data from the Aquia aquifer (Dai, 2000). The latter is presented here.

PROBLEM STATEMENT

The Aquia aquifer is a coastal plain leaky aquifer located in Southern Maryland (Figure 1). Calcium, magnesium, sodium, potassium and bicarbonate are the major ions in Aquia groundwater (Chapelle and Knobel, 1983). Water quality shows zonal bands with changes in concentrations of major cations that have been attributed to cation exchange and calcite and dolomite dissolution/precipitation (Appelo, 1994). A one-dimensional water quality model was previously developed by Appelo (1994) using PHREEQM. He estimated transport and exchange parameters by a try and error method.

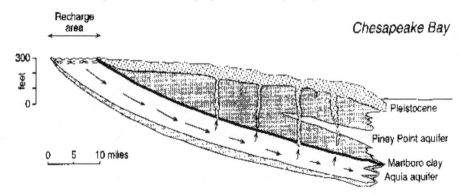

Figure 1. Cross section of the Aquia aquifer. Recharge occurs at the outcrop of the formation while discharge takes place evenly in the downstream part of the aquifer (adapted from Appelo, 1994)

MODEL FORMULATION AND RESULTS

The model represents a one-dimensional steady-state flow tube with a unit cross section area in which recharge takes place at x = 0. Leakage into the confining layers is evenly distributed over the second half of the flow tube. The flow tube has been discretized by means of 70 triangular elements and 72 nodes. Both spatial and time discretization ensure that Peclet and Courant numbers are below their required values of 2 and 1, respectively. Molecular diffusion is much less relevant than hydrodynamic dispersion and therefore has been disregarded. Cation exchange reactions are the main chemical processes in the aquifer. Gaines-Thomas convention is used for cation exchange and Na^+ is used as the reference cation. Other chemical reactions include aqueous complexation reactions and calcite and dolomite dissolution/precipitation. Primary aqueous species are: H_2O, Na^+, K^+, Ca_2^+, Mg_2^+, Cl^-, HCO_3^-, SO_4^{-2} and H^+. Calculations were performed at a constant temperature of 25 °C. The initial water was brackish as a result of mixing of seawater with fresh water during the deposition of the overlying Marlboro clay, which is a brackish-water clay. Initial and boundary component concentrations as proposed by Appelo (1994) are listed in Table 1.

Component	pH	Na^+	K^+	Ca^{+2}	Mg^{+2}	Cl^-	HCO_3^-	SO_4^{-2}
Initial	6.8	$8.74 \cdot 10^{-2}$	$1.9 \cdot 10^{-3}$	$4.38 \cdot 10^{-3}$	$9.92 \cdot 10^{-3}$	0.1018	$1.55 \cdot 10^{-2}$	$2.70 \cdot 10^{-4}$
Boundary	7.57	10^{-4}	$5 \cdot 10^{-5}$	$1.4 \cdot 10^{-3}$	0	10^{-4}	$2.8 \cdot 10^{-3}$	0

Table 1. Initial and boundary dissolved concentrations (mol/l), as proposed by Appelo (1994)

In order to interpret field data, parameters were estimated in a step-wise manner by following three steps. In Step 1 hydraulic heads at the boundaries were fixed to be 15.2 upstream and 1.5 m downstream. Proton exchange was modeled as a standard cation exchange reaction, $Na^++H-X = H^++Na-X$. Two hydraulic conductivities and dispersivities, CEC, three selectivity coefficients, initial concentrations of Na^+, K^+ and Mg^{+2} as well as boundary concentrations of K^+, Ca^{+2} and Mg^{+2} were estimated. The objective function corresponding to this step was $3.33 \cdot 10^3$. Computed curves for Na^+, K^+, and HCO_3^- show clear deviations from measured data near the downstream boundary where computed concentrations are lower than measured data. In addition, estimated initial concentrations of Na^+, K^+ and Mg^{+2} are too much lower than their prior estimates. In the second step hydraulic head was fixed only at the downstream boundary to a value of 1.5 m. A constant flux of 164.38 l/d, which was estimated with an additional inverse run, was specified at the upstream boundary (x = 0). Uniform leakage into the confining aquitard was assumed to occur along the second half of the aquifer. Appelo (1994) assumed that all the recharge leaks out from the second half of the aquifer. In order to test the plausibility of this assumption, groundwater discharge was also estimated. In this case, proton exchange was simulated via surface complexation by adding XOH as a primary species. Surface complexation reactions were expressed as $XOH_2^+ = XOH + H^+$ with $\log_{10}K=-7.4$ (at 25°C) and $XO^- = XOH - H^+$ with $\log_{10}K = 9.24$ (at 25°C). Related chemical parameters were obtained from Samper et al. (2000). Sorption site concentration was taken equal to 0.05 mol/dm^3 while adsorbent specific surface is 1000 m^2/kg. XOH was added as a sorption primary species and its initial concentration was estimated. The objective function decreases from $3.33 \cdot 10^3$ in Step 1 to $1.53 \cdot 10^3$ in Step 2 which results in a significant improvement of the fit of Na^+ and K^+. However, that of Mg^{+2} still presents some deviations while that of HCO3- is still not satisfactory because its concentrations at the downstream end are much lower than measured values. In Step 3 the hypothesis of methane oxidation was tested: Methane(aq) = HCO_3^- - $3H_2O$ + $9H^+$ + $8e^-$ with $\log_{10}K$ = -27.655 (at 25°C). By adding redox reactions into the geochemical system, the objective function decreases from $1.53 \cdot 10^3$ in Step 2 to $1.15 \cdot 10^3$. For the most part, estimated parameter values such as selectivities, initial and boundary concentrations are close to the values reported by Appelo (1994). Uncertainties in estimated parameters, as measured by their 95% confidence intervals, are small except for C_{0XOH}. The best fit for different components after 10^5 years is shown in Figure 2. Computed values match measured data for all six components except at the downstream end of the flow path where computed Mg^{2+} concentrations are slightly larger than measured data. This discrepancy could be due to a too low groundwater discharge through the downstream end. The estimated nodal leakage amounts to a 79.3% of the total recharge. The remaining 20.7% discharges through the downstream boundary.

CONCLUSIONS

Cation exchange, surface complexation, aqueous complexation, mineral dissolution and methane oxidation have been considered as part of the chromatographic separation of ions during displacement of different water types in Aquia aquifer. Optimum parameter estimates have been derived from the solution of the inverse problem of water flow and reactive solute transport. Estimated initial concentrations indicate that the initial water in the Aquia aquifer was not pure seawater but the mixing of seawater and fresh water. Estimated parameters are similar to the values reported by Appelo (1994). Estimated results indicate that a small but significant part of the flow (20.7%) makes it through the downstream end of the aquifer. For the most part computed concentrations match the observed peaks of Ca^{2+}, Mg^{2+}, K^+, Na^+, HCO_3^- and pH.

ACKNOWLEDGMENTS

This work was supported by: 1) FEBEX Project funded by ENRESA (Contracts # 70323 & 770045) and the European Union (Projects FI4W-CT95-0008 and FIKW-CT2000-0016), 2) the Spanish Ministry of Science and Technology (CICYT, HID98-282), and 3) University of La Coruña through a scholarship awarded to the first author.

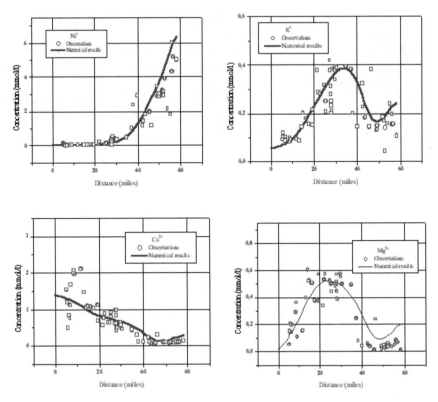

Figure 2. Measured (symbols) and computed concentrations (lines) of Na, K, Ca and Mg at the Aquia aquifer after 105 years (Step 3).

REFERENCES

APPELO, C. A. J., and D. POSTMA, Geochemistry, groundwater and pollution, Balkema, Rotterdam, 1993.

APPELO, C. A. J., Cation and proton exchange, pH variations and carbonate reactions in a freshening aquifer, Water Resour. Res., 30(10), 2793-2805, 1994.

CHAPELLE, F. H., and L. L. KNOBEL, Aqueous geochemistry and exchangeable cation composition of glauconite in the Aquia aquifer, Maryland, Ground Water, 21, 343-352,1983.

DAI, Z., Inverse Problem of Water Flow and Reactive Solute Transport in Variably Saturated Porous Media, Ph.D. Dissertation, 334 pp., University of La Coruña, La Coruña, Spain, 2000.

DAI, Z.. and J. SAMPER, INVERSE-CORE2D: A Code for inverse problem of water flow and reactive solute transport, Users Manual, Version 0, University of La Coruña, La Coruña, Spain, 240 pp., December, 1999.

GARCÍA-GUTIÉRREZ, M. , T. MISSANA, M. MINGARRO, J. SAMPER, Z. DAI, J. MOLINERO, Solute transport properties of compacted Ca-bentonite used in FEBEX project ,J. of Contaminant Hydrology (47)2-4, 127-137, 2001.

SAMPER, F.J., R. JUNCOSA, J. DELGADO and L. MONTENEGRO, CORE2D: A code for non-iso-thermal water flow and reactive solute transport, Users manual version 2, ENRE-SA, Tech. Pub., 06/00, 131 pp., 2000.

CONDITIONAL MOMENTS OF THE BREAKTHROUGH CURVES FOR KINETICALLY SORBING SOLUTES: HETEROGENEOUS REACTION PARAMETERS

Xavier Sánchez-Vila[1] and Yoram Rubin[2]

[1] *Dept. Geotechnical Engineering and Geosciences, Univ. Politècnica Catalunya, Barcelona*
[2] *Dept. of Civil and Environmental Engineering, University of California at Berkeley*

INTRODUCTION

Breakthrough curves (BTC) are usually analyzed using temporal moments. For a pulse injection the BTC corresponds exactly with the distribution of travel time (τ), that is, the time for a particle to move from the input location to the measurement point. Due to imperfect knowledge of the subsurface, travel time is treated as a random variable, and the goal is to derive its statistical moments. Travel time moments should be conditioned on all the available information (either hard or soft data), to account for all existing data. Conditioning helps reducing the uncertainty in the estimations, as measured by the estimated variance of the travel time (Rubin and Dagan, 1992).

CONDITIONAL TEMPORAL MOMENTS

Consider a sorbing solute that is moving through a heterogeneous medium under steady-state flow conditions. Assuming no local dispersion, the transport equation along the trajectory, valid at some representative elementary volume. becomes:

$$\frac{\partial C_1}{\partial T} + \frac{\rho_b}{\phi}\frac{\partial C_2}{\partial T} + V\frac{\partial C_1}{\partial \eta} = 0, \qquad (1)$$

where $C_1(\eta,T)$ is mobile concentration per unit volume of fluid; $C_2(\eta,T)$ immobile concentration per unit mass of soil; V normalized velocity; T normalized time; η normalized coordinate along the streamline; ϕ mobile porosity; and ρ_b bulk density. The geochemical model considered is that of kinetically-controlled linear mass-transfer between the mobile and immobile phases. This model depends on two potentially heterogeneous parameters, a normalized rate coefficient (k_2, dimensionless), and the distribution coefficient (K_d [L^3M^{-1}]). The governing equation is:

$$\frac{\partial C_2}{\partial T} = k_2 (K_d C_1 - C_2) \qquad (2)$$

For a pulse of concentration injected at time zero in a clean aquifer, we can find the mathematical expression for the conditional expected value of the mobile concentration at a given point located along the trajectory at normalized distance L:

$$< \overline{C}_1(L,s) >^C =< \exp(-s\tau(L) < R(s) > -s\psi(L,s)) >^C \qquad (3)$$

where $C_1(\eta,s)$ stands for Laplace transform of $C_1(\eta,T)$ (s Laplace variable);

$$\tau(L) = \int_0^{\eta(L)} V(\eta')^{-1}d\eta' \quad < R(s) >=< R(\eta,s) > \quad R(\eta,s) = 1 + \frac{\rho_b}{\phi}\frac{k_2(\eta)K_d(\eta)}{k_2(\eta)+s}$$

$$R'(\eta,s) = R(\eta,s) - < R(s) > \quad \text{and} \quad \psi(L,s) = \int_0^{\eta(L)} R(\eta',s)(V(\eta'))^{-1}d\eta$$

The conditional mean and variance of the travel time can be obtained from (3), as:

$$< \tau^{KIN}(L) >^C =< R(0) >< \tau^{NR}(L) >^C + < \int_0^{\eta(L)} \frac{R'(\eta',0)}{V(\eta')}d\eta' >^C, \qquad (4a)$$

$$\sigma_\tau^{2,KIN,C}(L) =< R(0) >^2 \sigma_\tau^{2,NR,C}(L) + 2 < R(0) > \sigma_{\tau\psi}^{KIN,C}(L,0)$$

$$+ \sigma_\psi^{2,KIN,C}(L,0) + 2\frac{\rho_b}{\phi} < \int_0^{\eta(L)} \frac{K_d(\eta')}{k_2(\eta')}\frac{d\eta}{V(\eta')} >^C. \qquad (4b)$$

^{KIN} stands for solute undergoing kinetically controlled reactions and ^{NR} for non-reactive solute; $<R(0)>=1+\rho_b/\phi<K_d>$ is the mean retardation factor. These moments are valid regardless of flow configuration.

A SIMPLIFIED ILLUSTRATIVE EXAMPLE

We consider a simple case of radial flow in a hydraulically homogeneous aquifer with heterogeneous retardation factor. The solute is injected at a distance from the well, D, and the well radius is d; the aquifer thickness is b; and the well is pumping at a constant rate Q. In this case the resulting expression for the mean travel time becomes:

$$<\tau^{KIN}(D)>^C = \left(1+\frac{\rho_b}{\phi}<K_d>\right)\frac{\pi b \phi (D^2-d^2)}{Q} + \frac{2\pi b \phi}{Q}\frac{\rho_b}{\phi}\int_d^D r<K_d'(r)>^C dr \tag{5}$$

The first term corresponds to the travel time for the non-reactive case times the mean retardation factor. The second term is the correction due to the variations in the conditional mean along the trajectory $(K_d'(r)=K_d(r)-<K_d>)$. When no data for conditioning is available $<K_d'(r)>^C=0$. If the K_d' values measured along the trajectory were mostly positive, the second term in the right hand side of (5) would be positive, leading to additional retardation in $<\tau^R_{KIN}(D)>^C$, and vice versa. On the other hand, it can be proved that in all cases the conditional mean travel time is larger or equal to that for a conservative solute. From (5), the K_d' conditional expected values are weighted by r (distance to the well). Therefore, the difference between the unconditional and conditional values of $<\tau^{KIN}(D)>$ can be more significant when measurements are taken far from the well; as the particle spends the largest part of its travel time at the larger distances, any delay produced by an enhanced retardation at these points would have a very significant retarding effect.

To illustrate this point, we consider $<\tau^R_{KIN}(r)>^C=a<K_d>(1-2r/D)$, that is a linear function of distance, with $a \in [-1,1]$ (a=0 corresponding to the unconditional case). Enhanced retardation close to the injection point (a=-1), leads to larger travel times (see Figure 1). The opposite is valid for a=1 (enhanced retardation near the well).

The second moment could also be analyzed for the general conditioning case, but in the following we will present some results only for the unconditioned case. In the example presented the variance of the travel time at the well is:

$$\sigma_\tau^{2,KIN,C}(D) = \frac{\rho_b^2}{\phi^2} \int_d^D \int_d^D \frac{<K_d'(r')K_d'(r'')>}{V(r')V(r'')}\, dr'\, dr'' + 2\frac{\rho_b}{\phi} \int_d^D \frac{1}{V(r)} < \frac{K_d}{k_2}(r) > dr \qquad (6)$$

If the following geostatisical model is adopted for K_d, $<K_d'(r')K_d'(r'')>=K_d^{G2}$ $\sigma_w^2 \exp(-|r'-r''|)$, we get that for the limit d-->0, (6) becomes:

$$\sigma_\tau^{2,KIN,C} = \left(\frac{2\pi b \rho_b}{Q} K_d^G \sigma_w\right)^2 \left[\frac{2}{3}D^3 + 2 - D^2 - 2(D+1)\exp(-D)\right] + \frac{2\pi b \rho_b D^2}{Q} < \frac{K}{k_2}$$

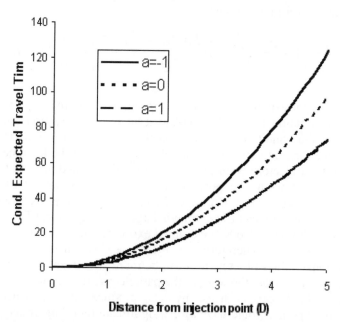

Figure 1: Conditional Mean Travel Time for a reactive solute vs. distance between the injection point and the pumping well. Conservative travel time is equal to unity and the mean retardation factor is 4.

Therefore at the limit for large distances the variance of travel time increases with the third power of the distance between injection and detection points in radial flow. This is quite different from mean uniform flow conditions, where the variance of travel time increases linearly with distance for large travel distances (Cvetkovic et al., 1998).

Acknowledgements. This work was partially funded by ENRESA.

REFERENCES

CVETKOVIC, V., G. DAGAN, and H. CHENG, Contaminant transport in aquifers with spatially variable hydraulic and sorption properties, Proc. R. Soc. London A, 454, 2173-2207, 1998.

RUBIN, Y, and G. DAGAN, Conditional estimation of solute travel time in heterogeneous formations-impact of transmissivity measurements, Water Resour. Res., 28(4), 1033-1040, 1992.

DETERMINATION OF PORE-SCALE TRANSVERSE DISPERSIVITY BY TAYLOR-ARIS DIS-PERSION IN A HELICAL SOIL COLUMN

M. A. Rahman[1], I. Benekos[2], O.A. Cirpka[1] and P.K. Kitanidis[2]

[1] *Universität Stuttgart, Institut für Wasserbau, Pfaffenwaldring 61, 70550 Stuttgart, Germany, Arifur.Rahman@iws.uni-stuttgart.de; Olaf.Cirpka@iws.uni-stuttgart.de.*

[2] *Stanford University, Dept. of Civil and Environ. Eng., Stanford, CA 95305-4020, USA, ybenekos@stanford.edu, peterk@stanford.edu.*

INTRODUCTION

Pore-scale dispersion plays a decisive role in the decay of concentration fluctuations, dilution of conser-vative solutes, and mixing of reacting compounds. Although pore scale transverse dispersivities are much smaller than the related longitudinal dispersivities, the mixing due to transverse dispersion controls, under certain conditions, the reactive behavior of interacting compounds in heterogeneous media.

The objective of the study is to develop a novel method for the determination of pore-scale transverse dispersion parameters that are difficult to obtain with the existing methods. We use a helical device (see Figure 1) the geometry of which induces shear flow in isotropic, homogeneous porous media. Applying a head difference between the inlet and outlet of the helix, the angular velocities are higher at the inside of the helix than at the outside. When a conser-vative solute is introduced, velocity differences lead to angular spreading of the solutes. The breakthrough curve of the flux-averaged concentration in the out-flow of the helix spreads inversely proportional to the local transverse dispersion coefficient. Conse-quently, small transverse dispersivity values cause strong longitudinal spreading and can therefore be detected easily and accurately.

TEMPORAL MOMENTS OF A BREAKTHROUGH CURVE IN THE OUTFLOW OF THE HELICAL DEVICE

We consider a helical domain as shown in Figure 1. The domain is characterized by the inner and outer radius r_1 and r_2, the pitch Δz, and the number of convolutions n. A head difference is applied between the inlet and outlet cross sections. If we assume that Δz is negligible in comparison to the radii and if we consider quantities that are averaged over the thickness of one whorl, the flow can be viewed as two-dimensional and the helix would simplify to a ring. In a ring, the angular coordinate j ranges only from 0 to 2π. For a small pitch $\Delta z > 0$ though many rotations are possible thus forming the helix. In our theo-retical analysis, the helix is semi-infinite and ranges from 0 to $+\infty$.

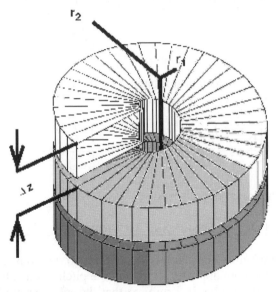

Figure 1. Visualization of the helical domain.

We analyze the breakthrough curves by their temporal moments. The k-th non-central and central temporal moment, M_k and M_{kc}, of the flux-weighted concentration are defined as:

$$M_k(\varphi) = \frac{1}{Q_{tot}} \int_{r_1}^{r_2} q_\varphi(r) \int_0^\infty t^k c(t,r,\varphi) \, dt \, dr \qquad (1)$$

$$M_{kc}(\varphi) = \frac{1}{Q_{tot}} \int_{r_1}^{r_2} \int_0^\infty \left(t - \frac{M_1}{M_2}\right)^k \frac{c(t,r,\varphi)}{r} \, dt \, dr \qquad (2)$$

in which Q_{tot} is the total discharge.

At the large-distance limit, we can derive the macrodispersion coefficient in a closed form for the limiting cases of a) no molecular diffusion and b) only molecular diffusion.

a) By neglecting the transverse dispersivity, $\alpha_t = 0$ ($\Rightarrow Dt = D$), we obtain: in which D is the effective molecular diffusion coefficient, θ is the porosity, and z_f is the thickness of the flight.

$$\lim_{\varphi \to \infty} \frac{\partial M_{2c}}{\partial \varphi} = \frac{(\Delta z - z_f)\theta}{Q_{tot}} \frac{r_2^4\left(4\left(\ln\frac{r_2}{r_1}\right)^2 - 9\ln\frac{r_2}{r_1} + 6\right) + r_2^2 r_1^2\left(4\left(\ln\frac{r_2}{r_1}\right)^2 - 12\right) + r_1^4\left(4\left(\ln\frac{r_2}{r_1}\right)^2 + 9\ln\frac{r_2}{r_1} + 6\right)}{24\ln\left(\frac{r_2}{r_1}\right)D} \qquad (3)$$

b) By neglecting the molecular diffusion, $D = 0$ ($\Rightarrow D_t = \alpha_t q_\varphi$), we obtain: in which α_t is the transverse dispersivity.

$$\lim_{\varphi \to \infty} \frac{\partial M_{2c}}{\partial \varphi} = \frac{\theta^2(\Delta z - z_f)^2}{Q_{tot}^2} \frac{\frac{4}{15}(r_2^5 - r_1^5)\ln\left(\frac{r_2}{r_1}\right)^2 + \frac{8}{9}(r_1^2 r_2^3 - r_2^5 + r_1^3 r_2^2 - r_1^5)\ln\left(\frac{r_2}{r_1}\right) + r_2^5 - r_1 r_2^4 - 2r_1^2 r_2^3 + 2r_1^3 r_2^2 + r_1^4 r_2 - r_1^5}{\alpha_t \ln\left(\frac{r_2}{r_1}\right)} \qquad (4)$$

in which α_t is the transverse dispersity.

EXPERIMENTAL COLUMN DESIGN AND METHODOLOGY

The helix is manufactured in stainless steel. It has 60 rotations. The outer diameter is 10 cm, the core diameter 3 cm, and the pitch has a value of 27 mm. The thickness of the flights is 2 mm, so that the effective thickness of the packing is 25 mm. The packing consists of glass beads with a grain size of 0.75mm –1 mm. The porosity is ≈40%.

Fluorescein is used as conservative tracer. It is detected by fiber-optic probes at the in- and outlet of the helix. Fluorescein was dissolved in deionized water at a concentration of 500µg/l. A constant dis-charge was applied by a head difference between the in- and outlet of the helix. Starting at some time t_0, the tracer solution was injected continuously into the porous medium. We measured the breakthrough curve at the outflow of the helix.

RESULTS AND DATA ANALYSIS

Five experiments were conducted each with different discharge rate to distinguish the contributions of molecular diffusion and hydrodynamic dispersion to transverse dispersion. The measured concentrations were normalized by the inflow concentration, so that the concentration values in the breakthrough curves, shown in Figure 2, range from zero to one.

The time length of the experiments ranged from a few hours to several days. Figure 3 shows the con-centration breakthrough curves in dimensionless

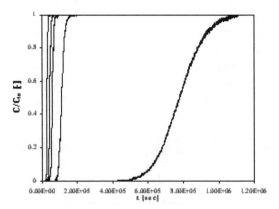

Figure 2: Normalized breakthrough curves as a function of real time for the different experiments

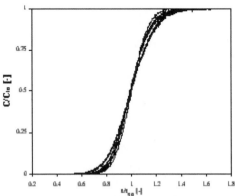

Figure 3: Normalized concentration breakthrough curves plotted in a normalized time axis. The time axis is normalized by the mean arrival time t_{50} of the tracer front.

axes. Here, the time is divided by the mean arrival time of the concentration front denoted by t_{50}. The curve in Figure 3 with the most spreading refers to the ex-periment with the lowest discharge rate, and the curve with the least spreading to that with the highest discharge rate.

The discharge rates were fairly high in all experiments. The mean rotational seepage velocity ranges from 0.27 rotations per hour to 7.5 rotations per hour. At these rates, molecular diffusion contributed marginally to local transverse dispersion. As a consequence, we were not able to estimate D from the data. In fact, the intercept of the regression analysis was negative. Therefore, we could determine only the value of the transverse dispersivity. We estimated the transverse dispersivity by inverting Eq. (4). Strictly, the latter equation holds only at the large-distance limit. Therefore, we used the resulting value α_t as initial guess in a Gauss-Newton scheme based on a numerical solution of the moment-generating equations accounting for the entire time range. Table 1 shows the initial guess for parameters α_t, D, and porosity q as well as their final estimates computed by the Gauss-Newton method. In neither case, we were able to determine the diffusion coefficient from the data.

Parameter	Initial guess	Final estimate
D [m^2/s]	Set to 0	Set to 0
α_t [m]	$7.27*10^{-4}$	$6.57*10^{-4}$
θ	0.404	0.405

Table 1: Initial guess and final estimate for parameters D, α_t and θ.

AN EXPERIMENTAL INVESTIGATION OF REACTIVE TRANSPORT

Carolyn Grammling[1], Charles Harvey[2] and Lucy Miegs[3]
[1] *Woods Hole Oceanographic Institute, Woods Hole, MA*
[2] *Massachusetts Institute of Technology, Cambridge, MA*
[3] *Sandia National Labs, Albuquerque N M*

Hydrodynamic dispersion, a mixing process that describes the spread of solute about the advective front, is classically modeled as a Fickian process. Because the dispersion coefficient is much larger than the effective diffusion coefficient at normal groundwater flow rates, a tracer-determined hydrodynamic dispersion coefficient will be largely a function of mechanical dispersion. However, the concentration of a species at the pore scale can be quite variable, and the concentration distribution of reactants at the pore scale has been shown to be controlled largely by molecular diffusion. Using concentrations of species that have been averaged across many pore spaces to predict the amount of reaction between them may consequently suggest an amount of reaction that is too great. A model that uses pore-averaged concentrations can thereby over-predict the amount of reaction occurring in a porous medium.

The purpose of this work is to rigorously examine this question by performing a direct comparison between the degree of bimolecular reaction observed in a laboratory column experiment at a given flow rate with the amount of bimolecular reaction predicted by an analytical model for the same flow rate. To perform these experiments we developed a laboratory method for directly imaging changing concentrations along a column. Using a charge-coupled device (CCD) camera, we can rapidly acquire high resolution images of the concentration changes in the column with time.

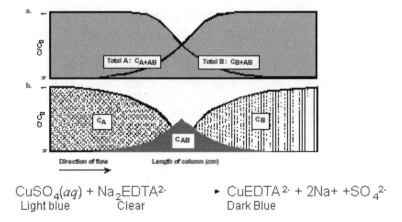

$$CuSO_4(aq) + Na_2EDTA^{2-} \longrightarrow CuEDTA^{2-} + 2Na+ +SO_4^{2-}$$

Light blue   Clear   Dark Blue

Figure 1. Schematics of reaction between $CuSO_4$ (C_A) and $EDTA^{4-}$ (C_B)within the column. a. The area under the left curve represents the total Cu^{2+} in the column. The area under the right curve represents the total $EDTA^{4-}$ in the column. b. At the center of the reaction front, all $CuSO_4$ and EDA^{4-} has been converted to $CuEDTA^{2-}$; the concentrations of CuSO4 and $EDTA^{4-}$ are zero. We integrate the central gray area over time to predict total $CuEDTA^{2-}$ produced in the column for a given flow rate.

Accurate visualization of fluid transport within a transparent porous medium requires matching the refractive indices of the injected fluid, the porous medium and the fluid saturating the medium. This is most easily done by matching the refractive index of a liquid (such as a Cargille fluid or an oil-based liquid) to that of glass beads or fused silica (R.I. ~ 1.46). For our experiments, we create a transparent porous medium by using sand-sized grains of a mineral (cryolite, with chemical formula Na_3AlF_6), with an index of refraction close to that of water (R.I. = 1.33).

In this study, a series of paired nonreactive fluid displacement and reactive colorimetric indicator experiments at different flow rates was conducted to observe the amount of mixing between two fluids in a transparent porous medium-filled chamber. The fluid displacement experiment is used to estimate the dispersion coefficient which is then used to construct a model of reactive transport.

In the reactive transport experiments, a light-colored fluid containing a chemical indicator mixes with a light-colored fluid with ions in solution, and they react to form a distinct color. The column is initially saturated with a solution of one reactant, which is then displaced by a solution with an equal concentration of the second reactant. As the two solutions mix at the interface, the reactants combine, forming colored product which is then transported through the column (Figure 1). We use an instantaneous bi-molecular chemical reaction of two solutes that goes to completion:

$$A+B\text{-->}AB \tag{1}$$

where the product AB is discernable within the column.

In both our fluid displacement and reactive colorimetric experiments, the change in color in the medium was imaged with a CCD camera, and the concentration distributions of the tracer and of the reaction product were quantified using an empirically determined product color intensity-concentration relationship. These results were then compared with an analytic solution for one-dimensional solute mass transport model coupled with reaction equations, where the dispersion coefficients were determined from the fluid displacement experiments. We will refer to reactive transport models that assume solute is completely mixed at the pore scale as standard pore-scale mixed (SPSM) models.

SPSM MODEL

The analytic solution for a simple bi-molecular reaction coupled with one-dimensional advective-dispersive transport that assumes complete pore-scale mixing is developed in three steps: (1) A solution is found for the combined concentrations of the invading reactant and its product; (2) from this solution, the solution is found for the combined concentration of the resident reactant and the product, and; (3) a solution is derived for the concentration of product alone.

For the spatially homogeneous system considered here, the product concentration C_{B+AB} is symmetric around the advective (plug flow) front at $x = vt$. Upstream of $x = vt$ the concentration of product is given by the concentration of C_{A+AB}, the invading solute, and downstream of $x = vt$ the concentration is given by C_{B+AB}, the displaced solute. The product concentration on both sides of the advective front is given by:

$$\frac{C_{AB}}{C_0} = \begin{cases} \dfrac{1}{2}\,erfc\left[\dfrac{x-vt}{2\sqrt{Dt}}\right] & \text{if } x < vt \\ \dfrac{1}{2}\,erfc\left[\dfrac{-x+vt}{2\sqrt{Dt}}\right] & \text{if } x > vt \end{cases} \tag{2}$$

This solution predicts a sharp peak of reactant that travels through the column at a velocity v. This peak is the maximum product concentration in the column and is always equal to $C_0/2$. The solutions for C_{A+AB} and C_{B+AB} indicate that, in the absence of reaction, both C_A and C_B would have a value of $C_0/2$ at x = vt (Figure 1a). So, the instantaneous reaction at the advective front sends the concentrations of both reactants to zero (Figure 1b) and holds the concentration of the product equal to half the initial concentration. According to this model, the concentration of the sharp peak should not change as the reactants are transported through the column.

The total amount of product formed may now be derived by integrating equation 14. Because C_{AB} is symmetric around x = vt, the integral is:

$$m_{AB} = 2\int_0^{vt}\left(\frac{1}{2}C_0 erfc\left(\frac{x-vt}{2\sqrt{Dt}}\right)\right)dx = 2C_0\sqrt{\frac{Dt}{\pi}} \tag{3}$$

where m equals the moles of product per unit cross-sectional area of the column. This result shows that the total amount of product continues to grow through time, but at a slower rate as the experiment progresses. This is the primary theoretical result that we will use to compare the SPSM model with our experimental results.

EXPERIMENT-MODEL COMPARISON

The comparisons between the amount of product CuEDTA^{2-} imaged within the column and the predicted amount of CuEDTA^{2-} from the SPSM model show that for all four flow rates the SPSM model consistently predicts more product formation than is observed. Figure 2 compares the total product formed, which is calculated by integrating the concentrations over the column, with the SPSM predictions (Eq. 3). The greatest amount of overprediction occurred at the fastest flow rate (Q = 150 ml/min): the model predicts concentrations of CuEDTA^{2-} that are about 20% more than observed concentrations. For all flow rates, with increasing time, there is an overall decrease in the rate of reaction as the experiments progress as the model predicts. The reaction zone widens, and reactant molecules must travel a greater distance to react.

The SPSM model predicts that the product concentration at the advective front will be half the maximum limiting reactant concentration; however, the observed product concentration peak for each flow rate was always smaller

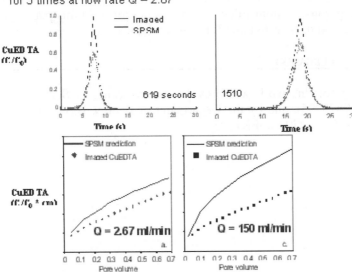

Figure 2. Predicted CuEDTA2- concentration in the column against imaged CuEDTA2- concentration. Model predictions of total CuEDTA2- formed in the column plotted against CCD camera-imaged CuEDTA2- for Q = 2.67 ml/min and Q = 150 ml/min.

(by at least 20 %) than the maximum predicted by the model, though it rises toward the predicted maximum over time. Product concentrations at the edges of the reaction zone, where reactant molecules have perhaps been better mixed, appear to be much better predicted by the model. We do not expect major imaging effects in the data (because the cryolite sand has a refractive index close to that of water); however, some apparent spreading of the reaction zone, or apparent decreased concentration of product, might occur as a result of refraction of light.

Our results indicate that complete pore-scale mixing does not occur. Both reactants may exist at the same location, even through the reaction is nearly instantaneous, when the location represents a volume containing a number of pores. One approach to modeling such behavior in porous media would be to determine an effective reaction rate coefficient representing the rate at which diffusive mixing occurs at the pore scale.

Our main result is that a model which assumes perfect mixing between two reactants as they are transported through a column will over-predict the amount of product that actually forms within the column. The method for visualizing transport at high spatial and temporal resolutions within a transparent, porous medium-filled column, as described in this paper, provides a new method of investigation for this problem.

ACKNOWLEDGMENTS

Funding for this work was provided by the National Science Foundation (EAR-9875995), and by the Department of Energy, Basic Energy Sciences division (DE-FG02-ooER15029).

SORPTION AND TRANSPORT BEHAVIOR OF HYDROPHOBIC ORGANIC CHEMICALS IN DIFFERENT GEO-SORBENTS OF BANGLADESH AND THEIR IMPACT ON GROUNDWATER

Md. Mokhlesur Rahman and Peter Grathwohl
Center for Applied Geoscience, University of Tuebingen
Sigwartstr. 10, 72076, Tuebingen, Germany.

This study focused on the determination of sorption and transport parameters for frequently used organic compounds (contaminants and pesticides) to see the effect in Bangladesh top soils and sediments and ultimate impact on groundwater. For a variety of organic compounds (TCE, 1,2-DCB, phenanthrene and carbofuran) batch and column experiments were carried out with deltaic, floodplain and residuum soils, aquifer sediments and peat. In general, the soils show almost linear sorption isotherms. The measured organic carbon normalized distribution coefficients (Koc) were in close agreement to calculated values based on the Karickhoff relationship. Slightly higher Koc values indicate that type and origin of organic matter varies within the observed geosorbents. In column experiments, the deltaic aquifer sediment showed non-equilibrium transport behaviour specially with phenanthrene while almost equilibrium condition was achieved during the column experiment with 1,2-DCB, TCE and carbofuran. The combination of batch and column experimental results together with materials (solids) and environmental properties and a use of equilibrium Ogata and Banks (1961) and non-equilibrium Rosen analytical model (1954) can provide tools for cost-effective soil and groundwater risk assessment.

INTRODUCTION

It is well established that sorption processes play an important role in the transport and disposition of hydrophobic organic compounds in the subsurface system. Therefore, a mechanistic understanding is crucial in order to properly assess the soil and groundwater contamination level. Due to intense irrigation and industrial use of organic chemicals, shallow groundwater in Bangladesh may be vulnerable to this contamination problem. Moreover, since groundwater is the major source of drinking water and remediations of contaminated sites are not even feasible for most of the countries in the world, a scenario-based integrated risk assessments models/guidelines are needed which will allow to predict risk of groundwater pollution, to categorize the sites for further use and remedial actions and decision making in a scientifically rational and cost effective way.

The main objective of this work is to assess the risk of groundwater pollution by environmental organic compounds based on material investigation, column percolation test and using contaminant transport modeling. The risk assessment procedure in this way will take the form of a scenario approach as it may be intended to apply to different situations in terms of classes/combination of pollutants and site-specific conditions, such as climatic conditions, permeability and distance between contamination and groundwater level. Such a scenario approach allows the determination a priori whether, under given site conditions (subsurface permeability, distance to groundwater table, type of material) and contaminant properties (volatile/non-volatile/water soluble etc.), a minor, medium or high risk of groundwater pollution exists.

MATERIALS AND METHODS

For this study, soil (collected on horizon basis), aquifer sediment (collected from a depth range of ca. 1-5 m) and peat samples were collected from three typical physiographic locations namely the deltaic area, floodplain area and terrace areas of Bangladesh. Physical characterization included grain size distribution, organic carbon content and particle density. Batch and column experiments were carried out with the chemical classes, which are frequently used in Bangladesh and have already caused groundwater pollution, were chosen for the study. These include pesticide-related compounds (carbofuran, 1,2-DCD), chlorinated solvents (trichloroethene) and PAHs (phenanthrene). Fluorescein was used as a nonsorbing tracer during the column experiment.

In the batch experiments, sorbed concentration was determined based on mass balance considerations. The Freundlich and linear models were used to fit the sorption isotherm data. Column experimental data were analyzed using the analytical solution for solute transport by Ogata and Banks (1961) and Rosen (1954).

RESULTS AND DISCUSSION

The results of sorption experiments are summarized in Fig. 1a for phenanthrene and Fig. 1b for 1,2-DCB, TCE and carbofuran.

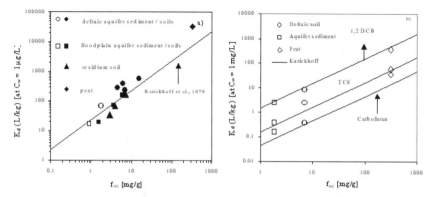

Fig. 1: Kd values vs. foc for the studied sorbents and comparison with the Karickhoff correlation: a) phenanthrene with all the collected solids and b) 1,2-DCB, TCE and carbofuran with deltaic soil, aquifer sediment and peat.

Floodplain and residuum soils show almost linear sorption isotherms ($1/n$ = 0.9 - 1.2) and revealed distribution coefficients close to values calculated by the Karickhoff correlation (Karickhoff et al., 1979). At given K_{ow} values, phenanthrene (PAH) in deltaic soil, aquifer sediment and peat exhibited slightly higher non-linearity ($1/n$ = 0.8 - 0.9) and higher K_{oc} values than floodplain and residuum soils. Stronger adsorption of PAHs to sediments was already observed by others (e.g., Chiou and Kile, 1998, Njoroge et al., 1998). For phenanthrene and the samples studied (deltaic soil, aquifer sediment and peat) the Karickhoff regression correlation underestimates the distribution coefficients. On the other hand, the distribution coefficients of less non-polar organic compounds, for example, 1,2-DCB, TCE and carbofuran can well be predicted by using the empirical Karickhoff correlation considering the degree of accuracy of the analytical methods.

Column experiments were carried out using deltaic aquifer sediment (silty sand) with phenanthrene, 1,2-DCB, TCE and carbofuran. The column experimental results are summarized in Fig. 2. For highly hydrophobic organic chemicals like phenanthrene as low as 26% of the equilibrium K_d was obtained during the column experiment. For less retarded solutes like 1,2-DCB, TCE and carbofuran as high as 90%, 85% and 60%, respectively of the equilibrium K_d was observed during the column experiments.

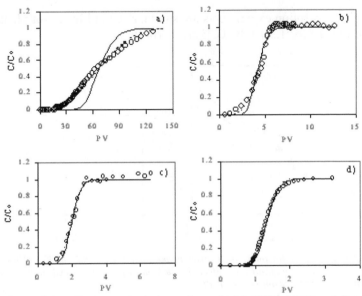

Figure 2: Breakthrough curves of: a) phenanthrene, b) 1,2-DCB, c) TCE and d) carbofuran with the deltaic aquifer sediment and fitted analytical solutions of Ogata and Banks (1961) and Rosen (1954). Legend used: symbols: experimental data; solid line: Ogata and Banks, 1961; dotted line: Rosen (1954).

Figure 3. shows the simulation results of phenanthrene transport through surface soil to the groundwater table using advective – dispersive – reactive transport equation of Ogata and Banks (1961) .

The simulation was done for the case of deltaic aquifer sediment (silty sand) having porosity of 35% and showing distribution coefficient (K_d) 44 L/kg with a strongly sorbing compound like phenanthrene. The point of compliance is considered 2m from groundsurface (typical depth to groundwater table in many parts of Bangladesh). Figure 3 - a predicts the solute transport with only retardation. As being of persistant organic contaminant, phenanth-

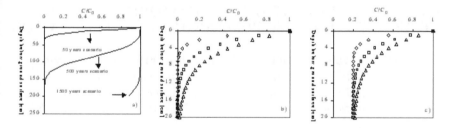

Figure 3: Simulation of equilibrium transport of organic solute through surface soil (seepage water) to the groundwater table. a) solute transport with retardation, b) solute transport with retardation and biodegradation (time 1000 years) c) same as of b) with 20% preferential flow (PF). Legend used: solid line: Ogata and Banks (1961); rectangle: HL 1 year; square: HL 5 year; triangle: HL 10 year.

rene would occur at the point of compliance after 1500 years. Figure 3 – b predicts the solute transport with retardation and biodegradation. As shown in the diagram, biodegradable compound may reach the groundwater in very low concentrations. After 1000 years of application, contaminant with a half life of 10 years will travel only 25 cm distance from the ground surface. Fig. 5 – c shows the same prediction as of 5 – b with 20% preferential flow (PF) i.e., 20% of the contaminant mass travels so quickly that sorption and biodegradation are not effective.

REFERENCES

CHIOU, C.T. and KILE, D. E. (1998): Deviations from sorption linearity on soils of polar and non-polar organic compounds at low relative concentrations. Environment Sci. Technol. 32, 338 - 343.

FREUNDLICH, H. (1909): Kapillarchemie. – Leipzig (Akademische Verlagsgesellschaft m.b.h.), 591p.

KARICKHOFF, S.W., BROWN, D.S. and SCOTT, T.A. (1979): Sorption of hydrophobic pollutants on natural sediments. Water Research. 13, 214 - 248.

NJOROGE, B.N.K., BALL, P.W. and CHERRY, R.S. (1998). Sorption of 1,2,4 – trichlorobenzene and tetrachloroethene within an authigenic soil profile: Changes in Koc with soil depth. J. Contaminant Hydrology. 29, 347-377.

OGATA, A. and BANKS, R.G. (1961): A solution of the differential equation of longitudinal dispersion in porous media. U.S. Geological Survey Professional Paper 411-A, Washington D.C.

ROSEN, J.B. (1954): General numerical solution for solid diffusion in fixed beds. Ind. Eng. Chem. 46(8), 1590 - 1594.

CYCLIC INCORPORATION OF MONITORING AND MODEL RESULTS TO OPTIMISE PUMP AND TREAT REMEDIATION

Johan R. Valstar[1], Rolf A.A. Hetterschijt, Frans J. Roelofsen,
Netherlands Institute of Applied Geoscience TNO
PO Box 80015, 3508 TA UTRECHT, The Netherlands
[1] *e-mail j.valstar@nitg.tno.nl, tel +31 30 2564707, fax +31 30 2564680*

INTRODUCTION

In former days pump & treat systems were designed to quickly flush contaminated aquifers. However many pump and treat remediation turned out to 'stagnate' and pump and treat as an effective remediation technique has been questioned (Freeze & Cherry, 1989; Keeley, 1989; Haley et al., 1991). After a preliminary rapid decrease of contaminant in the effluent in the first months during operation, the decrease of concentration tends to level off and mass removal is limited. Slow exchange of contaminants between 'mobile' and 'immobile' zones within the subsurface limit the progress of the pump and treat remediation. These slow exchange processes can be dissolution from Non Aqueous Phase Liquids, desorption of contaminants sorbed to organic carbon and diffusion of contaminants out of less permeable soil layers. Just enough groundwater and dissolved contaminants should be extracted to keep dissolution, desorption and diffusion processes going on. Griffioen and Hetterschijt (1998) showed that small groundwater velocities are large enough to do so. This will save costs as the capacity of the groundwater treatment plant will be much smaller (less contaminated groundwater has to be treated) and remediation time will be as long. The remaining problem is to control unwanted spreading of the contaminant: the groundwater extraction necessary to control the spreading exceeds the extraction necessary to remediate the contamination by orders of magnitude. Especially, control of contaminant plumes in high permeable aquifers re-quires extraction of several tens to hundred cubic meters of groundwater per day (see figure 1a).

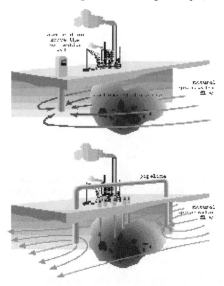

Figure 1. Traditional pump&treat [a: upper] and smart pump&treat using groundwater diversion [b: lower]

TNO has invented a concept of groundwater diversion to overcome this problem. Pristine groundwater is extracted upstream of a contaminated site and injected downstream of the contaminated site, see figure 1b. Extraction rates are chosen so that head gradients at the site are minimal and spreading of the contaminant plume can be controlled by a small ex-traction at the site.

OPTIMISED EXTRACTION RATES AS DESIGN CRITERION

By using the optimisation routines Modman (Green-wald, 1992) and Lindo (Schrage, 1991), a combined diversion and pump&treat remediation system has been designed for a site of Akzo Nobel in Weert, the Netherlands. Design criteria for these systems are the prevention of spreading of the plume, effective remediation by pump and treat, a large re-duction of the remediation extraction rates and a less strict minimisation of the diversion rates (ratio 10: 1). The control of the contamination was taken care of by demanding and inward groundwater flux at the most outer contamination contour lines which

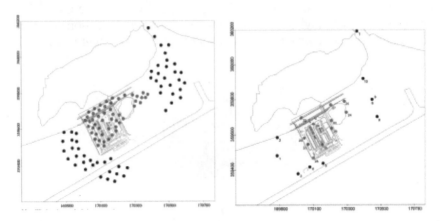

Figure 2. Potential well locations for the diversion and extraction system (left) and optimal selected well locations for the diversion and extracting system (right).

exceeds the dutch legal intervention value. A large number of potential locations for the diversion and remediation wells were selected (see figure 2 left).

Limited accessibility (buildings at the site and inaccessible wetlands next to the site) is the reason for the erratic spreading of the potential well locations.

For the design, the uncertainty of the subsurface has been taken into account. At the Akzo-site the subsurface consists out of two aquifers, of which the upper aquifer is only 10 me-ters thick. A discontinuous clay layer separates these aquifers. By incorporating the infor-mation from the bore hole data and geological knowledge, 5 different subsurface realisations have been generated which are all equally likely descriptions of the subsurface.

The combined diversion and remediation system has been obtained by opti-misation for these 5 different realisations. This resulted in 5 different well configurations (well location and extraction/injection rate). However, in reality only one well configuration will be im-plemented. Therefore using the five well configurations of the different realisations a 'mean' configuration was chosen, that will be implemented in reality, see figure 2 right. This system will only be sub-optimal as a better well configuration could be obtained when the subsurface would be known exactly. Unfortunately new data that can reduce the un-certainty only comes available after the installation of the system. Pumping rates will be adjusted based on this knowledge.

To obtain insight in the uncertainty of the optimal diversion and remediation rates, the 'mean' well configuration have been used in the optimisation of the diversion and reme-diation rates (well location are fixed, rates are optimised). The mean and maximum and minimal rates are shown in table 1.

Pumping rates m³/day	Minimum	Mean	Maximum
Diversion	600	670	700
Remediation	110	120	130

Table 1. Mean, minimum and maximum diversion- and remediation pumping rates [m³/day] at the site of Akzo Nobel.

ACKNOWLEDGEMENT

this research was funded by the Dutch organisation on soil quality management and knowledge transfer (SKB) and Akzo Nobel and carried out in co-operation with consultants of Tauw.

REFERENCES

FREEZE R.A., CHERRY J.A., (1989): What Has Gone Wrong? Ground Water vol. 27(4), 458-464.

GREENWALD, R.M., (1992): MODMAN – An Optimization Module for MODFLOW, Version 2.1, Documentation and user's guide, GeoTrans, Inc., Sterling.

GRIFFIOEN, J., HETTERSCHIJT, R.A.A., (1998): On diffusive Mass-Transfer Limitations in Re-lation to Remediation of Polluted Groundwater Systems, 6th International FZK/TNO Con-ference on Contaminated Soil, Edinborough, UK.

HALEY J.L., HANSON B., ENFIEDL C., GLASS J., (1991): Evaluating the effectiveness of Groundwater Extraction Systems, Groundwater Monitoring Rev. vol. 11(1), 119-124.

KEELEY, J.F., (1989): Performance Evaluation of Pump & Treat Remediations, Superfund Issue Paper, EPA/540/8-89/005, R.S. Kerr Environmental Research Lab., Ada OK, 14 pp.

SCHRAGE, L., (1991): LINDO: an optimization modeling system, 4th edition, The Scientific Press, San Francisco.

CONDITIONAL MOMENTS OF THE BREAKTHROUGH CURVES OF KINETICALLY SORBING SOLUTES

Alison E. Lawrence[1]*, Xavier Sanchez-Vila[2], and Yoram Rubin[1]
[1] Dept. of Civil and Environmental Engineering,
UC Berkeley, Berkeley, CA 94720
[2] Universitat Politècnica de Catalunya,
Gran Capità S/N, 08034 Barcelona, Spain

Abstract We present a methodology for calculating the conditional temporal moments of kinetically sorbing solutes based on the conditional temporal moments of non-reactive tracers. We present results showing the effect of the geochemical parameters on the reduction in uncertainty obtained by conditioning.

INTRODUCTION

Temporal moments are useful when characterizing subsurface transport, because concentrations measured in field tracer experiments are usually measured at various times at one or several locations downstream. In addition, regulations often concern the probability of exceeding a certain concentration before a certain time. Due to imperfect knowledge of the subsurface, the travel time, τ, which is the time for a particle to move from the input to the measurement location, cannot be fully predicted. The stochastic approach consists of considering τ as a random variable and deriving its statistical moments. Uncertainty in τ can be reduced by conditioning on hydrogeological or geophysical data. In Lawrence et al. (submitted), we present a concise methodology for estimating the conditional moments of BTCs for non-conservative solutes as a function of the conditional temporal moments of conservative solutes based on a Lagrangian methodology. We consider heterogeneous hydrological parameters and homogeneous geochemical parameters.

MATHEMATICAL STATEMENT OF THE PROBLEM AND GENERAL SOLUTION

We consider a non-conservative solute traveling from an injection point to a discharge location. The solute follows a certain streamline, which is unknown due to heterogeneity. Along this streamline, we can write the advection-dispersion equation, which includes a term that accounts for mass transfer between a mobile and an immobile phase. We use the general model proposed by Haggerty and Gorelick (1998), which considers a continuous distribution of mass transfer rate coefficients. Several common models, such as instantaneous equilibrium, two-site kinetics, and a lognormal distribution of rate parameters, can be obtained as special cases of this model. Disregarding the influence of pore-scale dispersion, the resulting equations are:

$$\frac{\partial C_1}{\partial T} + \beta_{tot} \int_0^\infty p(\alpha) \frac{\partial C_2(\alpha)}{\partial T} d\alpha + V \frac{\partial C_1}{\partial \eta} = 0, \qquad (1)$$

$$\frac{\partial C_2(\alpha)}{\partial T} = \alpha(C_1 - C_2(\alpha)) \qquad (2)$$

where C_1 is the mobile concentration per unit volume of fluid; C_2 is the immobile concentration per unit mass of soil; V is dimensionless velocity (V= v / U, where v is the actual velocity, and U is the mean velocity); T is dimensionless time (T = U t / I_Y, where t is actual time, and I_Y is the integral scale of the log-hydraulic conductivity, Y, in the mean flow direction); η is the coordinate along the streamline, non-dimensionalized by I_Y; β_{tot} is the dimensionless total capacity coefficient; and $p(\alpha)$ represents the volumetric fraction of the solid that reacts at a particular rate, α, where α is a dimensionless mass transfer rate coefficient. For a pulse of concentration injected at time zero into a clean aquifer, the concentration at the control point or plane at a distance L downstream is

$$\overline{C}_1(L, s) = \exp\left(-s\tau(L)\left(1 + \beta_{tot} \int_0^\infty \frac{\alpha p(\alpha)}{\alpha + s} d\alpha\right)\right) \qquad (3)$$

where $t(L) = \int_0^{\eta(L)} d\eta' / V(\eta')$ corresponds to the travel time of a conservative tracer along the trajectory from the injection point (η=0) to the control point or plane ($\eta(L)$). An overbar indicates the Laplace transform of a variable, and s is the Laplace variable. In this approach V and η, and thus τ, are random. Therefore, it is better to work with the conditional expectation of the breakthrough curve. The first two conditional reactive central temporal moments (mean and variance) are:

$$< \tau^R >^C = (1 + \beta_{tot}) < \tau^{NR} >^C, \tag{4}$$

$$\sigma_\tau^{2,R,C} = \sigma_\tau^{2,NR,C} (1 + \beta_{tot})^2 + 2\beta_{tot} < \tau^{NR} >^C \int_0^\infty \frac{p(\alpha)}{\alpha} d\alpha \tag{5}$$

where ^{C} stands for conditional, ^{R} indicates reactive, and ^{NR} stands for non-reactive.

ILUSTRATIVE EXAMPLE

For the geochemical model corresponding to a solute that undergoes reactions limited by two-site kinetics, the function $p(\alpha)$ is given by

$$p(\alpha) = \frac{\beta_1}{\beta_{tot}} \delta(\alpha - \alpha_1) + \frac{\beta_2}{\beta_{tot}} \delta(\alpha - \alpha_2) \tag{6}$$

To study the efficiency of conditioning, we use conditional moments for conservative solutes from Rubin (1991) that correspond to conditioning by 9 transmissivity values beginning at the injection point and continuing in the mean flow direction at a spacing of $1.25 I_Y$. We define a parameter that accounts for the reduction of the variance of the travel time from the unconditional to the conditional case.

$$\text{Percent Re duction} = \frac{\left| \sigma_\tau^{2,R,NC} - \sigma_\tau^{2,R,C} \right|}{\sigma_\tau^{2,R,NC}} 100\% \tag{14}$$

Figure 1 shows the effect of the total capacity coefficient on the percent reduction of travel time variance due to conditioning. $\beta_1 = \beta_2$ for all three curves. $\alpha_1 = 10$, $\alpha_2 = 0.1$ and $\sigma_Y^2 = 0.5$. As the total capacity coefficient increases, the effect of conditioning increases.

ACKNOWLEDGEMENTS

This work was partly funded by the National Science Foundation, ENRESA, and the Spanish Ministry of Education.

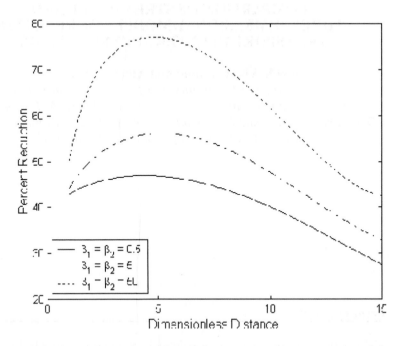

Figure 1: Effect of total on the percent reduction in the travel time variance due to conditioning for three different cases of the two-site model. For all curves, $\alpha_1=10$, $\alpha_2=0.1$ and $\sigma_Y^2=0.5$.

REFERENCES

HAGGERTY, R., and GORELICK, S. M., Modeling mass transfer processes in soil columns with pore-scale heterogeneity. Soil Sci. Soc. Am. J., 62(1), 62-74, 1998.

LAWRENCE, A. E., X. SANCHEZ-VILA, and Y. RUBIN, Conditional moments of the breakthrough curves of kinetically sorbing solute in heterogeneous porous media using multirate mass transfer models for sorption and desorption. Water Resour. Res., submitted.

RUBIN, Y., Prediction of tracer plume migration in disordered porous media by the method of conditional probabilities. Water Resour. Res., 27(6), 1291-1308, 1991.

COMPARISON OF STREAMTUBE AND THREE-DIMENSIONAL MODELS OF REACTIVE TRANSPORT IN HETEROGENEOUS MEDIA

Hari S. Viswanathan[1] and Albert J. Valocchi[2]
[1] Los Alamos National Laboratory, Earth and Environmental Sciences Division. Los Alamos National Laboratory, Los Alamos, NM 87545, USA
[2] Department of Civil and Environmental Engineering. University of Illinois at Urbana-Champaign, Urbana, IL 61801, USA

INTRODUCTION

Field-scale transport of reactive solutes is influenced strongly by physical and geochemical heterogeneity over a wide range of spatial scales. Accurate numerical simulation requires fine spatial and temporal discretization to resolve the smallest scales of heterogeneity, in addition to coupling large numbers of chemical components participating in geochemical and micro-biological reactions. Standard approaches based upon finite difference or finite element discretization of the governing set of convection-dispersion-reaction equations can lead to computational difficulties for large problems. To overcome these difficulties, several streamtube-based models have been presented in the literature. These models neglect transverse dispersion, and hence reactive transport occurs along independent one-dimensional stream-tubes. Therefore, streamtube models are well-suited for applications where the objective is to calculate solute flux breakthrough across a control plane.

We develop a reactive streamtube model by modification of the Finite Element Heat and Mass transfer code (FEHM), an existing flow and transport code. FEHM can simulate unsatu-rated zone conditions, heat flow, and mul-ticomponent reactive transport, and has been used ex-tensively by the Yucca Mountain Project. Because the same underlying numerical algorithms are used in both the FEHM and streamtube models, direct comparison of their relative performance is possible. We perform this comparison for a three-dimensional reactive transport example, demonstrating the large potential computational advantages of the streamtube approach.

REACTIVE STREAMTUBE MODEL

The first step for converting two- and three-dimensional simulations into streamlines is to map out path lines from the computed flow field. Numerous methods exist to accomplish this, and we use a "semi-analytical" particle tracking method outlined by Pollock (1988), since it was developed for block centered models such as FEHM. As the flow path and travel times are computed, we must also extract node-based chemical properties such as mineralogy, reactive site concentration, and distribution coefficient along each streamline. These properties are necessary for reactive transport calculations. Further details are given in Viswanathan (1999).

Next, the path lines provided by the Pollock (1988) method have to be converted into one-dimensional reactive transport simulations. In two dimensions, the process to convert streamlines into streamtubes is straightforward, however, the process is not nearly as straightforward in three-dimensions. We choose to follow Batycky et al. (1996) and use streamlines instead of streamtubes, since they are easily extended to 3D systems. The disadvantage of using streamlines over streamtubes is that they do not carry an explicit volumetric flux. For the problems presented in this paper we assume that a constant flux of solute enters at the inlet boundary, and thus we can assign a flow rate to each streamline based upon the flux at the inlet boundary. More complex algorithms will be required to simulate problems in which the influx is spatially variable or there is a nonuniform initial distribution of solute within the problem domain.

Given the volumetric flow rate associated with streamline j, Q_j, we can calculate the travel times, τ, and x, y and z positions at discrete intervals (i.e., "nodes") along a streamline using the Pollock method. Given the nodal coordinate positions along the streamlines and the corresponding travel time, we can calculate the effective linear travel distance, $\bar{x}$, and the effective average linear pore water velocity, $\bar{v}$, for each streamline segment. We can also compute an effective flow-cross-sectional area, A, and pore volume, V; A is simply the volumetric flow rate Q_j divided by the velocity $\bar{v}$, and V equals Q_j times the segment travel time. This procedure effectively generates a discretized one-dimensional solute transport model for each streamline. Since FEHM requires grid block volumes and inter-block areas, it can be used to solve the discretized transport equation. Finally, the concentration breakthrough at a given control plane can then be calculated using a flux weighted average of the concentration breakthrough curves from each of the streamtubes.

EXAMPLE SIMULATION

We consider ^{237}Np transport through a random permeability field to test the effectiveness of the RST method for contaminants that participate in nonlinear reactions. Characterization and performance assessment studies for the potential high-level nuclear waste repository at Yucca Mountain have identified ^{237}Np as a radionuclide of concern (Viswanathan et al., 1998). Other test problems are presented in Viswanathan (1999).

The problem domain is a cube 10 m on each side. The top and bottom are constant pressure boundaries, whereas the sides of the cube are no flow boundaries. The top and bottom boundaries were both set to the same pressure, and hence the flow in these problems is gravity driven and directed predominantly from the top to the bottom of the cube. A steady state flow field is calculated through the fully saturated block before the solute input is started. The porosity, ϕ, and the bulk rock density, ρ_b were set equal 0.27 and 2500 kg/m3, respectively. A log-normal distribution of permeability was generated using the turning bands algorithm. The geometric mean of the permeability is 1×10^{-12} m^2 with a ln(k) variance of 1.0 and a correlation length of 1 m. In or-der to make an accurate comparison, we required a fine grid spacing of 0.2 m for the CDR model (132,651 nodes) to limit the amount of numerical dispersion. A longitudinal dispersivity of 0.1 m is used for both models, and a transverse dispersivity of 0.01 m is used for the CDR model. Solute is released along the top boundary for 1 day and is collected at the bottom boundary. The geochemical processes we consider are the aqueous speciation of ^{237}Np into non- sorbing car-bonate/hydroxy complexes, and the sorption of NpO_2^+. The relationship presented by Smith et al. (1996) was used to relate the sorption parameters to the spatially variable permeability field.

Three aqueous components (NpO_2^+, H^+, and HCO_3^-) and one immobile component ($NpO_2^+(sorbed)$) are present in this example. Figure 1 shows the breakthrough of total aqueous ^{237}Np at the bottom of the domain. Both computational methods agree closely with RST showing a slightly higher peak concentration than CDR. The multiple peaks observed in the breakthrough curve were caused by heterogeneity. For this example, CDR required about 40 times more CPU time than the RST. In order to obtain an accurate result, 100 streamlines were used for this simulation. The required number of streamlines was obtained using trial and error by comparing the nonreactive tracer breakthrough from the RST with the high resolution CDR. We expect greater CPU savings for more complicated chemical systems since the CDR model becomes computationally expensive as the number of components increase. On the other hand, the com-putational advantage of the RST approach depends strongly upon the number of streamlines, and we expect that more streamlines will be necessary to obtain an accurate result for problems having a larger degree of chemical and physical heterogeneity.

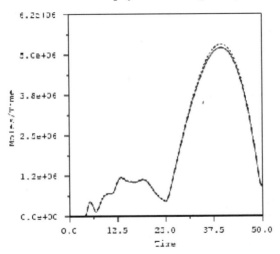

Figure 1: Comparison of the CDR (solid line) and RST (dashed line) techniques for reactive transport of ^{237}Np through a random permeability field.

REFERENCES

POLLOCK, D.W., Semianalytical computational of path lines for finite-difference models, Ground-water, 26, No. 6, 743-750, 1988.

SMITH, R.W., A.L. SCHAFER, A.F.B. TOMPSON, Theoretical relationships between reactivity and per-meability for monominerallic porous media, in Proceedings, XIX Symposium of the Scientific Basis of Nuclear Waste Management, edited by W.M. Murphy and D.F. Knecht, Mater. Res. Symp. Proc., 412, 1996.

VISWANATHAN, H.S., B.A. ROBINSON, A.J. VALOCCHI, and I.R. TRIAY, A reactive transport model of nep tunium migration from the potential repository at Yucca Mountain,

Journal of Hydrology, 1998.

VISWANATHAN, H.S. The development and application of reactive transport modeling techniques to study radionulcide migration at Yucca Mountain, NV, PhD Thesis, University of Illinois, LA-13642-T, Los Alamos National Laboratory Report, 1999.

MULTICOMPONENT EFFECTS ON THE TRANSPORT OF CATIONS UNDERGOING ION EXCHANGE IN FRACTURED MEDIA

Timothy J. Callahan[1], Paul W. Reimus[2], Peter C. Lichtner[2] and Robert S. Bowman[3]

[1] *College of Charleston, Charleston, SC 29424, e-mail: callahant@cofc.edu*
[2] *Los Alamos National Lab, Los Alamos, NM 87545, preimus@lanl.gov; lichtner@lanl.gov*
[3] *New Mexico Institute of Mining and Technology, Socorro, NM 87801, bowman@nmt.edu*

We developed a simple ion-exchange model to describe the transport of cations (lithium, sodium, and calcium) in fractured tuffaceous rock cores. The hydrodynamics of the system was characterized by injecting two nonsorbing anions having different diffusion coefficients. A numerical method based on a dual-porosity transport model was used to describe advection in the fractures and molecular diffusion in the porous matrix, using species-dependent diffusion coefficients. Although the arrival and rise in concentration of lithium during the tests could be explained quite well with a simple matrix retardation factor, the observed "tailing" of lithium was less than predicted, especially in rock types having a relatively high cation exchange capacity. By explicitly accounting for ion exchange reactions as well as charge balance in the dual-porosity model, simulations of lithium, sodium, and calcium transport in the fractured rocks were much improved. We conclude that accounting for ion exchange, as well as species-dependent diffusion, is necessary to properly interpret reactive transport experiments in fractured media, particularly when the injection concentrations of cations are high relative to the groundwater and when the cation exchange capacity of the rock type is large.

INTRODUCTION

Transport in fractured media is often described using a dual-continuum approach in which solutes or particles advect at different rates in two continua, such as fractures and unfractured porous matrix [see Tang et al., 1981; Callahan et al., 2000; and Guimera and Carrera, 2000 and references therein]. The dual-porosity model is one form of the dual-continuum concept, in which mass advects mainly or exclusively within the fractures with negligible or no advection occurring in the surrounding unfractured porous rock matrix. However, solutes can access the matrix by molecular diffusion. It is important to employ solute-specific matrix diffusion coefficients in the dual-porosity model. For the modeling efforts described below, the matrix diffusion coefficients were estimated by comparing the transport data of bromide and pentafluorobenzoate (PFBA) with the constraint that Br- is three times more diffusive than PFBA, based on the ratio of the respective diffusion coefficients in water [Callahan, 2001]. The dual-porosity model was shown to accurately describe the transport of nonreactive solutes in fractured volcanic tuff cores [Callahan et al., 2000]. Initial attempts to model the transport of a reactive solute (lithium ion) using a simple linear retardation model were inaccurate, especially for rock types of high sorption capacity. We hypothesized that the high concentration of Li^+ injected in the cores (relative to the other cations in the system, predominantly sodium and calcium) resulted in an asymmetric chromatographic separation of the solute breakthrough curves (BTCs). This was based on a previous study of Li^+ transport in laboratory columns containing crushed samples of similar volcanic tuff [Callahan, 2001]. The resulting BTC for Li^+ was a function of the ratio of Li^+ equivalents to the other cations in the system (Na^+ and Ca^{2+}) as well as the cation exchange capacity (CEC) of the crushed tuff.

The phenomenon of asymmetric chromatographic separation in high concentration tracer tests has been reported elsewhere [e.g., Valocchi et al., 1981a; b; Appelo, 1994; Vulava, 1998]; Lichtner [2000] presents a critique of the dual continuum approach with application to reactive transport. Our purpose was to determine whether a multicomponent approach that included ion exchange equilibria and species-dependent matrix diffusion coefficients could better describe the transport behavior of Li^+ in the fractured tuff cores. A better understanding of multicomponent effects in fractured media could lead to more accurate assessment of transport in contaminated aquifers, especially when predicting contaminant transport based on the behavior of tracers injected at high molar concentrations.

RESULTS AND DISCUSSION

The results for the tracer experiment in the lower Bullfrog Tuff core sample are presented below, as this sample had the highest cation exchange capacity.

This stratum of the Bullfrog Tuff Member (Crater Flat Tuff Formation) is defined based on its hydrologic properties [Geldon, 1993]. The Bullfrog Tuff Member is a moderately-welded ash flow tuff, rhyolitic in composition [Geldon, 1993; Callahan, 2001].

Experimental and best-fit model results are shown in Table 1 and Figure 1. Figure 2 shows the model results from both the single-component and ion-exchange models for Li^+ transport with the Li^+ data. This core exhibited the most asymmetric Li^+ BTC. Quantitative X-ray diffraction measurements on crushed samples of this rock type indicated 9 ± 3 wt. % smectite, 13 ± 3 wt. % analcime, and 4 ± 1 wt. % clinoptilolite [Anghel et al., 2000], which provided the majority of cation exchange sites in the core sample. The other rock types contained $\leq 2 \pm 1$ wt. % of these minerals and exhibited much lower cation exchange. The values of the ion exchange parameters $K_{Li\backslash Na}$, $K_{Li\backslash Ca}$, and CEC were much greater for this core compared to the other three, as was the Li^+ K_D value.

CONCLUSION

Using multiple solutes in tracer tests in fractured tuff provides information on the hydrodynamic dispersion within fractures, diffusive mass transfer between water in the fractures and water in the porous matrix, and the retardation behavior of reactive solutes, all from a single experiment. However, injecting high concentrations of chemicals into a system with a low ionic-strength water can drastically alter the transport behavior of cations compared to their behavior under low-concentration injection conditions. The traditional approach of estimating a retardation coefficient from tracer data is often used to predict the behavior of reactive solutes at low concentrations, but using this parameter obtained from high concentration tracer tests can lead to large discrepancies. We have shown that using an ion-exchange approach is necessary to explain the transport behavior of cations at high concentrations and to increase the applicability of tracer test interpretations to low-concentration conditions. This approach is superior to single-component models that infer sorption isotherm parameters from the transport behavior of a reactive solute, e.g., Freundlich and Langmuir sorption equations [Reimus et al., 1999] because the ion exchange equations more accurately describe the fundamental processes that affect Li^+ transport.

ACKNOWLEDGMENTS

Financial support for this work was provided by the U.S. Department of

Energy, Office of Civilian Radioactive Waste Management, as part of the Yucca Mountain Site Characterization Project. Thanks to Fred Phillips, Brian McPherson, and John Wilson for their discussions of the results, and to Dale Counce for the sample analyses.

REFERENCES

ANGHEL, I., H. J. TURIN, and P. W. REIMUS, Lithium sorption to Yucca Mountain Tuffs, Los Alamos Unrestricted Report LA-UR-00-2998, Los Alamos National Laboratory, Los Alamos, NM, 2000.

APPELO, C. A. J., Some calculations on multicomponent transport with cation-exchange in aquifers, Ground Water, 32(6), 968-975, 1994.

CALLAHAN, T. J., Laboratory investigations and analytical and numerical modeling of the transport of dissolved solutes through fractured rock, Ph.D. dissertation, New Mexico Institute of Mining and Technology, Socorro, 2001.

CALLAHAN, T. J., P. W. Reimus, R. S. Bowman, and M. J Haga, Using multiple experimental methods to determine fracture/matrix interactions and dispersion of nonreactive solutes in saturated volcanic rock, Water Resour. Res., 36(12), 3547-3558, 2000.

GELDON, A. L., Preliminary hydrogeologic assessment of boreholes UE25c #1, UE25c #2, and UE25c #3, Yucca Mountain, Nye County, Nevada, U.S. Geol. Surv. Water-Resour. Invest. Rep. 92-4016, Denver, CO, 85 pp., 1993.

GUIMERA, J. and J. CARRERA, A comparison of hydraulic and transport parameters measured in low-permeability fractured media, J. Contam. Hyd., 41: 261-281, 2000.

LICHTNER, P. C., Critique of dual continuum formulations of multicomponent reactive transport in fractured porous media, Dynamics of Fluids in Fractured Rock, B. Faybishenko, P. A. Witherspoon, and S. M. Benson (eds.), Geophys. Mon. 122, 281-298, Amer. Geophys. Union, 2000.

REIMUS, P. W. and M. J. HAGA, Analysis of tracer responses in the BULLION forced-gradient experiment at Pahute Mesa, Nevada, Los Alamos National Laboratory Report LA-13615-MS, Los Alamos, NM, 1999.

REIMUS, P. W., A. ADAMS, M. J. HAGA, A. HUMPHREY, T. CALLAHAN, I. ANGHEL, and D. COUNCE, Results and interpretation of hydraulic and tracer testing in the Prow Pass Tuff at the C-Holes, Yucca Mountain Project Milestone SP32E7M4, Los Alamos National Laboratory, Los Alamos, NM, 1999.

TANG, D. H., E. O. FRIND, and E. A. SUDICKY, Contaminant transport in fractured porous media: Analytical solution for a single fracture, Water Resour. Res., 17, 555-564, 1981.

VALOCCHI, A. J., R. L. STREET, and P. V. ROBERTS, Transport of ion-exchanging solutes in groundwater: Chromatographic theory and field simulation, Water Resour. Res., 17, 1517-1527, 1981.

VALOCCHI, A. J., P. V. ROBERTS, G. A. PARKS, and R. L. STREET, Simulation of the transport of ion-exchanging solutes using laboratory-determined chemical parameter values, Ground Water, 19, 600-607, 1981.

VULAVA, V. M., Cation competition in soil materials: Adsorption equilibria and transport, unpublished Ph.D. dissertation, Swiss Federal Institute of Technology (ETH), Zurich, Switzerland, 1998.

Modeling Parameters[a]	
Porosity of matrix	0.30
Solute mean residence time, τ (hr)	4.2
Peclet number, Pe	46.
Dispersivity in fracture $\alpha=L/Pe$ (m)	4.72×10^{-3}
Li$^+$ Retardation factor, R (-)[b]	6.9
Li$^+$ Partition coefficient, K_D (L kg^{-1})	0.95
Mass transfer coefficient,	0.0767 (Br)
MTC = $(n_m^2/B^2)D_m$ (hr^{-1})	0.0256 (PFBA)
Fracture aperture, B (m)[c]	1.00×10^{-3}
Matrix diffusion coefficient, D_m	2.4 (Br)
$(\times 10^{-10}$ m^2 s$^{-1})$[d]	0.8 (PFBA)
CEC (meq kg^{-1}), Measured	179.7
CEC (meq kg^{-1}), Fitted	179.7
$K_{Li\backslash Na}$[e]	9.1
$K_{Ca\backslash Na}$[e]	26.7

[a]*The Br and pentafluorobenzoate (PFBA) data were fit simultaneously by constraining the Dm ratio for Br: PFBA to 3:1. The matrix diffusion coefficient for Li$^+$ was assumed to be 2/3 the value for Br.*
[b]*Calculated from the Li$^+$ transport data from rising portion of the BTC using the Reactive Transport Laplace Transform Inversion code (RELAP) [Reimus and Haga, 1999].*
[c]*Based on the relationship B = (Q τ)/(L w), where t is the solute mean residence time.*
dDetermined from the MTC using the measured nm and the calculated B.
[e]*Equilibrium ion exchange coefficients, determined from best fit to the Li$^+$, Na$^+$, and Ca^{2+} data.*

Table 1. Best-fit model parameters for the fracture transport test, lower Bullfrog Tuff core.

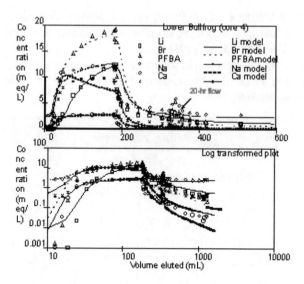

Figure 1. Transport data and RETRAN-M modeling results, lower Bullfrog Tuff core.

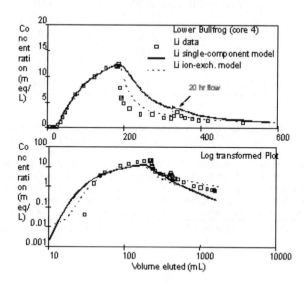

Figure 2. Comparison of single-component and ion-exchange model results, lower Bullfrog Tuff core.

MODELING GROUNDWATER FLOW AND REACTIVE TRANSPORT INCLUDING MICROBIOLOGICAL PROCESSES: A LARGE-SCALE CASE STUDY AT THE ÄSPÖ UNDERGROUND LABORATORY (SWEDEN).

Jorge Molinero, Javier Samper & Gouxiang Zhang
E.T.S. Ingenieros de Caminos, Canales y Puertos. Campus de Elviña s/n.
15192 A Coruña. Spain. Phone: (+34) 981-167000
Fax: (+34) 981-167170 / E-mail: molinero@iccp.udc.es

The Äspö Hard Rock Laboratory (Äspö HRL) is a prototype, full-scale underground facility launched and operated by SKB (the Swedish Nuclear Waste Management Company). The main aim of the Äspö HRL is to provide an opportunity for research, development and demonstration in a realistic rock environment down to the depth planned for a future deep nuclear waste repository. The Äspö HRL is located in the southeast part of Sweden, 400 km south of Stockholm. The underground facility consists of a 3,600 m long tunnel which starts with an access ramp and runs in two turns down to a depth of 450 m under the Äspö island. On March 13th, 1991 the access tunnel of the Äspö HRL intersected a vertical fracture zone at a depth of 70 m below sea level. This vertical fracture zone is known within the context of the Äspö HRL as the Redox Zone. Prior to tunnel intersection, a borehole was drilled and sampled in order to know undisturbed conditions of groundwater at the tunnel position. These samples provided a reference state for comparing the subsequent evolution of groundwater conditions. The Redox Zone Experiment carried out at the Äspö HRL provides a unique opportunity to study redox and other relevant geochemical, isotopic and microbiological processes, when an isolated vertical fracture zone is disturbed by the construction of a tunnel. The Redox Zone Experiment constitutes a long term experiment with a large and detailed chemical database at several control points.

Groundwater samples were collected in boreholes and tunnel walls during the Redox Zone Experiment. A sharp dilution front was observed in the tunnel three weeks after the start of the experiment. A dramatic decrease in Cl⁻ and cation concentrations was measured in samples collected from the roof of the tunnel. A short time later, dissolved Fe concentrations in the tunnel inflows decreased to near zero for a period of a few weeks. This could be taken as an indication of the arrival of an oxidation front to the tunnel position (Banwart et al., 1999). After 50 days both the significant dissolved Fe concentrations at all sample locations and the stable and continuously measured redox potentials (within the range -150 < Eh < -100) indicate that anoxic conditions prevail in the fracture zone. pH remained constant near a value of 8 throughout the experiment (Banwart ert al., 1999). Dilution of the saline native groundwater by fresh recharge water is the dominant process controlling the hydrochemistry evolution during the experiment. However, HCO_3^- and SO_4^{2-} concentrations increase significantly during the experiment at sampling points located at 70 m depth. Isotopic (Banwart et al., 1999) and microbiological (Pedersen et al., 1995) studies conclusively rule out SO_4^{2-} reduction during the experiment, and provide significant evidence supporting Fe(III) reduction as the respiration pathway for the oxidation of organic C in the fracture zone. Tullborg & Gustaffson (1999) report a large increase in ^{14}C activity in both dissolved organic and inorganic C during the experiment, providing evidence for a source of water containing young and oxidizing organic C. There is no conclusive explanation for the increase in dissolved SO_4^{2-} (Banwart et al., 1999). Sulfur isotope data (Wallin, 1995) show that SO_4^{2-} originating from either sea water, deeper groundwater or atmospheric deposition would not be consistent with the isotopic signature of dissolved SO_4^{2-} at sampled boreholes. Banwart et al. (1999) state that the hypothesis of anion exchange between SO_4^{2-} and HCO_3^- is an attractive explanation, mainly because any change in the isotopic composition would be reflected identically for ions in solution or those adsorbed. However, Bruton & Viani (1997) conclude that the total adsorption capacity expected for the fracture zone, is likely to be too small for anion exchange to have a significant impact on dissolved SO_4^{2-}.

A groundwater flow and reactive transport numerical model of the Redox Zone Experiment has been performed. The hydrogeochemical model accounts simultaneously for the following local-equilibrium chemical processes: aqueous complexation, acid-base, redox, cation exchange and mineral dissolution/precipitation, including more than 60 homogeneous reactions, as well as 5 heterogeneous reactions. Numerical simulations were carried out with CORE²ᴰ© (Samper et al., 2000), a finite element code developed at the

University of A Coruña for the solution of coupled groundwater flow, heat transport and multi-component reactive solute transport under fully or variably saturated conditions. Long term runs of the flow and transport numerical model were performed to simulate the undisturbed conditions (prior to tunnel construction). Initially, it was assumed that the domain contains only saline native groundwater. The numerical model was solved for 20,000 days with a fresh water recharge at the upper boundary. Calibration of the flow and transport parameters was performed in order to achieve a numerical solution consistent with available chemical information of undisturbed conditions at a depth of 70 m.. Computed concentrations for undisturbed (natural) conditions at the tunnel location agree for the most part with measured concentrations at a depth of 70 m. However, large discrepancies were found for sulfate, bicarbonate and iron which could possibly be affected by microbial processes, which were not considered in the model. Detailed research activities have been carried out at the Äspö HRL which provide firm evidence for microbial processes taking place at this site (Puigdomenech et al., 2001). Fermentation of Particulate Organic Carbon (POC) takes place in the shallow anaerobic zone where POC can be enriched and the intrusion of oxygen coming from the surface can be consumed by the aerobic metabolism near the surface. Fermentation provides the source of Dissolved Organic Carbon (DOC). As a result of fermentation processes, organic sulfur contained in POC is released as HS^-. Then, DOC and HS- are transported and oxidized in deeper parts of the aquifer containing Fe (III) mineral phases.

To overcome these limitations of the reactive hydrogeochemical model, a coupled reactive hydrobiogeochemical model was addressed which in addition to hydrochemical reactions accounts for microbial processes. This model was solved using BIO-CORE$^{2D©}$ (Zhang, 2001), a code which extends the capabilities of CORE$^{2D©}$ to cope with microbial proceses. BIO-CORE$^{2D©}$ deals with microbial metabolic competition, decay, metabiosis and endogenous respiration and considers the availability of substrates for attached microorganisms by coupling a diffusion layer model to account for biofilm resistance. Microbially-mediated processes considering Fe^{3+} as the electron acceptor to account for the oxidation of DOC have been included in the numerical model. The coupled groundwater flow, solute transport and reactive bio-geochemical model of Redox Zone Experiment of the Äspö HRL simulates also both natural and disturbed experimental conditions. Then consistent initial conditions for the Redox Zone Experiment are self-generated for each numerical simulation. Now, the numerical model is able to reproduce accurately the measured time evolution of dissolved bicarbonate and sulfate (Figure 1) as well as the rest of the chemical species considered in the reactive hydrobiogeochemical model. This result provides quantitative support for the hypothesis of microbially-mediated iron reduction-DOC oxidation processes playing a relevant role in the hydrochemical evolution of the Äspö Hard Rock Laboratory. These microbially-mediated processes can have a great relevance for the performance assessment of deep geological repositories in crystalline bedrocks.

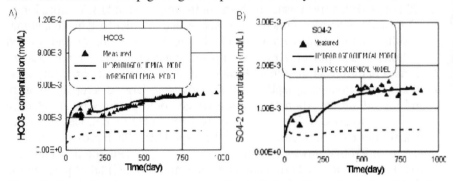

Figure 1. Comparison between measurements (symbols), hydrobiogeochemical model results (solid line) and hydrogeochemical model results (dashed line) for: A) time evolution of dissolved bicarbonates and, B) time evolution of dissolved sulfates.

REFERENCES

BANWART, S.; TULLBORG, E.-L.; PEDERSEN, K.; GUSTAFSSON, E.; LAAKSOHARJU, M.; NILSSON, A.-C.; WALLIN, B. & WIKBERG, P. (1996): Organic carbon oxidation induced by large-scale shallow water intrusion into a vertical fracture zone at the Äspö Hard Rock Laboratory (Sweden). Journal of Contaminat Hydrology, 21, 115-125.

BRUTON, C.J. & VIANI, B.E. (1997): Ion sorption onto hydrous ferric oxides: effect on major element fluid chemistry at Äspö (Sweden). In: Evolution of the Groundwater Chemistry at the Äspö Hard Rock Laboratory. Proceedings of the second Äspö International Geochemistry Workshop. SKB ICR97-04.

PEDERSEN, K.; ARLINGER, J.; JAHROMI, N.; EKENDAHL, S. & HALLBECK, L. (1995): Microbiological investigations. In: The Redox Experiment in Block Scale. Final Reporting of Results from the Three year Project. Chapter 7. SKB PR 25-95-06.

PUIGDOMENECH, I. (Editor) (2001): O2 depletion in granitic media The REX project. SKB TR-01-05.

SAMPER, J.; DELGADO, J.; JUNCOSA, R. & MONTENEGRO, L. (2000): CORE2D© : A Code for Nonisothermal Water Flow and Reactive Solute Transport. Users Manual Version 2. ENRESA Publicación Técnica 6/2000.

TULLBORG, E.-L. & GUSTAFSSON, E. (1999): 14C in biocarbonate and dissolved organics- a useful tracer?. Applied geochemistry, 14, 927-938.

WALLIN, B. (1995): Sulphur cycling in the Redox Zone. In: The Redox Experiment in Block Scale. Final Reporting of Results from the Three year Project. Chapter 6. Steven Banwart (Ed). SKB PR 25-95-06.

ZHANG, G. (2001): Nonisothermal Hydrobiogeochemical Models in Porous Media. Ph.D. dissertation. University of A Coruña (Spain).

AN EFFICIENT SOLUTION TECHNIQUE FOR THE NUMERICAL SIMULATION OF THERMALLY ENHANCED SOIL VAPOR EXTRACTION

Angela Winkler, Holger Class, Rainer Helmig
Universität Stuttgart

The remediation of NAPL-contaminated soils by thermally enhanced soil vapor extraction is in most practical cases a technology, which is very time-consuming and costly. It is therefore important to optimize this technology and remediation strategy for each specific contamination. Non-isothermal multiphase multicomponent models play an important role in this context since they allow extensive studies of different scenarios and sensitivity analyses of various parameters.

Conventional soil vapor extraction for NAPL recovery in the unsaturated zone is limited by the evaporation rate and by layers or lenses of low permeability. In order to increase the efficiency, thermally enhanced methods have been developed in recent years. One possibility is to inject a heat-carrying medium like steam or a steam/air-mixture. Both injection strategies are limited to temperatures around 100 °C at atmospheric pressure and are practicable for soils with small-scale heterogeneities. Another technique is the installation of thermal wells, e.g. heating lances. The heat transport occurs mainly by means of heat conduction and temperatures far beyond 100 °C can be achieved, so that this method can be applied for NAPLs of low volatility and for heterogeneous soils.

The numerical simulation of the coupled physical flow and transport processes during thermally enhanced NAPL recovery requires the use of efficient and powerful numerical schemes in order to save computation time. The applicability of a model depends further on the ability to reproduce the relevant processes on the scales of interest. For the model validation it is important to have enough data available and to quantify the influence of variable temperatures on the constitutive relationships, for example on the capillary pressure.

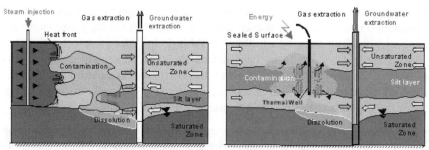

Figure 1: Thermally enhanced soil vapor extraction; heat transport by steam injection (left) and by thermal wells (right).

We apply a model concept that takes into account advective fluxes of the fluid phases water, NAPL and gas, also diffusive fluxes of the components (water, contaminant, air) in the gas phase, heat conduction, and mass/energy transfer due to evaporation, condensation, dissolution, and degassing. Phases may appear or disappear, in particular, we consider the disappearance and appearance of the liquid phases water and NAPL due to evaporation and condensation. The phase state indicates the algorithm, which phases are present locally in a control volume. We assume low concentrations of dissolved air and organic component in the water phase, and we use Henry's Law to calculate their mole fractions. The gas-phase mole fractions are computed using Dalton's Law and on the assumption that the Ideal Gas Law is valid for all gaseous components. We implemented a scaling of the capillary-pressure functions by considering the temperature dependence of the surface tension. Hysteresis effects are neglected.

An Eulerian approach is used to formulate molar balance equations, one for each mass component. We assume local thermal equilibrium. Thus, we can use a single balance equation for thermal energy locally averaged over the whole fluid-filled porous medium. Both equations are highly non-linear, and we apply a Newton-Raphson method to handle this. The matrix elements of the Jacobian are calculated by numerical differentiation. Time is discretized fully implicit (Euler method), and two different mass conservative schemes are available for spatial discretization, a Control-Volume-Finite-Element method (CVFE) and a Subdomain Collocation method (BOX).

The primary variables must be chosen according to the local phase state. For all phase states, we use pressure and temperature as primary variables. Should all fluid phases be present, we additionally take the liquid phase saturations to complete this set. For other phases states, we summarized the phase states and the corresponding primary variables in Table 1. In order to detect a changing phase state, we need criteria that indicate the appearance and disappearance of phases. Disappearance occurs when the corresponding saturation takes on a negative value. In the case of a phase appearance, we must distinguish between the liquid phases and the gas phase. This is also listed in Table 1.

phase state	present phases	primary variables	appearance of phase		
			water	NAPL	GAs
1	w,n,g	S_w, S_n, p_g, T	-	-	-
2	w	x_w^c, x_w^a, p_g, T	-	$x_w^c > x_w^c$	$p_{sat}^w + H_w^a x_w^a > p_g$
3	n,g	S_n, x_g^w, p_g, T	$x_g^w p_g > p_{sat}^w$	-	-
4	w,n	S_n, x_w^a, p_g, T	-	-	$H_w^a x_w^a + \sum_K p_{sat}^K > p_g$
5	g	x_g^c, x_g^w, p_g, T	$x_g^w p_g > p_{sat}^w$	$x_g^c p_g > p_{sat}^c$	-
6	w,g	x_g^c, S_w, p_g, T	-	$x_g^c p_g > p_{sat}^c$	-

Table 1: Phase states, primary variables, and substitution criteria for phase appearance

An efficient technique for solving large sparse systems of linear equations obtained from discretized PDEs is a multigrid method, which is implemented and parallelized in our simulator MUFTE_UG. To apply the multigrid method to systems with variable phase states, it is necessary to extend this method such that possibly occuring different primary variables can be transformed at the transitions between the grids.

One aim of this work was to compare temperature and saturation measurements from one-dimensional experiments with numerical results. The experiments were conducted in a glass column with a diameter of 10 cm and a height of 40 cm. Temperatures were measured in the direction of heat transport by having five ports in different positions. At the lower part of the column, a perforated plate kept the sand in position. The sand filling consisted of a coarse sand with an intrinsic permeability of 6.5E-10 m² and a porosity of 0.41. The circular heat source was placed at the top of the column, 2.5 cm above the first temperature sensor. The capillary pressure relationship was measured at isothermal conditions (20 °C). Density, viscosity and interfacial tension of water were measured as a function of temperature in a range between 20 °C and 95 °C. Further, the capillary pressure-saturation relationship of the sand was measured for both 20 °C and 70 °C. This information was implemented in the model. However, the interpretation of the experimental data and their matching by the numerical results is difficult due to the high degree of coupling of the processes. For example, heat losses have significant influence on the temperature and saturation curves in Figure 2.

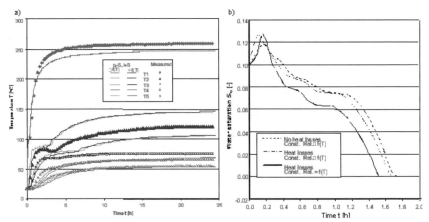

Figure 2: Comparison between numerical and experimental temperature and saturation curves for isothermal and nonisothermal constitutive relationships, resp.

The temperature profiles presented in Figure 2a as symbols were measured during the heating process of a coarse sand where the thermal-well temperature was kept constant at 300 °C. In comparison to these data, the results of the numerical modeling without and with temperature-dependent pc-S- and kr-S-relationship are also shown in the same diagram. Additionally, the development of the water saturation at one node with time is shown in Figure 2b for three different model runs. First, the heat transport was considered to be isolated from the surrounding medium, heat losses were neglected. The second run considered heat losses but not the temperature-dependence of the constitutive relationships, which was implemented only in the third run.

Both profiles of temperature and water saturation are not highly affected by the non-isothermal formulation of the constitutive relationships (capillary pressure, residual saturations). Only little differences can be recognized and no significant impact on a better matching of the measured data can be observed when using the nonisothermal relations. However, the two-dimensional discretization of the column can not accurately reproduce some 3D effects like condensation and accumulation of water at the colder glass walls. It is planned to further investigate the influence of such 3D boundary effects. Future work will also focus experimentally and numerically on non-isothermal three-phase systems, which likely will show a higher sensitivity to the nonisothermal constitutive relationships.

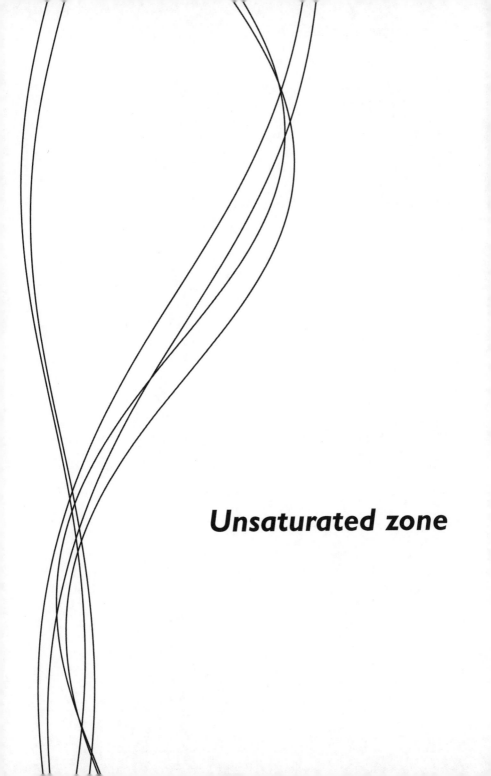

Unsaturated zone

FIELD STUDIES ON FLOW AND TRANSPORT IN THE VADOSE ZONE

Peter J. Wierenga
Department of Soil, Water and Environmental Science
The University of Arizona

Many laboratory studies have been conducted over the past 50 years to characterize the hydraulic and chemical properties of unsaturated soils and rock. These studies have provided much new information on and flow and transport processes in unsaturated media. They have also resulted in many new conceptual models, and variations of models, which describe the various phenomena observed during these laboratory studies. The number of well-controlled field studies is much more limited. Field studies are time consuming and costly, and therefore require longer term funding, greater organizational skills, and cooperation with scientists having different backgrounds and technical expertise. Scientists at national laboratories or scientists who have long-term support from national organizations are often in a better position to perform such studies. Field studies are needed to test computer models used for predicting contaminant transport from landfills, lagoons, nuclear waste disposal sites, agricultural fields, etc. Field studies are also needed to determine the values or ranges of values for the many parameters that go into the computer models. Finally, field data provide some sense of confidence in knowing what is out there. I have had support for my field studies for many years from the U.S. Nuclear Regulatory Commission. This led to cooperation for design and modeling with Dr. Richard Hills at New Mexico State University, Dr. Lynn Gelhar at MIT and Dr. Shlomo Neuman at The University of Arizona. In this talk, I present a broad overview of three-field experiments I conducted, one in New Mexico, and two in Arizona. These experiments have been described in journal articles and in reports published by the Nuclear Regulatory Commission, but such reports often lack interesting details, and general conclusions.

The first experiment was done in Las Cruces, NM, and was designed in cooperation with Dr. Gelhar at MIT. This experiment was initially designed to test deterministic and stochastic flow and transport models developed by Gelhar and associates, who were particularly interested in the role of tension dependent anisotropy on water flow in an unsaturated soil. To gain access to the deeper vadose zone, we dug a 6m deep trench, 26.4m long and 4.8m wide. This allowed us to insert tensiometers and pore water samplers in the undisturbed soil through the trench wall. Neutron probe access tubes were installed vertically through the surfaces of the two plots established on the two long sides of the trench. During excavation, 50 undisturbed core samples taken in each of nine soil horizons from 0.11m to 5.79m below ground surface. These samples were used to establish 450 soil-water retention curves in the laboratory. In addition, 450 saturated hydraulic conductivity values, 50 per layer, were determined in the field during excavation. Water and tracer were applied to the surfaces of the two plots with a precision drip system at rates of approximately 2 cm per day.

This study showed that despite significant variability in saturated hydraulic conductivity the movement of the wetting front in the dry unsaturated layered soil at this site was fairly homogenous. Visual observation of the trench face, and the tensiometer date indicated that the wetting front was nearly semicircular after 34 days of water application on the 4 m wide plot. There were no signs of preferential flow, or of flow through existing root channels and cracks. The overall motion of the wetting front was well predicted with a model based on the Richards equations, but there were significant differences between the observed and measured point values of water content due to spatial variability. Prediction of the point values of water content at this site was vastly improved by using similar media scaling, and by conditioning the hydraulic properties on the initial 2-D water content distribution (Rockhold et al 1966).

The second experiment was conducted on a 2,000-acre experimental farm near Maricopa, Arizona. A 50 x 50 m plot was instrumented with neutron probes, tensiometers and suction lysimeters down to 12 m below soil surface. A precision drip system was used to apply water and bromide at a rate of approximately 2 cm/day. The 27,000 drippers were placed on a 30 x 30 cm grid spacing and covered with plastic to prevent surface evaporation. An analysis of the first infiltration experiment at this site (Young et al., 1999) showed considerable spatial variation of the wetting front velocities (derived from the neutron probe data) over the 50 x 50 m area. However, the data also showed that the variability in effective water velocity i.e., the velocity calculated from ground surface to the depth of interest, decreased with increasing depth. While the coefficient of variation was close to 30% from 0-1m, it decreased to 9% at 2.5m. Thus it appears that as water moves relatively slowly through unsaturated layered soil profiles, the water front becomes more uniform. A one-dimensional model was used to describe bromide transport down to 3m. Bromide transport was more variable in space than water movement. This could be a reason to use more sophisticated deterministic or stochastic models for prediction. Such models have been shown to be able to capture the effects of preferential flow, immobile water, ion exchange and chemical or time dependent sorption processes. However, the latter models need many more parameter values, which are almost never available for field studies. Thomasson et al (2002) used an "effective retardation factor" in conjunction with the convection-dispersion equation to describe the bromide transport. This approach seems quite useful, although it does not shed light on the underlying processes controlling solute transport.

A third infiltration experiment (Yao et al, 2002) was conducted in fractured tuff at the Apache Leap Research Site near Superior, Arizona. At this site a large number of air permeability studies were conducted (Illman et al., 1998), but no water and tracer studies. A 9 x 9 m plot, subdivided in nine 3 x 3 m subplots was constructed on an area with visible surface fractures. Neutron probe access tubes, tensiometers and pore water samples were vertically installed in each of the nine plots at depths of 0.5, 1, 2, 3 and 5 m. The plots were flooded for about 2 years, during which time an average 5 cm waterhead was kept on each plot. Bromide was added to the water after 200 days, when the waterfronts in the nine plots had on average reached the 2 m depth. The spread in the water arrival times as measured by significant increases in rock matrix potentials, was quite large (10-80 days at 0.5 m). Bromide transport through the fractured tuff was highly variable. All stainless steel suction lysimeters performed well, yielding sufficient pore water for analysis. However, of the 45 lysimeters installed, only 15 showed bromide concentrations above background. Elevated bromide levels were encountered at all five depths. Six of the nine plots showed increased bromide levels at 0.5 m, three of nine plots at 1 and 2 m, one of nine plots at 3 m, and two of nine plots had increased bromide at 5 m. Analysis of this data in terms of modeling is a challenging proposition without having detailed information about fractures and fracture distributions. This information is difficult to get at the field scale.

Conducting large, well-controlled field experiments is a costly, time-consuming and challenging proposition. It takes patience, good cooperation with interested modelers, a good infrastructure, and, above all, a long-term source of funding. Hydrologists and soil scientists should work together to develop something like the well-known LTER sites (Long-Term Ecological Research sites funded by the National Science Foundation). We need long-term integrated field studies on contaminant migration in deep unsaturated rocks and soils. These need to be set up so that scientists from different disciplines and organizations (Universities, DOE, EPA, USGS, USDA, NRC) can participate. Site construction, management and data collection should be done centrally, at one or more well-selected locations, but data analysis should be open to any number of scientists and disciplines.

REFERENCES

WIERENGA, P. J., R. G. HILLS, and D. B. HUDSON. 1991. The Las Cruces Trench Site: Characterization, Experimental Results and One-Dimensional Flow Predictions. Water Resources Research 27:2695-2705

YOUNG, M. H., P. J. WIERENGA, A. W. WARRICK, L. L. HOFMANN, and S. H. MUSIL. 1999. Variability of wettings front velocities during a field-scale infiltration experiment. Water Resources Research 35:3079-3087.

ROCKHOLD, M. L., R. E. ROSSI and R. G. HILLS. 1996. Application of similar media scaling and conditional simulation for modeling water flow and tritium transport at the Las Cruces Trench Site, Water Resources Research 32:595-609.

ILLMAN, W. A., D.L. THOMPSON, V.V. VESSELINOV, and S. P. NEUMAN, Single-Hole and Cross-Hole Pneumatic Tests in Unsaturated Fractured Tuffs at the Apache Leap Research Site: Phenomenology, Spatial Variability, Connectivity and Scale, Report NUREG/CR-5559, prepared for the U.S. Nuclear Regulatory Commission, Washington, DC, September, 1998

YAO, T., P. J. WIERENGA, A. R. GRAHAM, C. J. MAI, and S. P. NEUMAN, Results of ponding infiltration and tracer experiments at the Apache Leap Research Site, Arizona, NUREG/CR, U.S. Nuclear Regulatory Commission, Washington, DC, 2002.

THOMASSON, M. L., P. J. WIERENGA and T. FERRE, 2002. Spatial variability of effective transport properties at the field scale. Journal of Hydrology (submitted).

UNDERSTANDING ISOTHERMAL AND NONISOTHERMAL FLOW IN PARTIALLY SATURATED FRACTURED POROUS MEDIA THROUGH FIELD TESTS AND MODELING

Yvonne Tsang
Earth Sciences Division
Lawrence Berkeley National Laboratory

Field tests and model analyses are complementary approaches to improve our knowledge of site characteristics and our understanding of governing processes. The understanding of field measurements and observations can be enriched through formulation of proper models. Models can either be simple, for deriving hydrological parameter distributions, or detailed and numerical, for evaluating complex coupled processes. Lessons learned from studies in underground drifts in partially saturated fractured porous media are presented in this paper.

Different approaches to field testing can be adopted, depending on how much is known about a particular site and what the specific objectives of the field investigation are. When great uncertainty exists pertaining to the hydrological attributes of a site, and when spatial heterogeneity dictates that the hydrological characteristics at one location are not representative of the entire site, then running "identical" and relatively simple tests at numerous locations may be required. This method of repetitive testing in multiple locations is described as a "systematic" approach to testing; it complements the more commonly practiced "feature-based" testing in which a test location is selected because of the special geological and hydrological features it exhibits. Such features may not be pervasive over the region of interest.

The approaches for analyzing and interpreting field data would also differ based on the types of data collected. When great uncertainty about processes exists, sophisticated numerical modeling of a site is not only inappropriate, it can even be misleading, because a "good" match between modeled and measured results may be obtained with an incorrect conceptual or structural model. On the other hand, when there is greater confidence in the hydrological attributes of a site, then detailed numerical modeling can be extremely valuable in giving a more in-depth understanding of the site's in situ processes.

In this paper, two field examples in partially saturated fractured porous volcanic tuff at Yucca Mountain, Nevada, the potential site for an underground high-level radioactive waste repository, are used to illustrate different approaches for bridging the gap between field testing and modeling.

The approach taken in the first example is to rely predominantly on systematic, multiple- location field data collection for developing knowledge of the hydrological attributes and parameter distributions governing isothermal flow. Modeling efforts in this example involve simple "order-of-magnitude" estimates. Comparison of these "model predictions" to a large volume of multiple-location data can provide an understanding of the hydrological attributes of a geological medium. The hydrological characterization of the lower lithophysal unit of the Topopah Spring welded tuff was carried out in an underground facility along a 5 m diameter drift at Yucca Mountain. The welded tuff in the lower lithophysal unit is intersected by many small fractures (less than 1 m long) and interspersed with lithophysal cavities ranging in size from 15 to 100 cm. The size and spacing of both the fractures and lithophysal cavities vary appreciably along the drift walls over an 800 m stretch. Because of spatial heterogeneity, we are adopting a systematic approach—testing in boreholes drilled at regular intervals along the drift, regardless of specific features in situ—to acquire knowledge of the hydrological characteristics of this unit. Field measurements in borehole sections isolated by inflatable packers include: (1) air-injection tests that measure fracture permeability, (2) liquid-release tests that determine flow characteristics and the ability of the open drift to act as a capillary barrier to divert water around itself, and (3) crosshole gas-tracer tests to measure the effective porosity of the rock mass. Testing is designed to have the borehole sections large enough (i.e., 2 m in section length) so that effects arising from small-scale heterogeneity from cavity size and fracture length are averaged out.

Comparison of collected data to simple, order-of-magnitude estimations is instrumental in leading to (1) insights into how flow is partitioned among fractures, matrix, and lithophysal cavities in the unsaturated rock; and (2) an understanding of how the flow channeling arising from spatial heterogeneity, together with the open drift acting as a capillary barrier, prevent water from entering the drift. The approach of simple order-of magnitude estimates for model prediction is easily utilized for hydrological characterization, using data collected at regularly spaced intervals along the drift. The systematic approach here complements the "feature-based" approach of other hydrological testing (in the same underground facility), in which the test locations are selected either by avoiding or focusing on specific features (such as large fractures or extra abundance of fractures or cavities).

Another approach was taken in the second example. In this instance, investigators used very detailed numerical modeling to predict the test outcome prior to commencement of field measurements. The experiment in question is a large-scale (a 60 m x 50 m x 50 m, test block, instrumented with thousands of sensors) and long-duration (eight years) thermal test in the middle nonlithophysal unit of the Topopah Spring welded tuff. In this unit, both short fractures (less than a meter in length) and long fractures (a few meters in length) are common, but lithophysal cavities are scarce. The site is well characterized by nearby smaller-scale tests and by densely spaced instrumentation within the test block. Introduction of heat into the rock mass sets in motion coupled thermal-hydrological processes such as heat transport by conduction and convection, phase transitions between liquid and vapor, and the movement of gaseous and liquid phases under pressure, viscous, and gravitational forces according to Darcy's law. The numerical model constructed for this experiment accounts for all the above thermal-hydrological processes, incorporates a complex, realistic test geometry in three dimensions, and utilizes site-specific characterization data as input parameters to the model.

Sophisticated numerical modeling is utilized to predict (in detail) the thermal-test outcome. Two categories of measurements are used to compare with model predictions: (1) temperature at close to 2,000 spatial locations, and (2) time evolution of moisture redistribution in the rock matrix and fractures, based on geophysical methods (electric resistance tomography, ground penetrating radar cross-hole tomography, and neutron logging) and air-injection tests. For the first category of data, temperature, statistics such as mean error and root mean error at different times are obtained to demonstrate the goodness of fit between model predictions and data. For the second category of data, simulated time evolution of drying and wetting (in the vaporization and condensation zones, respectively, of the rock matrix and fractures) is qualitatively compared to the trends of drying and wetting deduced from the geophysical and hydrological tomograms. The detailed numerical modeling approach works in a number of ways for the thermal test. It is appropriate because for thermally driven processes, the impact of fracture heterogeneity in the nonlithophysal unit is minimal for vapor transport. And though heterogeneity does impact gravity drainage of condensed water, the geophysical and air injection measurements used for comparison with modeled predictions are shown to be insensitive to these transient flow processes of liquid drainage in the fractures. It is also necessary for our numerical model to incorporate realistic three-dimensional test geometry such as drifts (that act as open boundaries) at a slight decline as well as the locations of temperature sensors. This is because most of the temperature rise in the test block is caused by heat conduction, hence in order to meaningfully evaluate thermal hydrological processes by comparing predicted and measured temperature we need to eliminate discrepancies arising from incorrect test geometry.

The two different modeling approaches illustrated in this paper each work for their particular situation. A simple order-of magnitude modeling approach is appropriate for the first example because large uncertainty for hydrological characteristics exists prior to collection of data. Thus, a large volume of collected data is utilized for determining the hydrological attributes of this lithophysal geological unit. The data from regularly spaced locations are also instrumental in allowing investigators to discriminate between phenomena resulting from fundamental flow processes and that from site-specific heterogeneity. In the second example, the dominant heat transfer processes serve to minimize the complexity of heterogeneity-induced flow effects. With sufficient sampling points for field measurements, it is appropriate to construct a numerical model that realistically represents the complex test geometry and boundary conditions to interpret the test data. Overall, the presence of thermally driven physical processes (such as heat conduction, heat convection, vaporization, and condensation) are confirmed by the modeled results.

Clearly, the choice of approach to be used in bridging the gap between measurements and modeling is guided by the state of knowledge about the site and the objective of the testing effort. These factors help in deciding the required amount and sufficient accuracy of measured data, as well as the degree of model sophistication that should be applied. Systematic characterization of hydrological parameter distribution does not necessarily require complex models. Rather, we advocate keeping the model simple and the interpretation straightforward to gain an overall understanding of the basic attributes of the geological medium under investigation. On the other hand, for a well-characterized site where we have confidence that both the governing processes and the effects associated with site features can be represented well, numerical modeling is a powerful approach. The model calibration and confirmation steps associated with complex numerical models greatly enhance the credibility of our modeling capability. They lend confidence that we can use models to predict the system behavior, even for a larger spatial scale and longer time duration than that of the field measurements.

METER-TO-KILOMETER SCALING OF PREFERENTIAL FLOW IN THE UNSATURATED ZONE

John R. Nimmo
USGS, Menlo Park, CA 94025, USA

Fast flowpaths in soil at the scale of about 1 m have been widely studied in agricultural and other applications for several decades (Beven and Germann, 1982). More recently, fast flowpaths on the scale of 10's to 1000's of m have been found to be significant within extensive unsaturated zones at some arid and semiarid locations (e.g. Bryant, 1992; Nimmo and others, 2001). Evaluating the scalability of these processes, in particular the issue of whether the same phenomena dominate across all scales, can facilitate the use of research findings from one scale to another and can also provide insight into the basic nature of these processes.

The basis of this presentation is a comparison of the maximum speed of convective transport, referred to here as vmax, among a variety of published studies. In many cases it is possible to estimate the minimum travel time of water over a particular scale length, generally the straight-line distance from the point of tracer application to the point of detection. This permits calculation of vmax for conditions of the study, by dividing this distance by the time between application and first detection of tracer, whether or not this was originally a stated objective.

Studies for comparison were selected according to several specific criteria. (1) The observations come from field experiments. (2) The preferential flow observed occurs within the unsaturated zone (above the lowest water table), though it may include perched water or other locally saturated conditions. (3) The transport observed indicates convective liquid transport, as opposed to gas or particulate transport. (4) The transport is "fast," by the criterion of being faster than would be predicted by traditional Darcy/Richards models with parameters typical of granular media.

Most of the smaller-scale studies were in agricultural fields with solution sampling at depth using tile drains, wells, or suction samplers (e.g. Kung et al., 2000). Other studies involved core sampling, neutron detection of infiltrating water, or collection of water at depth.

The larger-scale studies were mostly at sites with thick unsaturated zones in the arid and semiarid western US. Several were done within the Idaho National Engineering and Environmental Laboratory (INEEL), where the unsaturated zone comprises thick layers of fractured basalt interbedded with thinner sedimentary layers. In the INEEL Large-Scale Infiltration Test (LSIT), tracer was put into an artificial pond 200 m in diameter (Dunnivant et al., 1998), and detected near the bottom of a basalt layer extending to about 50 m depth. In the INEEL Spreading Area Tracer Test (SATT), tracer was applied to a large body of ephemeral surface water and later detected in the unsaturated zone as far as 2 km away (Nimmo et al., 2001). At Yucca Mountain, Fabryka-Martin et al. (1997) sampled at various locations throughout an 8-km long tunnel at 300 m depth in the unsaturated zone, and in 13% of the samples finding 36-Cl levels high enough to indicate nuclear-bomb-test fallout that marks the water as less than 50 years old. In the Cambric Migration Experiment at the Nevada Test Site (NTS), bromide tracer put into flowing water in an unlined ditch was detected in a suction sampler at 30.5 m depth in less than 92 days (Bryant, 1992).

For 36 tests from 23 studies, Figure 1 shows how vmax compares in a logarithmic plot of all results vs. scale length. The range of vmax for the studies in Table 1 is 0.03 m/day to 100 m/day, that is, about 3.5 orders of magnitude. The scale length in these 36 tests also spans a 3.5-order-of-magnitude range, from 0.4 to 2000 m.

For a standard of comparison for these results, consider that if vmax were truly independent of the characteristic length of the system, and if one had a representative statistical set of measurements covering a wide range, then that set of measured vmax would not show a consistent trend with length. The data in Figure 1 appear consistent with this sort of independence of vmax from scale. This is suggestive of scalability of v_{max} and the possibility that essentially equivalent phenomena are dominant at all scales.

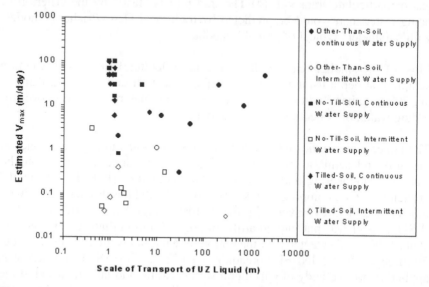

Figure 1. Estimated maximum rate of preferential flow over various distances in field tests. Solid circles represent cases where water for infiltration at the surface was supplied continuously; open circles represent cases of intermittent supply. The media are classified into three broad categories.

More surprisingly, the data suggest that within simple classifications based on input conditions, v_{max} varies little. Results could be grouped according to various features expected to affect the maximum flow rate, such as scale or type of medium, but the variable that most stands out is the surface conditions applied during the test. Where water is supplied by a pond or by continuous irrigation, vmax tends to be markedly greater than if the supply is intermittent. For 11 studies with continuous water supply, the arithmetic mean is 32.3 m/day with a standard deviation of 31.1 m/day. For four studies with water supplied intermittently at the surface from natural rainfall or normal irrigation practices, the mean is 0.8 m/day with a standard deviation of 1.47 m/day. Within each of these two groupings, this suggests that even such traditionally important variables as water content and hydraulic conductivity are not major factors in the determination of vmax. If this generalization is even approximately true, it would mean that the vmax values are not merely uncorrelated with scale, but for similar water input conditions are nearly constant.

Diverse media clearly have pores of different nature but these differences may not be strongly relevant to the travel time of initial convective transport. The dependence on water input conditions, particularly whether the supply is continuous or intermittent, may be the dominant influence. These results are encouraging for the development of models that may represent preferential flow more realistically, and that may be effective at all scales.

REFERENCES

BEVEN, K., and GERMAN, P., 1982, Macropores and water flow in soils: Water Resources Research, v. 18, p. 1311-1325.

BRYANT, E.A., 1992, The Cambric migration experiment--a summary report: Los Alamos National Laboratory LA-12335-MS.

DUNNIVANT, F.M., NEWMAN, M.E., BISHOP, C.W., BURGESS, D., GILES, J.R., HIGGS, B.D., HUBBELL, J.M., NEHER, E., NORRELL, G.T., PFIEFER, M.C., PORRO, I., STARR, R.C., and WYLLIE, A.H., 1998, Water and radioactive tracer flow in a heterogeneous field-scale system: Ground Water, v. 36, no. 6, p. 949-958.

FABRYKA-MARTIN, J.T., FLINT, A.L., SWEETKIND, D.S., WOLFSBERG, A.V., LEVY, S.S., ROEMER, G.J.C., ROACH, J.L., WOLFSBERG, L.E., and DUFF, M.C., 1997, Evaluation of flow and transport models of Yucca Mountain, based on Chlorine-36 Studies for FY97: Los Alamos National Laboratory LA-CST-TIP-97-010 (unpublished) ACC: MOL.19980204.0916, Los Alamos, New Mexico.

KUNG, K.J.S., STEENHUIS, T.S., KLADIVKO, E.J., BUBENZER, G., GISH, T., and HELLING, C.S., 2000, Impact of preferential flow on the transport of adsorbing and non-adsorbing tracers: Soil Science Society of America Journal, v. 64, no. 1290-1296.

NIMMO, J.R., PERKINS, K.S., ROSE, P.A., ROUSSEAU, J.P., ORR, B.R., TWINING, B.V., and ANDERSON, S.R., 2001, Kilometer-Scale Rapid Flow in a Fractured-Basalt Unsaturated Zone at the Idaho National Engineering and Environmental Laboratory, in Kueper, B.H., Novakowski, K.S., and Reynolds, D.A., eds., Fractured Rock 2001 Conference Proceedings, March 26-28, 2001, Toronto, 4 p.

UNSATURATED HYDRAULIC CONDUCTIVITY IN STRUCTURED SOILS FROM A KINEMATIC WAVE APPROACH.

M. Rousseau[1,2]*, R. Angulo-Jaramillo[2], L. Di Pietro[1] and S. Ruy[1]

[1] *Institut National de la Recherche Agronomique – Unité Climat, Sol et Environnement, Domaine St Paul, 84914 Avignon Cedex 9, France.*
* *e-mail: rousseau@avignon.inra.fr.*
[2] *Laboratoire d'étude des Transferts en Hydrologie et Environnement, Domaine Universitaire, B.P 53, 38041 Grenoble Cedex 9, France.*

Solving soil unsaturated flow and contaminant transport problems requires knowledge of soil hydraulic properties, namely hydraulic conductivity relationships. Although methods for calculating hydraulic conductivity of unsaturated soil from moisture retention data have been developed, a need to provide data to validate and compare methods remains. Few attempts have been made to develop, improve or compare methods for measuring hydrodynamic properties in the laboratory. It has been established that direct methods based on Darcy-Richards' theory fails to predict hydraulic conductivity near saturation, mainly because of pressure head gradients becoming too small for high moisture contents and approaching the order of magnitude of tensiometric measurement errors (Tamari et al., 1993). Therefore another theory, not requiring pressure head measurements, must be applied to assess hydraulic conductivity near saturation. It is interesting to apply the kinematic wave theory (Germann, 1985) to obtain the relationship between flux of drained water versus macropore moisture content and to identify this relationship with Brooks and Corey 's analytical form of hydraulic conductivity.

This study focuses on a structured soil where preferential flows occur and prevail on capillary effects within macropores; thus, the flux occurs mainly within macropores and the kinematic wave approach can be applied. Initial conditions of moisture content are assumed to be close to field capacity, defined in this work as volumetric water content after one day draining from saturation, when micropores are saturated and macropores are empty.

Estimating the relationship between water flux drained and macropore moisture content according to the kinematic wave theory (Beven and Germann, 1981) requires the knowledge of two parameters: a macropore-flux distribution index a and a conductance term b.

$$q = b\theta_{ma}^{a} \qquad (1)$$

Currently, parameters are estimated from the falling limb of the drainage hydrograph, applying an equation derived from the kinematic wave theory (Germann, 1985; Germann, 1990; Mdaghri-Alaoui and Germann, 1998; Germann and Di Pietro, 1999). A comparison between this current method and a new method using the evolution of the drained water flux versus macropore saturation after the end of rainfall to fit these parameters is explained below.

The objectives of this paper are twofold: i) compare the new method with the current one to estimate kinematic wave parameters and to test the sensitivity of these parameters to boundary and initial conditions; and ii) apply the kinematic wave theory to assess hydraulic conductivity between field capacity and saturation in order to complete hydraulic conductivity estimated by Wind (1968) evaporation method which is based on Darcy-Richards' theory.

The soil used in this study was a structured loamy clay soil from "La Valette" near Montpellier (France). An undisturbed soil sample was taken from the tilled topsoil; the column was 70 mm high and 150 mm in diameter.

Two types of experiments were performed on the same sample: i) infiltration experiments at field capacity -defined in this work as volumetric water content after one day draining from saturation-, in order to apply the kinematic wave theory, ii) evaporation experiments at saturation, in order to assess hydraulic conductivity using Wind's method (Tamari et al., 1993).

The new method requires the application of linear regression which is quite simple and gives minor uncertainties for the estimation of parameters a and b. Moreover, the fitting interval can be defined systematically for different rainfall intensity experiments. The drainage hydrograph simulation by the kinematic wave model is more consistent with parameters estimated using the new method (Fig. 1). On the other hand, it is of utmost importance that the initial moisture content of the soil sample be close to field capacity in order to apply the kinematic wave theory within its range of validity. For initial moisture contents below than field capacity, parameter a increases showing diffusive effects between the microporosity and macroporosity domains.

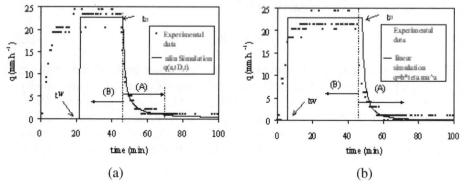

Figure 1. Simulation of the drainage hydrograph obtained for rain event 2 by the kinematic wave model. (a): parameter fitting from q(t). (b): parameter fitting from q(qma) (Eq. (1)). (A-interval: data used for model calibration; B-interval: hydrograph validation interval).

For high moisture contents (higher than field capacity), the kinematic wave theory makes it possible to complete the estimation of unsaturated hydraulic conductivity $K(\theta)$ obtained using Wind's method. This assumption was made comparing the analytic form of hydraulic conductivity given by Brooks and Corey (1964) and the kinematic wave's relationship (Eq.1); where the parameter h can be associated to the macropore-flux distribution index a and the term (K_s/θ_s^n) can be identified to the conductance term b (m.s^{-1}). Hydraulic conductivity data assessed by both the kinematic waves' theory and Darcy's theory seem consistent close to field capacity volumetric water content (Fig.2): there is less than one order of magnitude between the two groups of data. Three domains can be determined: i) moisture content is below field capacity, then Darcy's theory is applied, ii) moisture content ranges between field capacity and saturation, then the kinematic wave theory is applied; and, iii) at saturation, Darcy's law is applied.

Studies on different soils should be conducted to validate these preliminary results.

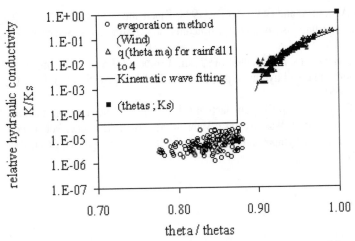

Figure 2. Hydraulic conductivity completed near saturation by $q(\theta_{ma})$ derived from kinematic wave theory.

ACKNOWLEDGMENTS

This research was partially funded by the "Programme National de Recherches en Hydrologie" (PNRH) French national program on hydrology research, on the project: Dynamique et mécanismes des écoulements préférentiels dans les sols, application au transport de pesticides (Dynamic and mechanisms of preferential flow in soils, application to pesticide transport). The senior author was also supported by an Engineer Doctor's Grant (BDI) from the "Centre National de la Recherche Scientifique" (CNRS).

REFERENCES

BEVEN K. and GERMANN P.F. (1981) Water flow in soil macropores. II. A combined flow model. Journal of Soil Science, 32 : 15-29

BROOKS R.H. and COREY A.T. (1964) Properties of porous media affecting fluid flow. J. Irrig. Drain. Div., Am. Soc. Civil Eng., 92 : 61-88

GERMANN P.F. (1985) Kinematic wave approach to infiltration and drainage into and from macropores. Trans. Am. Soc. Agric. Eng., 28 : 745-749

GERMANN P.F. (1990) Preferential flow and the generation of runoff. 1. Boundary-layer flow theory. Water Resour. Res., 26 : 3055-3063

GERMANN P.F. and DI PIETRO L. (1999) Scales and dimensions of momentum dissipation during preferential flow in soils. Wat. Resou. Res. 35 : 1443-1454

MDAGHRI-ALAOUI A. and GERMANN P.F.(1998) Kinematic wave approach to drainage flow and moisture distribution in a structured soil. Hydrological Sciences Journal, 43 : 561-578

TAMARI S., BRUCKLER L., HALBERTSMA J. and CHADOEUF J. (1993) A simple method for determining soil hydraulic properties in the laboratory. Soil Sci. Soc. Am. J. 57 : 642-651

WIND, G.P. (1969). Capillary conductivity data estimated by a simple method. In P.E. Rijtema and H. Wassink (ed.) Water in the unsaturated zone. Vol. 1. Proc. of the Wageningen Symposium, june 1966, IASH Gent brugge/UNESCO, Paris : 181-191.

CHARACTERIZATION OF SPATIAL VARIABILITY OF HYDROGEOLOGIC PROPERTIES FOR UNSATURATED FLOW IN THE FRACTURED ROCKS AT YUCCA MOUNTAIN, NEVADA

Quanlin Zhou, Gudmundur S. Bodvarsson, Hui-Hai Liu and Curtis M. Oldenburg

Earth Sciences Division, Lawrence Berkeley National Laboratory, Berkeley, California

INTRODUCTION

The unsaturated zone (UZ) at Yucca Mountain, Nevada, the potential site for a high-level nuclear waste repository, consists of alternating sequences of variably fractured and faulted welded and nonwelded tuffs. The thick UZ is grouped into five hydrostratigraphic units and furthermore into 35 hydrogeologic layers. To understand the complex property distributions and their effects on flow and transport, a large number of core-scale data have been obtained. These data have been used for calibrating mean layer-scale hydrogeologic properties for the three-dimensional mountain-scale UZ flow model. However, the lateral variability of hydrogeologic properties has not been investigated for the site characterization of Yucca Mountain. In this study, the spatial variability of three most sensitive properties (matrix permeability k_m, matrix α_m of van Genuchten characterization, and fracture permeability k_f) was investigated using inverse modeling.

DATA AVAILABLE

Core-scale measurements of state variables (water saturation, water potential and pneumatic pressure) of the ambient unsaturated flow at Yucca Mountain and hydrogeologic properties are available from drilling (core samples in 33 boreholes), and in situ field characterization in the Exploratory Studies Facility (ESF) and Enhanced Characterization of Repository Block (ECRB). Water saturation and potential measurements are employed to calculate their layer-scale values used for calibrating layer-scale matrix properties; pneumatic pressure measurements are very useful in estimating fracture permeability, the key parameter in the welded geologic units where fracture flow is dominant. Direct measurement of hydrogeologic properties has been conducted at different boreholes for porosity, intrinsic permeability, and capillary parameters (α and m for the van Genuchten characterization). The data are representative of small-scale properties at core scale. The local-scale measurements of intrinsic permeability and capillary parameters are used to calculate their prior layer-scale values for the calibration model.

CHARACTERIZATION OF LAYER-SCALE ROCK PROPERTIES

Two calibration steps are used to reduce the uncertainty in the estimated layer-scale rock properties. In the first step, mean values of seven sets of layer-scale properties (matrix permeability k_m, matrix α_m, matrix m_m, fracture permeability k_f, fracture α_f, fracture m_f, and fraction of active fractures γ_f) are calibrated using simultaneous inverse modeling (SIM). In the second step, the lateral variability of the three most sensitive sets of properties (k_m, α_m, and k_f) is further calibrated; all other sets of properties are fixed at their mean values obtained by SIM. The calibration process is conducted independently for each deep borehole.

In a calibration process, calibration of matrix properties and fracture permeability is done iteratively. First, matrix properties are calibrated using water saturation and potential data through steady-state unsaturated liquid flow simulation. Second, fracture permeability is calibrated using pneumatic pressure data through transient simulation of gas and liquid flow, and all matrix properties are fixed at their newly calibrated values. The iterative process continues until convergence is obtained. For a deep borehole of interest, the flow system is a one-dimensional vertical column from the top surface to the water table. The TOUGH2 code is used for the forward simulation of unsaturated liquid flow and two-phase gas-water flow. The ITOUGH2 code is used for parameter estimation.

Figure 1 shows the lateral variability of layer-scale   and   at different hydrogeologic layers. The solid line represents the vertical profile of mean value of these properties, while the dotted line represents the SIM result. The scatter

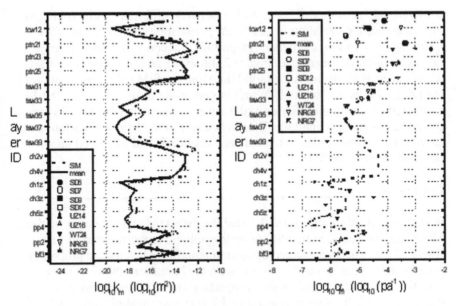

Figure 1. Spatial variability of matrix k_m and α_m at different hydrogeologic layers obtained by individual inverse modeling using borehole measurements.

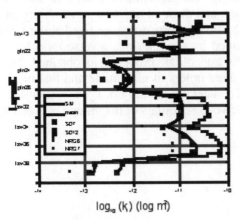

Figure 2. Spatial variability of fracture permeability k_f at different hydrogeologic layers at four boreholes with available measurements

points represent calibrated values at different boreholes obtained by individual inverse modeling. The lateral variability of   is two to three orders of magnitude. Most importantly, the lateral variability is smaller than the dominant vertical variability of permeability between different stratigraphic units. For example, the variation of the mean permeability between the TSw and CHn units is five to six orders of magnitude. Lateral variability of in general is one order of magnitude. Figure 2 shows the lateral variability of layer-scale , as well as mean value (solid line) and the SIM calibrated result (dotted line). The mean in the PTn unit is very close to its corresponding SIM calibrated result. In the TSw unit, the mean is smaller than the SIM result by half an order of magnitude. This is because in the SIM calibration, much attention was paid on the match between calibrated and measured pneumatic pressure at borehole SD-12.

CONCLUSION

In the conceptual model currently used for the site characterization of Yucca Mountain, the lateral variability of hydrogeologic properties and its effect on flow and transport is neglected by assuming uniform layer-scale properties at each hydrogeologic layer. In this research, the lateral variability of three most sensitive layer-scale hydrologic properties (matrix permeability k_m, and matrix α_m, and fracture permeability k_f) was investigated using individual inverse modeling. The calibration of the three properties at each deep borehole was performed using measurements of water saturation, water potential and pneumatic pressure, and those of intrinsic permeability and desaturation curve data. All other hydrologic properties are fixed at their optimal laterally averaged values obtained by simultaneous inverse modeling. Considerable lateral variability of hydrogeologic properties is obtained. The lateral variability of k_m is two to three orders of magnitude and that of α_m and k_f is one order of magnitude. The lateral variability of k_m is smaller than the dominant vertical variability of five to six orders of magnitude between hydrostratigraphic units.

TESTING AND MODELING OF SEEPAGE INTO UNDERGROUND OPENINGS IN A HETEROGENEOUS FRACTURE SYSTEM AT YUCCA MOUNTAIN, NEVADA

C. F. Ahlers, R. C. Trautz, P. J. Cook, and S. Finsterle
Lawrence Berkeley National Laboratory
M/S 90-1116, 1 Cyclotron Rd., Berkeley, California 94720
Rick_Ahlers@lbl.gov

Seepage is an issue of some importance for the proposed long-term geologic disposal of high-level radioactive waste at Yucca Mountain. Seepage into the tunnels in which the waste will be emplaced can mobilize the waste allowing it to enter the accessible environment through natural springs or man-made wells in neighboring valleys down gradient. A testing program was initiated to characterize the process of seepage into tunnels in Yucca Mountain in the same stratigraphic unit as the proposed waste emplacement tunnels. The seepage characterization data are used to create predictive models to assess the risk and magnitude of seepage under future conditions.

Off the main underground tunnel at Yucca Mountain, several niches, or short tunnels about 10 m long, were excavated to be used for seepage characterization. Three boreholes were drilled about 0.6 m above the crown of the niche and are labeled UL, UM, and UR in Figure 1. Air-injection testing was carried out in the boreholes above the niches. Intervals were isolated every 0.3 m along the boreholes by means of an inflatable packer system. The tests were analyzed to infer the fracture system permeability of the rock. After the air-injection tests were completed, liquid-release tests (LRTs) were initiated in some of the same intervals that were used for the air-injection tests. In this way, intervals with very low permeability could be identified, and LRTs in these intervals initiated at lower rates. LRTs of short duration were performed

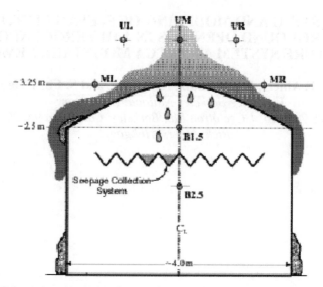

Figure 1. Schematic cross section showing the generalized layout of a niche, boreholes for testing, and seepage collection system. Cross section is perpendicular to the axes of the niche and boreholes. Note: upper boreholes are approximately 0.6 m above the crown of the Niche.

at Niche 3650, the first niche to be tested. A capture system was set up beneath the drift ceiling, as shown in Figure 1, so that potential seepage could be weighed and compared to the mass of water injected into the rock during that test. The seepage data for these tests included only the time of seepage initiation and the total mass of water that seeped. Multiple injection rates were tested in many of the intervals in order to capture the rate of injection below which no seepage occurs.

A three-dimensional, single-continuum model (predominantly representing the fractures) is used for simulation of the LRTs and any potential seepage. The seepage data are inverted to produce model-specific, seepage-relevant effective parameters. The seepage predicted by the model is mainly sensitive to variations of three model parameters, namely permeability (k), capillarity (1/a), and porosity (f). When seepage is first initiated and the seepage rate is not approximately steady, as is the case for the Niche 3650 seepage data, all three of these parameters are strongly correlated, i.e., a change in any of the three parameters will change the timing of seepage initiation and the shape of the seepage transient. Thus, these parameters cannot be determined independently by inversion of the seepage data alone. However, permeability may be fixed, and eliminated from the parameters to be calibrated, because it has been determined independently by the air-injection testing.

Five LRTs from one interval in borehole UM were selected for joint data inversion because they included seepage results for a range of injection rates. The resulting calibrated parameters give a very good match between the simulated and measured seepage. However, because of the correlation between the calibrated parameters, they are not independent, and there are likely to be other parameter combinations that are equally valid for reproduction of the data.

Review of the Niche 3650 data collection and analysis through regular discussions between the field-testing and modeling personnel resulted in several recommendations for improvements to testing and analysis for the purpose of producing model predictions of seepage due to long-term steady percolation:

1. The calibrated $1/\alpha$ and ϕ were found to be highly correlated, i.e., changes in either parameter similarly affect the calculated time of seepage initiation and cumulative seepage mass for each of the simulated Niche 3650 LRTs. Furthermore, the short-term LRTs only test a small portion of the fracture system that is responsible for the first arrival of water at the niche wall. These fractures may not be representative of the larger-scale fracture network that would be responsible for diverting water around the niche, which is the process of interest. Also note that porosity is not needed for predictions of seepage in response to long-term, steady percolation. Under these conditions, seepage depends on $1/\alpha$ (and k) only.

The following changes to data collection and analysis were proposed to reduce the parameter correlation and increase confidence that the estimated parameters are appropriate for their intended purpose. First, longer-term LRTs that result in near-steady seepage should be performed. Second, seepage data should be collected throughout the test, rather than just the cumulative-seepage mass at the end of each LRT, so that the near-steady seepage rate into the niche can be identified. Third, seepage-rate data should be inverted so that early-time mismatches between simulation and data do not affect the late-time match between simulation and data. Note that a mismatch in the early-time behavior is considered acceptable as we are interested in the average behavior of the network on the drift scale rather than the first arrival. In fact, forcing a match of the first arrival may induce an unwanted bias in the estimated parameters if the fracture connecting the injection interval with the niche ceiling is not representative of the average network behavior.

2. Because the shape of the niche ceiling strongly affects the diversion potential of the capillary barrier, it may be important to accurately reproduce the shape of the mined niche, especially if the niche ceiling has an extended flat area directly under the injection interval(s).

3. Evaporation of water as it enters the niche or in the collection system is a possible source of error for the analysis. The data inversion, as performed above, relies on the assumption that all the water is accounted for, i.e., that the mass of water injected is balanced by the mass of water remaining in the rock above (and around) the niche and the mass of water that seeps into the opening and is captured. If a significant portion of the water evaporated either before it dripped from the ceiling or while in the capture system, then this assumption is violated. There are several ways in which potential evaporation may be controlled or accounted for. The niche can be sealed and/or actively humidified during the testing in order to minimize the potential for evaporation. The capture system can be continuously drained into a sealed container to minimize the potential for evaporation of the collected water. Finally, a non-isothermal model with an active gas/vapor phase can be used for data inversion in order to capture potential evaporation effects.

4. Detection of water flowing in the rock at or near the spring line (or the highest point where the niche wall is still vertical) during LRTs would confirm that the injected water is being diverted around the niche and that the LRTs are, in fact, testing the diversion capacity of the capillary barrier formed by the niche.

During and after analysis of the Niche 3650 data, testing in two more niches (3107 and 4788) was performed. The LRT protocol was modified to address issues 1 and 3 raised above. Longer-term tests were run in order to allow a near-steady seepage rate to develop. The niches were closed and/or humidified in order to minimize the potential for evaporation both from the seepage face (i.e., the niche ceiling) and from the collection system. Finally, continuous drainage of the collection system and measurement of the seepage mass allowed the seepage rate to be calculated and a near-steady seepage rate to be identified for those tests where seepage occurred.

The data analysis was modified to address issues 1 and 2, raised above. The numerical meshes are constructed to reproduce the roughness of the niche ceiling, at the scale of the mesh discretization (10 cm). Only data from the near-steady seepage portion of the data are selected for inversion. This por-

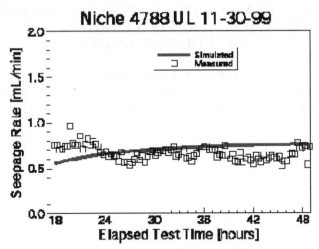

Figure 2. Comparison of typical results of the calibrated simulation to seepage rate data from Niche 4788.

tion of the data better characterizes flow through the relevant portion of the fracture system and should reduce the correlation between $1/\alpha$ and ϕ. Instead of inverting cumulative-seepage-mass data as was done previously, the inversion is performed on the seepage-rate data. This also helps reduce the correlation between $1/\alpha$ and ϕ and a potential bias in their estimates because errors in the simulated first arrival time due to ϕ are not propagated through the simulated seepage rate. Figure 2 shows a typical match between the results of the calibrated simulations and the seepage-rate data.

Data analysis begun soon after testing at Niche 3650 was initiated and collective review of field observations, data collection, and data analysis by all personnel led to an improved testing and analysis regimen for the remaining two niches (Niches 3107 and 4788).

ACKNOWLEDGMENT

This work was supported by the Director, Office of Civilian Radioactive Waste Management, U.S. Department of Energy, through Memorandum Purchase Order EA9013MC5X between Bechtel SAIC Company, LLC and the Ernest Orlando Lawrence Berkeley National Laboratory (Berkeley Lab). The support is provided to Berkeley Lab through the U.S. Department of Energy Contract No. DE-AC03-76SF00098.

A PHYSICAL AND STOCHASTIC DESCRIPTION OF INFILTRATION IN A LARGE-SCALE HYDROLOGIC MODEL

Hubert J. Morel-Seytoux
Hydrology Days Publications, 57 Selby Lane, Atherton, CA 94027-3926
Tel. and Fax: (415) 365 4080 / email: hydroprose@batnet.com

The problem of extrapolation of values of hydraulic characteristics of a soil from the "column" scale (cross section of 20 to 100 square centimeters) to a larger scale is a difficult one. The problem of uitlizing that information to derive appropriate laws of infiltration at the larger scale is even more daunting. Assuming that we have been able to quantify adequately the spatial variation of hydraulic conductivity in a statistical sense, knowing the underlying distribution form, and its parameters, etc., we can use our knowledge of soil dynamics to predict infiltration rate at the "column" scale (cross section of 20 to 100 square centimeters). The problem is in finding the infiltration rate at the scale say of 1 to 10 acres. One is usually satisfied with an estimate of the mean and of the variance of a property, say hydraulic conductivity, for the next larger scale, rather than insist on knowing precisely what the value is at every point on the "plot" (cross section area of 1 to 10 square meters). One then presumes that at the scale of the "plot" the soil behaves in a "stationary" manner, or, in other words, that it is rather homogeneous, though it may display random smooth fluctuations about a "constant" mean. Let us accept this assumption, at least, for the scale of a plot. It is tempting next to

assume that the "law of infiltration" for the column applies for the plot provided that one uses the proper "average" value of hydraulic conductivity.
However such procedure does not account properly for the physical phenomena. The problem is that the spatial variability has the insidious effect to
trigger an heterogeneity in the "process" of infiltration. The infiltration rate
is not given by the same equation if infiltration takes place at capacity or
below capacity. In one case infiltration rate equals rainfall rate; in the other
case infiltration rate equals capacity infiltration rate, a value quickly much
less than rainfall rate. In a region of high hydraulic conductivity, all the rainfall infiltrates; in a region of low conductivity ponding has occurred early and
infiltration rate is much smaller than the rainfall rate. Thus the problem is
not to plug an average value of conductivity in a single formula, but to average two different processes (symbolized by two different "laws of infiltration"). The problem is even worse because the weighting for the two formulas varies in time as more of the area ponds as time passes. Our goal in this
paper is to attempt to come up with a reasonable answer for the scale of a
"plot" (area of 1 to 10 square meters) or a "parcel" (100 square meters), as a
step toward the solution for the watershed scale. In this approach we need to
define (1) a "law of infiltration" , (2) the "law of chance" for the variability
of soil properties and finally (3) what we call the "rules of the game". What
is meant here by "rules of the game" is the set of assumptions made as to the
fate of the water that does not infiltrate at the point where it was supplied.

Utilizing accepted formulas for infiltration capacity and for ponding time at
a point scale, and laws of chance for the distribution of conductivity, laws of
infiltration for the plot or the parcel are derived analytically. In this derivation it is necessary to account for the fact that runoff from the ponded surfaces will cause "runon" and thus opportunity for infiltration in zones where all
the rainfall had infiltrated but some unfilled capacity still exists. The movement of the water on the surface can take place as sheet flow or through a network of microchannels. Thus other probability distributions enter into the
picture, those of the microchannels and of the slopes. Multiple integration in
space, time, process and chance (sample space) is required to derive the laws
of infiltration at a larger scale. Functional forms for the infiltration equations
at the parcel scale are derived under different assumptions (scenarios) regarding the spatial distribution of conductivity and/or the disposition of the
excess rainfall on the parcel. The derived functional forms are different from
the punctual infiltration equations that served as departure points. No effective (average) values of the hydraulic parameters exist that when plugged into
a punctual equation will provide a correct description for a parcel. Among

the scenarios investigated are: (1) the case when the parcel is assimilated to a huge size column (Single Huge Uniform Column case, or SHUC for short) for which the punctual equations are applied with an average conductivity, (2) the case when conductivity increases downslope (KID case) and (3) the case when excess rainfall, wherever generated, is immediately removed from the parcel through a system of microchannels (IRS case). Figure 1 shows a comparison of infiltration rates under the scenarios IRS and SHUC. When the (dimensionless) rainfall rate (ratio of rainfall rate over maximum value of hydraulic conductivity) is 1.1 the (dimensionless) ponding time in the SHUC case is 6.06 but for the IRS case the ponding time for the "entire" parcel is 72.73. Whereas in the SHUC case no excess rainfall is generated prior to ponding, in the IRS case partial ponding occurs immediately and excess rainfall is generated right away. The infiltration curves are very different. In the SHUC case the transition before and after ponding is brutal, infiltration rate decreasing very rapidly immediately after ponding, whereas in the IRS case the infiltration rate drops continuously and smoothly through time. Beside, in the SHUC scenario if the rainfall intensity is less than the mean hydraulic conductivity the column will absorb the totality of rainfall for ever, whereas with the IRS it will not and some excess rainfall will always be generated. When the rainfall rate is 1.5 the ponding time in the SHUC case is 2.67 and for the IRS case the ponding time for the "entire" parcel is 10.67. Which scenario is more realistic?

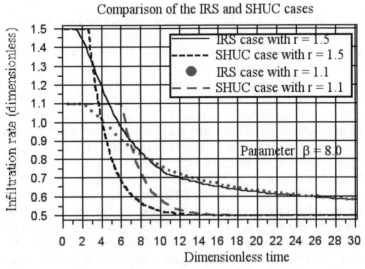

Figure 1. Infiltration rates under the IRS and SHUC scenarios for 2 different rainfall rates

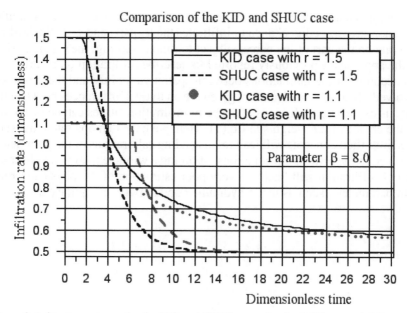

Figure 2. Infitration rates under the KID and SHUC scenarios for 2 different rainfall rates

Figure 2 shows a comparison of infiltration rates under the scenarios KID and SHUC. When the (dimensionless) rainfall rates are 1.1 and 1.5 the (dimensionless) ponding times in the SHUC case are respectively 6.06 and 2.67 but for the KID case the ponding times for the "entire" parcel are 0.0. The infiltration curves are not as different as in the IRS case. In the SHUC scenario if the rainfall intensity is less than the mean hydraulic conductivity (r<0.5) the column will absorb the totality of rainfall for ever, and the same is true with the KID case as a result of runon, which is not the situation in the IRS case.

CONCLUSIONS; WHICH SCENARIO TO USE FOR PARCEL INFILTRATION?

For the scenarios considered we found that the same results obtain for the IRS and the KDD scenarios on one hand and similar ones for the SHUC and KID scenarios on the other hand. The problem is in the mix of these two different parcel laws of infiltration. Presuming that a fraction fm of the parcel is well drained by microchannels and the runon occurs on the rest of the parcel, then the parcel infiltration rate is:

$$i_P = f_\mu i_\mu + (1 - f_\mu)i_S \qquad (1)$$

where im is the infiltration rate on the part of the parcel where excess rainfall does not have a second chance to infiltrate (the μ -part) and i_s is the infiltration rate on the part of the parcel subject to runon (spilling; theS -part). Most of the approaches previously reported to describe infiltration on a parcel did not account for the interactions between spatial variability and the processes involved. It should be clear that, given the analytical differences between the various expressions, all kinds of shape of infiltration curves can be generated by the choice of the weights in Eq.(1). Here we have demonstrated that such oversimplified concepts will lead to misleading calibrations of the parameters involved in the infiltration equations. Forcing a wrong equation on observed data of infiltration will lead to a very poor estimation of the physically relevant parameters, such as mean hydraulic conductivity or capillary drive.

AGGREGATION OF SOILS IN PRESENCE OF SPATIAL CHANGES IN TEXTURE FOR REPRESENTATION OF LARGE SCALE WATERSHED HYDROLOGICAL FLUXES

Jose M. Soria, Paolo Reggiani, Rafael Angulo-Jaramillo and Randel Haverkamp

Laboratoire d'Etude des Transferts en hydrologie et Environnement LTHE (UJF, INPG, CNRS, IRD), Domaine Universitaire, BP 53 38041 Grenoble Cedex 9, France

The present study investigates the impact of spatial change of soil texture on watershed-scale hydrological fluxes throughout the vadose zone. Hydrologist are interested in estimating the infiltration and evaporation fluxes through the land surface to calculate catchment water balances and simulate land-atmosphere interaction. In this context it is crucial to know whether the hydrological bare-soil fluxes across the land surface can be calculated by replacing the spatially variable soils within modelling entities such as subcatchments (e.g., Representative Elementary Watersheds of Reggiani et al., 1999) through an "equivalent" soil and by modeling the vadose zone as a single equivalent 1-D column; or if it is necessary to subdivide the unsaturated zone into smaller model entities, which are characterized by a single soil texture and which operate as parallel columns.

The principal aim of the study is to explore the hydrodynamic behavior of adjacent soil columns by answering three questions: i) is it possible to replace a group of soil columns by one single entity with equivalent hydrodynamic soil characteristics, while preserving the response signal of the groundwater recharge, infiltration or evaporation fluxes, ii) is it possible to simulate the flux behavior of a group of adjacent soil columns by one single equivalent flux obtained by weighting the fluxes of each individual soil column; and iii) is it possible to keep the columns as single entities and model them as vertical soil columns working in parallel? We will tackle the problem by studying the behavior of a rectangular domain separated into two columns of various widths. The results can easily be extrapolated to an arbitrary number of adjacent columns. To facilitate the analysis, we reduce the problem to two dimensions and apply a full FEM Richard's equation solver which is considered to represent "reality" in a synthetic fashion. We will refer to this analysis as the reference configuration. Next, we substitute the two adjacent soil columns by an equivalent artificial soil (i.e., equivalent hydraulic soil characteristics), based on aggregation principles of soil physics, and solve the Richard's equation for the equivalent domain by treating it as a single equivalent column. This situation is referred to as configuration 1. Finally, we solve the 1D Richard's equation for two adjacent columns separated by a no-flux boundary and calculate the total flux exiting the domain by weighting the individual fluxes of the two columns by their respective horizontal area projections and by comparing the resulting equivalent flux with that calculated by the full 2D simulation. This situation is referred to as configuration 2.

When schematizing the hierarchy of vadose zone flow processes, the first level consists in solving the Richard's equation subject to appropriate soil characteristics and initial and boundary conditions. This yields the distribution of water content in space and time. The second level consists in the integration of the water content profiles resulting in volumes as a function of time and, hence, fluxes. Consequently, test configuration 1, which deals with the equivalent soil characteristics, enters the process before the solution of the Richard's equation and the possible uncertainties introduced by replacing the "real" situation by an equivalent soil are amplified by the non-linearities of the solution of the transfer equation. Test configuration 2 (i.e., equivalent fluxes) enters the process after the solution of the Richard's equation, as the fluxes are computed with original soil characteristics for each soil column, and the equivalent flux is computed through a posteriori aggregation.

The hydraulic soil properties used for this study, are the van Genuchten [1980] water retention equation and the Brooks and Corey [1964] hydraulic conductivity function. These relationships require the knowledge of five parameters conveniently grouped into two categories: two shape parameters (i.e., m and h defining the shape of the water retention curve and that of the hydraulic conductivity function, respectively) which are dominantly related to soil textural properties; and three scale parameters of each water content (qS), pressure head (hg) and conductivity (KS) which are principally dependent upon soil structure. The shape parameters m and h can be related to the particle size shape parameters relative to the cumulative particle size distribution curve, taking into account the tortuosity of the soil through a semiphysical method (Haverkamp et al., 1998). Following this procedure, a link between the particle size distribution and the pore size distribution, and a link between the pore size distribution and the water retention curve can be established. This procedure is followed for the calculation of the equivalent soil characteristics.

The rectangular modeling domain is filled with two soils A and B with known particle size distributions and soil characteristic parameters m, η, θ_S, h_g and K_S. The soils taken from a large soil database, are chosen such that the texture dependent shape parameters m and h are different but the structure dependent scale parameters remain identical for both soils, i.e., θ_S=0.42 cm^3/cm^3; h_g=0.5 m and K_S=0.06 m/h. It allows to study the sole impact of changes in soil texture and excludes the influence of structure (less accessible under field conditions) on the modelling results. According to the USDA triangle of texture, soil A corresponds to a silt loam and soil B to a sand. The equivalent soil is produced by merging the particle sizes of the two soils A and B in an appropriate manner. For this purpose, the cumulative particle sizes curves for soil A and B are combined by extracting for each particle size diameter the cumulative frequency for soil A and B, weighting it by the respective composition percentages, and adding them up subsequently. The result of the procedure is a new equivalent cumulative particle size frequency curve, which lies in between the cumulative frequency curves of the soils A and B. The equivalent soil characteristic shape parameters are then calculated by the procedure mentioned above. As the scale parameters θ_S, hg and K_S are kept constant for both soils A and B, the new equivalent soil characteristics are fully defined. Three equivalent soils are considered for our study, composed by 80%-20%, 50%-50% and 20%-80% granulometric fractions of soils A and B. Obviously, any other prediction model (such as the pedotransfer function of Rawls and Brakensiek, 1985) could be used for the calculation of the equivalent soil characteristics, but as will be shown, the quintessence of the result will not change.

The numerical experiments used to test the three configurations (i.e., reference configuration, equivalent soil and equivalent flux configuration) are carried out on a rectangular domain composed by two soil columns. Depending on the soil combinations chosen (i.e., 80%A-20%B, 50%A-50%B or 20%A-80%B) different portions of the domain are occupied. Four different domain width scales are chosen w: 1 m, 10 m , 100 m and 1000 m, while the domain depth (6 m) is always kept constant. As mentioned above, the reference configuration consists of a 2D simulation of the vadose zone water movement allowing the soil columns to interact laterally. In this fashion the flow field through soil A impacts the flow through soil B and vice versa, and the two parallel soil columns are hydrodynamically coupled. A zero flux condition is imposed at the vertical outer limits of the domain. The two test configurations 1 and 2 only involve vertical 1D simulation of the domain without interaction in between the two soil columns. Two flux experiments are carried out for each soil combination, test configuration and domain width: infiltration and evaporation. For the case of infiltration, a constant flux (q=0.006 m/h) with free drainage at the bottom of the domain are chosen as boundary conditions, and a uniform pressure head (h=-10 m) throughout the entire domain as initial condition. The infiltration fluxes used for the comparison of the different test configurations, are analysed at a reference level of 1 m depth in order to avoid disturbance of the solution by the lower boundary condition. For the case of evaporation, a boundary condition corresponding to a constant pressure head *(h=-10000 m)* is imposed at the soil surface and a no-flux lower boundary condition is used. An initial condition at saturation (θ_s=0.42 cm³/cm³) is imposed uniformly throughout the domain. The evaporation fluxes at the soil surface are used for the comparison of the test configurations.

When increasing the horizontal length scale of the domain (w>10 m), the results calculated by the 2D reference solution for the test case of infiltration show a typical dual-modal behavior of the cumulated fluxes passing cross the reference level. Obviously, the sandy soil starts draining through the reference level long before the water content profile passes the loamy soil. The dual-modal behavior becomes more and more pronounced with increasing domain width. This is attributable to the fact that for larger width scales the contact zone of the two soils becomes negligible with respect to the domain size and the two columns behave as separate entities. For small domains (w£1 m), the order of magnitude of the interaction zone coincides with the size of the domain, therefore exhibiting mono modal behavior. Only for this case, an equivalent soil (configuration 1) could be used successfully to replace the two independent soil columns. For all other cases the equivalent soil is not able to reproduce the dual-modal soil water dynamics of the composed medium. Note that this conclusion is independent of the method employed to calculate the equivalent soil characteristics. Even when taking a different initial condition, such as a constant initial water content in A and B, similar results would have been obtained. Only A and B would then be inverted because A drains slower than B, but the dual-modal behavior would once again be observed. On the other hand, the equivalent flux method (configuration 2) gives very satisfactory results for domain scales w≥10 m. As the equivalent flux method is based on the concept of two separate soil columns, it does not obligatory give a mono-modal answer.

The dual modal behavior observed for the case of infiltration, is not noticeable for evaporation, as the kinetics of the evaporation fluxes are much slower. Therefore, the influence of w is less important. Nevertheless, the equivalent soil method does still not match the simulations of the reference case, while the equivalent flux method gives good results. This difference in behavior of the two test configurations is explained by the fact that the uncertainties introduced by replacing the "real" shape parameters by a set of equivalent shape parameters, are amplified by the non-linearity of the solution of the Richard equation. As the influence of the shape parameters on the flow behavior is more important in the dry part of the water retention curve rather than in the wet part, the estimations of the evaporation fluxes by the equivalent soil method are increasingly affected.

In conclusion, the results show that for a correct physically-based representation of hydrological fluxes across the vadose zone, textural changes need to be taken explicitly into account and cannot be considered by replacing spatial variable soils through an equivalent soil with equivalent soil characteristics. The experiments show that the flux signal reproduced by equivalent soils gives reasonable results only for very small domains, which are far smaller than the spatial scales at which hydrological fluxes need to be represented for watershed modeling purposes. This poses serious questions on the use of pedotranfer functions, for large surface areas. Moreover, if soils which are equal in terms of structure properties but differ in terms of texture, cannot be substituted through an equivalent soil, this will be even less the case for soils which differ in structure as well as texture, which is always the case in real-world situations. While texture changes over rather large spatial scales and can be linearly interpolated, structure is highly variable and changes over small spatial scales. This is an even stronger reason to exclude the possibility to find equivalent soils, which reproduce flux signals similar to the spatially distributed soil combinations.

REFERENCES

BROOKS, R. H., and A. T. COREY, 1964. Properties of porous media affecting fluid flow. Hydrol. Paper 3. Colorado State University, Fort Collins.

HAVERKAMP, R., C. ZAMMIT, F. BOURAOUI, and J.L. ARRUE, 1998. GRIZZLY, Grenoble catalogue of soils: Survey of soil field data and description of particle size, soil water retention and hydraulic conductivity functions. Laboratoire d'étude des Transferts en Hydrology et Environnement (LTHE), Grenoble, France.

RAWLS, W. J., and D. L. BRAKENSIEK, 1985. Prediction of soil water properties for hydrologic modeling. Watershed Management in the Eightis. Proc. Irrig. And Drain. Div., ASCE, Denver Colorado.

REGGIANI, P., M. SIVAPALAN, M. HASSANIZADEH, and W. GRAY, 1999. A unifying framework of watershed thermodynamics: constitutive relationships, Advances in Water Resources, 23: 15-39.

VAN GENUCHTEN, M. TH., 1980. A closed-form equation for predicting the hydraulic conductivity of unsaturated soils. Soil Sci. Soc. Am. J., 44: 892-898.

INFORMATION ENTROPY TO MEASURE TEMPORAL AND SPATIAL COMPLEXITY OF UNSATURATED FLOW IN HETEROGENEOUS MEDIA

David C. Mays[1,2], Boris A. Faybishenko[1] and Stefan Finsterle[1]
[1] Earth Sciences Division. Lawrence Berkeley National Laboratory
[2] Department of Civil and Environmental Engineering.
University of California, Berkeley

Geometric heterogeneity, coupled with the nonlinear interplay of gravity, capillarity, and applied pressure gradients, results in a rich variety of flow behaviors in unsaturated fractured rocks and porous media. In this paper, we develop a procedure to measure the complexity of these behaviors using information entropy, a statistical quantity which indicates the unpredictability, or complexity, of a physical process. We begin by recalling Shannon's definition [Shannon and Weaver, 1949]: for a given probability distribution function (PDF), information entropy is the negative expected value of the log-probability. In discrete form, this is:

$$H = -\sum_{i=1}^{N} P_i \log_2 (P_i)$$

where i is the bin number, N is the number of populated bins, and P_i is the proportion of data falling into the ith populated bin subject to the condition $\sum_i P_i = 1$. Relative entropy is defined as $H_R = H/\log_2(N_b)$, where N_b is the total number of bins.

Information entropy measures the degree to which the PDF constructed from a data set compares to the PDF corresponding to minimum information about the system. In our analysis, we take this minimum information PDF as the uniform distribution. If the data are predictable, corresponding to a peaked PDF, then the entropy is low. If the data are unpredictable, corresponding to a uniform PDF, then the entropy is high. Within this framework, the terms unpredictable, unstructured, and complex are analogous; we measure them with information entropy. Like thermodynamic entropy, information entropy explicitly depends on the enumeration of states, so the bin selection is important. If we have too few bins, we cannot resolve structure at small scales, and our calculated relative entropy will be artificially high. If we have too many bins, the data will be indistinguishable from a constant signal, and our calculated relative entropy will be artificially low.

To evaluate changes in entropy as a function of time or space, we break a multidimensional data set into segments along one of the independent variables, and then calculate the entropy for each segment using a constant set of bins defined along the other dimensions. This allows us to quantify changes in complexity. If there is a significant change in the nature of the physical process, this will be reflected in a change in entropy.

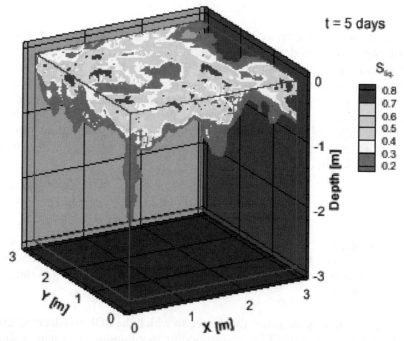

Figure 1: Numerical simulation of ponded infiltration into heterogeneous porous media. The initial condition is 1% saturation throughout.

As an example, we use entropy to evaluate the temporal and spatial complexity of simulated flow processes invoked by ponded infiltration into heterogeneous porous media, illustrated in Figure 1. The simulation is based on a numerical model of heterogeneous soil, produced by the software GSLIB [Deutsch and Journel, 1992], for which the transient response under ponded infiltration is calculated by the integral finite difference code TOUGH2 [Pruess et al., 1999]. We begin with a uniform saturation of S = 1% throughout the domain, then impose S = 100% along the top boundary.

To compute the entropy, we break the 3 m cube into 10 horizontal slices, each 30 cm thick, and then calculate the relative entropy of saturation data for each slice. Results for subsequent time steps are summarized in Figure 2. Initially, when S = 1% almost everywhere, we see the minimum value of relative entropy at all depths. Then, as time progresses, and water infiltrates into the porous block, the variability of saturation values becomes greater, generating higher relative entropy.

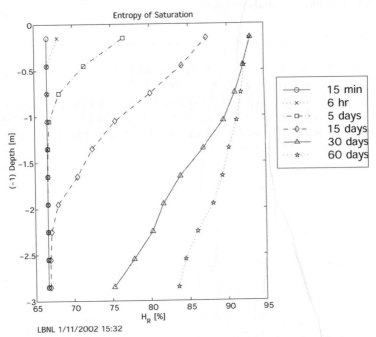

Figure 2: Entropy of saturation plotted against depth at various times. At early times, saturation is 1% throughout, so the relative entropy is minimum at 67%. At later times, saturation takes on a wide variety of values, so the relative entropy grows.

Results for capillary pressure data are complimentary. Initially, there is a wide variety of pressures in the heterogeneous block, reflected in high entropy. As the system approaches equilibrium, all pressures tend toward a common value, so the entropy of capillary pressure decreases. The average relative entropy for saturation and capillary pressure data is constant over time, within numerical limitations. This reflects the deterministic nature of the numerical simulation, and illustrates how this new approach allows us to conceptualize the infiltration process as a redistribution of entropy from capillary pressure to saturation.

Finally, we use information entropy to investigate the marginal value of additional data collection from boreholes. Using randomly selected "virtual wells," we show that computed entropy increases with additional virtual wells, but the rate of increase declines. Results are twofold: 1) the marginal value of each well declines, and 2) it would be difficult to design a monitoring system that is both economical and able to capture the full amount of information about spatial complexity.

REFERENCES

DEUTSCH, C.V. and A.G. JOURNEL, GSLIB: Geostatistical Software Library and User's Guide, New York: Oxford University Press, 1992.

PRUESS, K., C. OLDENBURG and G. MORIDIS, TOUGH2 User's Guide, Version 2.0, Lawrence Berkeley National Laboratory, Berkeley, CA, LBNL-43134, 1999.

SHANNON, C.E. and W. WEAVER, The Mathematical Theory of Communication, Urbana, IL: University of Illinois Press, 1949.

PORE CONNECTIVITY EFFECTS ON SOLUTE TRANSPORT IN ROCKS

Qinhong Hu[1] and Robert P. Ewing[2]
[1] *Lawrence Berkeley National Laboratory*
[2] *Iowa State University*

Plans call for nuclear waste to be confined in rock repositories, because diffusion in rock is relatively slow, assuring adequate time for radioactive decay. While fractures in the rock function as high-velocity flow pathways, solutes are both dispersed and retarded via diffusive exchange between the fracture and the rock matrix. If the matrix is even slightly below saturation, imbibition from active fractures will augment the diffusive movement of solutes from fracture to matrix, increasing diffusive retardation.

Hu et al. (2002 and unpublished results) examined imbibition of tracer-laced water into rocks, and observed three apparently anomalous results: first, while cumulative imbibition is generally expected to advance in proportion to the square root of time, in some rocks an advance approximately proportional to the fourth root of time was observed. Second, while a tracer concentration profile is expected to resemble the saturation profile during imbibition into initially dry media but show greater dispersion during imbibition into wet media, high apparent dispersion was observed during imbibition into initially air-dry Indiana sandstone. And third, an apparently anomalous increase in porosity was observed at the inlet face during imbibition into welded tuff, even though this face was prepared from the inside of a solid sample rather than from a weathered fracture face. The objective of this research was to investigate pore connectivity as a potential cause of these three anomalous observations, through comparison of experimental results with pore-scale imbibition simulations.

Rocks used were welded tuff, Berea sandstone, Indiana sandstone, and meta-graywacke. Cylindrical cores (2 cm length, 5 cm diameter) with epoxy-coated sides and exposed top and bottom faces were equilibrated in controlled humidity chambers to the desired water contents, approximately 2% (air-dry), 12.5%, and 76% saturation. They were then suspended, from an analytical balance, in a chamber with a water pan, such that the bottom face of the core contacts the free water surface. Imbibition was calculated from the cumulative change in suspended mass over time, with corrections for buoyancy resulting from changes in the water level caused by both imbibition and evaporative losses from the chamber. For welded tuff and Indiana sandstone, tracers were added to the water. After imbibition, small holes were drilled into the cores from both the inlet and air-exit faces, rock powder was sampled at 1 mm depth intervals, and tracer concentrations in the powder were measured.

The experiments were simulated using a pore-scale model, which conceptualizes the rock matrix as an assemblage of pore bodies connected by pore throats. Rocks with well-interconnected porespaces, such as non-cemented sandstones, have coordination (mean number of pore bodies to which each body is connected) in the range of $z = 4$–8. We used a cubic lattice ($z = 6$) and pruned connections at random to acheive lower coordinations. The stochastic process model anti-DLA (anti-Diffusion-Limited Aggregation) has been identified as an analog for stable displacement during imbibition (Lenormand, 1990). In anti-DLA, a random walker starts at a source location within phase A and diffuses until it reaches a phase B point, whereupon it stops, converting that point to A. As applied to our physical situation, free water at the inlet face of the core is the source point, and a random walker diffuses through water-filled pores into the core. Upon reaching a pore that is not occupied by water, it fills the pore, and a new walker is initiated.

Imbibition into Berea sandstone and welded tuff scaled with the square root of time, as expected. However, imbibition into metagraywacke (early time only) and Indiana sandstone scaled approximately with $time^{0.26}$. This scaling result matches predictions of percolation theory (Stauffer and Aharony, 1992) for 3-D diffusion at the percolation threshold, the coordination at which a sparsely connected porespace is only just connected. Simulations of imbibition capture the range of experimental data well. The slope of the straight section is 0.5 at high ($z > 1.68$) connectivities. Progressively lower pore coordination results in a lower imbibition rate, and eventually a imbibition scaling with $time^{0.26}$. Pore connectivity therefore provides a simple, unified explanation for the observed anomaly.

During imbibition into a dry medium, a solute concentration profile typically will resemble the saturation profile, with retardation changing the position but not the shape of the profile. In contrast, during imbibition into a moist medium, solutes will disperse by mixing with "old" water, and so a less sharp profile would generally be observed. This is seen for the case of tracer imbibition into welded tuff, where a more dispersed distribution is observed at 76% than at 12.5% initial saturation. However, against usual expectations, tracer concentration profiles for dye imbibition into air-dry Indiana sandstone show the high-dispersion pattern seen with imbibition into moist (76% initial saturation) tuff. Simulations using a pore coordination of z = 1.49 (at the percolation threshold) for "Indiana sandstone" and z = 1.68 for "welded tuff" show a pattern similar to those observed experimentally. The tracer concentration profile following simulated imbibition into the dry "tuff" is similar to the wetting front after adjustment for retardation, while that following simulated imbibition into the moister "tuff" shows more retardation and dispersion. The tracer profile in the simulated Indiana sandstone matches the experimental data fairly well. The explanation for this tracer profile in the "Indiana sandstone" lies not in dispersion mechanisms, but in the spatial distribution of accessible porosity.

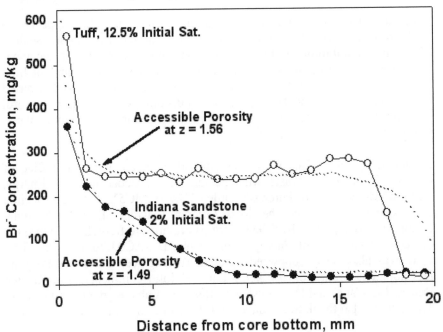

Recall that the Indiana sandstone core showed an imbibition scaling exponent of 0.26, in contrast to the more classical 0.5; an explanation can therefore be based on Indiana sandstone being at the percolation threshold. Near and at the percolation threshold, the porosity accessible from one end varies as a function of distance from the exposed face (Ewing and Horton, 2002). The modeled accessible porosity profile at low coordination matches the Indiana sandstone bromide concentration profile. The tracer profile is therefore apparently caused not by dispersion, but rather by the accessible porosity (see Figure).

In several of the welded tuff cores with initial saturation of 12.5%, bromide concentration in the millimeter closest to the inlet end was approximately twice the concentration through the rest of the core. This might have been thought a measurement error had it not been observed in multiple cores, with proportions of edge to plateau concentration ranging from 1.45 to 2.17. Again, pore connectivity considerations can explain the disparity. As with the tracer concentration profile in Indiana sandstone, it appears that the apparently anomalous reading at the inlet end results from differences in accessible porosity with position (see Figure).

Pore connectivity near or at the percolation threshold therefore appeared to be the root cause of all observed anomalies, explaining the temporal scaling of cumulative imbibition in Indiana sandstone and metagraywacke, the apparent dispersion during imbibition into air-dry Indiana sandstone, and the high tracer concentrations at the inlet edge of welded tuff. The anti-DLA-based imbibition model matched experimental results quite well, giving us a useful new simulation tool and helping to evaluate a simple and consistent explanation for the observed anomalies.

Acknowledgments:. This work was supported by the Director, Office of Civilian Radioactive Waste Management, U.S. Department of Energy, through Memorandum Purchase Order EA9013MC5X between Bechtel SAIC Company, LLC and the Ernest Orlando Lawrence Berkeley National Laboratory (Berkeley Lab). The support is provided to Berkeley Lab through the U.S. Department of Energy Contract No. DE-AC03-76SF00098. This work was also partly supported by an Earth Sciences Division's Program Development Grant from Berkeley Lab. Helpful comments from Karsten Pruess, Joe Wang, and Dan Hawkes of Berkeley Lab are greatly appreciated. The authors also thank Sonia Salah and Peter Lau for extra computer time.

REFERENCES:

EWING, R.P. and R. HORTON, Diffusion in sparsely connected porespaces. II. Steady-state distance-dependent processes, Water Resour. Res. (submitted), 2002.

HU, M.Q., T.J. KNEAFSEY, R.C. TRAUTZ, and J.S.Y. WANG, Tracer penetration into welded tuff matrix from flowing fractures, Vadose Zone J. (submitted), 2002.

LENORMAND, R., Liquids in porous media, J. Phys: Condensed Matter 2, SA79-88, 1990.

STAUFFER, D. and A. AHARONY, Introduction to Percolation Theory (2nd Ed.), Taylor and Francis, London, 1992.

PEDO TRANSFER FUNCTIONS – AN EXPLORATION USING ARTIFICIAL NEURAL NETWORKS

Lakshman Nandagiri, Amba Shetty and Somanath Kori
Department of Applied Mechanics & Hydraulics, Karnataka Regional Engineering College, Surathkal, Karnataka , India 574 157

Soil hydraulic properties need to be characterised in all applications of mathematical models that describe fluxes of moisture, energy and solutes in the unsaturated soil zone. The most important hydraulic property of an unsaturated soil is the water retention curve (WRC), which describes the relationship between volumetric moisture content (q) and the soil water pressure head (h). The drying WRC can be measured directly using ex-situ (laboratory) or in-situ (field) experimental procedures. Alternatively, it may be estimated using 'pedo transfer functions' (PTFs) which utilise information on more easily measured soil physical, chemical and morphological properties. The high degree of spatial variability exhibited by hydraulic properties, cumbersome experimental procedures and increasing use of distributed hydro-climatic models over large and heterogeneous spatial domains have favored the use of the PTF approach in estimating the WRC from routinely available soil survey data.

Considerable research attention has been devoted to the development of PTFs by the community of earth scientists. Since the underlying physics is complex and incompletely understood, majority of published PTFs possess the form of regression models relating either   moisture content at specific pressure heads to basic soil properties (point regressions models) or parameters of closed form functions for the WRC and soil properties (functional parameter models). The performances of PTFs developed in this manner are constrained by the limitations inherent to regression analysis, namely (i) the need to a priori specify the nature of relationship between the dependent variable and independent variables (i.e., linear, logarithmic, power , etc) and (ii) presence of cross correlations between the independent variables.

The present study is aimed at using Artificial Neural Networks (ANNs) as a tool to explore relationships between basic soil physico-chemical properties and unsaturated soil WRCs. ANNs are suited to complex problems where the relationships between the variables are not well understood and more importantly, their application does not call for a priori rationalisation about relationships between variables.

We used ANNs to explore relationships between basic soil properties and parameters of the van Genuchten water retention (WRC) function for a wide range of textural soil types available in the UNSODA database. Separate datasets of soils were created based on whether in-situ or ex-situ techniques had been employed to measure retention data. Our motive in creating separate datasets was governed by earlier findings that for a given soil the shape of the WRC obtained using in-situ measurements differs considerably from the one obtained using ex-situ measurements. A three layer feed-forward neural network model based on the back-error propagation algorithm was used to examine input-output relationships within each dataset. For each soil, twelve input variables (eight representative indices derived from particle size distribution data, dry bulk density, organic matter content, saturation water content and pH) were identified, but we experimented with five distinct neural models (M-1 to M-5) with increasing input parameterisations (3, 6, 7, 8 and 12 inputs respectively). Output variables in all cases were four parameters (ALPHA, N, WCR and WCS) of the van Genuchten water retention function which were obtained by application of the RETC optimisation scheme to measured retention data.

Our modeling approach involved a trial procedure to determine optimal network geometry, split sampling for training and testing the neural networks and use of ten different combinations of training-testing sets for each neural model application within each   dataset. Prediction accuracies of each neural model were evaluated in terms of the test-run root mean square error (RMSE) between observed and predicted values of the van Genuchten parameters.

Sensitivity analyses were carried out within the neural network framework with the twin objectives of highlighting differences in the behaviour of parameter sensitivities between ex-situ and in-situ based retention measurements and identifying within these, the relative importances of basic soil properties on each of the van Genuchten parameters.

A disadvantage of ANNs is that they do not provide a direct mathematical expression relating the variables. Therefore, we used results from the sensitivity analyses to screen inputs bearing relatively large significance on the output variables and used them to derive PTFs in the form of multiple linear regression equations.

We present results pertaining to differences in model performances between insitu and ex-situ datasets, influence of input parameterisation on predictions, non-uniqueness of ANNs as influenced by choice of training data, relative importances of soil properties on the shape of both in-situ and ex-situ measured WRCs and relative performances of ANNs and simple pedo transfer functions developed in this study.

From amongst the various ANN models developed for Database −1 and Database −2 (in-situ measured and ex-situ measured water retention data respectively), the one with the minimum number of inputs performed on par with those which used higher number of inputs. This justifies the argument that the performance of ANNs is not governed solely by number of inputs but rather on the information contained in them. The choice of a particular network geometry is highly problem specific and in the present study, a change in the input scenario demanded a change in the network geometry. This feature appears to be a major shortcoming in the general and routine application of ANNs. While the WRC parameters ALPHA, WCR and WCS could be estimated with a fair degree of accuracy from basic soil properties, the estimation of the other WRC parameter N, proved to be most difficult both in in-situ based and ex-situ based databases. The performance of our regression models although extremely poor for N, gave acceptable results with regard to the other van Genuchten parameters.

Experience gained in this study, clearly establishes the fact that ANNs are very useful in exploring complex relationships between multi-output-multi-input data. However, overall results with regard to performance of ANNs for the data of this study, showed that although they may not be very accurate and convenient estimating tools, they are indispensable as screening models. This capability may be exploited to identify the most important input variables that influence the outputs.

NUMERICAL SIMULATION OF TILE DRAINAGE IN CRACKING FIELD SOILS

Shrinivas Badiger[1] and Richard Cooke[2]

[1] *International Water Management Institute, Colombo, Sri Lanka.*
E-mail: s.badiger@cgiar.org
[2] *Department of Agricultural Engineering, University of Illinois at Urbana-Champaign, Urbana, USA.*

An understanding of temporal and spatial variations in flow from agricultural fields with tile drains is important in any attempt to predict contaminant loading from these fields. Study of drainage from fields with irregular tile systems installed in soils with preferential flow paths has been difficult due to the unavailability of suitable models. Most hydrologic and water quality studies in tile-drained fields have used traditional drainage models that are based on simplistic one-dimensional approaches or that are only applicable to parallel tile systems. In this paper, tile drainage is treated as an integral part of the soil-water continuum, along with concomitant processes such as infiltration, evaporation, transpiration, and macropore flow.

A general purpose, deterministic, variably saturated subsurface flow model, SWMS2D (Simunek, et al., 1994) was used to describe flow within the soil and towards a tile drain. The model solves Richard's two-dimensional formulation to simulate critical flow processes within the soil and across the atmospheric boundary. The subsurface module was adapted to include preferential flow described by 1D non-Darcian macroporous flow in vertically extending pores based on the works of Kohler et al. (2001). Tile drain was represented as a boundary condition prescribed at a single node, and by adjusting hydraulic conductivities in the surrounding elements.

MODELING APPROACH

Two different modeling approaches were tested to simulate subsurface flow to drains in a field site in east central Illinois. In the first approach, it is assumed that soil could be modeled as a continuous porous medium wherein, flow within the soil occurs two-dimensionally governed by Richard's equation. The model SWMS2D (Simunek et al., 1994) uses closed-form van Genuchten-Mualem functions (van Genuchten, 1980) to describe soil water retention and hydraulic conductivity, assuming that soil has a relatively uni-modal pore size distribution so that preferential flow through macro pores can be neglected. The second approach assumes that flow within the soil could be modeled in two interacting domains and is based on the works of Kohler et al. (2001). The flow domain consists of: (1) primary domain consisting of flow through the main soil matrix flow, similar to first approach; (2) secondary flow domain consisting of surface connected cracks and macro-pores in which flow occurs one dimensionally as non-capillary, laminar flow.

To estimate appropriate soil hydraulic properties, soil retention data derived from several undisturbed soil samples was used. The field retention data was fitted according to van Genuchten's hydraulic functions. The values of satu-rated hydraulic conductivity were estimated from the neural network predic-tions of Rosetta (Schaap, 1999) using the soil texture information and bulk density. To further simplify the process of calibration, field obtained strata information was approximated to consist of 4 layers. Parameters for the macropore region were not calibrated during this study. A fixed circular pore of 0.0001 m diameter was considered that vertically extends from the surfa-ce to the tile drain.

RESULTS

The model was tested for drain flows for an average rainfall year that had a good distribution of prolonged and short rainfall events and the results are pre-sented in Figure 1. The plots 1b and 1c show the time variant response of tile drainage and pressure head at a ground surface 10 m from the location of drain, to precipitation events (2a) occurring between April 01 and October 17.

The two simulation scenarios presented in Figure 1b represent tile drainage simulations using: (1) only micropore domain for 2D subsurface flow descri-bed by unimodal van Genuchten and Mualem functions (type-1), and (2) combined micropore domain and 1D vertical macroflow (type-2).

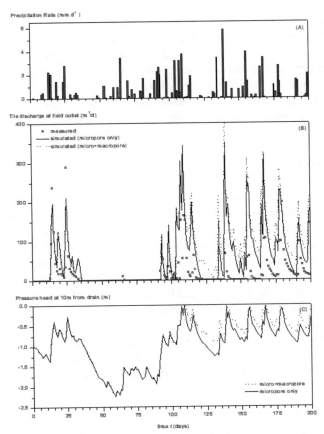

Figure 1. Precipitation (a), simulated and observed drain discharge (b), and pressure head at −10 m from the tile drain (c).

Simulation results show that type-2 scenario estimated higher magnitudes of response to rainfall events compared to type-1. Both, type-1 and type-2 flows were underestimated during periods t=100d through t=175d. A closer observation of the components of flow showed that meteorological and crop conditions simulated were underestimated primarily because the climatic data that was obtained from a station although topographically similar did not represent the study area. This was consistently observed for the periods during the summer when evaporative and crop water demands were generally high. However, the response from type-2 simulations was generally higher than type-1 and the additional flow was primarily due to macropores. Both the approaches exhibit poor fit of data in the recession periods and shows inadequacy of the moisture release properties described by calibrated hydraulic pro-perties. The complex switch in the soil hydraulic properties, from providing a direct flow link to tile during dryness, to reduction in hydraulic conductivity during wet periods leading to closure of macropores, poses a challenge to any simulation model. It explains the failure of both the modeling scenarios to represent multiple domain flows observed in the study site. Further studies that include integrated calibration approach for calibrating macropore param-eters may improve the tile responses immediately after a rain event.

CONCLUSIONS

Field-scale application studies indicated that the subsurface module simula-ted the occurrences of peak flows reasonably well. However, the failure of the subsurface model in simulating recession was primarily attributed to underestimated evapotranspiration demands during summer. Simulations with macropore inclusion provided better recession but did not necessarily have closer agreement with field conditions. Complex tile response observed in the field was recognized as a combination of rapid flows caused by short-circuiting of surface water through macropores during a rain event. Typical slow prolonged response after the rain events was due to characteristic low permeability of silty-clay-loam soils. Field-scale studies showed that the subsurface module could provide better predictions with more accurate des-criptions of soil hydraulic properties and climatic parameters.

REFERENCES

KOHLER, A., K. C. ABBASPOUR, M. FRITSCH, R. SCHULIN and M. T. VAN GENUCHTEN. 2001. Simulating unsaturated flow and transport in macroporous soil to tile drains sub-jected to an entrance head: Model development and preliminary evaluation. Journal of Hydrology. In press.

SCHAAP, M. 1999. Predicting soil hydraulic parameters from basic soil data. Rosetta Lite Version 1.0. Online User Manual. Riverside, Calif.: U.S. Salinity Laboratory-USDA.

SIMUNEK, J., T. VOGEL and M. T. VAN GENUCHTEN. 1994. The SWMS_2D code for simu-lating water flow and solute transport in two dimensional variably saturated media. Version 1.21. Research Report No.132. Riverside, Calif.: U.S. Salinity Laboratory-USDA.

VAN GENUCHTEN, M. T. 1980. A closed-form equation for predicting the hydraulic con-ductivity of unsaturated soils. Soil Science Society of America Journal 44:892-898.

INVERSE MODELING OF UNSATURATED HETEROGENEOUS MEDIA BY TWO-PHASE PRESSURE DERIVATIVE MATCHING

Kiyoshi Masumoto
Shimane University, Japan

INTRODUCTION

Inverse modeling is important to obtain a reliable groundwater simulation model for heterogeneous aquifer [e.g., Sun, 1994; Masumoto et al, 1998]. For reliable inverse modeling, the following problems must be solved: 1) sufficient measurements; 2) adequate parameterization; 3) adequate objective function; 4) adequate forward model; 5) high speed inverse analysis code. In this paper, to solve these problems for heterogeneous media in unsaturated condition, the following measures have been combined and applied to laboratory tests using a vertical sandstone plate: 1) air injection tests at multiple positions have been carried out for sufficient transient data; 2) to describe heterogeneity, inter-grid permeability has been treated as unknown with smoothing method for stable inversion; 3) the pressure derivative matching method, which is considered to be sensitive with transient data, have been used; 4) two-phase fluid flow model with capillary pressure, function of water saturation, has been considered; 5) the adjoint state method with quasi-Newton method (SSVM) has been used for efficient numerical inversion.

The validity of the pressure derivative matching for two-phase problems using transient data, obtained by laboratory test, is examined in this paper.

PRESSURE DERIVATIVE MATCHING METHOD FOR TWO-PHASE FLOW PROBLEMS

Numerical inversion by system states matching is based on a nonlinear optimization algorithm to minimize the performance index. In this study, Self Scaling Variable Metric Method (SSVM) [Oren and Luenberger, 1974], one of many quasi-Newton methods, was used to minimize the objective function.

To match the pressure derivative for two-phase problems, the author introduces the following objective function J' which includes J_{p2}, the term for derivative matching.

$$J' = G_{p1}J_{p1} + G_{p2}J_{p2} + G_{w1}J_{S1} + G_{sm}A_{sm} \tag{1}$$

where

$$J_{p1} = \sum_{n=1}^{Nt}\sum_{m=1}^{Nm} W_{p1}^{m,n}\left(p_{w,cal}^{m,n} - p_{w,obs}^{m,n}\right)^2 \tag{2}$$

$$J_{p2} = \sum_{n=1}^{Nt}\sum_{m=1}^{Nm} W_{p2}^{m,n}\left(\frac{p_{w,cal}^{m,n} - p_{w,cal}^{m,n-1}}{\Delta t^n} - \frac{p_{w,obs}^{m,n} - p_{w,obs}^{m,n-1}}{\Delta t^n}\right)^2 \tag{3}$$

$$J_{S1} = \sum_{n=1}^{Nt}\sum_{m=1}^{Nm} W_{S1}^{m,n}\left(S_{w,cal}^{m,n} - S_{w,obs}^{m,n}\right)^2 \tag{4}$$

where n is timestep index, Nt is the total number of timesteps, m is observation point index, Nm is the total number of observation points, W is weight, $P_{w,cal(obs)}$ is calculated (observed) water pressure, $S_{w,cal(obs)}$ is calculated (observed) water saturation, Δt is the timestep interval, and A_{sm} is a penalty function for smoothing parameter. The G terms are coefficients for the balance of each term.

We used the simultaneous solution method [Aziz and Settari, 1979] as the discretized governing equations for two-phase flow. p_a and S_w are the unknown parameters for the forward simulation. Water pressure $p_w = p_a - p_c(S_w)$ is calculated using capillary pressure p_c which is a function of S_w.

In this study, the method by Makhlouf et al. [1990], which can be classified into the discrete approach for adjoint state method [Sun, 1994], is applied to derive adjoint equations for two-phase derivative matching. The methodology presented in this study can also be applied to more complex models such as three-phase flow model. Calculation efforts for gradients of are almost the same as those required in the gradients of only J_{p1}.

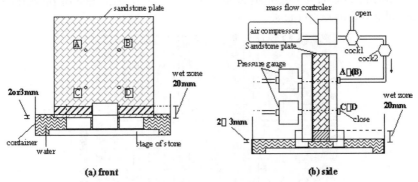

(a) front   **(b) side**

Fig. 1 Images of the air injection test system (injection at A)

LABORATORY AIR INJECTION TEST

To check the validity of developed inversion code, laboratory air injection tests were carried out using the apparatus shown in Figure 1. Four observation holes were made in the sandstone plate of dimensions 24cmx24cmx3cm, and one pressure transducer was attached to each hole. The apparatus was partly immersed in water to create two-phase conditions as shown in Figure 1.

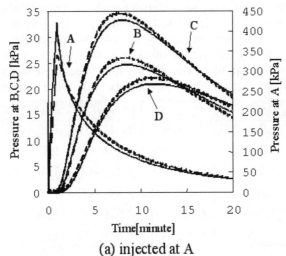

(a) injected at A

Fig. 2 Calculated and measured pressures obtained by numerical inversion from Case3.

Air injection was done at a controlled rate from one hole for a minute, then shut off for 19 minutes. Every hole was used as injection point, and pressure performances were obtained at all holes. A strict sequence of procedures was followed to keep the same initial condition.

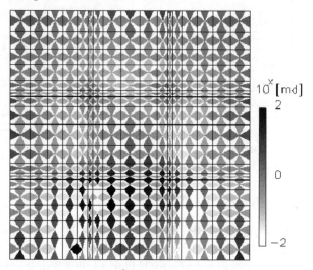

Fig. 3 Estimated permeability distributionÅ@(case3). Shaded 'diamonds' show estimated inter-grid permeability between neighboring grid blocks.

To perform numerical inversion of heterogeneous permeability distribution of the sandstone used for the lab test, absolute permeability at each inter-grid of discretized model was treated as an unknown parameter. Measurement error of flow rate by the storage of valve system was corrected. Numerical inversion was done simultaneously using four injection tests data. Only coefficient G_{p2} was changed to check the validity of pressure derivative matching.

	G_{p2}	J'	J_{p1}	J_{p2}	$G_{sm}*A_{sm}$
Case 1	1.00E-04	8.65E+02	1.31E+01	7.19E+06	1.33E+02
Case 2	1.00E-06	5.82E+01	8.04E+00	1.87E+07	3.15E+01
Case 3	1.00E-08	1.03E+01	<u>4.16E+00</u>	3.08E+08	3.07E+00
Case 4	1.00E-10	6.73E+00	4.89E+00	4.06E+08	1.80E+00
Case 5	1.00E-12	6.62E+00	4.84E+00	4.03E+08	1.78E+00
Case 6	0	6.62E+00	4.84E+00	no value	1.77E+00

Table 1 Values of each term in the objective function of numerical inversion for various G_{p2}

RESULTS AND DISCUSSION

When G_{p2}=1.0e-8 (Case3), we obtained the best matching results. Figure 2 shows one example. The estimated permeability distribution of Case 3 is shown in Figure 3. Each term of objective function at 100 inverse iterations is shown in Table 1. We have obtained the smallest J_{p1} from Case3 (underlined in Table 1), even considering Case6, the usual objective function (G_{p2}=0). It means that derivative matching method is effective if adequate weights are used.

CONCLUSIONS

1. The adjoint state method was developed for pressure derivative matching of two-phase flow model which includes capillary pressure. Using the algorithm, objective function added by pressure change rate term can be minimized with the same computing effort required for usual objective function.

2. Using multi-point air injection tests data, obtained in laboratory, heterogeneous permeability distribution of a sandstone plate could be obtained with good matching of pressure performance.

3. Pressure derivative matching for two-phase flow problem is effective for transient pressure data matching when adequate weightings in objective function are selected.

REFERENCES

AZIZ, K. and SETTARI, A: Petroleum Reservoir Simulation, Elsevier Applied Science Publishers, 476pp. 1979

MAKHLOUF E.M., W.H. CHEN, M.L. WASSERMAN and J.H. SEINFELD: A general history matching algorithm for three-phase, three-dimensional petroleum reservoirs, SPE 20383, 1990

MASUMOTO, K., TOSAKA, H. and KOJIMA, K.: New Algorithm for Identifying Hydraulic Property Distribution of Rock Mass by Simultaneous Fitting of Pressure and its Change rate at Multi-Points in Multi-Wells, J. Groundwater Hydrology of JAGH, Vol.40, No.3, 273-287,1998(in Japanese with English abstract)

MASUMOTO, K., VALLE, M: Confidence intervals of hydraulic properties estimated by highly efficient numerical inversion with pressure change rate matching, Proceedings of the International Symposium 2000 on Groundwater,IAHR in

Omiya, 375-380, 2000

MASUMOTO K.: Pressure Derivative Matching Method for Two Phase Fluid Flow in Heterogeneous Reservoir, paper SPE 59462 presented at the 2000 SPE Asia Pacific Conference on Integrated Modelling for Asset Management in Yokohama Japan, 2000

OREN, S.S. and LUENBERGER, D.G.: Self-scaling variable metric (SSVM) algorithms, Part1: Criteria and sufficient conditions for scaling class of algorithms, Management Science, Vol. 20, 845-862, 1974

SUN, NE-ZHENG: Inverse Problems in Groundwater Modeling, Kluwer Academic, 1994

IMPLEMENTATION OF DETERMINISTICALLY-DERIVED HYDROSTRATIGRAPHIC UNITS INTO A 3D FINITE ELEMENT MODEL AT THE LAWRENCE LIVERMORE NATIONAL LABORATORY SUPERFUND SITE

Kayyum Mansoor[1], Michael Maley[2], Zafer Demir[3] and Fred Hoffman[1]
[1] Lawrence Livermore National Laboratory, Livermore, California
[2] ETIC Engineering, Inc., Pleasant Hill, California
[3] Weiss Associates, Emeryville, California

The Lawrence Livermore National Laboratory (LLNL) facility is a highly developed research facility that is implementing an extensive ground water remediation program. In 1982, multiple plumes of volatile organic compounds (VOCs), predominantly trichloroethene (TCE) and tetrachloroethene (PCE), were discovered in ground water beneath LLNL.

In 1987, LLNL was placed on the U.S. Environmental Protection Agency's National Priority List. The environmental investigation covers an area of about 2 square miles to depths over 300 ft. As part of the environmental cleanup activities, LLNL operates a large ground water extraction system to remediate the VOC plumes beneath the site. In 2000, this system included a total of 80 ground water extraction wells connected to 25 separate treatment facilities. These combined facilities treated about 308 million gallons of ground water at an average combined flow rate of 600 gpm, and removed about 270 kg of VOCs in 2000. To better manage this large complex remediation system, a finite-element numerical model was developed.

The site is underlain by a thick sequence of heterogeneous alluvial sediments. Defining ground-water flow pathways in this complex geologic setting is required. The application of a deterministic approach was applied to define hydrostratigraphic units (HSUs) (Figure 1) on the basis of identifiable hydrau-

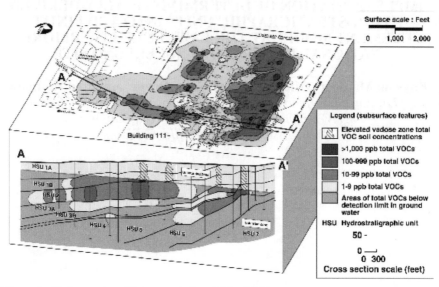

Figure 1: Hydrostratigraphic conceptual model for LLNL.

lic behavior and contaminant migration trends using a systematic analysis of independent data sets which included long-term hydraulic tests, ground water elevations, ground water chemistry data, soil chemical data and, borehole lithologic and geophysical logs. The conceptual model based on this approach indicates that ground water flow and contaminant transport occurs within packages of sediments bounded by thin, low-permeability confining layers. These layers were found to significantly limit hydraulic communication between the HSUs even after years of pumping and form the primary hydraulic controls within the alluvial sediments at LLNL (Noyes et al. 2000, in press). The primary assumption of the conceptual model is that between these confining layers, if fully saturated, the ground water is considered to be relatively well mixed and that ground water flow and contaminant transport is essentially parallel to the HSU boundaries (Noyes et al. 2000, in press).

To assess the conceptual model and enhance subsurface remediation efforts, a three dimensional finite elements ground water flow and contaminant transport model was developed for HSUs 1B and 2 using FEFLOW (Diersch, 1998). The model area covers about 7 square miles located in the eastern section of the Livermore Valley. The model is constructed of 13 elemental layers where layers 1-6 represent HSU 1B; layer 7 represents the thin confining layer; and layers 8-13 represent HSU 2. The model was descritized into 222,908 nodes with a mesh refinement scheme to improve accuracy, reduce potential errors and to optimize computational efficiency.

A deterministic approach applied in the development of boundary conditions and aquifer parameters. A temporal varying Type 1 boundary condition was applied to the eastern and southwestern portion of the model to simulate influx drainage from the east and outflow to an adjacent ground water basin, respectively. Other sources included rainfall recharge evenly applied to the upper elemental model layer and a recharge flux applied to simulate inflow thought a treatment-facility discharge pond. Major sinks include the discharge of ground water to of the Arroyo Las Positas stream and the onsite and offsite extraction and remediation wells.

The model was simulated with multiple steady-state flow periods and transient transport under confined conditions. To account for temporal variation of boundary conditions, the model was separated into 36 stress periods from April 1988 to December 2000. These stress periods are primarily related to significant changes in the LLNL ground water extraction system.

The first of two model calibration steps was performed with 8 stress periods, and the calibration focused primarily on obtaining a hydraulic conductivity distribution. These 8 stress periods were selected to represent distinct boundary conditions and ground water extraction rates. The goal was to define a representative hydraulic conductivity distribution for each HSU that would apply under all conditions experienced at the site through time. Initial hydraulic conductivity parameters were estimated using the non-linear parameter estimation tool, PEST (Doherty, 1994) constrained with hydraulic test data and an assessment of observed permeability tends. The second calibration step was to extend the ground water elevation matching to all 36 steps. Boundary conditions and other aquifer parameters were adjusted to minimize differences between observed and modeled peizometric surfaces to achieve a reasonable calibration for the entire stress history. There is overall good agreement between observed and modeled ground water elevations for all stress periods.

To calibrate the transport model, initial TCE and PCE source plumes were modeled forward and compared to quarterly plume maps from December 1991 to December 2000. The transport model was calibrated by comparison of model simulations and quarterly plume maps. Where discrepancies were noted, adjustments were made in either the flow model or in transport parameters. This process was repeated until an overall good agreement between observed and predicted plumes of PCE and TCE was achieved. By history matching TCE and PCE data for 10 years of remediation, the model was considered capable of making accurate forecasts of conditions into the future. Therefore the numerical model was able to provide decision support for wellfield management and other remediation decisions. In addition, the history matching by the transport model provided additional confirmation that the thin confining layers that defines the HSU conceptual model, represents field conditions.

The calibrated flow and transport model is currently used at LLNL to refine the conceptual model, to optimize ground water remediation efforts, and to support long-range planning and budgeting for the Superfund cleanup activities. For example we had evaluated different remedial designs based on hypothetical resource constraints. One evaluation involved predicting the effectiveness of a remedial system by operating wells along the site boundary only. The model was able to provide input to evaluate the long-range costs by demonstrating that the aggressive strategy would require 50 years to get all but the source areas below regulatory levels whereas the reduced strategy would require over 250 years. The model has proven useful for wellfield management to adjust flow rates in wells to keep stagnation points from inhibiting cleanup. Current modeling scenarios include capture zone analysis, pumping interference evaluation, extraction well placement, optimal pumping rates, mass removal projections, and long-range remediation assessment.

Through detailed analysis, a conceptual model was defined based on field observation that flow and transport is contained between thin confining layers within the heterogeneous alluvial sediments, and little communication occurs across them. This approach was used for the development of both the conceptual and numerical models. The results of the numerical modeling exercise validated the HSU approach by successfully modeling ground water flow and plume behaviors in different HSUs. The calibrated model has been applied to refine the conceptual model, support wellfield management decisions and provide future performance evaluations for planning and budgeting. Future work includes defining more heterogeneity within an HSU and incorporating this into a numerical model, and developing numerical models for the geologically complex deeper HSUs.

ACKNOWLEDGEMENTS

This work was performed under the auspices of the U.S. Department of Energy by the University of California, Lawrence Livermore National Laboratory under contract No. W-7405-Eng-48. The authors also would like to thank Charles Noyes of LLNL for support with the conceptual model, Jacob Bear of Technion Institute for ongoing support of modeling projects at LLNL, Souheil Ezzedine of Weiss Associates for support on numerical solutions, and Gary Weissman of Michigan State University for work on the nature of HSU boundaries.

REFERENCES

Doherty, J., L. Brebber, and P. Whyte. 1994. PEST – Model Independent Parameter Estimation. Watermark Computing, Corinda, Australia.

Diersch, H.-J.G. 1998. FEFLOW: Interactive, Graphics-Based Finite-Element Simulation System for Modeling Groundwater Flow, Contaminant Mass and Heat Transport Processes, User's Manual, Release 4.7. WASY Institute for Water Resources Planning and Systems Research Ltd., Berlin, Germany.

Noyes C.D., M.P. Maley, and R.G. Blake, in press. Defining Hydrostratigraphic Units within the Heterogeneous Alluvial Sediments at Lawrence Livermore National Laboratory, Ground Water.

MULTISCALE FINITE ELEMENT METHODS FOR MISCIBLE AND IMMISCIBLE FLOW IN POROUS MEDIA

Ruben Juanes[1] and Tadeusz W. Patzek[1,2]

[1] *Civil and Environmental Engineering. University of California at Berkeley. 631 Davis Hall, Berkeley, CA 94720-1710*

[2] *Earth Sciences Division. Lawrence Berkeley National Lab. One Cyclotron Road, Mailstop 90-1116, Berkeley, CA 94720-1710*

INTRODUCTION

Flow and transport in fractured porous media are, very often, processes not dominated by diffusion. This makes the mathematical problem almost hyperbolic, which naturally develops sharp features in the solution. Classical numerical methods produce a solution that either lacks stability, resulting in nonphysical oscillations, or accuracy, by showing excessive numerical diffusion.

Development of novel numerical methods for the complete equations of multiphase compositional flow in multidimensions must necessarily start from simplified models in one space dimension. These reduced model problems should display, however, the key features that pose difficulties in obtaining satisfactory numerical solutions such as, for instance, wild nonlinearity, shocks or near-shocks, boundary layers and degenerate diffusion. The key point of the proposed formulation is a multiscale decomposition of the variable of interest into resolved (or grid) scales and unresolved (or subgrid) scales, which acknowledges the fact that the fine-scale structure of the solution cannot be captured by any mesh. However, the influence of the subgrid scales on the resolvable scales is not negligible. A novel idea of subgrid stabilization by means of the concave hull of the flux function is introduced. By accounting for the subgrid scales, the oscillatory behavior of classical Galerkin is drastically reduced and confined to a small neighborhood containing the sharp features, while the solution is high-order accurate where the solution is smooth. This ensures that the numerical solution is not globally deteriorated. The method does not emanate from a monotonicity argument and, therefore, it does not rule out small overshoots and undershoots near the sharp layers. To prevent this situation, a subscale-driven shock-capturing mechanism is presented. The generality of the proposed formulation makes it amenable to further extensions.

NUMERICAL FORMULATION: THE MULTISCALE APPROACH

We model miscible and immiscible flow in porous media with the scalar conservation law:

$$\partial_t u + \nabla \cdot \mathbf{F} = q, \quad x \in \Omega, \quad t = [0,T], \tag{1}$$

where u is the conserved quantity, F is the total flux, and q is the production rate. In the nonlinear case, the total flux has the form $F=f(u)-k(u)\nabla u$, where f is the hyperbolic part of the flux and k is the diffusion tensor. Both are allowed to be nonlinear functions of the unknown u. We consider Dirichlet and Neumann boundary conditions:

$$u = \bar{u} \text{ on } \Gamma_u \subset \partial\Omega, \quad \mathbf{F} \cdot \mathbf{n} = \bar{F} \text{ on } \Gamma_n = \partial\Omega \setminus \Gamma_u, \tag{2}$$

and the initial conditions $u(x,t=0)=u_0(x)$. In the linear case, $F=au-k\nabla u$, and we define the linear advection-diffusion operator $Lu:= \nabla\cdot(au-k\nabla u)$.

Consider the functional spaces $V:=\{\varpi\in \hat{I}W: v=u \text{ on } \Gamma_u\}$, $V_0:=\{\varpi\in \hat{I}W: v=0 \text{ on } \Gamma_u\}$ where the appropriate choice of the Sobolev space W depends on the form of the diffusion tensor. The weak form of the problem is to seek $v\hat{I}V$ for each fixed $t\in (0,T]$, such that

$$(\partial_t u, v) + a(u,v;u) = l(v) \quad \forall v \in V_0, \quad u(x,t=0) = u_0(x), \tag{3}$$

where

$$(\partial_t u, v) = \int_\Omega \partial_t u \, v \, d\Omega,$$

$$a(u,v;w) = \int_\Omega \mathbf{f}(w) \cdot \nabla v \, d\Omega + \int_\Omega \mathbf{k}(w)\nabla u \cdot \nabla v \, d\Omega, \tag{4}$$

$$l(v) = \int_\Omega q \, v \, d\Omega - \int_\Gamma \bar{F} \, v \, d\Gamma$$

In the linear case, the only difference with respect to Eq. (3) is that $a(u,v) \equiv a(u,v;u)$ is now a bilinear form.

Let $V_h \subset V$, and $V_{h0} \subset V_0$ be conforming finite element spaces of piecewise polynomials. The standard Galerkin approximation of Eq. (3) is to find $u_h \in V_h$ for each fixed t, such that

$$(\partial_t u_h, v_h) + a(u_h, v_h; u_h) = l(v_h) \quad \forall v_h \in V_{h,0}, \tag{5}$$

and $u_h(x,t=0)$ is the projection of the initial function $u_0(x)$ onto space V_h. The standard Galerkin method lacks stability for the near-hyperbolic problem, as shown in the numerical simulations.

The key idea of the multiscale formulation [1] is to consider the trial function space V and the test function space V_0 as the direct sum of two spaces:

$$V = V_h \oplus \tilde{V}, \quad V_0 = V_{h,0} \oplus \tilde{V}, \tag{6}$$

where V_h and $V_h^{\,0}$ are the spaces of resolved scales and $\tilde{V}$ is the space of sub-grid scales. This decomposition acknowledges the fact that the subscales cannot be captured by the finite element mesh, but their influence on the grid scales is not negligible. We now split the original linear problem:

Grid scales : $(\partial_t(u_h + \tilde{u}), v_h) + a(u_h + \tilde{u}, v_h) = l(v_h) \quad \forall v_h \in V_{h,0},$

Subscales : $(\partial_t(u_h + \tilde{u}), \tilde{v}) + a(u_h + \tilde{u}, \tilde{v}) = l(\tilde{v}) \quad \forall \tilde{v} \in \tilde{V}.$ $\tag{7}$

The subscales are modeled analytically using an algebraic subgrid scale (ASGS) approximation [2], $\tilde{u} = \tau R u_h$, where τ is called the relaxation time, and $R u_h := q \partial_t u - L u_h$ is the grid-scale residual. After integration by parts on each element, the equation for the grid scales reads:

$$\tag{8}$$

$$(\partial_t u_h, v_h) + a(u_h, v_h; u_h) + \sum_e \int_{\Omega^e} \tilde{u} L^* v_h \, d\Omega + \int_{\Gamma^e} \tilde{u} b^* v_h \, d\Gamma = l(v_h) \quad \forall v_h \in V_{h,0},$$

where L^* is the adjoint of L, and b^* is the associated boundary operator. The final equation for the resolved scales includes the usual Galerkin terms and some additional volume and boundary integrals evaluated element by element. Since the subscales are proportional to the grid scale residual, the method is residual-based and, therefore, automatically consistent.

Application of the multiscale approach to the nonlinear problem is not straightforward because the form a(u,v;w) is not linear in w. Our approach is based on an incremental formulation and a multiple-scale decomposition of the increment: $u \approx u_h + \tilde{\delta u}$ This allows us to split the problem into a grid-scale problem and a subscale problem. The final equations are formally identical to those of the linear case, but now involve a linearized advection-diffusion operator. We further improve the method by incorporating a shock-capturing technique, based on increasing the amount of numerical dissipation in the neighborhood of layers. We propose a novel, dimensionally consistent, subscale-driven artificial diffusion, given by $k_{sc} = C_{sc} (|\tilde{\delta u}|/U_{sc}) h|a(u_h)|$, where U_{sc} is a characteristic value of the solution near the shock, and C_{sc} is a constant coefficient.

REPRESENTATIVE SIMULATIONS

Under certain simplifying assumptions, the case of one-dimensional **miscible flow** corresponds to a linear advection-diffusion equation, with $f(u)=au$, $k(u)=\varepsilon$. We solve the problem with parameters: $a=1$, $\varepsilon=10^{-4}$, $q=1$. A backward Euler time-stepping scheme and a fairly coarse grid (the element Peclet number is 250) was used. Standard Galerkin method produces a globally oscillatory solution at all times, while the solution obtained by the ASGS method is nonoscillatory and captures sharply the moving ramp-plateau interface and the boundary layer (Figure 1).

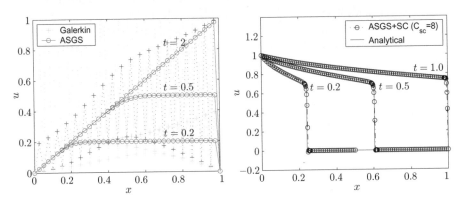

Figure 1. Linear advection-diffusion with sources

Figure 2. Buckley-Leverett flow

One-dimensional **immiscible flow** of two fluids is described by the Buckley-Leverett equation. Here we employ $f(u)=q_T u^2/(u^2+(1-u^2))$ and $k(u)=\varepsilon u(1-u)$

with values: $q_T=1$, $\varepsilon=10^{-4}$. We used backward Euler time-stepping and different grids (for the results shown the element Peclet number is about 100). Classical Galerkin gives a globally oscillatory solution, especially for long simulation times. The subgrid scale approach, in particular when shock-capturing is included, provides a solution that is free from oscillations and not overly diffusive (Figure 2).

CONCLUSIONS

We have presented a successful numerical method for the solution of nonlinear conservation laws, which is based on a multiscale decomposition of the variable of interest, and applied it to the problems of miscible and immiscible two-phase flow in porous media. To the best of our knowledge, this approach is entirely new in the context of flow in porous media. The proposed modified subgrid scale method with shock-capturing shows exceptional performance in the test cases studied. We are now extending this methodology to multiphase compositional flows in multidimensions.

REFERENCES

[1] T. J. R. HUGHES. Multiscale phenomena: Green's functions, the Dirichlet-to-Neumann formulation, subgrid scale models, bubbles and the origins of stabilized methods. Comput. Mehtods Appl. Mech. Engrg., 127:387-401, 1995.
[2] R. CODINA. On stabilized finite element methods for linear systems of convection-diffusion-reaction equations. Comput. Mehtods Appl. Mech. Engrg., 188:61-82, 2000.

SEASONAL VARIATION IN BIOAVAILABILITY OF RESIDUAL NAPL IN THE VADOSE ZONE

Arturo A. Keller & Mingjie Chen
Bren School of Environmental Science and Management
University of California, Santa Barbara, CA 93106
e-mail: keller@bren.ucsb.edu

Since Monitored Natural Attenuation (MNA) of organic pollutants is considered more frequently, it is important to understand the controlling processes and their dependence on seasonal fluctuations in soil temperature and moisture. Assuming that the climatic conditions are static over the course of life of the project can result in significant error in the estimated time to clean up a site, with potential risk to receptors and/or liability to owners. For this work, we modified a multiphase model (UTCHEM v.6) to account for boundary conditions present in the vadose zone including rainfall infiltration and gas exchanges, estimating the soil temperature profile, considering temperature dependence of physicochemical properties, and kinetic interphase mass transfer. The model also includes biodegradation, which is limited by moisture content, oxygen and pollutant availability, and temperature. Based on these modifications, the water table is allowed to rise and fall following seasonal variations in rainfall infiltration and atmospheric temperature. We also allow the exchange of chemicals across the soil-atmosphere interface, which has a significant effect on the predicted rate of pollutant disappearance. The model is then used to study the effect of seasonal variations in soil temperature and moisture, driven by actual climatic conditions. Using data from an actual site in Sacramento, California, we create a number of synthetic examples to illustrate the role of the various fate and transport processes and their dependence on seasonal variation. The results indicate that although biodegradation is an important process, the water table fluctuations and diffusive processes also produce significant transfer of NAPL components to the atmosphere. The relative importance of these processes depends mostly on the assumptions made with respect to rainfall infiltration rate, which in this case has a significant effect on the fate and transport of NAPL residual.

LARGE-SCALE CONSTITUTIVE RELATIONSHIPS FOR UNSATURATED FLOW IN FRACTURED ROCKS

Hui-Hai Liu[1], G.S. Bodvarsson[1] and David Hudson[2]

[1] *Earth Sciences Division, MS90-1116, Ernest Orlando Lawrence Berkeley National Laboratory, Berkeley, California*

[2] *U.S. Geological Survey, Sacramento, California*

During the last decade, the need to investigate the feasibility of using the unsaturated zone of Yucca Mountain, Nevada, as a potential permanent storage facility for geological disposal of high-level nuclear wastes has generated intensive research interest in modeling flow and transport in unsaturated fractured rocks. Modeling flow and transport in unsaturated fractured rocks is also of interest in other active research areas, including environmental remediation in arid and semiarid regions.

The continuum approach is commonly used for modeling field-scale flow and transport in fractured rocks. In this approach, the fracture network and the rock matrix are treated as overlapping and interactive continua with different flow and transport characteristics. Key parameters for an unsaturated flow model based on the continuum approach include constitutive relations (relations between capillary pressure, saturation, and relative permeability) for both the matrix continuum and the fracture continuum.

For many reasons, the constitutive relationships for the porous tuff matrix are often measured at a core scale on the order of centimeters, while a typical numerical gridblock size is on an order of meters for field-scale modeling studies. In this case, upscaling is needed to determine large-scale relationships based on the small-scale measurements. Although considerable progress has been made for upscaling flow and transport parameters under saturated conditions, studies related to upscaling unsaturated properties for porous media are very limited. This is mainly because of the complexity of unsaturated flow in heterogeneous porous media.

On the other hand, constitutive-relationship models originally developed for porous media have often been borrowed for modeling unsaturated flow in the fracture continuum. This can be highly questioned because unsaturated flow mechanisms within a fracture network are not necessarily the same as those in a porous medium. The previous use of porous medium models, including the Brooks-Corey (1964) model and van Genuchten (1980) model, is mainly because of lack of a more appropriate model for the fracture continuum.

It has become well known that gravity-driven fingering flow is a common flow mechanism in unsaturated fractures. How to handle this important mechanism with different numerical approaches still remains an issue under active research. Within the context of the continuum approach, the large-scale constitutive-relationship models for the fracture continuum must consider effects of fingering flow to provide physically correct simulation results for unsaturated flow in fractures.

The objective of this paper is to briefly review the recent progress we have made in developing large-scale constitutive relations, with special attention given to the issues mentioned above. Specifically speaking, we, taking advantage of large air entry values for the rock matrix, developed a closed-form upscaling formulation for constitutive relations for rock matrix. Based on subgrid-scale numerical modeling results, we proposed a new constitutive-relationship model for unsaturated flow in fracture network by improving the corresponding models for porous media. To incorporate the fingering flow at fracture network scale into the continuum approach, we also developed an active fracture model.

INTEGRATION OF PERCHED WATER AND CHLORIDE DATA IN MODELING FLOW PROCESSES WITHIN THE UNSATURATED ZONE OF YUCCA MOUNTAIN, NEVADA

Yu-Shu Wu and Jianchun Liu

Earth Sciences Division, Lawrence Berkeley National Laboratory
Berkeley, CA 94720, USA

This paper presents a modeling study incorporating field-measured perched water and chloride data into a 3-D large-scale unsaturated zone (UZ) model of Yucca Mountain, Nevada, a potential underground site for a high-level nuclear waste repository. Model calibration using these field data is intended to improve the model capability of evaluating the current conditions and predicting future conditions of the UZ, so as to aid in the performance assessment of the proposed repository system. The modeling approach is based on a continuum formulation of coupled multiphase fluid flow and tracer-transport processes through fractured porous rock, using a dual-continuum concept. The methodology includes (1) manually calibrating the fluid and rock parameters in the perched zones to match the observed perched-water body and (2) forward simulations to match the measured chloride pore-water concentration data at depths.

Quantitative investigation of fluid flow, heat transfer, and radionuclide transport at Yucca Mountain is an essential step for characterizing the site, designing the repository, and assessing the natural system's performance. Numerical modeling has played a crucial role in understanding the UZ fluid movements and evaluation of hydrogeologic, thermal, and geochemical conditions within the overall waste-disposal system. The numerical model rely critically, among other factors, on incorporation of the best-estimated model parameters, normally obtained through model calibration, combining field, laboratory, and modeling investigations.

The UZ model covers a total area of approximately 40 km2 of the Mountain (Figure 1). Depending on the local topography, thickness varies from 500 to 700 m, overlying a relatively flat water table. The proposed repository would be located in the highly fractured Topopah Spring Welded unit, more than 200 m above the water table with an approximate area of 1,000 m east-west and 5,000 m north-south. Hydrologic processes in the UZ occur in a hetero-geneous environment of layered, anisotropic, fractured volcanic rocks, con-sisting of alternating layers of welded and nonwelded ash flow and air fall tuffs.

The TOUGH2 and T2R3D codes were used for flow and transport simulation respectively. The plan view (x-y) of the 3-D numerical grid is shown in Figure 1. The proposed repository is located near the center of the model domain. Each gridblock in the plan view represents a vertical column in the 3-D grid. Fracture-matrix interactions in the model are handled using the dual-permeability model. The ground surface of the mountain is the top boundary and the water table is the spatially fixed bottom boundary. Present-day mean infiltration is applied to the top boundary as a source term. The water table is the bottom boundary and all lateral sides are no-flow bounda-ries. The input parameters for rock and fluids include fracture, matrix, and transport properties of each model layer. Special matrix and fracture proper-ties are applied to faults in each hydrogeological unit.

The presence of perched-water bodies in the vicinity of the potential reposi-tory at Yucca Mountain provides invaluable insight into the heterogeneity of the UZ formation, water movement, and the surface infiltration history of the mountain. To calibrate the 3-D model against observed perched-water condi-tions, rock properties have been modified locally. For the perched-water con-ceptual model, fracture and matrix permeability parameters within perched zones have been manually calibrated from a series of 3-D modeling studies. The simulation results of steady-state flow are presented and discussed in terms of (1) comparisons with matrix liquid saturation and (2) matching with observed perched-water bodies. Simulated results with the perched-water conceptual model have been checked against observed saturation, water potential, and perched-water data at all boreholes where data are available. Figure 2 shows the match between observed and modeled vertical-saturation and perched-water locations at borehole SD-12.

Geochemical data provide additional information to analyze flow processes of the UZ system. Pore-water chemical concentration data can be used to calibrate the UZ model to bound the infiltration flux, flow pathways, and transport times. Distribution of chemical constituents in both liquid and solid phases of the UZ system depends on many factors, such as hydrological and geochemical processes of surface precipitation, evapotranspiration, the fracture-matrix interactions of flow and transport, large-scale mixing via lateral transport, and the history of climate changes and surface recharge. In the present chloride-transport modeling, chloride is treated as a conservative tracer transported through the UZ and the modeled chloride concentrations are compared with the measured pore-water chloride data. The model results are in reasonable agreement with the field data.

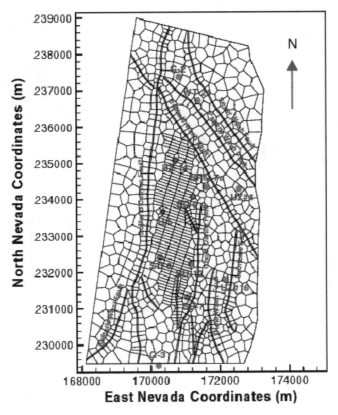

Figure 1. Plan view of the 3-D UZ model grid, showing the model domain, faults incorporated, and borehole locations at the Yucca Mountain.

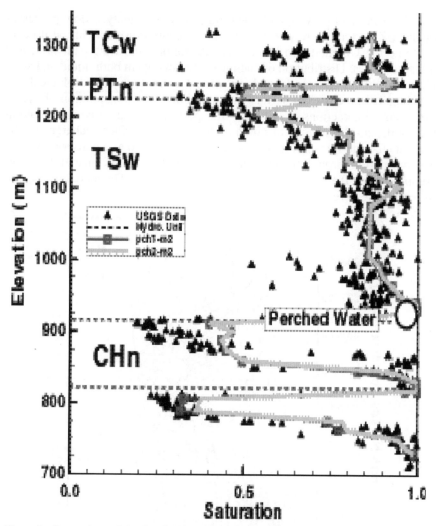

Figure 2. Comparison of simulated and observed matrix liquid saturations and perched-water elevations for borehole SD-12 (Dashed lines represent interfaces between hydrogeological units).

Index of authors

Abdul Hameed, Md.
Abriola, L.M.
Ahlers, C. F.
Ahmed, S.
Ahn, J.
Aines, R. D.
Angulo-Jaramillo, R.
Arifur Rahman, Md.
Attinger, S.
Avis, J.D.
Badiger, S. M.
Barth, G. R.
Beauheim, R.L.
Beckie, R.
Bellin, A.
Benekos, I.
Bodvarsson, G.S.
Bolshov, L. A.
Bowman, R. S.
Brauchler, R.
Brimhall, G.
Burrage, K.
Burrough, P.r A.
Callahan, T. J.
Campbell, B.
Carle, S.
Carrera, J.
Cirpka, O.A.
Class, H.
Coldewey, W.G.
Connelly, M. P.
Cook, P. J.
Cooke, R. A.
Copty, N.
Cronin, A.A.
Chaika, Y.
Chambré, P. L.
Chen, Guan-Z.
Chen, J.
Chen, M.

Chen, Wen-Fu
Chen, Z.
Chiang, Chung-J.
Christensen, F. D.
Chrysikopoulos, C. V.
Dagan, G.
Dai, Z.
Datta-Gupta, A.
de Marsily, G.
Delay, F.
Demir, Z.
Denisov, Y.M.
Detwiler, R. L.
Di Pietro, L.
Dietrich, P.
Dominic, D. F.
Doss, S.
Doughty, C.
Dranikov, I. L.
Drellack, S. L.
Dykhne, A. M.
Eisenberg, F.i-Jo
Engesgaard, P.
Ewing, R. P.
Ezzedine, S.
Faybishenko, B. A.
Ferris, J. R.
Fienen, M. N.
Findikakis, A. N.
Finsterle, S.
Finsterle, S. A.
Fogg, G. E.
Froukh, L. J.
Gabeva, D.
Gandhi, R. K.
Gee, G. W.
Gelhar, L. W.
Ginn, T. R.
Glass, R.J.
Göbel, P.

Goldberg, D. E.
Goltz, M. N.
Gonzales, J. L.
Goovaerts, P.
Gopalakrishnan, G.
Gorelick, S. M.
Grammling, C.
Grathwohl, P.
Green, C. T.
Grote, K.
Halford, K. J.
Halinah, T.
Hanley, W.
Harris, D. B.
Harvey, C.
Haverkamp, R.
Helmig, R.
Hetterschijt, R.A.A.
Hiester, U.
Hill, M. C.
Hirayama, T.
Hoffman, F.
Holden, P. A.
Holmén, J. G.
Hopkins, G. D.
Hopmans, J.W.
Hsu, Kuo-C.
Hubbard, S. S.
Hudson, G. B.
Illangasekare, T. H.
Inoue, Y.
Jacobs, B.
James, S. C.
Jeannin, Pierre-Y.
Jing, X.
Johnson, V. G.
Juanes, R.
Kalin, R.M.
Karasaki, K.
Kashyap, D.

Shvidler, M.
Simmons, A.
Singhal, D.C.
Smith, L.
Smith, L.
Smith, R. W.
Soria, J. M.
Spane, F. A.
Starke, B.
Stauffer, F.
Stigsson, M.
Striegel, K.-H.
Tanaka, M.
Teles, V.
Teutsch, G.
Theurer, T.
Thilo, A. C
Timmins, B.
Trautz, R.G.
Travis, B. J.
Tsang, Chin-F.
Tsang, Y.
Tuller, M.
Unger, A.
Valocchi, A. J.
Valstar, J. R.
van der Voort, I.
van Gaans, P.
van Helvoort, Peter-J.
van Tonder, G.
Vasco, D. W.
Vasvari, V.
Viswanathan, H. S.
Walker, D. D.
Wang, Chung-H.
Wang, E.
Wang, H.
Wang, J. S.Y.
Ward, A. L.
Weissmann, G.

Wierenga, P.
Wildenschild, D.
Wilson, A. M.
Williams, D.
Winkler
Winkler, A.
Wu, Yu-S.
Xu, T.
Yabusaki, S.
Yang, Q.G
Yang, Y.S.
Yoden, T.
Yohmei, T.
Yoneda, M.
Yucel, V.
Zhan, H.
Zhang, D.
Zhang, G.
Zhang, Z. F.
Zhenxue, D.
Zhou, F.
Zhou, Q.
Zhou, Qi Y.
Ziagos, J.
Zimmerman, R. W.
Zimmermann, S.
Zlotnik, V. A.
Zurbuchen, B. R.